# MANAGEMENT OF TECHNOLOGY VI

# MANAGEMENT OF TECHNOLOGY VI

# Proceedings

## THE CREATION OF PROSPERITY, BUSINESS AND WORK OPPORTUNITIES THROUGH TECHNOLOGY MANAGEMENT

## THE SIXTH INTERNATIONAL CONFERENCE ON MANAGEMENT OF TECHNOLOGY MOT 97

25–28 June 1997
Göteborg, Sweden

Official Conference of
IAMOT – The International Association
for Management of Technology

Horst Mueller, Jan-Gunnar Persson and Kenth R. Lumsden

SMR – The Swedish Society of Mechanical Engineers,
Naval Architects and Aeronautical Engineers
Stockholm, Sweden

ISBN 91-630-5611-9

*Additional copies may be obtained by contacting:*

SMR       The Swedish Society of Mechanical Engineers,
          Naval Architects and Aeronautical Engineers
Mail      SMR, P.O.Box 5164, S-102 44 Stockholm
Office    Jungfrugatan 38/Tyskbagargatan 12
Phone     +46 8 6679320
Fax       +46 8 6679705
Internet  smr@swipnet.se

*Quantity discounts available.*

In co-operation with SKF

# Table of Contents

# THE SIXTH INTERNATIONAL CONFERENCE ON MANAGEMENT OF TECHNOLOGY

*The IAMOT MOT 97 Conference is held under the Patronage of His Majesty Carl XVI Gustaf, King of Sweden*

## The Honorary Committee

| | |
|---|---|
| Peter Augustsson, CEO | SKF |
| Michael Treschow, CEO | Atlas Copco /From May–97: Electrolux/ |
| Jörgen Linder, Lord Mayor | City of Göteborg |
| Bertil Pekkari, Group Vice President | The Esab Group |
| Ulf Dinkelspiel, CEO | Exportrådet, Swedish Trade Council |
| Clas Åke Hedström, CEO | Sandvik |
| Lars G Malmer, Group Vice President | SKF |
| Bo Berggren, CEO | STORA |
| Lennart Spetz, CEO | Western Sweden Chamber of Commerce |
| Göran Tunhammar, CEO | SAF, Swedish Employers' Confederation |
| Christer Heinegård, Deputy Director General | NUTEK, Swedish National Board for Industrial and Technical Development |
| Bengt Halse, CEO | SAAB |
| Heinrich Blauert, CEO | VI, Association of Swedish Engineering Industries |
| Anders Sundström, | His Excellency The Secretary Ministry of Trade and Industry of Trade and Industry |
| Leif Gustafsson, CEO | SSAB  Swedish Steel |
| Robert W. Hendry, CEO | SAAB Automobile |
| Sören Gyll, CEO /Through April–97/ | VOLVO |
| Bertil Jonsson, President | LO, The Swedish Trade Union Confederation |

## Conference Focus

Our World is developing at a speed, unthinkable just some decades ago. The key issues and main triggers of these rapid evolutions, are always the abilities of meeting global needs, desires and visions of people and their leaders. As all technology development is carried out and monitored by man, it should also be reasonable to state that the paths of evolutions can be adjusted in appropriate directions by man.

The way of enhancing economic prosperity for countries, industries, and businesses is depending upon effective and efficient management of technology. This area will determine business competitiveness which is no longer a matter of choice, but a matter of survival in the global marketplace.

Representatives from major international organisations, corporations, educational institutions, and government agencies will convene, for the sixth time, to share the latest research and experience in the exploding field of technology management.

This is an unequalled opportunity to join the world's leading experts representing many countries from five continents to address techno- socio-economic issues and problems at all levels.

At the macro and micro levels, from nations to individual firms, organisations are acknowledging the link between innovation and economic success. The application of technology, not just its development, is the key to surviving in the competitive global economy. Organisations that continuously innovate and are able to apply these innovations are those that will thrive in the next decade.

The Sixth International Conference on Management of Technology, as in previous conferences provides a forum for the exchange of research results, concepts, and practical industrial experiences.

Presentations and stimulating discussions among leading scholars, policy makers, academics, and practitioners provide the opportunity to explore new ideas, establish new personal contacts, and continue the exchanges begun in prior conferences.

The conference provides an interdisciplinary perspective on current and future issues and problems. The theme for the Sixth Conference MOT 97 is

*The creation of prosperity, business and work opportunities*
*through technology management*

## Acknowledgements

Special thanks are due to the following reviewers who have supported the editors with reviewing all the papers submitted:

| | | |
|---|---|---|
| Tarek M. Kahlil | University of Miami | USA |
| Bo Lindström | The Royal Institute of Technology, KTH | Sweden |
| Robert M. Mason | Case Western Reserve University | USA |
| Hans Björnsson | Chalmers University of Technology, CTH | Sweden |
| Gunnar Eliasson | The Royal Institute of Technology, KTH | Sweden |
| Kenth Lumsden | Chalmers University of Technology, CTH | Sweden |
| Bo Brismar | Huddinge University Hospital | Sweden |
| Bo Carlsson | Case Western Reserve University | USA |
| Leo Alting | Technical University of Denmark | Denmark |
| André Maisseu | University of Versailles | France |
| Lars Sjöstedt | Chalmers University of Technology, CTH | Sweden |
| Dean Abrahamson | University of Minnesota | USA |
| Ingvar Andersson | CIT Chalmers Industriteknik | Sweden |
| Louis A. Lefebvre | University of Montreal | Canada |
| Jan-Gunnar Persson | The Royal Institute of Technology, KTH | Sweden |
| Bengt-Åke Lindberg | Scania | Sweden |
| David J. Bennett | Aston University | UK |
| J-C Persson | IVF, The Swedish Institute of Production Engineering Research | Sweden |
| Richard Smith | Arizona State University | USA |
| Sören Sjölander | Chalmers University of Technology, CTH | Sweden |
| John Ettlie | University of Michigan | USA |
| Mats Johansson | Chalmers University of Technology, CTH | Sweden |
| Thore Hagman | Chalmers University of Technology, CTH | Sweden |
| Tomas Engström | Chalmers University of Technology, CTH | Sweden |
| Roland Örtengren | Chalmers University of Technology, CTH | Sweden |
| John Wedel | Chalmers University of Technology, CTH | Sweden |

We are also very grateful to persons willing to stand by and help every time when it was necessary:

| | | |
|---|---|---|
| Sten Drakenberg | SMR, Production Committee | Sweden |
| Per Engström | ABB, Management & Process Consult | Sweden |
| Harald Sten | SMR, Production Committee | Sweden |
| Mikael Zaar | SAAB Military Aircraft | Sweden |
| John O. Aje | University of Maryland | USA |
| Fredrick Betz | National Science Foundation | USA |
| Alain Bienyame | University of Paris - Dauphine | France |
| Christian Dambrine | Association Nationale de la Recherche | France |

| Richard Dasher | Stanford University | USA |
| Dennis A. Guthery | American Graduate School of Int'l Mangement | USA |
| Ken Keys | Ferris State University | USA |
| Isak Kruglianskas | University of Sao Paulo | Brazil |
| Yutaka Kuwahara | Hitachi Europe Ltd. | UK |
| Susumu Kurokawa | Massachusetts Institute of Technology, MIT | USA |
| Horst Mueller | Chalmers University of Technology, CTH | Sweden |
| Joseph C. Paradi | University of Toronto | USA |
| Roberto Sbragia | University of Sao Paulo | Brazil |
| Istvan J. Toth | TRW Inc. | USA |
| Rias J. Van Wyk | University of Capetown | South Africa |
| Stan Waslylyk | Jones, Day, Reavis & Pogue | USA |
| Hiroyuki Yamasaki | Mitsubishi Electric Corp. | Japan |

### Special Thanks to the Key-Note Speakers from Industry:

| Michael Treschow | President and CEO, Atlas Copco |
| Göran Wennergren | Consul General of Japan |
| Siwert Gårdestig | CEO, Sahlgrenska University Hospital |
| Christer Heinegård | Deputy Director General, Nutek, Swedish National Board of Industrial and Technical Development |
| Peter Augustsson | President and CEO, SKF |
| Jeffrey Herbert | Chairman and CEO, Charter Plc and Chairman of the Esab Group |
| Arne Wittlöv | President and CEO, Volvo Aero Corporation |
| Bertil Pekkari | Group Vice President & Technical Director, the Esab Group |
| Peter Westman | Director of R&D and Quality, SSAB Swedish Steel |
| Stig-Göran Larsson | Vice President Research&Development, SAAB Automobile |
| Pär Malmberg | Director Group Technical Development, SKF Group |
| Per-Olof Edin | LO, the Swedish Trade Union Confederation |

## The Main Sponsors

| SKF | Main Sponsor | STORA | Paper |
| THE ESAB GROUP | Main Sponsor | Skandia Tryckeriet | Printer |
| SAAB | Main Sponsor | Salomongruppen | Graphic design |
| SCANDINAVIAN AIRLINES | Main Sponsor | Skandinaviska Enskilda Banken | Social activity |
| SSAB | Main Sponsor | Hasselblad | Social activity |
| SCANIA | Main Sponsor | City of Göteborg | Social activity |
| VOLVO | Main Sponsor | Spin-Off Companies at | |
| ATLAS COPCO | Main Sponsor | Chalmers Science Park | Work |

## The Conference Co-chairmen

**Dr. Tarek M. Khalil, Dean**
University of Miami
The Graduate School
Ferre Building 210, 1000 Memorial Drive
Coral Gables, Florida 33146 USA
Telephone: +1 305-284-4154
Fax: 305-284-5441
Internet: tkhalil@umiamivm.ir.miami.edu

**Dr. Robert M. Mason, Professor**
Case Western Reserve University
Weatherhead School of Management
10900 Euclid Avenue
Cleveland, Ohio 44106-7235 USA
Telephone: +1 216-368-4777
Fax: +1 216-368-4776
Internet: rmm3@pyrite.cwru.edu

**Jan-Gunnar Persson, Professor**
Royal Institute of Technology KTH
Engineering Design
S-100 44 Stockholm, Sweden
Telephone: +46 8-790-7868
Fax: +46 8-202-287
Internet: jgp@damek.kth.se

## The Scientific Committee

David Bennett, Professor
Aston University
Aston Business School, UK

John Ettlie, Professor
University of Michigan, USA

Louis Lefebvre, Ph.D.
Ecole Polytechnique Montreal,
Canada

Robert M. Mason, Professor
Case Western Reserve University
Weatherhead School of Management
USA

Richard Smith, Professor
Arizona State University, USA

Hans Björnsson, Dean
Chalmers University of Technology
CTH, Sweden

Tarek M. Khalil, Dean
University of Miami
The Graduate School, USA

Bengt-Åke Lindberg, Tekn Dr
Scania, Sweden

Jan-Gunnar Persson, Professor
Royal Institute of Technology
KTH, Sweden

Horst Mueller, Administration
Chalmers University of Technology
CTH, Sweden

Bo Carlsson, Professor
Case Western Reserve University
USA

Louis A. Lefebvre, Professor
University of Montreal,
Canada

Bo Lindström, Dean
Royal Institute of Technology
KTH, Sweden

Sören Sjölander, Professor
Chalmers University of Technology
CTH, Sweden

## The Organising Committee

Jan-Gunnar Persson
KTH

Lennart Elg
Nutek, (Corresponding member)

Gösta Ferneborg
The ESAB Group

Horst Mueller
CTH

Lars-Torsten Olsson
SMR

## The International Advisory Committee

Dr. John O. Aje, Director
University of Maryland, USA

Dr. Alain Bienyame
University of Paris - Dauphine
France

Dr. Dennis A. Guthery, Director
American Graduate School
of Int'l Management, USA

Dr. Yutaka Kuwahara
Hitachi Europe Ltd., UK

Dr. André Maisseau
University of Versaille, France

Dr. Richard Smith, Professor
Arizona State University, USA

Dr. Stan Waslylyk
Jones, Day, Reavis & Pogue
USA

Dr. David J.Bennett
Aston University, UK

Dr. Christian Dambrine
Association Nationale
de la Recherche, France

Dr. Ken Keys, Director
Ferris State University, USA

Dr. Susumu Kurokawa
Massachusetts Institute
of Technology MIT, USA

Dr. Joseph C. Paradi
University of Toronto, Canada

Dr. Istvan J. Toth, Director
TRW Inc., USA

Dr. Hiroyuki Yamasaki
Mitsubishi Electric Corp.
Japan

Dr. Fredrick Betz
National Science Foundation, USA

Dr. Richard Dasher
Stanford University, USA

Dr. Isak Kruglianskas
University of Sao Paulo, Brazil

Dr. Louis A. Lefebvre, Professor
Ecole Polytechnique de Montreal
Canada

Dr. Roberto Sbragia
University of Sao Paulo, Brazil

Dr. Rias J. Van Wyk, Professor
University of Capetown
South Africa

## The Conference Secretariat

Bernt Kjellander       Ulla Mueller       Lars-Åke Moureau       Horst Mueller

# Paper Index and Conference Program
# with Paper Presentations

## SESSION A+F   5
### Management of technology education & Application of technology to learning organisations
Paper Session
Chairman Dr. Hans Björnsson, Dean School of Technology Management, Chalmers University of Technology, Sweden
Friday June 27, 1997 Keiller Room 11.00–13.00 hours

## SESSION A+F   6
### Management of technology education & Application of technology to learning organisations
Paper Session
Chairman Dr. Robert Mason, President of IAMOT, Case Western Reserve University, USA
Friday June 27, 1997 Keiller Room 16.00–19.15 hours

## SESSION B+E   4
*Enterprise integration and integrated information systems & Cultural differences
in innovation, entrepreneur ship and technology management*
*Paper Session*
*Chairman Dr. Gunnar Eliasson, Professor, The Royal Institute of Technology, Sweden
Friday June 27, 1997 Gabrielsson Room  11.00–13.00 hours*

## SESSION B+E   5
*Enterprise integration and integrated information systems & Cultural differences
in innovation, entrepreneur ship and technology management*
*Paper Session*
*Chairman Dr. Tarek M. Khalil, Dean The Graduate School & Founder of IAMOT, University of Miami, USA
Friday June 27, 1997 Wingquist Room  16.00–18.30 hours*

## SESSION B+E   6
*Enterprise integration and integrated information systems & Cultural differences
in innovation, entrepreneur ship and technology management*
*Paper Session*
*Chairman Dr. Gunnar Eliasson, Professor, The Royal Institute of Technology, Sweden
Friday June 27, 1997 Gabrielsson Room  16.00–19.15 hours*

## SESSION B+E 7
### Enterprise integration and integrated information systems & Cultural differences in innovation, entrepreneur ship and technology management
Paper Session
Chairman Dr. Prasanta K. De, Professor, X.L.R.I. Jamshedpur, India
Saturday June 28, 1997 Chalmers Room 08.45–10.45 hours

## SESSION B+E 8
### Enterprise integration and integrated information systems & Cultural differences in innovation, entrepreneur ship and technology management
Paper Session
Chairman Dr. Sushil, Professor, Indian Institute of Technology, India
Saturday June 28, 1997 Chalmers Room 11.15–12.45 hours

## SESSION C+J 1
### National technology policies & Service and government sector technology management with health engineering
Key-Note Session
Chairman Professor Jan-Gunnar Persson, President of SMR, The Royal Institute of Technology KTH, Sweden
Wednesday June 25, 1997 Congress Hall 14.30–15.30 hours

## SESSION C+J 2
### National technology policies & Service and government sector technology management with health engineering

*Paper Session*
*Chairman Professor Jan-Gunnar Persson, President of SMR, The Royal Institute of Technology KTH, Sweden*
*Wednesday June 25, 1997 Broström Room 16.00–17.30 hours*

## SESSION C+J 3
### National technology policies & Service and government sector technology management with health engineering

*Paper Session*
*Chairman Professor Jan-Gunnar Persson, President of SMR, The Royal Institute of Technology KTH, Sweden*
*Wednesday June 25, 1997 Broström Room 17.30–19.00 hours*

## SESSION C+J 4
### National technology policies & Service and government sector technology management with health engineering

*Paper Session*
*Chairman Dr. Bo Carlsson, Professor, Case Western Reserve University, USA*
*Friday June 27, 1997 Broström Room 11.00–13.00 hours*

## SESSION D+M 1
### Technology for the sustainable society & IT, intellectual property with MOT and economics
Paper Session
Chairman Dr. Leo Alting, Professor, Technical University of Denmark
Wednesday June 25, 1997 Wingqvist Room 16.00–17.30 hours

## SESSION D+M 2
### Technology for the sustainable society & IT, intellectual property with MOT and economics
Paper Session
Chairman Dr. André Maisseu, Professor, University of Versailles, France
Wednesday June 25, 1997 Wingqvist Room 17.30–19.30 hours

## SESSION D+M 3
### Technology for the sustainable society & IT, intellectual property with MOT and economics
Key-Note Session
Chairman Professor Jan-Gunnar Persson, President of SMR, The Royal Institute of Technology KTH, Sweden
Thursday June 26, 1997 Congress Hall 08.45–10.00 hours

## SESSION G   4
### Methods in technology management
*Paper Session*
*Chairman Dr. Louis Lefebvre, Professor, University of Montreal, Canada*
*Friday June 27, 1997 Zachrisson Room  08.45–10.30 hours*

## SESSION G   5
### Methods in technology management
*Paper Session*
*Chairman Dr. Louis Lefebvre, Professor, University of Montreal, Canada*
*Friday June 27, 1997 Zachrisson Room  11.00–13.00 hours*

## SESSION G   6
### Methods in technology management
*Paper Session*
*Chairman Dr. Louis Lefebvre, Professor, University of Montreal, Canada*
*Friday June 27, 1997 Zachrisson Room  16.00–19.15 hours*

## SESSION G    7
### Methods in technology management

## SESSION H    1
### Technology transfer

## SESSION H    2
### Technology transfer

## SESSION H  3
### Technology transfer
Key-Note Session
Chairman Dr. Robert Mason, President of IAMOT & Professor, Case Western Reserve University, USA
Thursday June 26, 1997 Congress Hall 14.30–15.45 hours

## SESSION H  4
### Technology transfer
Paper Session
Chairman Dr. Tarek M. Khalil, Dean The Graduate School & Founder of IAMOT, University of Miami, USA
Friday June 27, 1997 Kjellberg Room 11.00–13.00 hours

## SESSION H  5
### Technology transfer
Paper Session
Chairman Dr. David Bennett, Professor, Aston University, UK
Friday June 27, 1997 Kjellberg Room 16.00–19.15 hours

## SESSION H 6
### Technology transfer
Paper Session
Chairman Dr. Robert Mason, President of IAMOT & Professor, Case Western Reserve University, USA
Saturday June 28, 1997 Wingqvist Room 08.45–10.45 hours

## SESSION H 7
### Technology transfer
Paper Session
Chairman Dr. David Bennett, Professor, Aston University, UK
Saturday June 28, 1997 Kjellberg Room 08.45–10.45 hours

## SESSION H 8
### Technology transfer
Paper Session
Chairman Dr. David Bennett, Professor, Aston University, UK
Saturday June 28, 1997 Kjellberg Room 11.15–12.45 hours

## SESSION I 4
### Industrial technology management
*Paper Session*
*Chairman Dr. Tarek M. Khalil, Dean The Graduate School & Founder of IAMOT, University of Miami, USA*
*Friday June 27, 1997 Kjellberg Room 08.45–10.30 hours*

## SESSION I 5
### Industrial technology management
*Paper Session*
*Chairman Dr. Gunnar Eliasson, Professor, The Royal Institute of Technology KTH, Sweden*
*Friday June 27, 1997 Gabrielsson Room 08.45–10.30 hours*

## SESSION I 6
### Industrial technology management
*Paper Session*
*Chairman Dr. Robert Mason, President of IAMOT & Professor, Case Western Reserve University, USA*
*Saturday June 28, 1997 Wingqvist Room 11.15–12.45 hours*

## SESSION K+L   6
### Systems of innovation and technology & Creation of work opportunities
Paper Session
Chairman Professor Jan-Gunnar Persson, President of SMR, The Royal Institute of Technology, Sweden
Saturday June 28, 1997 Zachrisson Room 11.15–12.45 hours

# Author Index

# 001

# From Transistors to Integrated Circuits: a Shift of Innovation

# Communities in Japan

by

**Leonard H. Lynn**
**Weatherhead School of Management**
**Case Western Reserve University**
**Cleveland, Ohio 44106**

**USA**

**Telephone: [216] 368-6048**
**Fax: [216] 368-4785**
**e-mail lhl@cwru.po.edu**

Key words: innovation communities, integrated circuits, Japan, technological change, technological discontinuities, technology communities, technology imports, technology policy.

Topic letter and category: C (National technology policies); H (Technology transfer...); K (Systems of innovation...)

**For oral presentation**

**The Sixth International Conference of Management of Technology -- MOT 97**
**25-28 June 1997**
**Goteborg, Sweden**

1

# From Transistors to Integrated Circuits: a Shift of Innovation Communities in Japan

Two remarkable instances of technological leapfrogging by the Japanese have posed anomalies for researchers interested in technology management and technology policy. The first involved the transistor (particularly as embodied in the transistor radio), the second the integrated circuit (particularly as first embodied in electronic calculators).

The transistor was invented in the U.S. at Bell Laboratories in 1948. The transistor radio, the overwhelmingly most important early commercial product using transistors, was pioneered by Texas Instruments in collaboration with a smaller U.S. firm in 1954. Yet Japan, which had never been a major factor in world electronics markets, borrowed this technology and by the end of the 1950s was dominant in the market for both transistors and transistor radios. A number of authors have been puzzled by several aspects of this experience. At the most general level, it has been wondered how the Japanese managed to move from a position of extreme weakness in electronics technology to quickly become the primary beneficiaries of the new transistor technology (Malerba, 1985). Even more puzzling, earlier research suggested that this leapfrogging over U.S. industry was accomplished in the face of Japanese government meddling which is said to have slowed Sony's introduction of the transistor technology from Bell Laboratories (Trezise, 1976; Fransman, 1995; Goto, 1993). Further, the Japanese case was anomalous in that Japan's traditional electron tube producers, unlike their U.S. counterparts, quickly came to dominate this new technology and, unlike their European counterparts, showed no signs of being more sluggish innovators than the American venture capital firms entering the industry. Both the economics and organization theory literatures suggest that this should not have happened (note, for example, Tilton, 1971; Tushman and Anderson, 1986).

In an earlier paper (Lynn, forthcoming), I suggest some answers to these puzzles. First of all, I argue that the level of electronics technology in Japan in the late 1940s and early 1950s did not lag nearly as much as is generally imagined. I show that, contrary to previous accounts, government was not a major barrier to the introduction of transistor technology by Sony or any other firm. Indeed, using the "Innovation Community Framework" (Reddy et al., 1991; Lynn et al. 1996; Lynn et al., forthcoming) I suggest that government played a critical role in supporting use of the new technology by Japanese firms. As part of the coordinating "superstructure level" of the innovation community government researchers were the first in Japan to learn about the invention of the transistor. They conducted the most important early research in Japan on this technology. They organized study groups that included scientists and engineers from all the major electronics firms to diffuse information on transistors, presented papers at conferences, and developed prototypes of commercial transistor-based products, including the radio. Later, the Japanese Ministry of International Trade and Industry (MITI) *facilitated* the import of transistor-related technologies. It did this by standing behind the Japanese firms (including small unknown firms like Sony) buying the technology from such U.S. giants as Western Electric and RCA. For some technologies MITI intervened to lower royalty and other fees for Japanese purchasers. Still later, MITI, other government agencies, and various industry associations worked to develop export markets for the Japanese transistor radio producers, some of which had had very little international experiences.

Aside from government and industry associations, the Japanese sogo shosha (general trading companies) were also important parts of the coordinating superstructure of the Japanese transistor radio innovation community. The sogo shosha helped the Japanese commercializers of the

2

technology both to acquire the technology and to develop international markets for their products. The strength and efficiency of the superstructure of the Japanese innovation community for the transistor radio explain much of the success of the "substructure" (the firms actually making the transistor radios and their components).

In the 1960s the U.S. again took the lead in semiconductor technology with the IC. Like the transistor, the IC was invented in the U.S. This time the major inventions were by Texas Instruments (TI) and Fairchild in 1959 and 1960. Again the lead for crucial commercial products based on the new U.S.-developed technology was lost to Japan. There were differences, however. While, it is commonly believed that one reason the U.S. lost its dominance in transistor technology was that U.S. antitrust laws forced AT&T to share the technology at low cost with any firm, domestic or foreign, that wanted it, this was not the case with the IC. Indeed, TI was determined to make sure the Japanese did not get IC technology at a bargain price. The Japanese also had other disadvantages when it came to the IC. The earliest important markets for the technology were in defense applications. Since the Japanese firms had no market for ICs to be used in missiles and other high technology defense applications, the U.S. firms quickly widened their lead in the types of ICs most suited for these purposes. Further the more complex IC production technology required far more complex "complementary assets" in the form of specialized production equipment than had been true with transistors. The U.S. infrastructure for the provision of these complementary assets was far stronger than that of Japan.

Nonetheless, Japan's success with ICs paralleled that with transistors. Just as TI had pioneered a prototypic model of the first major transistor consumer product, the pocket radio, TI also pioneered a prototypic model of the first mass IC consumer product, the handheld electronic calculator. And just as the Japanese quickly came to overcome this initial American lead to dominate the market for transistor radios, so too they quickly came to dominate the market for IC calculators (Reid, 1984). And, just as success with the relatively low-technology transistor radio led to strength in transistor technology, success with the relatively low-technology calculator led to strength in IC technology. In the late 1960s calculators accounted for some 60% of the demand for ICs (Omichi, 1990). Japanese strength in integrated circuits, in turn, supported its growing strength in IC production equipment. By the early 1990s the Japanese semiconductor manufacturing equipment industry had taken clear leads in technology and in world market share in many critical sectors (JEI, 1991).

In this paper, I argue that the Japanese success with ICs demonstrated remarkable flexibility and purposefulness on the part of the Japanese innovation community. The next section of the paper depicts the processes by which this happened. As a result of these processes the Japanese not only took the markets for IC calculators, but quickly became very strong in the production of semiconductor chip production equipment, chips and much computer equipment. A concluding section suggests some implications for policy and strategy of this account and also suggests future research.

**Transistor and IC Innovation Communities**

The innovation community framework, like perspectives focusing on "technology communities (Tushman and Anderson, 1986)," " national innovation systems (Nelson, 1993)," and "technological systems (Carlsson, and Stankiewicz, 1991), attempts to provide a systematic approach to analyzing the institutional environment for technological innovation. Unlike these other approaches it focuses on the organizations directly involved in the commercialization of a specific

3

new technology. The innovation community, accordingly, is smaller and more tightly bounded than that in other formulations. This allows more specified comparisons and points to issues of how broader institutional frameworks change with the progress from one technology to another. The innovation community framework also draws on the ecological literature to propose a distinctive structuring of the institutional environment (Astley and Fombrun, 1987). This includes a coordinating superstructure and a substructure consisting of firms producing the innovation and its major inputs. The superstructure includes non-market organizations, such as government, professional societies and trade associations, and also occasionally profit-making organizations such as the Japanese sogo shosha. These organizations route information and other key inputs to the elements in the substructure responsible for the innovation. The substructure includes the firms competing to commercialize the innovation as well as those supplying complementary assets such as production equipment or components. The purpose of the framework is to guide comparative research on technological innovation. Elsewhere we have suggested, for example, that different community configurations may make patterned differences in the speed or nature of innovation. We have suggested, for example, that more comprehensive superstructures are more conducive to discontinuous change. One stream of research based on this framework would emphasis cross-national comparisons -- providing a way of examining "national systems of innovation" (Reddy et al., 1991; Lynn, 1994b; Lynn et al., 1996; Lynn et al., forthcoming). This paper is primarily concerned with looking at the transition from one innovation community to a related one centered on a more advanced innovation. It also seeks to provide information that may allow comparisons between these innovation communities in Japan with those in the U.S. and elsewhere.

**Superstructure.** The primarily superstructural, or "coordinating," organizations in the Japanese innovation community that commercialized the transistor radio were governmental, though professional societies, industry associations and trading companies were also important (Lynn, forthcoming).

The Japanese government played four important roles in the commercialization of Japanese transistor radios: 1. creating technologies that overcame key barriers or demonstrated possibilities; 2. ensuring that firms in the substructure (the actual producers) were well aware of the new technology and encouraged to employ it; 3. coordinating technology imports to ensure that Japanese firms got the technology on favorable terms *and that they shared it with other Japanese firms*; and 4. helping to develop markets, especially export markets, for the innovation.

Government laboratories were the first in Japan to engage in semiconductor research after World War II. They were the first in Japan to make transistors, to make junction transistors, and to make experimental demonstration transistor radios. Study groups, including researchers from all the important electronics firms were organized by government researchers. The Ministry of International Trade and Industry (MITI) coordinated all technology imports in the 1950s and 1960s, intervening in negotiations to keep Japanese firms from bidding against each other to raise the price of a technology, guaranteeing royalty payments to make foreign firms more willing to sell to relatively-unknown Japanese partners, and making it difficult for a Japanese firms to monopolize an imported technology (Lynn, 1994a). MITI worked with industry associations and others to ensure the quality of Japanese transistor and transistor radio exports, and to forestall protectionism on the part of the countries importing these products.

Not surprisingly, government played similar roles in the case of ICs. The Electronics Technology Laboratories (ETL, which was attached to the Agency for Industrial Science and Technology of MITI) was first in Japan to produce a transistor. ETL was also first in Japan to produce a successful experimental IC. The success, as we shall see, provided a major stimulus to the electronics firms when it was announced in a Japanese business newspaper in January 1961 (Nishizawa and Ouchi, 1993; Nakagawa, 1981; SEIJ, 1991)

MITI also continued to play a role in coordinating technology imports through the early and mid 1960s. A critical technology allowing the viable production of ICs was the Fairchild planar process. In September 1963 MITI approved an exclusive agreement for NEC to import this technology. The agreement was "exclusive, " but MITI pressured NEC to sublicense the technology to all the other Japanese firms (Omichi, 1990; Fransman, 1995). MITI had frequently acted similarly in the 1950s and 1960s to prevent firms from monopolizing foreign technologies (Lynn, 1994a).

In early 1962 TI filed for Japanese patents on ICs (though the public release of the patents did not take place until June 1965). TI was more hesitant than Fairchild about selling rights to its patents to the Japanese. The company hoped to use the technology to leverage its way into the Japanese market. Indeed, in January 1964 TI applied to the Japanese government for permission to establish a wholly owned subsidiary in Japan. The main purpose of the plant was to supply IBM with semiconductors for use in computers. The TI application reinforced the conviction on the part of MITI officials that the IC technology was distinctively strategic to Japan. (Omichi, 1990). The Japanese patent office stalled in reviewing the TI patents (indeed the key patent was not awarded to TI until 1989).

Government and industry worked together in an effort to develop a response to the TI proposal for a wholly owned subsidiary. The Japan Electronics Industry Development Association (JEIDA - - an industry association formed in 1958 under MITI through the 1957 Temporary Measures for the Promotion of the Electronics Industry Law) established a special "TI Patent Countermeasures Committee." Foreign investment in ICs was still restricted at the time, but TI threatened to withhold its IC patents from the Japanese if it were not allowed to established its subsidiary. Meanwhile TI strengthened its position by filing for a series of eleven related patents (Nakagawa, 1981; JEIDA, 1988).

The Japanese government took its time in developing an initial response to TI's application. Finally, in September 1966 MITI imposed three conditions on the application: 1. instead of forming a wholly owned subsidiary, TI would have to establish a fifty-fifty joint venture with a Japanese partner; 2. TI would offer its basic patents to Japanese firms at a "reasonable" price; and 3. TI would exercise self-restraint to avoid making too harsh an impact on the Japanese firms. TI balked at the conditions, particularly the one requiring it to take a Japanese partner. TI argued that the subsidiary would have to spend a percentage of sales (about 16%) on R&D that would be unacceptable to Japanese partners, and also that a Japanese partner would simply rotate its people in and out of the joint venture, threatening its viability (Nakagawa, 1981).

MITI was faced with a dilemma. The Japanese semiconductor industry could not advance without access to the TI patents (some $500 million a year in exports to the U.S. that already used IC technology were at risk), yet a strong TI presence in Japan would also threaten the new industry. MITI continued to stall, a tactic the Ministry often used in trying to pressure foreign firms. MITI also sought to arouse Japanese public opinion against TI through judicious leaks to the press. MITI compared the proposed entry of TI into the Japanese market to the sudden (and to the Japanese shocking) appearance in Tokyo Bay of the American fleet of "Black Ships" a century earlier. The Black Ships had forced Japan to open itself to foreign trade. TI's senior managers

5

were outraged by MITI's stalling. TI's lawyers approached the government almost weekly. The deadlock continued through 1967. Finally, in 1968, TI agreed to MITI's conditions. At least one writer characterizes this as a TI victory (Reid, 1984) in which MITI backed down to a stubborn TI. A larger group (Anchordoguy, 1989; Nakagawa, 1981; Business Week, 1968, 1968a; Tatsuno, 1986.) argues that it was a MITI success. TI accepted a Japanese joint venture partner (with Sony), though the agreement was only for three years -- after which TI took full ownership. TI agreed to limit production of the joint venture so that its market share in Japan would be less than 10%. Perhaps, more importantly, MITI had delayed TI's entry into Japan. Tresize (1976) claims that this hurt Japan because it delayed the access of Japanese calculator producers to the latest IC technology. Other writers (e.g. Anchordoguy, 1985; Tatsuno, 1986) argue that by delaying the entry of TI into Japan, MITI gave the Japanese IC producers time to become competitive. Given the subsequent success of the Japanese in the electronic calculator and other industries this view seems plausible.

Despite the various efforts of MITI the Japanese firms were hobbled by the need to pay high royalties to the American providers of technology. Between them TI, Fairchild and Western Electric charged a royalty equal to 9.55% of Japanese sales of integrated circuits. Some Japanese firms also made additional payments for technological guidance to RCA and GE. To help alleviate the burden MITI offered subsidies to the Japanese producers under a national project for the development of ICs to be used in computers. Special loans were given by the Japan Development Bank to future support the industry. Just as MITI had helped promote exports of transistors and transistor radios, so too it helped in the case of integrated circuits (JEIDA, 1988).

Often working with government, Japanese business associations were also important parts of the Japanese superstructure. In the case of the transistor radio such organizations as the Japan Machinery Exporters Associations were central. In the case of ICs reference has been made to JEIDA. This organization itself was formed in the late 1950s under government coordination, but with the help of other industry associations such as the Electronics Machinery Industry Association (which represented firms producing radios, television sets and their components). Smaller more focused associations were also important. Just after TI filed for the Japanese patents on ICs, for example, some thirty resistor makers organized a "Circuit Miniaturization Research Association" to carry out cooperative research on semiconductor technology. Other associations were formed in the early 1960s focusing on materials, electronic computers and other sectors. Some of these associations imported semiconductor materials for analysis by the Japanese. Still others promoted Japanese IC exports (Omichi, 1990; JEIDA, 1988; more generally on such trade association activities see Lynn and McKeown, 1988). Professional societies such as the Physics Society provided venues in which information about the new technologies was announced to the industry and wider publics (Lynn, forthcoming).

The sogo shosha had also been important in the commercialization of transistor radio in Japan. At a time when few Japanese companies had overseas offices, and few Japanese managers had traveled outside Japan, the sogo shosha developed key contacts in the U.S. and Europe and helped researchers traveling from Japan to collect information. The sogo shosha also helped Japanese firms buy the technologies and production equipment they needed. Sony's agreement to purchase rights to the transistor technology from Western Electric in 1953 was negotiated with the help of a former Japanese sogo shosha employee. Marubeni's agent in the U.S. from 1953 to 1957, Kimura Ichitaro, helped some 280 Japanese engineers in the electronics industry on visits to the U.S.. Almost all of them visited Bell Laboratories, some also went to RCA and General Electric. Kimura was not an expert in semiconductors, but after successfully helping engineers from Toshiba and other companies was increasingly asked to help visitors. At the time members of the relatively small Japanese business community in New York helped each other out regularly, even when such help extended to competitors. Even rival sogo shosha would ask Kimura to arrange visits for their clients to semiconductor facilities in the U.S. (Marubeni, in return, would ask for assistance from other sogo shosha in areas where they had better developed contacts). Kimura was not an expert in semiconductors, he would often rely on the help of U.S.-based engineers from electronics firms such as Hitachi. Here too there was a remarkable spirit of cooperation at the time. A Hitachi manager might find himself helping engineers from arch-rival Toshiba (SEIJ, 1991).

During the 1950s the sogo shosha expanded their presence in the U.S. By the 1960s, an increasingly important role of the sogo shosha became identifying and importing the various forms of production equipment needed by Japanese manufacturers of semiconductors. A major problem was that U.S. suppliers had little interest in the Japanese market (growth was rapid in the U.S.), and were unwilling to provide after-sales support to Japanese customers. Reliability and quality problems were monumental. Additionally, MITI pushed Japanese firms to begin producing the equipment themselves, and sometimes made the import process difficult (SEIJ, 1991)

This provided opportunities for Japanese entrepreneurs. Two young semiconductor experts at the sogo shosha Nissho Iwai's U.S. office organized a new firm, Tokyo Electron in November 1963 to fill part of the gap. Tokyo Electron initially served as a service oriented importer of semiconductor production equipment to Japan. The company not only found the best equipment to sell Japanese clients, but also serviced the equipment. Later Tokyo Electron made arrangements for Japanese manufacturers to provide some of the equipment, and also itself became a producer (SEIJ, 1991, Gilder 1989). Traditional Japanese strengths in optics, photography and precision machinery provided a strong basis for the movement of Japanese firms in this new industry.

Substructure. The main elements of the substructure of the Japanese innovation community involved in commercializing the transistor radio included Sony (the first firm to market transistor radios in Japan), such firms as Toshiba and Hitachi (its major rivals in this product), Kobe Kogyo (an early rival for both the transistor and the transistor radio), and firms such as Alps and Mitsumi that developed key complementary assets such as miniaturized speakers and condensers. While some of the firms were also major elements in the substructure of the community commercializing ICs and IC-based calculators, there were important changes. Sony was not amongst the leaders, and such components as miniaturized speakers and condensers were not crucial complementary assets. The new key firms were NEC in the production of the introduction of IC technology to Japan, NEC and Sharp working to develop calculators, and such producers of IC production and test equipment as Tokyo Electron, Nikon, Kokusai Electric, and Ando Electric.

The first successful IC was made by Jack Kilby of Texas Instruments in October 1958. With Kilby's mesa IC, each separate transistor, diode and resister had to be interconnected by hand. In 1959, Robert Noyce of Fairchild, invented the planar IC, which was based on a more practical method for interconnecting circuit elements. In March 1960 Texas Instruments produced an IC for customer evaluation. In 1961 Fairchild manufactured the first commercial integrated circuits. The major market for ICs at the time was the defense industry. In 1962 Texas Instruments received a contract to develop ICs for Minuteman missiles. The first commercial use of the IC was in a hearing aid in December 1963, but in the early 1960s experts predicted that military applications would dominate demand for ICs (Braun and Macdonald, 1982; Kelly 1976; Wolff, 1976; Reid, 1984).

7

Meanwhile in Japan, the January 1961 announcement that ETL had produced a successful experimental IC shocked many researchers in the business community. Several firms had been relying on their ties with U.S. firms to gain an edge in the next generation of semiconductor technology. Mitsubishi Electric was attempting to commercialize the (ultimately unsuccessful) molectronics process being developed by Westinghouse Electric. Hitachi, Toshiba, Kobe Kogyo and others were trying to commercialize RCA's (ultimately unsuccessful) micromodule technology (Aida, 1992; SEIJ, 1991).

Managers at NEC were the first in Japan to get detailed information on the development of the IC in the U.S.. This was in late 1959. NEC had a close relationship with Fairchild because it had bought exclusive rights to the Fairchild patents for the planar production of transistors (Aida, 1992). In February 1960 NEC set up an IC development team. Initially the Japanese seemed to pose little challenge to the U.S. firms. As was noted above, many of the early applications for ICs were for defense in highly sophisticated applications. As with the transistor, the hearing aid provided another, rather small, niche. As with the transistor radio, however, the IC calculator provided the Japanese with a cheap high-volume consumer product based on a less sophisticated version of the technology. By quickly dominating this market, the Japanese moved to a position of strength with regard to the overall technology.

Some sources attribute the first electronic calculators (which used discrete transistors, not ICs) to a British company, Bell Punch, which had a machine on the market in 1963 (Dummer, 1983; Valery, 1975). Others say it is impossible to tell who first developed an electronic calculator (Braun and Macdonald, 1982). In any case, the Japanese quickly came to dominate this market based on their relatively low labor costs at the time (Malerba, 1985). One of the Japanese firms that was to become a leader with this product, and then with IC-based calculators, was Sharp (then called Hayakawa Electric). Sharp's top management had been attempting to enter the computer industry, but without much success. It was excluded from a national R&D program on computers by MITI, because its technology lagged behind such other major firms as Toshiba, Hitachi and NEC. In 1962 Sharp decided to give up on computers and concentrate on calculators. Company engineers worked with a professor at Osaka City University, and by March 1964 had an electronic desktop calculator ready for the market. The machine weighed 25 kilograms and cost about $U.S. 1,500 -- but was much faster than mechanical calculators (Moritani, 1990).

The next step would be a transition to the IC-based calculator, and development work was begun in both the U.S. and Japan. In 1965 TI (ironically the firm that had developed the first transistor radio, but then given up the market to the Japanese) began development of a hand held IC calculator. Meanwhile in Japan, Sharp was working on a desktop IC calculator with NEC, the most advanced Japanese company in the development and commercialization of IC technology. In 1967 Sharp and NEC successfully developed an IC desktop calculator. By the early 1970s Sharp and the other Japanese firms had about 85% of the U.S. market for electronic calculators. TI successfully introduced its hand held IC calculator in 1971 and briefly regained control of the U.S. market for calculators, but within a decade some 70% of the U.S. market belonged to the Japanese again (Reid, 1984).

One reason for the Japanese success was that firms like Sharp decided to use the MOS-IC technology (which had been developed by RCA in 1962), rather than the more sophisticated bipolar chips favored by U.S. firms. The MOS-ICs were slower, but consumed less power, were cheaper, and were more compact. For the MOS-IC technology Sharp initially had to go outside

Japan. The supplier of their chips was an American firm, North American Rockwell (Moritani, 1990; Nakagawa, 1981).

With the control of the market for IC calculators and soon other relatively low-technology IC commercial products, the Japanese IC producers increased their strength. In 1971 seven of the top ten semiconductor producers were American and three were Japanese. By 1981 five were American, four Japanese (the other was the Dutch company Philips). By 1988 only three U.S. firms remained in the top ten, compared to six Japanese firms. In 1980 U.S. firms were still the undisputed leaders in the production of semiconductor manufacturing equipment, by the early 1990s Japanese firms had supplanted them as leaders (JEI 1991, Omichi, 1990).

## Conclusions

Two contradictory images have guided our impressions of the development of technology in Japan. One image, particularly fashionable in the 1980s was of a juggernaut guided by elite bureaucrats in MITI and top managements of leading firms who would pick technologies likely to emerge as "winners," and then ensure that industry had the resources to exploit these technologies. In reaction to this another image emerged in which government and patterns of industrial relationships in Japan had nothing to do with Japan's technological successes, indeed had hindered that success.

This paper suggests substantial problems with both of these images. The Japanese superstructures were immensely flexible. New associations were formed as needed, the government role shifted -- withdrawing from some areas as firms became increasingly able to handle R&D and other functions on their own. The substructure saw the rise of firms that had been relative outsiders such as Sony in the case of the transistor radio and Sharp in the case of the electronic calculator, and the emergence of new firms such as Tokyo Electron. Initiatives came from a number of places, including private firms as well as government researchers. There was little sign of entrenched interests fighting rearguard actions to slow progress (note Rosenkopf and Tushman, 1996). Still, the picture painted here is not one of laissez faire. There was a substantial amount of co-ordinative activity from governmental and other superstructure organizations. These activities reduced the costs to firms of building conduits to international flows of technology. MITI rather than engaging in anticompetitive coordinating policies, as some have suggested, seemed to spur competition by such means as preventing the monopolization of imported technology and aggressively diffusing information on the new technologies.

Other factors also account for the Japanese success. One was that Japan had strength at the substructure level to allow creation of efficient providers of complementary assets. Japan's leadership in cameras, precision equipment and printing, for example, provided expertise to undergird a semiconductor production equipment industry. As has been noted by others (e.g. Gilder, 1989), the Japanese orientation towards low cost civilian products versus high technology defense oriented products turned out to be an advantage rather than, as initially believed, a handicap.

These areas should be explore further through explicitly cross-national comparisons between Japan, the U.S. and Europe. Comparisons with the more recent experiences of the NIEs also are needed. Of particular policy relevance may be that the Japanese case suggests the possibility of procompetitive technology import control policies for developing economies.

References

Aida, Y. (1991). *Denshi Rikkoku Nihon on Jijiden, I*. Tokyo: NHK.

... (1992). *Denshi Rikkoku Nihon on Jijiden, II*. Tokyo: NHK.

Anchordoguy, Marie (1989). *Computers, Inc.* Cambridge: Harvard University Press.

Astley, W. & C. Fombrun (1987). "Organizational Communities: An Ecological Perspective.' In. S. Bacharach & C. Fombrun (eds.), *Research in the Sociology of Organizations: 163-185*. Greenwich: JAI Press.

Braun, E. & S. Macdonald (1982), *Revolution in Miniature*, 2nd Ed., Cambridge: Cambridge University Press.

*Business Week* (1968). "TI Gives in to Tokyo." January 27: 132.

*Business Week* (1968a). "International Outlook.: May 4: 100.

Carlsson, Bo & R. Stankiewicz (1991). "On the Nature, Function and Composition of Technological Systems." *Journal of Evolutionary Economics*. I: 93-118.

Dummer,. G.W.A. (1983). *Electronic Inventions and Discoveries*, New York : Pergamon..

Fransman, Martin (1995). *Japan's Computer and Communications Industry*. Oxford: Oxford University Press.

Gilder, George (1989). *Microcosm*. New York: Simon and Schuster.

Goto, Akira (1993). "Technology Importation: Japan's Postwar Experience." pp. 277-304 in J. Teranishi & Y. Kosai (eds.) *The Japanese Experience of Economic Reform*. London: Macmillan.

Japan Economic Institute (JEI) (1991). *JEI Report*. 21:a. June 7.

Japan Electronics Industry Development Association (JEIDA) (1988). *Denshi Kogyo Kai 30-nen no Ayumi*. Tokyo: JEIDA.

Kelly, Jack S. (1976). "Invention of the Integrated Circuit," *IEEE Transactions on Electron Devices*. ED-23, 7 (July): 648-654.

Lynn, Leonard H. (forthcoming). "The Commercialization of the Transistor Radio in Japan: The Functioning of an Innovation Community." *IEEE Transactions on Engineering Management*.

... (1994a). "MITI's successes and failures in Controlling Japan's Technology Imports." *Hitotsubashi Journal of Commerce and Management*. 29: 15-33.

... (1994b). "Japan's Systems of Innovation: A Framework for Theory Guided Research." In S. Beechler & A. Bird, *Research in International Business and International Relations*: 6: 161-188..

Lynn, Leonard H., J.D. Aram & N.M. Reddy (forthcoming). "Technology Communities and Innovation Communities." *Journal of Engineering-Technology Management*.

Lynn, Leonard H. & T.J. McKeown (1988). *Organizing Business: Trade Associations in the U.S. and Japan*. Washington, D.C.: University Press.

Lynn, Leonard H., N.M. Reddy & J. Aram (1996). "Linking Technology and Institutions: The Innovation Community Framework." *Research Policy*: 25: 91-106.

Malerba, Franco (1985). *The Semiconductor Business*. Madison: University of Wisconsin.

Moritani, M. (1990). *Gijutsu Kaihatsu no Showa-shi*. Tokyo: Asahi.

Nakagawa, Y. (1981). *Dokyumento Nihon no Handotai Kaihatsu*. Tokyo: Diamond.

Nelson, Richard (ed.) (1993). *National Innovation Systems*. New York: Oxford.

Nishizawa, J. & A. Ouchi (1993). *Nihon no Handotai Kaihatsu*. Tokyo: Kogyo Chosakai.

Omichi, Y. (1990). *Handotai Gyokai*. Tokyo: Kyoikusha.

Reddy, N., J. Aram & Leonard H. Lynn (1991). "The Institutional Domain of Technology Diffusion." *The Journal of Product Innovation Management*: 295-304.

Reid, T.R. (1984). *The Chip*. New York: Simon & Schuster.

Rosenkopf, Lori & M. Tushman. (1996). *The Coevolution of Community Networks and Technology*. Working Paper. Philadelphia: Wharton.

Semiconductor Equipment Industry of Japan (SEIJ) (1991). *"Handotai Rikkoku" Nippon*. Tokyo: Nikan Kogyo.

Tatsuno, S. (1986). *The Technopolis Strategy*. New York: Prentice-Hall.

Tilton, John (1971). *International Diffusion of Technology: the Case of Semiconductors*. Washington: Brookings.

Trezise, P. with Y. Suzuki (1976). "Politics, Government, Economic Growth," pp. 753-811 in H. Patrick & H. Rosovsky (eds.). *Asia's New Giant*. Washington, Brookings.

Tushman M. & P. Anderson (1986). "Technological Discontinuities and Organizational Environments." *Administrative Science Quarterly*, 31: 753-811.

Valery, Nicholas (1975). "Coming of age in the calculator business." In *New Scientist*. Calculator Supplement 68:973 (Nov. 13): ii-iv.

Wolff, Michael F. (1976). "The Genesis of the Integrated Circuit,' *IEEE Spectrum*. August: 45-53.

# 002

THE IMPACT OF R&D ON INNOVATIVE AND BUSINESS
PERFORMANCE: A COMPARISON
BETWEEN UNITED STATES AND BRAZIL

Author:
Roberto Sbragia
Faculty of Economics, Business Administration and Accountancy
University of Sao Paulo
Brazil

| | |
|---|---|
| Tel: | +55-11-210-4640 |
| Fax: | +55-11-816-8044 |
| e-mail: | rsbragia@usp.br |

Co-authors:
Alden S.Bean, Roger L.Whitely and Jeannie M. Russo, CIMS/Lehigh
University, United States, Phone 1.610.758-3427, Fax 1.610.758-3655
Isak Krugliankas and Tales Andreassi, FEA/University of Sao Paulo,
Brazil, Phone 55.11.210-4640, Fax 55.11.816-8044

## ABSTRACT

Databases regarding Industrial R&D Indicators are being implemented since
1992 in Brazil, by ANPEI- National Association for R&D of the Industrial
Companies, and United States, by IRI- Industrial Research Institute
following similar methodologies. This paper is intended to present a
comparative analysis using data of both cases focusing on the impact of
the R&D intensity on the innovative and business performance of the
firms.
Common indicators and longitudinal analysis will be used in order to
explore the idea that business performance, at some extent, is related to
the R&D effort.

Key Words:       Industrial Technology/R&D
                 Technology/R&D Management
                 Technology/R&D Performance

Topical Category: I 2

Oral Presentation

# Strategy-Driven Technology in International Competition

**Submitted by:**

William B. Werther, Jr.,Ph.D.
Samuel N. Friedland Professor of Executive Management
School of Business Administration
414 Jenkins Building
University of Miami
Coral Gables, Florida 33124
Phone:     (305) 284-2706
  Fax:     (305) 284-2655

**Key Words:**

Strategy
Technology
Technology Convergence
Context Management
International Competition
Entrepenuership
Technology Management
Alliance Management

**Topical Categories:**

(A), (B), (E), (H), (I)


**Oral Presentation**

# Strategy-Driven Technology in International Competition

## (Abstract)

Great firms and entire industries have been launched through
entrepreneurial efforts that applied emergent technologies to
recognized problems. Early recombinant DNA pharmaceutical
research, personal computers and their software are current
examples; historical examples are found at the origins of
telephone, automobile, aerospace, and other industries--only
distantly associated with their founding entrepreneurs. However,
as technology-driven industries transcend their entrepreneurial
beginnings and become mature, the underlying technologies tend to
converge around the "best" technology--at least as perceived by
the end-users.

Technology convergence shifts the basis of competition from
superior technologies to other conditions, such as efficiency,
quality, or ease-of-use.  This strategic shift does not negate
the importance of technology; the application of the underlying
technology remains essential to the industry's players. However,
as technologies converge, the source of sustainable competitive
demands either a new technology or superiority in non-
technological areas. The changing requirements faced by industry
maturity demand that technologists not only manage the underlying
technologies but also their context.

"Context management" recognizes that competitive advantage
also can be found outside the technology-oriented elements of the
firm's value added chain. Simply put, superiority in non-
technological areas may even be more heavily valued by the
customer. Strategy formulation for technology-driven firms,
therefore, must embrace both the technological and contextual
issues in order to achieve successful technology management.
Defining the scope of technology management to exclude strategic
thinking and its relevant contexts often leads to technology
leaders becoming marketplace followers, even losers.

Relying on a life-cycle paradigm and theory base, the
proposed paper provides a framework for identifying likely
transition points that differentiate technology-driven from
strategy-driven approaches to technology management. Then the
contextual elements of strategic-driven technology management are
discussed, outlining the minimum necessary elements associated
with the industry/firm evolution into a mature industry. These
elements include productivity, quality, service, speed, and
alliance options, since these are often key variables in ensuring
a successful transition. The paper concludes with propositions
that identify needed pathways for future research.

# Strategy-Driven Technology in International Competition

Once a technology is perceived to be useful on the basis of a cost/benefit analysis, the technology and its applications are ultimately driven by their interaction with markets. These market-technology interactions often unleash strong, competitive forces that eventually dominate the technology, shaping it to the dictates of the marketplace (Nevens, Summe, and Uttal, 1990).

Analysis of many businesses suggests that they move through rather predictable stages that constitute a life cycle. Though the duration of each stage, and therefore the entire life cycle, is highly variable, both the sequence of the stages and the implications for the technology are predictable within broad parameters because each stage of the life cycle is characterized with common, business-related responses, regardless of the underlying technologies.

At the same time, technological solutions tend to converge around a single technology or family of technologies that are deemed to be the "best" solution from the end-user perspective. This technological convergence further accelerates the subordination of the technology to the marketplace. In time, the once innovative technology becomes a given in the marketplace and, thus, ceases to be a source of competitive advantage. In fact, the technology becomes a necessary but insufficient condition of competitive success (Werther and Kerr, 1995).

Leaders who have put their emphasis on the technology side of technology management often discover that their once innovative technology is not longer innovative enough to fend off competitors who have sought competitive advantage in areas outside of technology. The predictability of the technology/business life cycle combined with the tendency toward technological convergence suggests noteworthy implications for the strategic management of technology.

This paper outlines the theory and implications of the technological/business life cycle. Then attention focuses on the tendency of technological convergence. The paper ends with a discussion of strategic and operational implications for the management of technology.

## Industry/Technology Life Cycles

Technologies, organizations, and the industries they create, evolved through predictable stages, often referred to as a life cycle. This life cycle emerges only against the backdrop of competition; monopolistic or government-controlled industries can distort, even delay, the onset of each stage within the life cycle. The invisible hand of competition, as Adam Smith referred to it in his seminal, 1776 book, An Inquiry into the Wealth of

Nations, derives from decision makers pursuing their best
interests. These individual efforts have collective impact,
however, that results in a predictable and sequential series of
stages that shape the firm and its industry life cycle.

As outlined by Figure 1, the initial relationship between
technology an business purpose is one of experimentation, seeking
to find the right cost/performance relationships. At this early
stage the relationship between supply and demand is almost always
uncertain because the actual costs/benefits to the end-users are
not well defined. In fact, it is this uncertainty that causes
many firms with good technologies to fail. Often these firms lack
the management skills to deal with the complexity of integrating
technology with operations to produce a salable product. Or, even
if they can overcome this roadblock, barriers of marketing and
insufficient capital often loom large. But when the technology is
compelling enough and the entrepreneur finds the combination of
technology, operations, and capital, the technology-based
business moves to the next level.

Simply put, the growth stage of the life cycle results when
the cost/benefit relationships become both obvious and favorable
to the end-users and management is able to acquire the capital to
integrate the production and marketing. Here demand typically
outstrips supply. This undersupply combines with a beneficial
technology begins to attract others into the market with similar
technologies or technologies that achieve similar end results.
These new entrants contribute not only additional supply to the
industry, they contribute new approaches and new solutions.

Efforts to standout from competitors often take two
directions as the growth stage continues. One approach is the
price approach.  Here competitors seek to standout on the basis
of price, attracting the cost-conscious buyer. Often, new
entrants into the market with copying strategies have little else
to offer but low prices because established competitors have gain
reputational, geographic, or other advantages. Budget and Value
Rent-A-Car companies recognized this need when entering the North
American rental car market against well-established players like
Hertz and Avis, so they incorporated their proposed point of
competitive advantage into their name. The other approach is to
differentiate the product on some other, non-price basis, such as
quality, prestige, or design, for example. To illustrate the
point, consider that Mercedes Benz sells prestige; Volvo safety.

Publicizing these approaches combined with the price-
lowering effects of increased competition, tend to expand the
market--attracting still more new entrants, expanding the
quantity available, publicizing the technology, and putting
pressure on players for still lower prices. In the absence of
outside intervention or regulation, this beneficial-to-buyers
cycle continues until the market exhibits a situation of

oversupply.

The mature stage is characterized by supply exceeding demand. At first, this imbalance might only reveal itself during an economic downturn. But, in time, the oversupply persists even at the top of the business cycle, as the worldwide automobile market suggests. Though demand may still be growing during the mature stage, the growth has usually slowed, taking on an increasingly cyclical nature. Competitors discover surplus capacity and are willing to sell products at steep discounts in order to maintain cash flow and utilization of sunk capital investments. More precisely, many producers are willing to sell at a price below total costs but above marginal costs, setting off a price war. Late entrants who have not achieved economies of scale are decimated by the ensuing price war. The result is the beginning of industry consolidation. Bankruptcies become common in the industry and remaining players begin to merge to reduce competition or to gain economies of scale. The industry continues with fewer players facing squeezed margins.

Eventually, the slowing sales stagnate and begin an irreversible, long-term drop. Here the industry has entered the decline stage, with many of the weaker firms still around having entered this stage individually before the entire industry. Though this stage can be profitable--for example, money is still being made selling vacuum tubes--the industry attractiveness is often low, making it difficult to attract talent and capital. Of course, oblivion is not inevitable. The industry may undergo a long-term decline over decades or it may be renewed by a new technology--as boom boxes renewed the portable radio businesses.

Technology Convergence
        Chief Technology Officers and corporate strategists might argue that the concern over the stages of the life cycle concept do not apply to technology-driven firms (Adler and Ferdows, 1990). The argument often made is straightforward: Our technology is unique, even guarded with patents. Therefore, we can stand above the ensuing price war and use our technology to differentiate our products throughout the so-called mature stage. Though the reasoning is seductive, it is seldom accurate. Instead, even truly unique technology-derived competitive advantage becomes marginalized by competitors. Consider Apple Computer, as an example. Its graphic user interface (GUI) was, and by many accounts, remains a superior technology. But the onslaught of the Windows technology from Microsoft and the ever more powerful generations of Intel microprocessors (WINTEL) have consigned Apple to a declining role with an unattractive future. Sony's Betamax for home use was considered technologically superior; its gone from the consumer market. Polaroid, which has held onto the self-developing market with its unique technology, is a minor player in the photographic industry. In each of the examples, the technology was superior, even unique, but the

competitive results were eclipsed by others. What happened?

Although an analysis of Apple, Sony, and Polaroid would reveal differences in strategy and execution, each was a victim of technology convergence. Personal computers are converging around the "WINTEL" technology interface; home video recorders have converged around the VHS standard; and, photography has converged around 35 millimeter, not instant photography. As the technology becomes more widely accepted and standardized, individual technological attributes may not be sufficient to overcome the convergence trend. While Sony's Betamax or Apple's GUI were superior technologies unique to their firms, for example, the end users preferred the longer playing times of VHS or the greater availability of software for the WINTEL platform.

As an industry moves from the beginning toward the end of its life cycle, technology as the driver quickly gives way to strategy. Firms that blindly hang on to their technology-based solutions as though they were some primitive gods, the worship of whom are guaranteed to deliver salvation, are often disappointed to find out that technology is a fickled and false god. Again, consider Apple, Sony's Betamax, or Polaroid.

As suggested by Figure 2, the impact of technology in shaping the industry declines as the industry moves from the introduction to the growth stage. By the beginning of the mature stage, the industry has largely converged on a given technology. Holdouts for other technologies may survive in a niche, but they typically find that their "unique" technology is increasingly marginalized by the mainstream technology developments. Sadly, too, it is often too late to change over to the main technology because in so doing the firm would face start-up costs and have little unique to add in an industry that has become increasingly competitive and price conscious. Still worse, a firm that has relied on technology as its point of difference would likely find that it has insufficient marketing and distribution competencies to compete with well established, mainline players. What would Apple offer if it adopted the WINTEL technology? Compaq and IBM along with Dell and Gateway would not yield share willingly and Apple would have little compelling to offer customers not already provided by existing WINTEL players.

Though there can be no doubt that technology can ignite an industry by finding a more effective or efficient solution to a problem, when that technology is widely available or been superceded by technologies that provide the end user with similar results, it ceases to be a source of competitive advantage. When a unique technology delivers a "me too" result, or worse, a result that is seen as less than that of competitors, competitive survival is neither likely nor, from an efficient use of resource, desirable.

## Strategic Technology Management

The purpose of strategy is to gain a sustainable source of competitive advantage. Technology can deliver that advantage initially. But, when the industry matures and the technologies converge, industry success depends less and less on the underlying technology and more and more on the strategic management of technology. That is, competitive success shifts from technology to the broader context in which that technology is delivered (Erickson, Magee, Rousel, 1990). Return to the personal computer (PC) market for an example. When Apple pioneered many of the innovations that make up the PC or when IBM validated the PC as a business tool, Compaq Computers did not exist. Today, Compaq is the largest seller of PCs in the world. While Apple tried to ride its proprietary technologies into the future and IBM sought technological advantage in its (superior but failed) OS2 software, Compaq pursued rigorous cost cutting in its manufacturing of the technology standard for the industry, the WINTEL platform--a marriage of technologies it neither developed nor furthered.

Or consider an even older example from the plain paper copier industry. Here Xerox enjoyed such a commanding lead in technology (plain paper copying via the Haloid process) and strategy (through its worldwide distribution partners and its innovative leasing arrangements) that the company name became a verb in many languages--as in, "Please xerox this for me." Japanese manufacturers collectively unseated Xerox by pursuing a low-cost, high reliability strategy. Japanese producers developed a strategy of giving purchasers a better value than Xerox--a better value in terms of price and reliability. Xerox, believing in its technological competencies--which were considerable compared with the weak management capabilities of its senior executives--and seeking short term profitability, essentially abandoned the low-end market pioneer by the Japanese in favor of more expensive (and profitable) high-end machines. With a beachhead established, the Japanese moved up the value-added scale, eventually dominating the photocopier market. Only by shifting from a technological orientation to a strategic one that involved a total quality management approach to management was Xerox saved from the long-term decline phase of its life cycle.

The point of these examples is that even technological pioneers--such as Apple, IBM, and Xerox--typically succeed in the long run based more on their strategic management of technology than on the actual technologies themselves. Admittedly, technologies are often the minimum necessary condition for entry into an industry. But success across the industry life cycle depends on transitioning the management of the firm from a technological orientation to a managerial one that embraces strategic planning for the product over its entire life cycle (Bahrami and Evans, 1989). What is ultimately required of management is vision--the ability to see the future of the industry and articulate that vision in an ennobling way that motivates technical and non-technical team members to coordinate their actions in preparation for that future.

The need for such a vision by senior management demands looking beyond the experimentation issues of the introduction phase or the operational issues of the growth stage. Instead, what is needed is a clear understanding of the position the product will hold when the industry has matured and reached slow growth. Though mature industries may be less glamorous than the launch of new technologies, the mature stage often necessitates limited additional investment and can be a source of free cash flow needed to prime the technological pump and the next round of technological innovation. Undoubtedly, it is this realization that successful, mature products are needed to generate the surplus revenues that fund innovation that drove Jack Welch, the CEO of General Electric, to demand that his subordinate managers make GE products number one or number two in market share or, failing that, deliver to him either a plan to do so or to sell off the lagging division.

Fortuitously, chief technology officers and other senior executives have at their disposal a tool commonly used in technology-driven organizations, namely, cross functional teams composed of not only technologist, production specialists, and marketing experts, but also strategists. Though the need for vision remains a demand on senior management, cross functional teams can embrace organizational strategists or outside consultants to plan how the new technology will emerge from the introduction to growth and then to mature stages. What this requires is a perspective that goes beyond solving just the immediate problems facing the team but to identify what actions are needed now to ensure that the technology-based product remains dominate throughout the growth and mature phases.

Though the requirements for life cycle success will vary from technology to technology and from market to market, observations of successful firms suggest several minimum conditions need to be planned for from the early stages, preferably before product introduction takes place (Adler, Riggs, and Wheelright, 1989). Paramount among the contextual variable surrounding the technology appear to be plans to radically drive the per unit cost down in ways that lead to high (though not necessarily the "best") quality. While the technology is still undergoing modifications in later stages, fast-time-to-market capabilities are necessary to gain what is called, first mover advantage--the benefits of being first to a market (Dumaine, 1989; Eisenhardt, 1990). But, like a good boxer who wants to get in the first punch, first mover advantage needs to be backed by a counter punch that destablizes (and, hopefully, demoralizes) competitors when they respond (Gomory, 1989; Gupta and Wilemon, 1990).

At a deeper level, the cross-functional team must identify the core competencies needed to deliver increasing value to customers (Prahalad and Hamel, 1990). In the introduction phase, for example, the need for smooth, efficient manufacturing in the mature stage seems remote, if relevant at all. But, that need to be a low cost (if not the low cost) producer is usually the hallmark of firms that dominate their industry--or want to do so. Ultimately, the challenge for senior management is to get members of cross-functional teams to learn to think strategically, building that particular learning function into the teams in such a way that they pass on to new team members a strategic technology management perspective (Senge, 1990).

Conclusions

From a management viewpoint, the creation or identification of a technology that is subsequently operationalized is often a major effort, particularly when that technology presents a significant technological or commercial breakthrough. The result is that a long, and often vexing problem has been solved. But the identification or creation of the technology and its subsequent operationalization are but two of the necessary three steps to long-term, commercial success. Admittedly, there will be no technological-driven success without the technology and the technology is useless without being operationalized into to usable and presumably profitable venture. But these two steps do not ensure long-term, competitive success.

Needed is a strategic perspective that goes beyond merely operationalizing the technology and putting it into the marketplace. Strategy forms the third leg of a successful approach to technology management. Unfortunately, technologist seldom have the training to think strategically, instead focusing on the creation/operationalization for which they are trained. Yet, interestingly, technologist have an array of tools that can overcome this deficiency. Primary among these are experience with cross-functional work teams.

When integrating technologies from different areas, it is common to assemble a team whose members can draw on their different sources of expertise. Often, one even finds marketing representatives on these teams, who serve as the voice of the customer. By going a step further and integrating corporate strategist into the product planning stages, technology leaders can move beyond the tactical plans of operationalization to the strategic plans of how to dominate the sector or industry created by the newly emerging technology.

References

Adler, Paul, Henry Riggs, and Steven Wheelwright, "Product Development Know-How: Trading Tactics for Strategy," Sloan Management Review, Fall, 1989, pp.7-17.

Adler, Paul S. and Kasra Ferdows, "The Chief Technology Officer," California Management Review, Spring, 1990, pp. 55-62.

Bahrami, Homa and Stuart Evans, "Strategy Making in High-Technology Firms: The Empiricist Mode," California Management Review, Winter, 1989, pp. 107-128.

Dumaine, B. "How Managers Can Succeed Through Speed," Fortune, February 13, 1989, p. 54. Among firms classified as "high technology," the interdependence between the timely use of technology and competitive advantage is even more obvious. As Dumaine reports: An economic model developed by the McKinsey & Co. management consulting firm shows that high-tech products that come to market six months late but on budget will earn 33% less profit over five years. In contrast, coming out on time and 50% over budget cuts profits only 4%.

Eisenhardt, Kathleen M., "Speed and Strategic Choice: How Managers Accelerate Decision Making," California Management Review, Spring, 1990, pp. 39-54.

Erickson, Tamara J., John F. Magee, Philip A. Roussel, and Kamal N. Saad, "Managing Technology as a Business Strategy," Sloan Management Review, Spring, 1990, p. 74.

Gomory, R.E., "From the 'Ladder of Science' to the Product Development Cycle," Harvard Business Review, November-December, 1989, pp.99-105. And, as Gomory observed: "One cannot overestimate the importance of getting through each turn of the cycle more quickly than a competitor. It takes only a few turns for the company with the shortest cycle time to build up a commanding lead."

Gupta, Ashok K., and David L. Wilemon, "Accelerating the Developments of Technology-Based New Products," California Management Review, Winter, 1990, pp. 24-44.

Nevens, T.M., G.L. Summe, and B. Uttal "Commercializing Technology: What the Best Companies Do," Harvard Business Review, May-June, 1990, pp. 154-163.

Prahalad, C.K. and Gary Hamel, "The Core Competence of the Corporation," Harvard Business Review, May-June, 1990, pp. 79-91.

Senge, Peter M. "The Leader's New Work: Building Learning Organizations," Sloan Management Review Fall, 1990, pp. 7-23.

Werther, Jr., William B. and Jeffrey L. Kerr, "The Shifting Sands of Competitive Advantage," Business Horizons (Volume 38, No. 3) May-June, 1995, pp. 11-17.

## Industry/Technology Life Cycles

| Stage | Name | Description |
|-------|------|-------------|
| I | Introduction | Experimentation with the technology and business purpose integration; the supply and demand relationships are uncertain. |
| II | Growth | Successful integration generally leads to (often rapid) growth, as the technological solution is more widely recognized as superior to pre-existing solutions; typically demand is growing and exceeds supply. |
| III | Maturity | Maturation of the industry is generally characterized as widely agreed upon technological configurations and distribution systems with slow to stagnant growth; over the business cycle, average supply exceeds demand even though demand may be flat to growing. |
| IV | Decline | The decline of the technology-based industry results from the base technology being superceded by a new one and/or a declining end-user interest; over the business cycle, average supply exceeds demand and demand is declining. |

Figure 1.  Industry/Technology Life

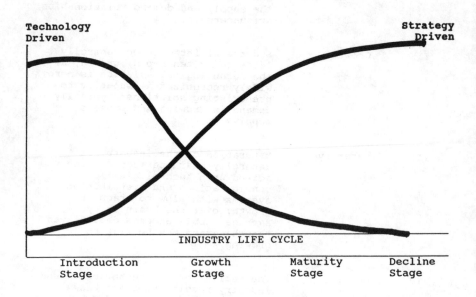

## Strategy and Technological Convergence

## Over the Industry Life Cycle

**Technology
Driven**

**Strategy
Driven**

INDUSTRY LIFE CYCLE

| Introduction<br>Stage | Growth<br>Stage | Maturity<br>Stage | Decline<br>Stage |

Figure 2.  Strategy and Technological Convergence over the
Industry Life Cycle

# 004

Prof. Dr.-Ing. Georg Obieglo
Fachhochschule Reutlingen--Hochschule für Technik und Wirtschaft
Reutlingen University of Technology and Business Administration

## Learning by Doing--Diploma Thesis in a Company
### Study Structure

Fachhochschulen in Germany are, in comparison to classical universities, a very new type of higher education institution. One characteristic of these schools is that to date legislation has only allowed courses of study in engineering, business management and social sciences. A further characteristic is that in many federal states (cultural policy is a responsibility of federal states in Germany) the valid regulations call for two practical semesters of approximately six months each, to be integrated into the course of study. The third characteristic is the consequential procedure for appointing professors. With very few exceptions, the professors at Fachhochschulen have already had their own professional experience in business. The course of study lasts eight semesters, including the two practical semesters, and ending with the completion of a diploma thesis written in conjunction with a firm. As a rule, accompanying exams are taken each semester. This type of structure is well-organized. In comparison to some other German institutions of higher education, the length of study at Fachhochschulen is short and time-efficient. After students have successfully completed all necessary exams and tests, they are required to spend a semester doing work and research at a chosen firm and to write a diploma thesis. Graduates receive an academic degree, for example Diploma-Engineer with the addition of FH (Fachhochschule), to distinguish the title from that of other types of schools.

The experiences of Fachhochschulen concerning each of these characteristics have been extremely positive in their first 25 years. The close relationship between study programs and real business, made possible through the practical study semesters, the practical experience of the professors and--to be explained later--the chance for students to complete their thesis within a company all enormously increase the chances for graduates to succeed in their job search. In the following example, you will see how a beneficial partnership between the academic and professional fields can be an advantage for all three partners: student, school, and business.

### The Work Thesis

#### Length

As the program is designed, students are required to carry out and complete a work thesis at the end of their studies. The requirements are laid out in the exam regulations, with a term of three to six months, always after all other semesters. This period is counted from the receipt of the topic to completion and delivery of the paper to the examination office.

#### Style and Tasks

The work thesis is a chance for students to prove that during their semestes of study, they have learned to scientifically analyse a topic, seek potential solutions, and formulate one of these solutions. There are no set rules for the topic or the project style. Therefore, various theoretical, experimental, and mixed formats are possible. Students have not only the ability to choose topic areas for their thesis, but also location and representing professor during the completion of the thesis.

## Location

Considering the various topics and styles for theses, students may also choose from a variety of locations to complete their project. It can be written at the school, at home, or at the library (when the work is theoretical). It can be completed in the laboratory or the computer center of the school, or alone and exclusively in a firm. It can, however, also be written in a mixed form, part at school, part at the firm. The way in which the thesis is completed depends very heavily upon the topic, the argument, and also the availability of the necessary laboratory and equipment.

## Working in the Industry

It is understandable that a school which finds such importance in practical training also seeks close cooperation with business in this last semester of the program. The following are a few aspects of organisation, problems and trends regarding such a partnership.

## Organisation

As the program is organised, students are required to have a clearly outlined topic with descriptions of the tasks and a representing professor. The following two examples are variations of the way theses have been carried out in the last few years.

## Variation A

The firm sends a list of possible thesis topics to a professor at the school, who either keeps it for students to look at or posts it on the bulletin board. Contact to the firm is kept through the professor, who, after matching the firm with a students, receives an outline of the topic together with a description of the scope of the work. With these papers, he makes suggestions for improving the topic and at the same time acknowledges his role as representing professor.

## Variation B

The student contacts the firm on his or her own, or has already had contact with them through a former practical semester. After the student and the firm have decided to work together, the student must find a representing professor. This professor receives the topic suggestions and scope of tasks. The process then continues as in Variation A.
In general, the representing professor makes an agreement with the student that he or she will report regularly to the professor about his or her progress and any problems that may arise. Toward the end of the project, the professor will make a visit to the firm in order to become informed about the student's attained goals, the construction of the research and, most importantly, the student's work performance at the firm. The completed and returned thesis is then registered and graded by the professor and a reader. The professor's previous visit to the firm also plays a considerable role in his or her analysis of the thesis.

## Positive Aspects

The exceptional feature of the work thesis lies in the aspect of working in a potential future career area and in the exposure to real occupational situations. The student takes a look at current problem issues within the field. He or she recognizes not only the limitations of finding solutions, but also the association of solutions with costs. He or she gains perspectives into organisational decision-making and work structures, which in many ways are carried out very differently than they are taught in school. He or she also acquires impressions of the working climate of a firm and the activities of those responsible in regard to modern management. He or she gains experience in meeting deadlines, which is an invaluable practice for later occupational life. The student also experiences the feeling of working on a topic which is an integral part of the firm's success.

## Problems

We must consider also the other side of the coin regarding the thesis. One of the main problems, especially for the firms which are new to this procedure, lies in the overload of themes in a thesis. Through patient discussion, a compromise must be found between the requirements of the firm, the completion of a topic and the timetable that the student is given by the school.
A further problem is, in some cases, the lack of support within a firm. Above all for experimental work, it is necessary that the required machines be available, that other departments support the work being done, and that a research system be set up and/or adapted. If the representatives in the firm are not willing to provide the necessary arrangements in a timely manner, the student may lose a considerable amount of valuable time waiting for technical clarifications or the sequence of a research structure.
A final problem is the firm-oriented implementation of a thesis. For example, the student could be used only as a gopher used to carry out endless measurements to gain the respective knowledge for further decisions without really being involved in the problem. Or, the written thesis could be filled with firm-specific abbreviations and names which are not understandable when read by a third party.

## Trends

Regarding the implementation of the work thesis, the following trends have developed in the last few years. Many firms take advantage of the students' practical semester in order to prepare them to come back for their final thesis. The reason behind this technique is that, after a six-month relationship, the firm has a reasonably good idea of how the student works and also of his or her ability to work with the others at the firm. If the firm has had a good impression of the student, it is motivated to continue its cooperation and perhaps hire him or her later as a permanent employee.
The completion of a thesis is also advantageous because the firm can use this concrete project as a clear example of the student's abilities. The same holds true for the student, who has many opportunities to look intensively at the firm. The increasing internationalisation of business brings with it the reality that an applied semester abroad is becoming more and more interesting even for students of technical disciplines. Along with the possibility of completing a work thesis abroad comes an excellent opportunity to gain international experience without losing a semester from studies. There are some departments at our school of which 90% of the students complete their thesis at a firm, and from those firms 30% are located abroad. In those cases, it is understandable that the thesis would be written in the respective language of the firm.

## Conclusion

The completion of the work thesis, which is a very important part of studies at a polytechnic university, has greatly increased in cooperation with a company. Students are most widely interested in completing their theses abroad when possible, either within Europe or even further. To make this possible, both firms and the school administration are challenged to provide the necessary opportunities for writing the thesis. After many years of experience with this concept, we can guarantee that the thesis in a company, "learning by doing," offers the following advantages

> for students:
> --getting to know a company
> --working on an interesting project
> --a work topic closely related to later occupational activities
> --additional connections to help in finding a career after studies
>
> for the school:
> --education oriented toward real occupational situations
> --good cooperation with businesses
> --the attractiveness of the school and its graduates
>
> for the firm:
> --the treatment of a topic by an unbiased third party
> --capable, motivated help for its own employees
> --the working through of a problem not exclusively with cost pressures involved
> --the acquisition of an employee that can work with the team
> --swift adaptation of an entry-level employee into the company

# 005

# EFFECT OF INTEGRATED MANUFACTURING STRATEGIES ON MANUFACTURING PERFORMANCE: A STUDY OF SOME EUROPEAN MULTINATIONALS

[1]H. Paul
School of Management
Asian Institute of Technology
PO Box 4, Klongluang, Thailand 12120
Tel. +66 2 5246143/Fax. +66 2 5245667
E-mail: hpaul@ait.ac.th

B. Suresh
Central Purchasing
Eletrolux AB, Sweden

Keywords: Integrated Manufacture, Competitive Performance, Manufacturing Strategy

**Topic L, Category 2**

**Suitable for Oral Presentation**

[1]Corresponding author.

# EFFECT OF INTEGRATED MANUFACTURING STRATEGIES ON MANUFACTURING PERFORMANCE: A STUDY OF SOME EUROPEAN MULTINATIONALS

H. Paul, School of Management, Asian Institute of Technology, Bangkok, Thailand

B. Suresh, Central Purchasing, Electrolux AB, Stockholm, Sweden

## ABSTRACT

Advanced manufacturing may be deemed to operate on an integrated plane supported by three pillars - computer integrated manufacturing(CIM), total quality control(TQC) and just-in-time(JIT) or their variants. These technologies are based on the broader classification of new manufacturing technologies into design, production and planning methods. Integrated manufacturing strategies are formulated with coherent decisions in these three technologies to transform the entire manufacturing function to gain superior competitive performance. This competitive advantage is manifest in performance factors of cost, quality, delivery and flexibility. Although the concept of integrated manufacturing means that these technologies work jointly and interactively to bring together previously independent elements of manufacturing, they also can and do work independently.

This paper presents the results of a study to determine the effect of integrated manufacturing strategy incorporating CIM, TQC and JIT on competitive manufacturing performance. Multiple regression is used to determine the effect of integrated manufacturing strategy on competitive performance measures. Both one-way(for each of CIM, TQC, JIT) and three-way analyses (CIMxTQCxJIT) were performed to analyse the individual and interactive effects of these technologies on the performance factors. The results of this analysis indicate that all three technologies are positively related, both individually and interactively, with competitive performance factors, although some more than others.

## INTRODUCTION

The application of advanced technologies in manufacturing firms forms an integral component of world class manufacturing. Perhaps the best way to highlight world class manufacturers is to describe them as operating on an integrated manufacturing plane which is supported by the three pillars: Computer Integrated Manufacturing (CIM), Total Quality Control (TQC) and Just In Time (JIT) [Gunn, 1987]. These practices can work alone to impact on one or more competitive performance factors of cost quality, delivery and flexibility. For example, manufacturing automation(CIM) may lower unit cost, increase quality, facilitate faster delivery, and make manufacturing more flexible in terms of products and volumes. TQC alone through employee involvement may impact on the four performance factors. Similarly, JIT methods may enhance all these performance factors. Moreover, integration of various stages of manufacturing operation may also be facilitated by some independent application of any of the three practices. For example, JIT eliminates inventory buffers between production stages, and facilitates laying out of plants by product families to eliminate physical distribution between successive stages. These three practices work in tandem to change the way goods are produced; in fact, their joint application has dramatically transformed the entire manufacturing function. These practices are based on the broader classification of AMT into the functional areas of design/manufacturing, manufacturing/operations and production planning and control[Paul and Suresh, 1990]. Although these can work as stand-alone systems, the concept of integrated manufacturing highlights the fact that they also work interactively to bring together previously independent elements of production [Mortimer, 1985 and Schonberger, 1986].

The objectives of this paper is to formulate hypotheses on the interactive effects components of integrated manufacture (CIM, TQC and JIT) on external performance measures(cost, quality, delivery and flexibility) and to test the relationships between them. These relationships should provide the justification of AMT at plant level, for it has a direct effect on the operational issues of cost, quality, delivery and flexibility. However, the components of integrated manufacture and external performance measures must be "measured" before the relationships could be established. The methodology for doing this is described later.

## Hypotheses on Effects of Integrated Manufacturing

One of the salient features of integrated manufacturing is that CIM, TQC and JIT individually and jointly affect the nature of performance measures in manufacturing. For example the combination of JIT and TQC is challenging because maintaining total quality in plants that switch rapidly between products ( a feature of JIT) is difficult; processes have to be brought back into acceptable tolerances each time a new set up is made. Hence it can also be hypothesised that each of the singular facets of integrated manufacturing is positively related to each of the competitive performance measures.

Hypothesis 1a: Facets of integrated manufacturing practices using AMT (CIM, TQC, JIT) are positively related to cost.

Hypothesis 1b: Facets of integrated manufacturing practices using AMT (CIM, TQC, JIT) are positively related to quality.

Hypothesis 1c: Facets of integrated manufacturing practices using AMT (CIM, TQC, JIT) are positively related to delivery.

Hypothesis 1d: Facets of integrated manufacturing practices using AMT (CIM, TQC, JIT) are positively related to flexibility.

The possible combinations of integrated manufacturing practices will have a greater impact on the performance of the plant rather than concentrating on a singular facet. A logical extension of this argument is that the simultaneous use of all three facets of integrated manufacturing places the highest demands on the plant, making the value of performance measures even greater than it is with a single combination. On the basis of these arguments, the interactions of CIM, TQC and JIT affecting performance measures in manufacturing is hypothesised.

Hypothesis 2a: The interactive effects of integrated manufacturing practices using AMT (CIM, TQC, JIT) are positively related to cost.

Hypothesis 2b: The interactive effects of integrated manufacturing practices using AMT (CIM, TQC, JIT) are positively related to quality.

Hypothesis 2c: The interactive effects of integrated manufacturing practices using AMT (CIM, TQC, JIT) are positively related to delivery.

Hypothesis 2d: The interactive effects of integrated manufacturing practices using AMT (CIM, TQC, JIT) are positively related to flexibility.

## Questionnaire Development and Data Collection

An effort is made in this study to define and measure integrated manufacturing more comprehensively than have previous studies. CIM measures the extent to which a firm has implemented computer/automated technologies for manufacturing. Total Quality Control measures the extent to which a firm uses techniques to promote continuous improvement, putting quality at source, and fulfilling customer needs. JIT measures the extent to which a firm attempts to cut costs through reduced inventories and lead times and by controlling such features as the number of suppliers, size of deliveries, and the total number of parts. Three different scales with a total of 27 items for the three integrated manufacturing practices(CIM, TQC and JIT) were developed.

Similarly, four different scales with a total of 12 items for the four external measures of manufacturing performance were developed. Cost objectives are frequently measured using labour, materials, inventory turnover; and unit costs. When comparing across firms with different products, and different product mixes, a common denomination to measure manufacturing becomes quite difficult.

Quality measures include percent defective or rejected, the frequency of failure in the field and cost of quality. An external measurement for quality is meeting customer requirements. In this research, a manufacturing driven definition of quality was used by measuring it in terms of defects or percentage of products that pass final inspection without rework. This was done because the unit of analysis in the research did not include customer opinions.

To measure delivery performance percentage of on time shipments, average delays, and expediting response may be used. Overall the best standard measurement for delivery is the percentage of orders delivered on time.

While there are many ways to define flexibility, it is related to being able to change manufacturing in response to changing market needs. Flexibility may be measured with respect to product mix, volume, and cycle time for new products. The measure used in this research is the cycle time: the time from placement of order for raw material, through production and distribution to the final customer.

The unit of analysis in this study were plants of European manufacturing firms which use advanced manufacturing technology extensively. In order to provide a broad perspective, a diverse range of manufacturing firms were pursued. For example, diversity was sought in the group of technologies, range of industries, size of operations, products, experience with automated technology and production processes and activities. The firms chosen in this study were from: computers and telecommunications, automobile and machinery, aerospace, and chemical and pharmaceutical sectors. Some thirty-five firms participated in this study.

For the selected plant the initial contact people were the plant managers. A questionnaire measuring CIM, TQC and JIT was distributed to each plant manager. Each plant manager was also independently asked to give their perception of how the plant's performance fared compared to their competitors in the industry and questions on the manufacturing strategy framework. Each plant manager was also asked to provide the names of a manager in each of three functions in manufacturing: operations, quality and production control. An expert panel of 10 plant managers had identified these three functions as the most likely to be affected by integrated manufacturing. By surveying across these three functions, one could examine the effects of integrated manufacturing on producing the finished goods as well as support activities that goes into producing these goods. This will lead to the comparison of performance measures in manufacturing.

The plant managers also provided the names of the functional managers. Functional managers were asked about the facet of manufacturing pertinent to their areas of expertise: CIM for operations, TQC for quality, and JIT for production control. This information was used to corroborate the information provided by plant managers. In addition each functional manager was asked questions about their perception of integrated manufacturing and its relationship to performance measures of cost, quality, delivery and flexibility for their firms. A questionnaire on items for measurement of the three scales of integrated manufacturing practices(CIM, TQC, JIT) and the four scales of external measures of manufacturing performance(cost, quality, delivery, flexibility) was developed in close consultation with the panel of ten plant managers. Each item for each scale was measured by a Likert scale. The perceptual measures for all the items for a given scale were aggregated to arrive at a total scale measure. The questionnaire was administered to plant and manufacturing functional managers in operations, quality and prodsuction control of the 35 participating firms. A total of 128 responses were received.

**Reliability and Validity of Measurement Scales**

In order to determine the ability of the scales to yield consistent measurement a reliability analysis of the measurement instrument is needed. Different forms of reliability assessment, such as test-retest, alternative forms, and internal consistency, were considered. Because respondents would probably not participated in the repeated administration of the same questionnaire or its different form, reliability was operationalised as internal consistency. Cronbach's alpha[Cronbach, 1951] was used to check for internal consistency of items in each scale. This coefficient alpha is a first approximation of the average correlation coefficient of each item with each other item [Nunnally, 1978].

Many researchers agree that a Cronbach's alpha of 0.7 is considered an adequate level of internal consistency[Nunnally, 1978]. For research using new scales, like this study, Nunnally suggests that an alpha value of 0.6 would be acceptable. Other researchers accept a lower alpha value. Jones and James [1979] claimed that their scales, with alpha values from 0.44 to 0.81 provided an acceptable measurement instrument, because of the smaller number of items in the scales. In order to be conservative, the limit set for alpha for this study was 0.6. The reliabilities of the scales are shown in Table 1 for integrated manufacturing practices and competitive performance measures. All of the Chronbach's alphas exceed the minimum level of 0.6.

TABLE 1
RELIABILITY ANALYSIS - INTERNAL CONSISTENCY OF SCALES

| Scale | Chronbach's Alpha |
|-------|-------------------|
| INTEGRATED MANUFACTURING | |
| CIM | 0.69 |
| TQC | 0.71 |
| JIT | 0.75 |
| COMPETITIVE PERFORMANCE MEASURES | |
| Cost | 0.73 |
| Quality | 0.75 |
| Delivery | 0.78 |
| Flexibility | 0.77 |

Validity measures the extent to which a scale measures what it is intended to measure. A scale could be reliable, but could measure the "wrong" thing and thus be invalid. Construct validity refers to the ability of the scale to measure the overall construct it intends to measure, usually as one dimension. In this study, factor analysis was employed to investigate construct validity. If the factor analysis indicates there is more than one factor for a scale, then two or more different dimensions of the construct are being measured by the scale. This means the scale should be split into two or more parts or nuisance questions should be eliminated from the scale to insure that it measures a single construct.

After achieving a single factor, the eigenvalues are checked to insure that they exceed 1.0 and the loadings of individual items on the scale are examined[Kim and Mueller, 1978]. For this study, any factor loading of an individual item with less than 0.23 is regarded as low, and those items are removed from the scale. A second factor analysis is then conducted with the remaining items to check if the new combination loads on one factor. Tables 2 and 3 show the results of the factor analysis using maximum likelihood estimates for integrated manufacturing practices and competitive performance measure constructs. Each scale loaded on a single factor, with item loadings all greater than 0.23 and eigenvalues are all greater than 1.0. These results indicate that the scales have good construct validity.

# TABLE 2
## CONSTRUCT VALIDITY - INTEGRATED MANUFACTURING PRACTICES

| Scale | Categorise Items to Factors | | | | | | | | | | | Eigen Value | Variance Explained |
|---|---|---|---|---|---|---|---|---|---|---|---|---|---|
| | 1 | 2 | 3 | 4 | 5 | 6 | 7 | 8 | 9 | 10 | 11 | | |
| CIM | .62 | .58 | .67 | .64 | .63 | .55 | .68 | .59 | .61 | .60 | .65 | 1.84 | .69 |
| TQC | .68 | .69 | .71 | .72 | .70 | .73 | .59 | .65 | | | | 2.34 | .73 |
| JIT | .59 | .61 | .58 | .71 | .68 | .65 | .66 | .70 | | | | 2.14 | .77 |

# TABLE 3
## CONSTRUCT VALIDITY - COMPETITIVE PERFORMANCE MEASURES

| Scale | Categorise Items to Factors | | | Eigen Value | Variance Explained |
|---|---|---|---|---|---|
| | 1 | 2 | 3 | | |
| Cost | .42 | .56 | .58 | 1.15 | .65 |
| Quality | .65 | .72 | .71 | 1.42 | .73 |
| Delivery | .78 | .80 | .82 | 2.36 | .83 |
| Flexibility | .69 | .63 | .65 | 1.35 | .68 |

## The Results

Multiple regression enables the researcher to predict the level or magnitude of a dependent variable based on the levels of more than one independent variable[Cohen and Cohen, 1975]. To test the hypotheses, multiple regression was used to predict the impact of the three integrated manufacturing practices on each competitive performance criterion. In the first step, a one-way interaction of the integrated manufacturing variables (CIM, TQC, JIT) was determined. A significant incremental $R^2$ in this step could be interpreted as support for the hypotheses 1a -1d, i.e., each of the singular facets of integrated manufacturing is positively related to each of the competitive performance measures. In the second step, a three-way interaction of all the components of integrated manufacturing (CIM x TQC x JIT) with the performance measures were investigated. Significant incremental $R^2$ in this step could be interpreted as support for hypotheses 2a - 2d.

Tables 4 - 7 show the results of the regression analysis for each of the competitive performance measures. From the tables, it is seen that the individual aspects of integrated manufacturing bear a relationship to competitive performance measures. All the facets (CIM, JIT, TQC) have a positive effect on the performance measures in operations, quality and production control. There are also several significant incremental effects on the three functions. CIM shows a more direct effect in delivery and flexibility in the operations and production control. TQC shows good effects in cost and quality in operations, quality and production control. JIT shows significant

## TABLE 4
### RESULTS FOR MULTIPLE REGRESSION ANALYSIS FOR COST

| Variables | b | Operations ΔR² | R² | F | b | Quality ΔR² | R² | F | b | Production Control ΔR² | R² | F |
|---|---|---|---|---|---|---|---|---|---|---|---|---|
| 1-way Interaction | | 0.19 | 0.16 | 1.70 | | 0.21 | 0.22 | 3.85 | | 0.12 | 0.22 | 5.31 |
| Constant | 5.63 | | | | 8.53 | | | | 7.11 | | | |
| CIM | 0.25 | | | | 0.27 | | | | 0.22 | | | |
| TQC | 0.28 | | | | 0.41 | | | | 0.56 | | | |
| JIT | 0.31 | | | | 0.39 | | | | 0.31 | | | |
| 3-way Interaction | | 0.09 | 0.25 | 3.48 | | 0.09 | 0.29 | 0.52 | | 0.04 | 0.32 | 3.26 |
| Constant | 9.61 | | | | 6.58 | | | | 5.42 | | | |
| CIM x TQC x JIT | 0.62 | | | | 0.61 | | | | 0.58 | | | |
| Overall F | | | | 4.72 | | | | 3.30 | | | | 2.54 |

## TABLE 5
### RESULTS FOR MULTIPLE REGRESSION ANALYSIS FOR QUALITY

| Variables | b | Operations ΔR² | R² | F | b | Quality ΔR² | R² | F | b | Production Control ΔR² | R² | F |
|---|---|---|---|---|---|---|---|---|---|---|---|---|
| 1-way Interaction | | 0.23 | 0.23 | 5.58 | | 0.13 | 0.14 | 6.01 | | 0.28 | 0.28 | 4.73 |
| Constant | 1.52 | | | | 5.27 | | | | 4.66 | | | |
| CIM | 0.39 | | | | 0.36 | | | | 0.28 | | | |
| TQC | 0.36 | | | | 0.47 | | | | 0.55 | | | |
| JIT | 0.52 | | | | 0.61 | | | | 0.58 | | | |
| 3-way Interatcion | | 0.48 | 0.48 | 1.92 | | 0.34 | 0.31 | 5.42 | | 0.35 | 0.33 | 5.66 |
| Constant | 1.63 | | | | 4.99 | | | | 5.63 | | | |
| CIM x TQC x JIT | 0.48 | | | | 0.53 | | | | 0.41 | | | |
| Overall F | | | | 4.32 | | | | 6.28 | | | | 5.33 |

36

## TABLE 6
### RESULTS FOR MULTIPLE REGRESSION ANALYSIS FOR DELIVERY

| Variables | Operations | | | | Quality | | | | Production Control | | | |
|---|---|---|---|---|---|---|---|---|---|---|---|---|
| | b | $\Delta R^2$ | $R^2$ | F | b | $\Delta R^2$ | $R^2$ | F | b | $\Delta R^2$ | $R^2$ | F |
| 1-way Interaction | | 0.22 | 0.12 | 4.89 | | 0.09 | 0.25 | 3.85 | | 0.08 | 0.32 | 1.91 |
| Constant | 2.71 | | | | 3.88 | | | | 3.78 | | | |
| CIM | 0.55 | | | | 0.58 | | | | 0.61 | | | |
| TQC | 0.32 | | | | 0.19 | | | | 0.21 | | | |
| JIT | 0.31 | | | | 0.28 | | | | 0.23 | | | |
| 3-way Interatcion | | 0.21 | 0.43 | 2.34 | | 0.10 | 0.31 | 3.67 | | 0.33 | 0.41 | 1.83 |
| Constant | 5.89 | | | | 4.87 | | | | 4.72 | | | |
| CIM x TQC x JIT | 0.67 | | | | 0.60 | | | | 0.61 | | | |
| Overall F | | | | 3.92 | | | | 2.93 | | | | 3.65 |

## TABLE 7
### RESULTS FOR MULTIPLE REGRESSION ANALYSIS FOR FLEXIBILITY

| Variables | Operations | | | | Quality | | | | Production Control | | | |
|---|---|---|---|---|---|---|---|---|---|---|---|---|
| | b | $\Delta R^2$ | $R^2$ | F | b | $\Delta R^2$ | $R^2$ | F | b | $\Delta R^2$ | $R^2$ | F |
| 1-way Interaction | | 0.10 | 0.32 | 5.58 | | 0.08 | 0.22 | 3.45 | | 0.12 | 0.19 | 2.55 |
| Constant | 5.71 | | | | 3.30 | | | | 4.72 | | | |
| CIM | 0.62 | | | | 0.41 | | | | 0.39 | | | |
| TQC | 0.29 | | | | 0.21 | | | | 0.20 | | | |
| JIT | 0.33 | | | | 0.37 | | | | 0.41 | | | |
| 3-way Interatcion | | 0.41 | 0.44 | 1.92 | | 0.38 | 0.46 | 2.53 | | 0.39 | 0.47 | 3.46 |
| Constant | 6.11 | | | | 5.77 | | | | 3.87 | | | |
| CIM x TQC x JIT | 0.71 | | | | 0.61 | | | | 0.58 | | | |
| Overall F | | | | 2.92 | | | | 2.18 | | | | 1.89 |

effects on cost, quality, delivery and flexibility in the three functional areas of operations, quality and production control. These findings provide support for hypotheses 1a - 1d.

All the three way interactions of CIM, TQC, and JIT also show a positive effect on competitive performance measures. These show a more consistent significant incremental effect when compared with the one way interactions. These findings also provide support for hypotheses 2a - 2d. The interactive effects of integrated manufacture influence all the four performance criteria.

## Conclusions

The paper provides a descriptive view of the relationship between some facets of integrated manufacturing with competitive performance measures. Multiple regression is used to analyse the impact of facet of integrated manufacturing(CIM,TQC,JIT) on each competitive performance criterion. The scales to measure the facets and the performance criteria show good fit for internal consistency and construct validity. Good incremental effects were shown when each of the facet of integrated manufacturing was tested with each of the performance criteria in operation, quality and production control. More consistent, significant relationships are seen with the three-way interactions. These prove that manufacturers have mastered cost, quality, delivery and flexibility, all at once to a degree.

## References

1. Gunn, T. G., *Manufacturing for Competetive Advantage: Becoming a World Class Manufacturer*, Ballinger Publishing Company, Cambridge, Mass., 1987.

2. Paul, H. and Suresh, B., "Integrating advanced manufacturing technology with manufacturing strategy, *Proc. of 5th International Conference on Manufacturing Strategy*, Operations Management Association, U.K., June 1990.

3. Mortimer, J., *Integrated Manufacture*, Springer-Verlag, Berlin, 1985.

4. Schonberger, R. J., *World Cl;ass Manufacturing: The Lessons of Simplicity Applied*, The Free Press, New York, 1986.

5. Cronbach, L. J., "Coefficient alpha and the interval structure of tests", *Psychometrica*, Vol. 16, 1951, pp297-334.

6. Nunnally, J. C., *Psychometric Theory*, McGraw Hill, New York, 1978.

7. Jones, A. P. and James, L. R., "Psychological climate: dimensions and relationships of individual and aggregated work environment perceptions", *Organizational Behaviour and Human Performance*, Vol. 23, 1979, pp201-250.

8. Kim, J. and Mueller, C. W., *Introduction to Factor Analysis*, Sage Publications, Beverly Hills, Ca, 1978.

9. Cohen, J. and Cohen P., *Applied Mul;tiple Regression/Correlation Analysis for Behavioural Sciences*, Lawrence Eribaum Associates, Hillsdale, New Jersey, 1983.

# 006

**First Author**
Roberto Sbragia
Management Department
Faculty of Economics, Business Administration and Accountancy
University of Sao Paulo
Brazil
Phone: 55.11.210-4640
Fax: 55.11.816-8044
E-mail: rsbragia@usp.br


**Co-author**
Isak Kruglianskas
Management Department
Faculty of Economics, Business Administration and Accountancy
University of Sao Paulo
Brazil
Phone 55.11.210-4640
Fax 55.11.816-8044
E-mail: kruglia@usp.br

**Title**

The Innovative Behavior in the Brazilian Industry: Are Firms Succeeding?

Key Words:    Industrial Technological Innovation/R&D
Technological Innovation/R&D Management
R&D Management/ Performance Evaluation


**Topical Category**

I, 2, Oral Presentation

# THE INNOVATIVE BEHAVIOR IN THE BRAZILIAN INDUSTRY: ARE FIRMS SUCCEEDING?

## 1. Introduction

The Brazilian business environment is currently undergoing major changes, among which the increasingly important presence of global competition; technological evolution; strategic alliances; regulation policies; reorganizing the chain of production; making companies leaner and eliminating verticalization; quality and productivity changes; the labor force, and others. This context provokes issues such as how do companies differ in their struggle for survival? How to they change and develop in time? Are they able to remain competitive? What forces can and should be explored?

The answers are not apparently obvious. Nevertheless, studies involving major companies (Pavitt and Patel, 1994) show that more than 90% of the successful companies presented a high stability in time, as well as great technological competence, measured by the growing incorporation, as well as a routine, of innovative programs and the ability to explore business areas with a quickly expanding technical content. Indeed, in the last two decades it has been increasingly clear that technological innovation plays a key role in the performance of industrial organizations, clearly indicating the political attention that will be given to this phenomenon (Smith, 1992).

This study looks at the innovative behavior of a significant group of Brazilian companies between 1993 and 1995, attempting to analyze and interpret the intensity of their technological effort and the possible impacts on their innovative and business performance. For this end it uses information contained in the National Association for R&D of Industrial Companies Database( Base de Dados da ANPEI - Associação Nacional de P&D das Empresas Industriais), implemented in 1992 to guide decisions in the country's political arena and in technological management from both a macro- and a micro-economic viewpoint.

Along these lines, the following section presents the main methodological aspects that support the study both conceptually and instrumentally. Then the indicators of approximately 400, 630 and 500 companies that registered their data with ANPEI in fiscal years 1993, 1994 and 1995, respectively, are described and interpreted. Finally the main conclusions of the study and some closing comments are reported.

## 2. Methodological Aspects

One of the major difficulties found in analyzing the innovative behavior of industrial companies is the availability of data, both in terms of input - R&D Intensity - and output - R&D results. The existing indicators in several countries, even among the most industrialized ones, are considered to be in their early stages and limited, both in terms of concept and of practice.

Thus, after 1992, significant surveys have been conducted in countries like the US and Canada, in the Americas; the UK, Germany, Italy, France, Holland and several Nordic countries, in Europe; and Japan and South Korea, in Asia. At the same time, since 1975 and especially after 1990, international organizations like the OECD have proposed and recommended definitions and indicators to be employed in such surveys in order to create a common comprehension geared to uniformity (OECD, 1975; OECD, 1992; OECD, 1994; OECD, 1996).

In Brazil this type of effort has been in progress since 1992 (Sbragia, 1994; Sbragia & Kruglianskas, 1995; Sbragia & Kruglianskas, 1996a; Sbragia & Kruglianskas, 1996b) under the aegis of ANPEI, an association that resembles others in the US (the IRI); Canada (the CRMA); Mexico (ADIAT); Europe (EIRMA); Korea (KITA); Japan (JATES) and Australia (EIRMA). We are talking about the ANPEI database on "Technological Innovation Business Indicators", whose main principles are described further ahead.

### 2.1. Conceptual Model

In concept, as deployed in ANPEI, the contents of the database can be seen in a simplified way through the model in Figure 1, where companies' innovative improvement is portrayed by means of associated indicators, both in terms of input and output. These indicators may be stratified in several ways, with a priority for the industrial sector to which the companies belong (SIC Classification - Standard Industrial Classification, that goes up to 4 digits); size (micro, small, mid-sized, large and mega-companies) and source of capital (private or public capital).

### 2.2. Concepts, Definitions and Approaches

Based on the literature and other similar experiences abroad, especially the IRI's - Industrial Research Institute, USA, (Whiteley, Bean & Russo, 1996), the ANPEI Database, in terms of concepts, definitions and methodological principles, has sought:

- to add the theoretical contributions involved in the problem of quantifying the National Expenditure on Science and Technology (DNTC - Dispêndios Nacionais em Ciência e Tecnologia), whose theoretical framework is represented by the Frascati Manual (OECD, 1975). However, considering the common practice found in the companies as regards the objective and the profile of the technical and scientific activities conducted, it is believed that the acronym R&D&E (Research, Development and Engineering) better represents the business space currently occupied by activities of industrial innovation (OECD 1992 and LINK, 1994). Along these lines, the acronym R&D&E was employed by the ANPEI Database and, in view of its development during the time this study took place, has added elements to R&D (Research and Development), including: Technological Services (prospecting studies, trials, tests and technical analysis, technical documentation, human resources skills training, manufacturing start-up and new product marketing), the Acquisition of Embodied and Disembodied Technology, both in the country and abroad, and Non-Routine Engineering, that is, engineering activities more closely related to the innovative process such as design, tooling up, industrial engineering, implementation of quality assurance procedures, and re-designing the facilities.

Figure 1: Conceptual Model of a Database on Technologically Innovative Business Indicators

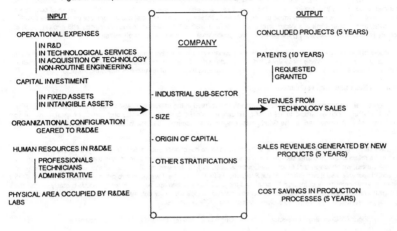

| INPUT | COMPANY | OUTPUT |
|---|---|---|

INPUT

OPERATIONAL EXPENSES

  IN R&D
  IN TECHNOLOGICAL SERVICES
  IN ACQUISITION OF TECHNOLOGY
  NON-ROUTINE ENGINEERING

CAPITAL INVESTMENT

  IN FIXED ASSETS
  IN INTANGIBLE ASSETS

ORGANIZATIONAL CONFIGURATION
  GEARED TO R&D&E

HUMAN RESOURCES IN R&D&E

  PROFESSIONALS
  TECHNICIANS
  ADMINISTRATIVE

PHYSICAL AREA OCCUPIED BY R&D&E
LABS

COMPANY

- INDUSTRIAL SUB-SECTOR

- SIZE

- ORIGIN OF CAPITAL

- OTHER STRATIFICATIONS

OUTPUT

CONCLUDED PROJECTS (5 YEARS)

PATENTS (10 YEARS)

  REQUESTED
  GRANTED

REVENUES FROM
  TECHNOLOGY SALES

SALES REVENUES GENERATED BY NEW
  PRODUCTS (5 YEARS)

COST SAVINGS IN PRODUCTION
  PROCESSES (5 YEARS)

- to adopt an appropriate balance between the breadth and depth of the information requested from the companies so as not to overload the respondents but also avoiding superficial information. It is recognized, however, that respondents are key people in the search for quality of the information generated, and must be the ongoing target of training and guidance.

- to give morel emphasis, at this point in time, to the company's compliance with the Database system than to the exactitude, reliability or completeness of the information supplied by it, presuming that such criteria will be met, to a greater extent, in a subsequent phase, with the progressive evolution of its participants, both in the understanding of the concepts and definitions arising from the system and in the structuring of the internal accounting processes to register and provide the information requested. It is realized, however, (FASB, 1974), "that the rules that refer to the activities that should be identified as R&D are designed to accommodate a large variety of aspects included under this acronym. Compliance with these rules should result in the possibility of obtaining a reasonable degree of comparison between the companies that report their data. The differences among the companies are such, however, that a precise interpretation of R&D activities and of the underlying costs - both in terms of companies and of the industrial sub-sectors - cannot be considered realistic. Thus, although the database can always develop methodologically, there will always be a certain variability in the available data".

- to ensure the reliability of the information produced by the system, not identifying the companies, that are randomly coded by 4 digits, and only divulging data assembled based on a minimum number of 4 cases in the different strata.

2.3. Procedures and Instruments

The database's data collection instrument is the "Annual Report on Business Indicators of Technological Innovation", that contains a series of instructions to be filled in, as well as complementary information to aid the people who provide the data. However, before receiving and filling in the Report, the companies is previously registered in the Database, based on its Registry Form, that gives its name, geographical location, size, source of capital and contact person for the Database. Based on this preliminary information ANPEI attributes a code to the company that, as well as being subsequently transferred to the Report for the appropriate processing, is communicated to the company for each and every interaction with ANPEI. Thus, it is ensured the anonymity of the participants and the confidential nature of the information, giving the database the required credibility to continue in the mid- and long-term.

It is important to emphasize that, in its current phase, the project to implement the database includes a strategy of inducing companies to measure certain elements within a learning approach. It combines several mechanisms in order to do this, such as:

- the strengthening of an operational base in São Paulo, at ANPEI's facilities, with sufficient staff, equipment and material to operate the system and deploy the process of distribution and receipt of the data collection tools vis-à-vis the different companies;

- the decentralization of the actual data collection on a regional level, with company guidance centers, visits and demands for answers in the states of Bahia, Minas Gerais, Rio de Janeiro, Paraná, Santa Catarina and Rio Grande do Sul, duly supported by the central office in São Paulo, also responsible for this particular state;

- the selective involvement of the entities that represent the Brazilian industry, such as trade associations and industry state departments, so as to attract the interest of this type of user and enter, more easily, into the potential universe of companies that participate in the system. The premise is that, in its self-sustaining phase, the database will operate on a network system, with ANPEI as the central link of a chain comprised by several entities that represent industrial regions and sectors, each of which are responsible for supporting the data collection procedures vis-à-vis their associate companies;

- The dissemination of the information produced by the database as a way to reveal, notably to companies, the results that the system is able to produce. Along these lines, individual statements of the main business technological indicators are devised and distributed to all the companies that comprise the database, with the aim of making benchmarking feasible.

2.4.    Firms Represented in the Database

Figure 2 shows the distribution of the companies represented in the database between 1993 and 1995 (ANPEI, 1993; ANPEI, 1994; ANPEI, 1995) according to the most significant industrial sub-sectors, the size and origin of capital, considering that more than 80% of the cases are in the Southeastern region of the country (São Paulo, Rio de Janeiro, Minas Gerais and Espirito Santo).

It's interesting to note that the features of the companies do not change substantially from one year to the other, except for their size. As refers to the industrial sub-sectors, considering the five most representative ones in the period (that correspond to 60% of the cases), we observed that Machinery/Equipment comes first, followed by Chemicals/Chemical Products, Electronic Instruments/Components, Metal and Primary Metal Products. As for the size, there was a relative growth between 1994 and 1995 of the mid- and small companies compared to large- and mega-companies, perhaps better portraying Brazilian reality. As for the origin of capital, we can finally see a small increase of multinational companies to the detriment of a smaller participation of state-controlled companies, that in 1995 began to answer for more than 97% of the cases.

Figure 2: Company Sub-sectors, Size and Origin of Capital represented in the ANPEI Database

| Segments | % of Cases by Fiscal Year | FY 1993 (n = 401) | FY 1994 (n = 630) | FY 1995 (n = 500) |
|---|---|---|---|---|
| Sub-sectors | Chemical/Chemical Products | 14,7% | 13.8% | 13,7% |
| | Industrial machinery/Equipment | 11,7% | 16.5% | 15,9% |
| | Transport Equip/Auto parts | 11,5% | 6,4% | 8,3% |
| | Electronic Components/Equip | 10,2% | 9,1% | 9,6% |
| | Metal Products | 8.0% | 8,6% | 8,1% |
| | Primary Metals | 5,3% | 6,7% | 7,7% |
| | Others | 38,5% | 38,9% | 36,7% |
| Size | Micro | 5,8% | 9,1% | 9,2% |
| | Small | 16,2% | 26,8% | 26,8% |
| | Medium | 33,0% | 32,8% | 36,4% |
| | Large | 41.2% | 28,4% | 26,0% |
| | Mega | 3,8% | 2,9% | 1.6% |
| Capital Origin | Domestic, Private | 79.3% | 84,5% | 80,2% |
| | Multinational | 15,7% | 11,4% | 17,0% |
| | State-controlled | 5,0 | 4,0% | 2.8% |

**3. Results**

3.1 Profile of the Companies Analyzed

Figure 3 presents the main features of the companies that share the ANPEI Database in terms of size (number of employees and sales revenues) and economic performance (profitability) between 1993 and 1995. It's interesting to observe that, although approximately 3,500 companies were registered, the number of active participants has varied throughout this period in the range of 400 to 600 cases, of which only 25% are common every year.

It can be seen that  the participating companies presents, in average values per company, a marked drop in the period, both in the number of employees (approximately 55%) and in sales revenues (26%). But we can also see a trend towards improved economic performance, as average  profitability rose from a sharply negative figure in 1993 to positive figures, or at least close to zero in the following years. These indicators are fairly in tune with the Brazilian situation at the beginning of the decade, that shows a tendency to reorganization and cutting off the fat of industrial companies, allied to a recovery capacity of the especially troublesome years that marked the end of the 1980s and the beginning of the 1990s.

42

Figure 3: Profile of the Companies Surveyed

| INDICATORS (average figures per company) | FY 1993 (n=401) | FY 1994 (n=630) | FY 1995 (n=500) |
|---|---|---|---|
| Number of Employees | 1,979 | 1,456 | 902 |
| Gross Sales Revenues ($ 000) | 210,012 | 152,281 | 155,199 |
| Gross Sales Revenues/Nr. of Employees ($ 000) | 106,5 | 104,50 | 172,0 |
| Net Profit/Gross Sales Revenues (%) | -23.55 | 6.42 | -0.64 |

In fact, we can see an increase of approximately 70% of the productivity of the "human resources" factor in 1995, measured by Gross Sales Revenues/Number of Employees, that rose, in round numbers, from $ 106 thousand and from $ 104 thousand in 1993 and 1994, respectively, to $ 172 thousand in 1995.

3.2. Intensity of R&D Effort

The data in Figure 4 quantify the intensity of R&D&E efforts expended by companies participating in the database. These figures must be taken as the best estimates of the resources devoted to technical and scientific activities by the firms surveyed.

Figure 4: Intensity of the R&D Effort of the Companies Surveyed

| R&D&E INTENSITY (average figures per company) | FY1993 (n=401) | FY1994 (n=630) | FY1995 (n=500) |
|---|---|---|---|
| R&D&E Expenditures ($) | 3.050,544 | 2.2270,849 | 2.203.095 |
| R&D Expend./R&D&E Expenditures (%) | 49.65 | 50.34 | 56.64 |
| Technological Services Expend./R&D&E Expenditures (%) | 22.75 | 18.09 | 15.88 |
| Technology Acquisition Expend./R&D&E Expenditures (%) | 9.12 | 12.61 | 10.63 |
| Non-Routine Engineering Expend./R&D&E Expenditures (%) | 18.47 | 18.97 | 16.85 |
| Capital Investments for Technological Innovation | 805,162 | 1,319,147 | 914,879 |
| R&D&E Staff (Technical and Administrative, full time equivalent) | 35 | 31 | 35 |
| Technical Staff (professionals and technicians) /R&D&E Staff (%) | 87.06 | 75.52 | 87.76 |
| Professionals (bachelors, masters and Ph.Ds) /Technical Staff in R&D&E (%) | 57.11 | 55.80 | 50.36 |
| Ph.Ds in R&D&E/R&D&E Technical Staff (%) | 1.72 | 2.10 | 4.24 |
| R&D&E Expenditures per Technical Staff in R&D&E ($) | 86,562 | 120,653 | 106,076 |
| R&D&E Expenditures per Professional in R&D&E ($) | 142,791 | 212,232 | 204,851 |

OBS: The number of cases varies according to each item of information, as not all the companies provided all the additional data.

Data indicates that, in terms of intensity of R&D&E effort per company, there were no great changes in the 93-95 period. This confirms that corporations have adjusted to new conditions by concentrating on human resources productivity increases. It is interesting to note that the reduction of the R&D Expenditures per company, especially between 1993 and 1994, did not necessarily signify that the companies are spending less. What happened, in fact, was a relative reduction of the size of the companies that participated in the database during the period, as we have already explained. On the other hand, the growing evolution of the participation of the expenses in R&D "strictu sensu" in the global R&D&E expenses may indicate the direction of the corporate effort towards activities with a more innovative content, reinforced by the relative increase of the participation of doctors in the total workforce, that grew approximately 2.5 times between 1993 and 1995. All this seems to indicate a quality improvement in terms of the degree of innovation of the technological projects.

3.3. Results of the R&D Effort

The numbers in Figure 5 try and portray some of the impacts of R&D&E activities in the companies that participated in the ANPEI database between 1993 and 1995. This impact should not be seen as the direct and sole result of the technical and scientific group, but as the integration of the efforts of several interactive groups/units such as top management, marketing,

43

production, suppliers, and others. They are partial output indicators, some of which are difficult to quantify and to precise, of the activities of technological innovation developed by the companies surveyed.

Figure 5: Results of the R&D Efforts in the Companies Surveyed

| RESULTS OF THE R&D&E EFFORT (average figures per company) | FY 1993 (n=401) | FY 1994 (n=630) | FY 1995 (n=500) |
|---|---|---|---|
| Projects concluded in the year in regard to those initiated in the last 3 years (%) | 61.88 | 58.04 | 58.44 |
| Patents registered in the country (annual average for the last 10 years) | 0.85 | 0.69 | 0.93 |
| Revenues from Sale of Technology to third parties in the year ($) | 945,881 | 129,130 | 238,854 |
| Revenues from New Products introduced into the market in the last 5 years/Gross Sales Revenues for the year (%) = NPI | 39.00 | 39.38 | 37.45 |
| Production Cost Savings in the year, resulting from process improvements introduced in the last 5 years/ Gross Profit for the year (%) = CSI | 3.48 | 3.79 | 4.27 |
| R&D&E Yeld = Gross Profit x (NPI+CSI) ($ 000) | 22,145 | 17,289 | 9,057 |
| Return on R&D&E = R&D&E Yeld/R&D&E Expenditures | 7.25 | 7.61 | 4.11 |

OBS: The number of cases varies according to each item of information, as not all the companies provided all the additional data.

In tune with previous analyses, it is not observed, in general, major variations in the data that refer to the impact of R&D&E activities in the period analyzed. Nevertheless, both in the item that refers to Revenues from the Sale of Technology to third parties and to R&D&E Yeld, estimated based on the application of a factor (New Product Index - NPI plus Cost Savings Index - CSI) on the Gross Profit (Tipping, Zeffren & Fusfeld, 1995), it is detected very high values for 1993, which can be partially explained by the relatively high presence of large and mega-companies in the Database that year. Indeed, these companies showed revenues arising from technological sales much higher (approximately tenfold) than the others (ANPEI, 1994), as well as absolute values for Gross Profit. However, when we take the indicator that refers to the R&D&E Return (R&D&E Yeld divided by R&D&E Expenditures), it is noted a decrease of almost 50% from 93 to 94, showing perhaps that the firms are getting back more slowly, through the introduction of new products in the market and the reduction of the cost of production processes in the last five years, the resources allocated to innovative activities. This may be mirror the re-directing of the innovative effort previously demonstrated, that is, add a relatively greater emphasis to the more slowly maturing activities, as is the case of basic and applied research and experimental development.

In any case, it must be clear that any analysis of the indicators of results of innovative effort are very complex and limited because of the time lapse and also because they are difficult to measure. Perhaps longer series, complemented with sensitivity and correlation analyses, will allow us to obtain more powerful and reliable conclusions.

## 4. Conclusions and Final Considerations

The conclusions we can draw from the innovative behavior of industrial Brazilian companies based on the ANPEI database should be seen in view of several limitations, that not only result from the inherent lack of precision and representativeness of the data, given the features of the Database, but also because different cases were analyzed between 1993 and 1994, although there was indeed a small common core. Thus any conclusion must be interpreted within a preliminary and tentative effort and is, therefore, subject to future confirmation.

Thus we can show, initially, that most of the companies in the Database, mostly represented by the mid-sized and large companies, show a trend towards stability between 1993 and 1995, both in terms of the intensity of the R&D&E effort and in terms of the possible resulting impacts converging, in average figures per company, to:

- operational expenses in R&D&E close to $ 2.2 million/year, that represent approximately 1.2% of the Gross Sales Revenues, as well as a capital investment in technological innovation of approximately $ 1 million/year;

- an innovative quality improvement, mirrored by an emphasis on R&D "strictu sensu" higher than 50% in regard to the total effort in R&D&E, and a greater participation of Ph.Ds in the technical staff close to 4%.

- a total staff dedicated to R&D&E, including technical (professionals and technicians) and administrative personnel converging to approximately 35 persons per company;

- the participation of the technical staff in the total R&D&E staff of approximately 80%, and of professional in the total number of technical staff of approximately 55%.

- operational expenses of approximately $ 100,000 per technical staff and $ 200,000 per professional;

- a number of projects closed approximately 60% of those initiated in the last 3 years;

- a number of patents registered in Brazil close to 1, considering the annual average for the last 10 years;

- a revenue arising from new/modified products introduced into the market in the last 5 years close to 39% of the current sales revenues;

- cost savings, resulting from the improvements introduced into the production process in the last 5 years, equal to approximately 4% of the current Gross Profit.

It is important to emphasize that these indicators, although they show a possibly timid behavior on the part of Brazilian industry in view of the statistics of more industrialized countries, also showed an apparently significant answer of the companies in view of our recent industrialization, the difficult economic situation that marked the country for the last 15 years, the new paradigms of global competition, the new challenges that result from economic opening and the recent tools of industrial and technological policies implemented in the country.

Figure 6: National Expenditure on Science and Technology in Brazil

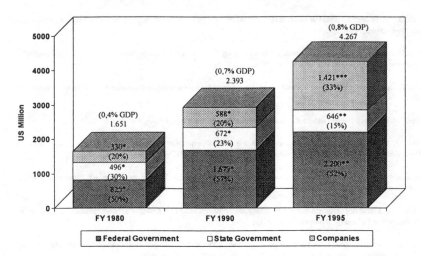

*NPCT/UNICAMP, 1990    **MCT/CNPq, 1995    ***ANPEI, 1996

In fact, as Figure 6 shows, for the last fifteen years, since the beginning of the 1980s, Brazilian industry used to participate with no more than 20% of the National Expenditure on Science and Technology (NEST), estimated, at the time, as $ 1.6 billion, or 0.4% of the Gross Domestic Product (GDP). Of that total, however, large state-controlled companies certainly contributed with more than 80%. At present the participation of the industry attains at least 33% of the NEST, currently estimated at $ 4.2 billion, or 0.8% of the GDP. More important than this growth, however, is that state-controlled companies now answer for only 30% of the business expenditure, and the private sector is responsible for the remaining 70%. All this shows the importance of establishing indicators that refer to the innovative behavior of the Brazilian industry and its possibility of comparison/and the possibility of comparing it with that of other countries, both developing and already developed.

**Bibliographical References:**

ANPEI - Indicadores Empresariais de Capacitação Tecnológica: Resultados a Base de Dados
Relatório nº 3, Ano Base 1993, Dezembro/1994.

ANPEI - Indicadores Empresariais de Capacitação Tecnológica: Resultados a Base de Dados
Relatório nº4, Ano Base 1994, Dezembro/1995.

ANPEI - Indicadores Empresariais de Capacitação Tecnológica: Resultados a Base de Dados Relatório n°5, Ano Base 1995, Dezembro/1996 (To be edited).

FASB (Financial Accounting Standard Board) - Statement of Standards: Accounting for Research and Development Costs, NY, December, 1994.

MCT/CNPq - Dispêndios Nacionais em Ciência e Tecnologia 94: CNPq/COOE - Coordenação de Estatística e Indicadores de C&T, Brasília, DF, 1995.

NPCT/UNICAMP - Ciência e Tecnologia no Brasil. Campinas, 1994.

Link, Albert N. The Classification of Industrial R&D. National Science Foundation, Research on Research and Technological Program, Washington D.C., 1994

OECD. The Frascati Manual: The Measurement of Scientific and Technical Activities. Organization for Economic Cooperation and Development, Paris, 1975.

OECD. Proposed Guidelines for Collecting and Interpreting Technological Innovation Data; Oslo Manual. Organization for Economic Cooperation and Development, Paris, 1992

OECD. Definiciones y convenciones principales para la medición de la investigación y el desaarrollo experimental. Resumen del Manual Frascati de 1993. Paris, 1994.

OECD. Oslo Manual (second edition). Committee for Scientific and Technological Policy. Paris, 1996.

Pavitt, K & Patel, P. Technological Competences in the World's Largest Firms: Characteristics, Constraints and Scope for Managerial Choice. Fourth International Conference of The Management of Technology, Miami, 1994

Sbragia, R. R&D Spending at the Firm Level in Brazil: Implementation of a Database for International Comparisons. Fourth International Conference on Management of Technololy. Miami/USA, February-March 1994.

Sbragia, R. & Kruglianskas, I. R&D at the Firm Leve: the implementantion of a Database in Brazil. European Conference on Management of Technology, Birmighan, England, July, 1995.

Sbragia, R. & Kruglianskas, I. R&D at the Firm Level: a comparative analysis between ANPEI (Brazil) and IRI (United States). Fifth Internacional Conference of Management of Technology, Miami/USA, February/1996a.

Sbragia, R & Kruglianskas, I. R&D in Brazilian Industry: Recent Indicators. Research-Technology Management, Volume 39, No. 3, May-June, 1996b.

Smith, K. Technological Innovation indicators: experience and prospects. Science and Public Policy, number 19, volume 6, December 1992

Tipping, J. W, Zeffren, E. & Fusfeld, A R. Assessing the Value of Your Technology. Research-Technology Management, September-October, 1995

Whiteley, R.L., Bean, A S. & Russo, M.J. Meet Your Competition: Results from the 1994 IRI/CIMs Annual R&D Survey. Research - Technology Management, Volume 39, No. 1, January-February, 1996.

# 007

## DEFINING MANAGEMENT ROLES IN COMPLEX PROJECT ORGANIZATIONS

Author:
Antonio C.A. Maximiano
University of Sao Paulo
Brazil
Phone:
Fax: +55 11 816 8044

ABSTRACT

The Organization of large and multifunctional projects is a complex task which involves the need to define not only the project manager's role but also those of several other participants, inside and outside the company.

In this paper, a case study is presented of a major European industrial company and the solutions if provided to solve this problem in its Brazilian operation.

The paper describes how this company redefined its industrial function and then had to make a decision on how to redeplay is formerly centralized R&D function. A team was gathered which attempted and succeeded in designing a policy to adjust the R&D division to a new concept in project management. In this concept, new product development is carried out by means of a large mulifunctional organization linked to higher management.

The "reengeneering" of the authority and responsibility lines in this policy was achieved with the help of the authority and responsibility lines in this policy was achieved with the help of a linear organization chart, a classic tool for this purpose.

The paper presents a description of how this project was undertaken, from problem definition to implementation of decisions.

Oral Presentation

# 008

## THE REINVENTION OF SAFETY MANAGEMENT IN GOVERNMENT SPACE INDUSTRY

Author:
Aysar P. Sussan
LYNN University,
Testing Center
3301 College Ave.
Ft. Lauderdale, Florida 33314
USA

| | |
|---|---|
| Tel: | +1-954-452 1557 |
| Fax: | +1-954-476 4888 |
| e-mail: | sussana@polaris.ncs.nova.edu |

Co-authors
Gaston A. Ray
Safety Engineer
P.O. Box 4127
CSR 1230
Patrick Air Force Base, Florida 32925 USA

| | |
|---|---|
| Tel: | +1-407-494 5155 |
| Fax: | +1-407-494 5626 |

## ABSTRACT

In today´s public sector we are witness to changes that align future government administrative practices with that of the private sector. These changes are coming slowly, yet cautiously, and under the concept of **Reinvention,**

Computer Sciences Raytheon (CSR) is contracted by U.S. Air Force to support the tracking of NASA, U.S. Navy space and missile programs. CSR´s fourteen hundred plus employees have responsibilities that include communications, electronics, and air field operations. The mission of the safety department at CSR was studied internally on the efficient and effective use of their resources (people, energy, materials, space, time, and money).

Reinvention is an approach whereas we study our process, our customers, and our ways of conducting business. The concept of Reinvention is based on the combination of two management theories, Scientific Management, and Human Relations Management.

The success of the safety department at CSR was measured by the application of the above two theories. Upon completion of the study the safety department initiated the following:

| Accident in 1995 | | Accident in 1996 |
|---|---|---|
| Employees not trained | 8.4% of the total group | 4.2% of the total group |
| Employees trained | 7.3% of the total group | 3.6% of the total group |

| Year | No. of accidents | Cost of accidents |
|---|---|---|
| 1994 | 22 | $37,552.12 |
| 1995 | 23 | $6,210.25 |
| 1996 | 12 | $1,440.00 |

Oral Presentation

# 009

Paul Hyland
InCITe (Innovation & Continuous Improvement Technologies) Research Group
Faculty of Business & Technology
University of Western Sydney, Macarthur
PO Box 555
Campbelltown
NSW 2560
Australia
Telephone: (61) 46 203217
Fax: (61) 46 266683
E-mail: p.hyland@uws.edu.au

Co-authors:

Sarah Caffyn
CENTRIM (Centre for Research in Innovation Management)
University of Brighton
Falmer
Brighton
BN1 9PH
UK
Telephone: +44 1273 642187
Fax: +44 1273 685896
E-mail: S.J.Caffyn@bton.ac.uk


Ross Chapman
InCITe (Innovation & Continuous Improvement Technologies) Research Group
Faculty of Business & Technology
University of Western Sydney, Macarthur
PO Box 555
Campbelltown
NSW 2560
Australia
Telephone: (61) 46 203245
Fax: (61) 46 266683
E-mail: r.chapman@uws.edu.au


Max Silano
CENTRIM (Centre for Research in Innovation Management)
University of Brighton
Falmer
Brighton
BN1 9PH
UK
Telephone: +44 1273 642193
Fax: +44 1273 685896
E-mail: M.Silano@bton.ac.uk

Title of paper:
Using continuous improvement to gain competitive advantage : A comparison of companies in
Australia and the United Kingdom

Keywords:
Continuous improvement; quality; manufacturing; deregulation; competition; survey; UK; Australia.

Topic A: Applications of technology to learning organisations
Category 2: Empirical and experimental
Suitable for oral presentation only

## Introduction

Deregulation exposes previously protected industry sectors to the harsh realities of global competition. In order to remain viable these industries must consider and implement best practice management strategies and technologies. The globalisation of markets and the increasing pace of technological change has meant that organisations and their managers must constantly strive to improve what they do and to seek relevant new knowledge to maintain competitive advantage. Successful implementation of company-wide quality management and continuous improvement principles and practices has become an essential part of this process. This paper looks at recent changes in the manufacturing environment in Australia and the UK, and compares the findings of a survey of the practice of continuous improvement in these countries.

## Economic Reform and Industry Competitiveness in Australia and UK

In a broad sense Australia's reforms have addressed the same areas as those of other countries. This deregulation began in the 1980s and includes:
- trade and exchange rate reforms
- foreign investment reforms
- industrial reforms
- public sector reforms
- tax reforms
- banking system reforms
- capital market reforms

The pace of reform has often been subject to political expediency and in this respect Australia would be no different than other countries which have deregulated their economies. In the UK there have been major changes in the economic and legislative environment in which UK businesses operate since the Conservative Party came to power in 1979. Deregulation, privatisation of public utilities and other state owned enterprises, employment legislation and the emasculation of trade unions have helped to create a business environment characterised by increased competition and more flexible working arrangements.

Questions have been raised as to whether the rate of reform can be sustained in Australia (Eade, 1995). The decisions made by Government in areas such as infrastructure investment will have implications for long-term growth and the rate at which the benefits from deregulating the economy can accrue. In some sectors of the economy, the pace of change varies depending on the impact of regulation, the rate of infrastructure investment, the rate of direct sectoral investment and foreign competition. In the UK businesses are hampered by an inadequate transport infrastructure. According to a recent CBI report, "historic levels of under-investment and lack of a coherent national transport strategy have left the UK with a transport network which compares poorly with that found in other major European countries" (Confederation of British Industry, 1995).

In reviewing the progress of Australia's liberalisation policy, the Hilmer report (1991) saw the task of reform as urgent and recommended a broad policy approach rather than one which was specially tailored for each sector. If it is to survive and succeed in a global market place, industry, and manufacturing firms in particular, must prepare themselves to accept the logic of competition. In other words, while companies may have greater opportunities to export products, they will inevitably face increased competition from imports. As a consequence, the emerging global order requires that the industries become internationally competitive. In Australia the manufacturing sectors benefited most from protectionism and were able to develop despite in-built inefficiencies in many industries. These inefficiencies became exposed primarily by the emerging economies of south-east Asia following deregulation. Nevertheless, in the aggregate, the effects of deregulation on Australian trade have been positive. During the past ten years exports of manufactures have grown at an annual rate of 16 per cent and now comprise 19 percent of total exports.

The Australian Government has placed the onus on private industry and the individual firm to maximise the potential benefits of a deregulated economy, an approach similar to that adopted by the UK Government since 1979. To achieve this firms need to react to the changing environment and build advantages for themselves. To minimise the adverse impacts of deregulation firms need to implement a strategy of organisational renewal (Das, 1996). One way that Australia's domestic producers can better position themselves to respond to competition is to learn from the experiences and mistakes of industries in other countries, such as the UK, which have preceded them down this often bumpy road.

The present openness of the UK economy is reflected in the high level of foreign direct investment (FDI) in both directions[1]. Overall, between 1981-92, the UK has been the second largest recipient and the third largest source of FDI worldwide (and the largest source when FDI is expressed as a percentage of GDP) (Confederation of British Industry, 1995). The UK is now regarded favourably to other European countries as a place for manufacturing. According to BMW's Chairman, Herr Pischetsrieder, "Structural change has made Britain by far the most attractive place to invest in Europe." The UK is also attractive to investors from beyond Europe and in 1995 gained 40% of all investment in the EU originating from American and Japanese companies. In the year up to March 1995 there were 434 inward investment projects in the UK, mostly in manufacturing, expected to create over 37,000 new jobs. Although some of these investments were for completely new plants the majority were expansions on existing facilities. Among the major factors attracting companies to the UK are: the consistent welcome given to foreign investment by the UK government and most regional authorities; the aptitude and adaptability of the UK workforce, combined with relatively low labour costs and flexible working arrangements; a highly regarded science and technology base; and regional assistance (44% of output from foreign-owned manufacturing operations is situated in the UK's assisted areas).

Along with the opening up of the business climate in Britain, the increasing involvement by UK firms in collaborative activities suggests that they have become more receptive to external ideas and influences. In 1995 as many as 82% of manufacturing firms were collaborating with academics and almost as many were working with other companies. Although most of this collaboration takes place within the UK there is growing commitment to working with overseas companies, in particular with US businesses (CBI/NatWest, 1996).

At a global level, increased competition means that workplace reforms will have to be continually implemented if domestic industries are to remain viable. Businesses need to know what the likely impediment to such reforms are. Recent research in Australia and overseas has provided useful information on competitive strategies for organisations faced with higher levels of competition. For instance, in Australia Nunes et al (1993), found reforms were less likely to be implemented in industries with lower levels of competition and high union density. Dow (1992) observed that Australian firms found that the best way to achieve significant change was through a policy of openness and involvement. Most of the good news stories, however, tend to focus on a small number of leading edge firms. Hilmer (1991, p.27) identified a need for significant improvement in the development and use of competitiveness and productivity measures by Australian firms. While quality of product or service has long been recognised as essential for organisational success, recent studies have identified a need for what has been termed *competitive quality* (Hamel and Prahalad, 1994). This term has been used to describe the requirement for companies to go beyond the skilled application of tools and techniques to include a shift in values, beliefs and assumptions guiding organisational activities. Competitive quality is based on a systems perspective, continuous improvement, high productivity and customer orientation (Dean and Bowen, 1994).

In Australia, recent research (Brown and Van der Wiele, 1996) suggests that many firms are now viewing the development of effective quality systems and subsequent certification as a part of general business improvement, rather than a marketing driven activity. This has resulted in identification and documentation of the key processes of the business followed by

---

[1] The data in this paragraph is drawn from (Confederation of British Industry, 1995).

matching them to the ISO 9000 elements (rather than the reverse) and developing appropriate documentation out of an examination of the existing processes rather than forcing externally derived documentation onto often unmatched processes. This development is very much in keeping with key findings of the multinational IQS study into quality management practices (1991) and the Ernst & Young report (1994) on quality practices and ISO 9000 quality system standards in Australia. The latter survey found that "Almost all respondents reported streamlined systems and improved procedures [*from quality system implementation and certification*] and envisaged significant business benefits when combined with continuous improvement techniques."

In the UK there are a growing number of initiatives which are raising awareness of these wider issues and encouraging companies to improve their quality systems by adopting a more holistic approach. Such initiatives include, for example, BS5750/ISO9000; the model and associated award developed by the European Foundation for Quality Management; the UK Quality award; Best Factory Awards; national associations such as the British Deming Association, and the National Association for Quality through Teamwork; and industry and regionally-based quality clubs.

Many British companies are now rising to the challenges posed by the competitive international environment. For example, from the early 1980s, the UK made steady progress in improving stock turn and closing the gap with the US and Japan (Confederation of British Industry, 1995, p17). However, the nature of "quality" makes it hard to measure objectively and make comparisons. For example, two international studies of the automotive component industry reached different conclusions about quality in UK plants. A McKinsey study covering the period 1987-91 concluded that "Britain leads Europe in terms of quality" (Rommel et al., 1996). It found that 67% of companies were above average in terms of quality (behind Japan with 85% but ahead of the US on 44% and of all the other European countries in the study). According to the authors, "Quality has improved greatly in Britain since the beginning of the 1990s... British top management has now devoted itself intensely to quality, more so than that of any other country in Europe." However, the Andersen study of 1994 found that UK plants had the second lowest quality in Europe (Andersen Consulting, 1994). The sharp contrast in the conclusions relating to quality may be the result of the small sample size in both studies and different ways of calculating "quality". Both studies recognise the beneficial impact of the Japanese transplants on indigenous supplier firms in terms of increasing volumes and pressure to improve quality; they also agree that the UK suffers from poor productivity.

By taking a broader strategic view of quality, it has been shown that the twin goals of improving productivity and quality are *not* incompatible, that both can be improved simultaneously. In fact, the increasing pace of globalisation and technological change has meant that productivity and quality improvements must occur simultaneously if organisations are to retain or increase their competitive advantage. While certain industries have demonstrated this competitive pressure towards continuous improvement, there remains large variation in the development of management approaches to quality across different industries and between different organisations and nations.

Around the world the development of Continuous Improvement (CI) is increasingly being viewed as an essential requirement to maintain competitive advantage and to assist firms in sustaining ongoing business improvement. Continuous Improvement has been defined as "a company-wide process of focused and continuous incremental innovation" (Bessant et al., 1994). It is thus complementary to the more radical change normally considered under the terms technological innovation or Business Process Re-engineering (BPR). Bessant et al. (1994) argue that there are six critical requirements for successful long term implementation of CI:

- A clear strategic framework – CI must be clearly incorporated into the organisation's strategic agenda and goals.
- Strategic management – CI needs to be well planned and to include regular targets and milestones, both in the short and longer term, which are well communicated along with measurement and display routines.

- An underlying supportive culture – a widespread recognition of the importance and value of CI, an acceptance that everyone in the organisation has something to contribute to the process.
- An enabling infrastructure – the adoption of organisational structures which promote efficient two-way communication and decentralised decision-making.
- CI needs to be managed as a process – this involves the adoption of learning or problem solving processes.
- A supporting toolkit – the availability of a set of common problem solving tools (and training in their application) to help employees engage in CI.

While CI has been regarded as a key element in quality programs for some time, there is a growing recognition of its application in other areas such as flexibility, cost-reduction, inter-firm relations and support process improvement (Robinson, 1991 and Bessant et al., 1994). An examination of the level of development of CI principles and practices across all aspects of a company's operation could provide a significant indicator of that company's potential future competitive situation. In the following section we report on the findings of the initial results from a study of CI implementation in Australian and UK manufacturing firms.

*Results of a Study of Continuous Improvement in Australian and United Kingdom Manufacturing Industry*

The survey reported here was carried out as part of a wider investigation of CI being co-ordinated by the Eureka project, EuroCINet. Members of EuroCINet, a European-wide network of researchers working in the field of CI, agreed to carry out a survey which would produce in the short-term an overview of the prevalence and organisation of CI in the participating countries. Issues that emerged from this as being of particular relevance or interest could then be investigated more thoroughly using appropriate methodologies. Over the period March 1995 – March 1996 the survey has taken place in the following countries: Sweden, Denmark, The Netherlands, Finland, the UK, and Australia. Other countries planning to conduct the survey include Ireland and Germany. Each country is producing its own analysis. During 1996 the data from each country was merged by InCITe researchers in Australia in order to allow international comparisons to be carried out.

The survey was conducted by postal questionnaire. To enable inter-country comparisons to be made a set of core questions was agreed. These form the bulk of the questionnaire used in each country, but individual countries were able to include additional questions if they wished. A common coding scheme was adopted. Guidelines were agreed on the type of company to survey, in terms of size (number of employees) and manufacturing areas (SIC codes).

The following statement appeared prominently on the questionnaire: "The term Continuous Improvement is used here to describe a systematic attempt to involve all employees in incremental improvement."

The UK and Australian questionnaires comprised 32 questions in five sections covering:
- Company background
- General characteristics of the organisation in the business unit, and previous experiences of change efforts
- Issues concerning the organisation and operation of CI
- Support for CI, and the tools used in the CI process
- The effects of CI

The respondents were representative of a wide range of firms in terms of turnover and number of employees, as shown in Tables 1 and 2.

Table 1 - Annual Turnover

| Range (DM)* | UK | UK% | Aust | Aust% |
|---|---|---|---|---|
| < 21 m | 24 | 16.9 | 131 | 31.2 |
| 21 - 100 m | 64 | 45.1 | 155 | 36.9 |
| > 100 m | 35 | 24.6 | 80 | 19.0 |
| Missing Data | 19 | 13.4 | 54 | 12.9 |
| Total | 142 | 100.0 | 420 | 100.0 |

* converted using exchange rate on Dec 16, 1996

Table 2 - Number of Employees

| Range | UK | UK% | Aust | Aust% |
|---|---|---|---|---|
| < 100 | 11 | 7.7 | 184 | 43.8 |
| 101 - 500 | 92 | 64.8 | 170 | 40.5 |
| > 500 | 32 | 22.5 | 52 | 12.4 |
| Missing Data | 7 | 4.9 | 14 | 3.3 |
| Total | 142 | 100.0 | 420 | 100 |

As many as 65% of the UK companies responding to the survey reported the presence of widespread and sustained or systematically applied continuous improvement activities. The corresponding figure for the total Australian sample was 47%.

The strategic value of CI has been recognised by more companies in the UK than in Australia. In the UK 65% of respondents to this question said that CI was considered to be of strategic importance, with less than a third (30%) considering it to be of operational importance and only 4% stating that it is of minor importance. In Australia 44% of companies stated that it is of strategic importance, 48% said it was of operational importance, and 8% felt it to be of minor importance.

This is reinforced when we look at the spread of CI within the organisation. Nearly two thirds of the UK companies (64%) report that CI is practised throughout the entire unit including functions such as design, purchasing and sales, compared to 48% of Australian firms. In just over half (52%) of the Australian companies CI is limited to the manufacturing function, including support areas such as maintenance engineering, compared to just under a quarter of UK companies.

Thus the UK companies appear to be further down the CI road in terms a systematic implementation of CI on a company-wide basis. It is surprising then to find that the Australian firms in the survey have been working with CI for longer than the British sample. CI had been in place for more than four years in just over a third (35%) of the Australian companies responding to this question, compared to a fifth (20%) of UK firms. The proportions of early users, i.e. those with up to two years experience of CI, were 39% for Australia and 51% for the UK.

The managers in both Australia and the UK responding to the survey reported that quality and price were the most important competitive measures (sales-winning criteria). Time-to-market, customised products and delivery lead-time did not rank highly in terms of sales-winning criteria.

Whilst the survey collected data on a variety of elements of quality management and continuous improvement, in this paper we will focus on four particular aspects: the main motives for implementing a CI strategy; the focus of CI activity; the supporting mechanisms for the change process involved; and tools used to ensure the success of the change process. Each of these characteristics was measured on a five point Likert scale and each scale is described in more detail below.

Tables 3 to 6 present the means of each of the variables under consideration (measured on a five point Likert scale) for Australia and the UK. A description of the two extremes of the five point scale applicable to the relevant variable is provided below the title for each of the four tables. One way Analysis of Variance (ANOVA) tests were carried out to test for significant differences between the mean values for the two countries. In this test, the lower the significance figure, the greater is the difference between the two countries; the difference becomes significant when the figure is 0.05 or less. In each table the parameters down the left hand side of the table have been ranked in decreasing order of significance.

Table 3 - Main Motives For Continuous Improvement
(1 = Not Important, through to 5 = Of Critical Importance)

| CI Main Motives | | | | |
|---|---|---|---|---|
| | Mean | | ANOVA Statistics | |
| Variable | UK | Australia | F values | Signf. |
| Increase employee commitment | 4.05 | 3.65 | 12.5753 | 0.0004 |
| Reduced production lead times | 3.74 | 3.43 | 6.7544 | 0.0096 |
| Improve organisation, cooperation and communication | 3.93 | 3.68 | 4.9662 | 0.0263 |
| Increase employee skills | 3.62 | 3.39 | 4.4839 | 0.0347 |
| Because CI is a management directive | 1.76 | 2.01 | 3.5945 | 0.0586 |
| Increase production volume | 3.03 | 3.21 | 1.8252 | 0.1773 |
| Improve administrative routines | 2.88 | 2.77 | 0.8851 | 0.3473 |
| Improve delivery reliability | 3.89 | 3.79 | 0.7925 | 0.3738 |
| Improve safety and physical environment | 3.20 | 3.30 | 0.6292 | 0.4280 |
| Because our customers ask for CI | 2.30 | 2.41 | 0.5598 | 0.4547 |
| Increase manufacturing productivity | 4.00 | 4.16 | 0.3784 | 0.5387 |
| Improve quality conformance | 4.10 | 4.14 | 0.1432 | 0.7053 |
| Cost reduction | 4.03 | 4.01 | 0.0204 | 0.8866 |

It can be seen from Table 3 that the main motives given for the introduction of CI were, in priority order (according to the means for the UK and Australia), quality conformance improvement and cost reduction, with increasing manufacturing productivity and delivery reliability improvement also seen as important. These four characteristics were seen as important in both Australia and UK, but firms in the UK gave a significantly higher rating to increasing employee commitment and attitude towards change than Australian firms. Interestingly, customer requests and management directives were not seen as important motives for change. Based on the ANOVA test, there were significant differences between the two countries for motives for working with CI considered in this table, in particular, reduced production lead times, increasing employees skills and improving organisational cooperation and communication were rated significantly higher by UK companies.

Respondents were asked the frequency with which CI is directed towards certain activities (Table 4). In both countries CI activities are most often concerned with trying to reduce manufacturing costs and improve manufacturing quality. This is to be expected since, as we have seen, cost reduction and improving quality were some of the most important motivators for adopting CI amongst both UK and Australian firms. One of the most significant differences between the two counties is the greater emphasis on employee commitment among British companies, which reflects the importance attached to this by UK respondents as noted above.

Table 4 - Focus of the Continuous Improvement Activity
(1 = Not Frequent, through to 5 = Very Frequent)

| Focus of CI Activity | | | | |
|---|---|---|---|---|
| | **Mean** | | **ANOVA Statistics** | |
| **Variable** | **UK** | **Australia** | **F values** | **Signf.** |
| Set-up time | 3.38 | 2.67 | 15.9427 | 0.0001 |
| Machine up-time and speed | 3.16 | 2.68 | 10.7463 | 0.0011 |
| Employee commitment | 3.60 | 3.30 | 5.4632 | 0.0198 |
| Buffer stock, lay-out and physical flows | 3.14 | 2.87 | 3.6395 | 0.0571 |
| Safety | 2.99 | 3.21 | 2.4432 | 0.1187 |
| Employee skills | 3.45 | 3.31 | 1.5678 | 0.2111 |
| Manufacturing quality | 3.82 | 3.90 | 0.4862 | 0.4860 |
| Product design | 2.95 | 2.86 | 0.3792 | 0.5383 |
| Work methods and tools | 3.40 | 3.33 | 0.3417 | 0.5592 |
| Administrative routines | 2.72 | 2.66 | 0.2583 | 0.6146 |
| Material waste | 3.35 | 3.37 | 0.0217 | 0.8830 |
| Manufacturing costs | 3.89 | 3.87 | 0.0209 | 0.8852 |

Table 5 - Support For Continuous Improvement
(1= Not Important, through to 5 = Of Critical Importance)

| Support Methods for CI | | | | |
|---|---|---|---|---|
| | **Mean** | | **ANOVA Statistics** | |
| **Variable** | **UK** | **Australia** | **F values** | **Signf.** |
| Use of Total Productive Maintenance | 4.06 | 2.70 | 53.36 | 0.0000 |
| Support from staff functions | 3.59 | 4.30 | 41.0205 | 0.0000 |
| Promoting on notice boards | 3.31 | 2.57 | 31.6112 | 0.0000 |
| Promoting via competition and awards | 3.10 | 2.09 | 28.4590 | 0.0000 |
| Work in teams / work groups | 4.22 | 3.74 | 16.057 | 0.0001 |
| A general problem solving format | 3.57 | 2.88 | 14.362 | 0.0002 |
| A suggestion scheme | 3.00 | 2.37 | 14.3494 | 0.0002 |
| Promoting through internal media | 3.11 | 2.51 | 14.0125 | 0.0002 |
| Incentive systems | 3.06 | 2.35 | 11.2863 | 0.0009 |
| Use of formal policy deployment | 3.38 | 2.81 | 10.81 | 0.0011 |
| Face to face communications | 3.71 | 4.03 | 9.2831 | 0.0024 |
| Monitoring CI process | 3.78 | 4.18 | 2.7873 | 0.0957 |
| Training in problem solving tools | 3.88 | 3.69 | 2.3241 | 0.1281 |
| Use of ISO 9000 | 3.66 | 3.51 | 1.1791 | 0.2781 |
| Supportive leadership | 4.10 | 4.37 | 0.9306 | 0.3352 |
| Regular shop floor visits by management | 3.77 | 3.81 | 0.1097 | 0.7407 |

Table 5 examines the various support mechanisms regarded as most important in accomplishing CI in the business unit. It can be seen from this table that firms in both countries consider supportive leadership to be very important, and both groups have a similar view on the value of management visits to the shop floor. Based on the ANOVA test, a range of support methods were identified as rating differently in the UK and Australia. UK companies used Total Productive Maintenance, teamwork, and formal policy deployment more than Australian companies which tended to use face-to-face communication and formal staff support.

Table 6 - Problem Solving Tools
   (1= Not Important, through to 5 = Of Critical Importance)

| Problem Solving Tools | Mean | | ANOVA Statistics | |
|---|---|---|---|---|
| Variable | UK | Australia | F values | Signf. |
| Creativity tools/Idea generation tools | 3.86 | 2.97 | 44.1247 | 0.0000 |
| Display/visualisation tools | 3.73 | 2.88 | 43.1851 | 0.0000 |
| Failure Mode and Effect Analysis (FMEA) | 3.47 | 2.57 | 33.1712 | 0.0000 |
| Standardisation tools | 3.63 | 2.89 | 29.1885 | 0.0000 |
| 5S (cleaning, sorting, systemisation etc.) | 3.36 | 2.56 | 16.3998 | 0.0001 |
| 7 "new" quality tools (7MP tools) | 3.05 | 2.42 | 13.7788 | 0.0002 |
| Problem identification tools/checklists | 3.72 | 3.96 | 4.6281 | 0.0320 |
| Processing mapping tools | 3.45 | 3.17 | 4.2643 | 0.0396 |
| Quality Function Deployment (QFD) | 2.88 | 2.56 | 2.5975 | 0.1081 |
| 7 basic quality tools | 3.48 | 3.33 | 1.2105 | 0.2719 |

Table 6 examines the perceived importance of a variety of problem solving tools used in the implementation of CI activities  The results indicate that the majority of companies appear to concentrate on the simple tools which may be rapidly implemented rather than those that may require long term planning and data collection. Problem identification tools or check-lists are considered to be most important by these companies, while the 7 basic tools (e.g. Pareto charts, fishbone or cause-and-effect diagrams) and process mapping tools are also regarded as important. UK firms are more likely to attach importance to the more sophisticated tools such as Failure Mode and Effect Analysis (FMEA) and the 'Seven New Tools' (also known as the 'Seven Management and Planning Tools') than Australian firms.

*Implications of the survey results*

The comparison of the results of the UK and Australian surveys shows that in some respects there are strong similarities between manufacturing firms in the two countries.  For example, improvements in manufacturing productivity, manufacturing quality and cost reduction were important motivations for both UK and Australian companies; in both countries CI is most frequently directed at improving manufacturing quality and reducing costs; and both sets of respondents considered management visibility on the shop floor and supportive leadership to be important.

However, there are also some marked differences between the practice of CI in the UK and Australia.  For example, around two thirds of the UK companies claimed to have widespread and sustained or systematically applied CI activities; to consider CI to be of strategic importance; and to practice CI throughout the entire unit. Fewer than half the Australian firms reported a similar level of progress in these areas. This suggests that, in general, UK firms are more advanced in terms of establishing a CI as a part of "normal" operations (or that the UK respondents are more optimistic – or dishonest! – than their Australian counterparts).

These differences cannot be attributed to the length of time the companies have been doing CI, since the Australian firms have been working with CI for longer than the British.  It seems that the UK companies have made more progress in a shorter space of time, achieving a more advanced stage of CI. For example, one would expect a company to begin by using the simpler, easier to apply CI tools and move onto the more complex or novel techniques (e.g. QFD, the 'Seven New Tools') at a later stage. However, Table 6 suggests that more UK than Australian companies have recognised the importance of the more sophisticated tools.    The Australian companies also attached less importance to display tools and creativity tools, many of which are simple and easy to use, than do the UK firms.

There are various possible explanations for the more thorough implementation of CI in the UK than in Australia. UK companies may have felt the impact of deregulation of the economy more deeply and therefore are more committed to programmes like CI which can help them become more competitive. British companies may be more exposed to influences from the USA, where many of the recent developments in employee involvement and quality, including an emphasis on applying these practices to non-manufacturing areas, have taken place. UK firms in some sectors, notably automotive components, now supply Japanese transplants and have become subject to more stringent quality, delivery and cost requirements than hitherto. On the other hand, many of the Australian firms using CI are subsidiaries of overseas companies and are slow to risk taking on change programs unless told to do so by the parent organisation.

The pace of change in the environment in which the companies in these countries operate is unlikely to slow down in the foreseeable future. In fact, the day-to-day demands placed on these firms by increased competition, changing customer needs and changing government industry policy are likely to become even more intense. Thus there will be a growing need to improve the skills, commitment and cooperation of all employees in manufacturing organisations as they are forced to respond to these developments. With this in mind it is interesting to note that, as shown in Table 3, UK firms view the need to increase employee commitment and employee skills as a motive for CI to a far greater extent than do Australian companies (the difference was significant for both these variables). Several government initiatives are encouraging UK companies to invest in improving employee skills and motivation in order to enhance overall business performance. According to the CBI, "The UK has made significant progress towards raising the levels of education and training, but the gap with other nations remains." (Confederation of British Industry, 1995 p.23). A growing number of companies are participating in the Investors in People scheme, launched in 1991, which provides a framework for improving business performance through people development. By 1995, more than half of organisations with over 200 employees had committed to achieving the IIP standard, as well as nearly a quarter of firms below that size.

*Conclusions*

Deregulation policies have opened up the economies of the UK and Australia to trade in both directions i.e. to imports as well as to exports. This has a number of implications for firms operating in these countries, including:
• existing inefficiencies are shown up;
• increased competition;
• a shift in the source of competition from within the country to world-wide.

Moreover, as customers are able to access products from a global market place they become more demanding and increasingly look to factors other than price alone when purchasing commodities. Although price normally remains a major consideration in purchasing decisions, factors such as quality, timeliness and reliability also become important. To survive in the long term and become competitive at a global level, manufacturers need to overcome their inefficiencies, establish a competitive (sales-winning) edge, and put in place an ongoing process that allows and encourages changes to all aspects of their organisations. This is possible, it is argued, by adopting a concept of competitive quality.

One of the elements of competitive quality is continuous improvement. To get the maximum benefit from CI, the focus needs to move from a purely manufacturing emphasis to encompass all business processes. The survey findings suggest that a greater proportion of UK firms are taking this holistic, strategic approach to CI than is the case in Australia. The strategic approach to CI involves developing the skills, commitment and participation of all employees. If enough companies do this the national skills base will be enhanced. This itself is one of several factors which attracts inward investment which in turn translates into more jobs and, as seen in the UK, if the transplants have high standards there is a knock on effect in improving business performance in the local supply chain.

*References*

Access Economics and The Allen Consulting Group Pty Ltd. (1991), Developing Australia's National Competitiveness, A report prepared for the Business Council of Australia. Melbourne.

Andersen Consulting (1994). Worldwide Manufacturing Competitiveness Study: The Second Lean Enterprise Report. Arthur Andersen & Co.

Bessant, J., Caffyn, S., Gilbert, J., Harding, R. and Webb, S. (1994). *Rediscovering Continuous Improvement*, Technovation, 14 (1) pp.17-29

Brown, A. and Van der Wiele, T. (1996). *A Typology of Approaches to ISO Certification and TQM* , Australian Journal of Management, 21 (1), pp. 57-67.

Caplen, B. (1996). *Bulls, bears and tigers*, Euromoney, May, pp.32-37.

Confederation of British Industry (1995). *Making it in Britain IV*, Fourth annual report of the National Manufacturing Council, 9 November. London, UK.

CBI/NatWest (1996). Innovation Trends Survey, Issue 7. London, UK.

Das, R. (1996). *Deregulation and liberalisation in India: The managerial response*, Journal of general management, 21 (3), pp.48-58.

Dean J. W. Jr. and Brown, D. E. (1994). *Management Theory and Total Quality: Improving Research and Practice Through Theory Development*, Academy of Management Review, 19, pp.392-418.

Dow, D. (1992). *The future of the manufacturing sector in Australia*, Practising Manager, 12 (2), pp.16-19.

Eade, P. (1995). *Can India keep up the pace of reform?*, Euromoney, March, pp.1-4.

Garvin, D. A. (1988). Managing Quality: The Strategic and Competitive Edge, The Free Press, New York.

Hamel, G. and Prahalad, C. K. (1994). Competing for the Future: Breakthrough Strategies for Seizing Control of Your Industry and Creating the Markets of Tomorrow, Boston, Harvard Business School Press.

IQS (1991). International Quality Study: The Definitive Study of the best International Quality Management Practices . Top-Line Findings, A Joint Project of the American Quality Foundation and Ernst & Young, Cleveland, OH.

Hilmer, F. (1991), *Coming to grips with competitiveness and productivity*, Discussion Paper No. 91/01, for the Economic Planning Advisory Council, February.

Hilmer, F. (1993), *Report by the Independent Committee of Inquiry into Competition Policy in Australia*, National Competition Policy, Canberra, AGPS.

Hilmer, F. (1995), *Competition policy: Underlying ideas and issues*, Discussion Paper No. 337, Centre for Economic Policy Research, Australian National University, November.

Hoekman, B.M. and Mavroidis, P.C. (1993), *Competition, Competition Policy, and the GATT*, Policy Research Working Paper No. 1228, The World Bank, December.

Lewis, S. (1994). *All systems go*, Asiamoney, July-August, pp.34-36.

Nunes, N., Crockett, G., and Dawkins, P. (1993). *The impact of competition and trade unions on workplace reform and organisational and technological change*, Australian Economic Review, Iss. 102, pp.71-88.

Porter, M.E. (1985). Competitive Advantage: Creating and sustaining superior performance, The Free Press, New York.

Quiggin, J. (1996), *Estimating the results of Hilmer and related reforms*, Discussion Paper No. 338, Centre for Economic Policy Research, Australian National University, January.

Robinson, A. (1991). Continuous Improvement in Operations, Productivity Press, Cambridge, MA.

Rommel, G., Brück, F., Diederichs, R., Kempis, R.-D., Kaas, H.-W., Fuhry, G. and Kurfess, V. (1996). Quality Pays, Macmillan Press Limited, Basingstoke, UK.

Schutte, H. (ed.) (1994). The Global Competitiveness of the Asian Firm, Macmillan, London.

Siddiqi, A. R. (1992). *India charts a new course*, Chemical Engineering, 99 (8), pp.35-39.

Sohal, A. and Eddy, T. (1994). Quality Practices in Australian Manufacturing Firms, A Joint Report by Monash University and Ernst & Young, Melbourne.

The Mobil Survey (Fifth Cycle) of ISO 9000 Certificates Awarded World-wide (1996). Mobil Europe Ltd. London, UK.

Zhao, X., Maheshwari, S. K. and Zhang, J. (1995). *Benchmarking Quality Practices in India, China and Mexico*, Benchmarking for Quality Management & Technology, 2, (3) pp20-40.

# 011

# ANTECEDENTS AND RAMIFICATIONS OF TECHNOLOGY MANAGEMENT IN THE AFTERMATH OF REENGINEERING

Authors:
Eliezer Geisler and William Drago
Dept. of Management
College of Business
University of Wisconsin-Whitewater
Whitewater, WI 53190
USA

Te:         +1-414-472-3971
Fax:        +1-414-472-4863
e-mail:     geislere@uwwvax.uww.edu

## ABSTRACT

This paper addresses the role that management of technology (MOT) plays in the aftermath of business process reengineering. Based on studies that author conducted of the effects of reengineering, the paper is a comprehensive study of the organizational and managerial aspects of MOT as they are imbedded in the concepts of reengineering. In addition, the paper explores the positive and negative effects of reengineering, with the focus on how MOT can alleviate some of these effects. Various models are presented and some cases of reengineered corporation are discussed.

Oral Presentation

# 012

## CORE QUALITY DESIGN, CQD, IN NEW PRODUCT DEVELOPMENT, NPD.

Author:
Jan Österlund, Dr Sci
Royal Institute of Technology, Stockholm Sweden
Storhagsvägen 41
125 54 Älvsjö
Sweden
Tel:        +46-08-88 35 55
Fax:        +46-08-88 35 55

## ABSTRACT

New design methods focusing on Functional Requirements analysis enable creation of a concept guiding the following design work of making drawings, programs, prototypes etc. Axiomatic Design is one such method that allows solving of design problems before the start of the design work finalizing an NPD process. The structure of functional requirements, FR, and conceptual solutions in form of design parameters, DP, is broken down and mapped down to the detail level. It is made by successive definition of FR´s and corresponding DP´s into a tree structure of independent solutions. The broken down FR structure in the concept enable a continuous verification of the design work. Each step of design is verified by the parameters originated in the step against the according FR´s from the concept. Comparison of the design result to the corresponding requirements from the design concept is the base in the CQD method. The method includes also optimal use of competence resources to get very thorough conceptual solutions. This will reduce failures and iterations in the following design work.
Thus, the method gives the right product quality at decreased cost and project time.

Oral Presentation

# 014

# Globalized Manufacturing and Technology Transfer Strategies - The Development of a Technology Valuation Model

David Bennett, Kirit Vaidya and Zhao Hongyu,
*Technology and Innovation Research Centre, Aston Business School, Birmingham UK*

and
Wang Xing Ming
*The Business School of the People's University of China, Beijing, China*

## ABSTRACT

As manufacturing becomes increasingly globalized the value of technology has become a crucial question when being transferred from suppliers to acquirers. Under many forms of transfer arrangement the value of technology cannot be considered in isolation from the nature of the arrangement itself which could range from one-off transactions to an equity joint venture or other forms of close partnership. The distribution of costs, risks and benefits varies substantially between types of arrangement as well as the specifics of the agreement. Previous research by the authors into the transfer of technology between the UK and China has revealed that the issue of reaching mutual agreement on the value of technology was a major handicap to many transfer negotiations.

This paper describes the framework and progress with development of a technology valuation model. The main focus of the research is on machine tool technology being transferred from the UK to China. The results will assist companies in developing their technology transfer and global manufacturing strategies. The overall aim of the research is to develop a model using empirical data gathered from both countries to identify the factors that both technology suppliers and acquirers consider when valuing transferred technology. The model will provide a framework for assessing the components of value, their relative weights, the balance between them and how they are related to the form of collaboration between the supplier and acquirer.

## Introduction

The growth of globalized manufacturing has been especially rapid over recent years and international technology transfer, coupled with cross border manufacturing, is now seen as an effective means of accessing foreign markets and resources. This is especially the case with transfers between developed and developing countries (Kaplinsky 1990, Roessner and Porter 1990). An example can be seen in China's machine tool industry which has maintained a rapid annual growth since the mid 1980s. Its annual output value doubled by the end of 1993 compared with 1985 making it among the world's top five machine tool industries in terms of output value. Despite this dramatic increase in output, the industry's production capacity still cannot meet the rapidly increasing domestic demand which in recent years has grown annually at around 17% per annum making it currently the world's third largest market for machine tools. The shortage of domestically produced machine tools of sufficient quality has resulted in large numbers of imports from the major industrialised countries. Machine tool imports now represent nearly 65% of total sales value of machine tools in China.

Although this situation suggests that China may look like a continuing destination for future foreign machine tool exports this is unlikely to be the case without accompanying technology transfer since the Chinese government imposes import tariffs of, on average, 30% on machine tools. As a consequence the rate of decrease of local manufacturers' share of the domestic market has slowed from about 10% per annum between 1992 and 1994 to about 2% since 1995. Also investment incentives in the form of tax reductions and the lower costs of labour and materials favour the transfer of foreign technology to local manufacturing sites. As a result foreign machine tool manufacturers have shown considerable interest in establishing technology collaborations with Chinese partners.

There is still, however, a question concerning the value of technology that arises in most technology transfer negotiations and collaboration arrangements (Bruijn & Jia, 1993). There have been many cases where multinational enterprises proved reluctant to conduct inter-firm transfers due to the value of technology not being fully appreciated by acquirers (Hymer, 1976; Teece, 1982). There are also many foreign companies that have experienced time-consuming negotiations in trying to establish the value of technology with Chinese partners and customers, with many failing to reach an agreement.

Previous research by the authors into the transfer of technology between the UK and China has revealed that the issue of reaching mutual agreement on the value of technology was a major handicap to many transfer negotiations. Suppliers often felt that the acquirers tried to drive down prices without appreciating the full benefits of the technology and by contrast acquirers felt that suppliers always wanted to charge higher prices and did not appreciate the availability of alternatives or local development capabilities. From research carried out to date the following are the main factors which make it difficult to determine a value for technology which is acceptable both to the supplier and acquirer (Bennett et al, 1997).

i)    Differences in the perceived strategic and commercial importance of the technology.
ii)   Differences in the form of collaboration.
ii)   Differences in perception concerning the technology gap.
iii)  Differences in perception of product standards.
iv)   Differences in the amount of in-house and sub-contract production.

**Research focus and design**

From the point of view of the owner the value of technology depends on how it is used. It can be retained or transferred to a third party. Costs associated with its development, production and supply need to be taken into account. Apart from these costs, the value of technology is also affected by the actual or potential threat from alternative competing technologies and barriers against entry into markets. For the potential acquirer the important considerations are the cost of the technology, its own absorptive capacity and the benefits to be gained from the technology. Therefore it involves a company's overall strategy, market position, the form of transfer arrangements and collaboration between the owner and the acquirer. As the study of these issues requires investigating both sides of any transfer arrangement the research design includes analysis of available data on technology transfer transactions, UK and Chinese company case study analyses and questionnaire surveys in both countries.

The main aspects of the research are:

i)    Development of the concept of value within the context of technology transfer arrangements.
ii)   Definition and assessment of the major determinants of value from the perspective of the supplier and acquirer of technology.
iii)  Identification of judgmental factors, subjective influences and uncertainties which have a bearing on the agreed value of the technology in the transaction, the transfer arrangement and collaboration (if appropriate) after the transfer.
iv)   Assessment of the relative importance of the judgmental and objectively determinable factors and uncertainty in valuing the technology.
v)    Testing the robustness of the model within wider context (initially by applying it to the steel industry).
vi)   Development of a generic framework with potential for application in other industries.

## The conceptual model and framework for technology valuation

As a starting point the value of technology is considered as the "gain" which can be made by ensuring its best possible use. However, as the technology may be used solely by the owner or shared with others, its value to owners and acquirers (actual or potential) will depend on their different perspectives. The effectiveness and value of technology are dependent on upstream factors (cost and quality of components, processes and services required to develop and produce the technology). The technology also adds value downstream (for example, by enabling more efficient production of better quality components). Based on these considerations, four components have been identified for incorporation into the technology valuation model.

1.    "Owner's value". This is the current worth of the technology to the owner based on the cost of its development, production and distribution together with the cumulative costs of any other upstream activities (for example, those incorporated in the cost of components and other inputs) and opportunity cost considerations (for example, where the market value of the technology is lower than the cost of its development because of obsolescence).

2.    "Substitute value" . This is the price that the acquirer could expect to pay for an equivalent technology from another source. This may be either the price of alternative technologies in the market, if such a market exists, or the cost of the acquirer developing its own technology.

3.    "Traded value". This is the income that could be derived if the technology was sold-on by the acquirer or its value if the acquirer was bought-out by a third party. If the acquirer is a listed share holding company the traded value could be reflected in the change of its share price.

4.    "Transfer value". This is the potential worth of the technology to the acquirer, taking into account the proportion of added value generated further downstream in the value chain which could be captured by the acquirer.

These four value components have a bearing on whether a transfer of technology can be agreed, the "transaction value" of the technology, and the form of the agreement. The value of technology to the current owner will be based on the distinctive differentiation advantages it offers as well as the cost base which itself depends on its own costs and the costs upstream in the value chain. The substitute value influences the decisions of both the potential acquirer and the owner. Potential acquirers of technology will, in addition, be concerned with the traded value since it provides an indication of the gain if the technology is subsequently resold. Transfer value is of the greatest importance to the acquirer since it represents the "worth" of the technology taking into account the downstream value added that can be captured. Transfer value would also be of relevance to the supplier where a royalty is to be paid or a share of benefits can be gained in return for the use of the technology by the acquirer.

The focus of the research is on the transaction between the owner and the acquirer. Therefore development of the model has concentrated on the owner's and the transfer values with the two other value components influencing the price of the technology cost and the form of transfer arrangement through the decision making processes of the owner and the acquirer.

Several authors (for example Baker and Freeland 1975, Sounder and Mandakovic 1986) have identified a number of factors to be taken into account in selecting and valuing technology and the authors' case study research confirms the importance of these. They include uncertainty of commercial and technical success, the resource requirements to develop the technology, the degree to which the technology contributes to established missions and the current life-cycle stage of the technology. Further, the nature of technology makes the question of its value even more complex. While some technology embodied in hardware and even some software in the form of expertise can be readily bought and sold in the market, this is not true of most technology for a number of reasons:

i)    To a greater or lesser extent, potential suppliers of the technology may have developed knowledge and capabilities which cannot be easily transferred.
ii)   Suppliers may not wish to transfer their core knowledge and capabilities crucial to their own competitive advantage unless the benefits of making the transfer exceed the costs.
iii)  Acquirers and suppliers of the technology may be uncertain about the capability needed to absorb the technology and the market conditions for the "product" to be made by the technology.
iv)   Both suppliers and acquirers may be concerned about achieving an acceptable distribution of costs, risks and benefits from the transfer.

The value of technology must therefore take into account the actual types of transfer or sharing arrangements. The distribution of costs, risks and benefits vary substantially between types of arrangements as well as the specifics of the agreements.

**Development of Owner's Value**

For the owner, technology is a part of its organisational knowledge which gives it distinctive capabilities and competitive advantages. It has been noted that a concern with making technology available to another enterprise is the possible loss of the competitive advantage embodied in the technology. Nevertheless, a clear conclusion from previous research was that firms seek to maximise the benefits from their established technology by transferring it to a foreign enterprise in order to develop access to an expanding market. Further, the likelihood of other firms with competing technologies entering the market and barriers against entry into markets for the products of the technology can sway the balance in favour of transferring technology instead of retaining it within the enterprise.

In summary, the influences on the way the owner perceives value are:

i)   The distinctive features of the technology being considered.
ii)  The costs of development, production and distribution.
iii) The availability and cost of bought-in components and software incorporated into the
     owner's processes and products.
iv)  The actual or potential threat from competing technologies.
v)   Barriers against entry into target markets.

A model of the cost structure of machine tool technology based on the analysis of specific products in UK companies has been developed and is being validated with assistance from the collaborating companies (see Figure 1).

**Figure 1. The Cost Structure of Owner's Value**

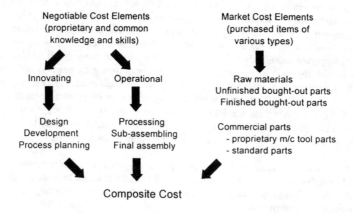

In order to examine the features of the technology being transferred, a distinction has been made between process and product technology. Further the know-how and skills which are part of the technology have been separated into two types:

i) Innovating types such as design, development, process planning.
ii) Operational types such as processing, sub-assembling and final assembly skills.

The innovating components are 'key' to improving and updating technological capability. If the owner wishes to protect a technological advantage the emphasis will be on transferring operational capabilities only. If the key technology is to be transferred then the value will need to reflect the owner's intellectual investment in development together with an adequate return.

From the owner's perspective the costs of the technology can also be separated into two further types. First, there are those that are incurred internally by virtue of the fact that they are linked with 'proprietary' activities. Second, there are costs incurred externally through buying-in parts, know-how and skills. In practice it is necessary to clarify what parts of both are to be transferred and what additional components and know-how the acquirer may need to obtain in order to make effective use of the technology.

## Development of Transfer Value

For the potential acquirer the important considerations in determining transfer value are the cost of the technology, its own capacity to absorb and use the technology and the benefits to be derived from it. There are a number of reasons why the acquirer's perception of owner's value could be lower than that of the owners themselves. The acquirer may not appreciate that the knowledge required to use the technology successfully cannot be gained simply from design drawings. In many cases there are differences in product quality standards and specifications between the supplier's and acquirer's markets and therefore the acquirer may need to carry out modifications to the technology to make it suitable for local customers. The acquirer may also not appreciate that the technology is dependent on availability and use of components supplied to exacting standards by specialist contractors. For example, a typical Chinese machine tool manufacturer will buy-in only 10% of parts in terms of workload, whereas a UK manufacturer's bought-in element will be around 60%.

Earlier work by members of the team found that almost 60 per cent of Chinese firms wished to acquire foreign technology to improve their competitive capability (Bennett et al, 1996). In the machine tool industry, the role of foreign technology is to improve competitive capability by offering better products with higher performance and enable access to new markets. For example, using imported technology is almost essential for Chinese firms to sell their machines to joint ventures in the automotive sector. In addition, acquirers may need to make wider changes to their organizations in order to effectively absorb and make the best use of the transferred technology. These may include establishing a separate unit which is isolated from those parts of the enterprise that are subject to the social and welfare obligations of state enterprises in China. The corollary of this type of organizational arrangement may be to create a shareholding company or joint venture with the foreign supplier of the technology.

In principle the technology transferred could be a product, process or a combination of both. The team has found that in most cases the primary transfers in the machine tool sector have been of product technology, though in order to reach the high standards in manufacturing the products it has been necessary to improve processes as well.

For the acquirer the value of the technology is realised by the number of products it sells and the higher prices customers will pay for the advantages offered by the product. This will often require a totally different marketing approach to the one traditionally used by enterprises in China (see case A). This often requires the supplier of the technology to become involved in the marketing despite the acquirer assuming the transfer would be of technology hardware and production know-how only.

The advantages of using transferred technology include the following:

i)     Better quality.
ii)    Greater reliability.
iii)   Greater accuracy.
iv)    Ease of operation and control.
v)     Faster and/or more efficient operation.
vi)    Less time for preparations and repairs and cheaper maintenance.
vii)   Aesthetic factors (e.g. more compact and attractively styled machines).

Transfer value is actually a balance between the acquisition gains and costs (see Figure 2).

## Figure 2. The Development of Transfer Value

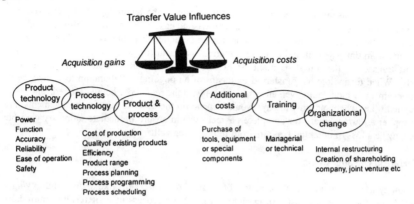

Transfer Value Influences

Acquisition gains — Acquisition costs

Product technology / Process technology / Product & process

Power
Function
Accuracy
Reliability
Ease of operation
Safety

Cost of production
Qualityof existing products
Efficiency
Product range
Process planning
Process programming
Process scheduling

Additional costs / Training / Organizational change

Purchase of tools, equipment or special components

Managerial or technical

Internal restructuring
Creation of shareholding company, joint venture etc

The acquirer gains by offering a 'better' product to existing and/or new customers and from entering new market segments. The gain arises from capturing a part of the additional value to the customer of the new product as opposed to existing or competing products. The costs to the acquirer include the actual price paid for the technology together with any equipment and training costs and the cost implications of any organizational changes that are required.

An acquirer cannot be certain that they will be able to learn and use the technology and that there will be a sufficiently large gain. This raises the questions of who pays the transaction costs associated with the technology transfer, for example the technical and management training, and whether the acquirer is willing to pay for the technology in full at the outset. It has been noted that acquirers often wish to share their risks with suppliers in return for longer term benefits. For this reason and because many Chinese enterprises are short of funds there is often an unwillingness to pay for the technology 'up front'.

### Owner's value and transfer value in the context of strategic alliances

Since the technology transfer process often involves an arrangement for sharing gains, costs and risks the valuation of technology cannot be isolated from the suppliers' as well as acquirers' overall strategies for technological collaboration. There are many specific factors which could substantially influence value in a collaborative transfer process. The following are the main factors which have been identified from the research so far when determining the owner's value and transfer value in the context of strategic alliances:

i) Relative perceptions of the time taken to transfer technology and market the end product.
ii) Quantification of intangibles (e.g. know-how).
iii) Assessment of the content of the transferred technology.
iv) Time taken to assimilate the technology.
v) Payment arrangements.
vi) Expectations of each side's performance.

More generally the influencing factors can be summarised into three broad aspects, i.e.

# 1. Commercial considerations

For commercial reasons suppliers will expect the costs of the technology to be covered by a monetary return. Acquirers on the other hand will wish to ensure the future benefits derived from its use can cover their payments for the technology. In practice there are likely to be two types of payment; an initial payment and a future (deferred) payment (or payments). If the transfer is a one-off transaction the initial payment could comprise the whole amount including notional profits. When technology is transferred by means of an ongoing collaboration there may be an initial payment (which could even amount to zero) with the remainder being deferred. The terms of payment (i.e. when and how to pay) would depend on the specific transfer arrangements. For the supplier an arrangement for complete payment would ensure immediate monetary gain but there may be a loss of potential benefits from future added value.

# 2. Technical considerations

Technology transfer is not simply a matter of **change of ownership** like selling and buying a consumer product. Nor is it just **selling rights of use** but a process of **transferring know-how for production and use of the technology**. The time required for the transfer process and the effort necessary for learning and absorption depend on the degree of sophistication of the technology and the technological gaps, including the quality and capacity of equipment and the stages of knowledge, between suppliers and acquirers (Bohn 1994). More specifically different types of technology will require differences in the transfer process. Machine tool manufacturing technology, for example, requires more systematic know-how and skills to ensure the accuracy and reliability of the whole machine. Moreover, some key know-how cannot be transferred in the form of drawings, nor routine instructions, but through an experience-based learning process. Therefore the value of technology may not be fully appreciated by acquirers until they actually absorb the technology and thus are able to make complete advantage of its use. At the same time suppliers may also suffer a loss if their gain derived from transferring technology is based mainly on futures sale of end products. As a result both suppliers and acquirers could consider the technology was wrongly valued, with the former claiming the value to be too low and the latter claiming it was too high.

# 3. Strategic considerations

Owners of technology need to decide how best it can be exploited, either by internal activities or by external collaboration. If collaboration can add more value they need to consider which transfer arrangement provides the best return while minimising costs and risks. This often provides a strong incentive for establishing a globalized manufacturing strategy based on the identification of target markets and exploiting local advantages which, if a partner is involved, will include their technological, managerial and marketing capabilities. However, the owner will probably wish to retain some control over the technology and to manage the potential threat of competition. By the same token, acquirers need to be aware of the gaps between their strategic aspirations and current capabilities in order to judge the potential contribution of acquired technology to their future competitiveness and further development. These considerations raise the question of valuing technology within the context of a strategic alliance where a collaboration involving joint efforts, shared costs, benefits and risks, lead to mutually reinforced competitive strength, improved performance and increased benefits. The following case examples are from the authors' research and demonstrate the complexity of valuing technology within the context of a strategic alliance. The names of all the companies have been changed.

**Case A: Technological Collaboration Between Beijing Great Wall Machinery (BGWM) and "Millco".**

Millco has a worldwide reputation for its high quality machine tools. In order to secure and protect its access to the Chinese market Millco's UK subsidiary decided to transfer its technology for manufacturing CNC machining centres. Due to the sophistication of the machine the technology acquirer was required to have appropriate capabilities. BGWM, being a technologically based company, though not a traditional machine tool manufacturer, was considered to have superior technological capacity than many other Chinese enterprises and a co-production partnership was established in 1993. Millco supplied technology for its best selling machine, a vertical machining centre from its latest product range. This comprised provision of designs, training, and the supply of parts and assemblies for a given number of machines. The total contract value was US$ 6 million with stage payments according to the transfer process which was divided into four phases. At each phase it was intended that the local content should be increased, until eventually Millco supplied only key components. The price paid for the technology, which included provision of training, was considered by BGWM to be high with only 9% discount given on CKD kits compared with the price of complete machines when sold in China. BGWM, however, agreed to the asking price having assessed the benefits of sharing Millco's good reputation and capability to supply advanced technology and high quality.

After three years of collaboration BGWM was able to build and market a good quality machining centre so from a technical point of view the transfer was successful. However, the collaboration was not without commercial problems as in 1994 and 1995 BGWM only managed to sell very few machines. As a result, the value realised by the seller and the acquirer was small and Millco doubted the strategic benefits from continuing to collaborate with BGWM.

From the beginning of 1996 BGWM changed its marketing strategy from selling single machines to focusing on designing production lines and therefore winning orders for complete sets of associated machines. As a result its sales of the machining centre in 1996 were greater than those of any other CNC machine tool in China. Not only has transfer value been greatly improved but the strategic significance of the collaboration has also been recognised by Millco. Negotiations for a further collaborative agreement were therefore initiated to include more transferred technology, its value reflecting the partners' mutual strategic benefits.

**Case B: Technological Collaboration Between Shanghai General Machine Co (SGMC) and "Autoco".**

Autoco is one of the largest machine tool companies in the world. Its UK factory produces special purpose machines, particularly for the automotive industry. In 1991 it acquired a company that a few years previously had established a technology transfer agreement with SGMC . The terms of the agreement were that SGMC made an initial payment for drawings and training and undertook to pay a royalty of around 10% on future sales. Parts could either be purchased from Autoco or acquired locally since the machines were not permitted to be sold in China under the Autoco name.

The advantages of transferring technology to SGMC were considered to be that it is located in the coastal region where there is superior infrastructure support and there are also several major automotive customers in Shanghai. The transferred technology was for the manufacture of a transfer line. By 1996 SGMC had just two transfer lines nearing completion. Due to technical factors, however, SGMC continued to have difficulty winning orders, even with Autoco's technology. For transfer lines customisation and reliability are very important issues. Each application, and consequently each machine, is different and specialised skills such as sequencing of operations are crucial. Customers demand a guarantee of high reliability because module breaks-downs cause the whole transfer line to stop. Both these issues require the manufacturer to have considerable 'know-how' about the whole manufacturing process. Such know-how cannot be simply transferred via a sale of drawings and a short period of training but requires a build-up of experience coupled with a good absorptive capacity and resource commitment on the part of the acquirer. SGMC does not have the technological know-how for manufacturing such a special purpose machine but neither can it accumulate the necessary experience since it is unable to win orders from customers. As a result Autoco cannot make any gains from royalties.

Autoco recognised that the agreement it had inherited was based on low expectations and commitment and was bound to have limited success since it recognised that SGMC could not acquire the technology solely from the drawings and training. With the increased market potential resulting from the growth of the Chinese automotive industry and SGMC's improved access to this market Autoco is reconsidering the partnership and seeking to modify its agreement. In view of the previous problems, however, it will need to collaborate more closely with SGMC. The collaboration should provide a phased programme of transfer with opportunities for SGMC to gain experience and to gradually absorb technology. The initial phases may involve SGMC just carrying out final assembly with Autoco being responsible for the remainder of manufacturing and marketing.

The two case studies suggest that the issue of technology valuation goes well beyond establishing the initial agreement on price. In Case A the transfer value changed along with BGWM's improving sales performance while in Case B the initial payment only provided an opportunity to generate transfer value in the future. In the event this became more difficult to realise than was thought. Both cases clearly indicate that valuing technology is not a matter of setting up and negotiating a price but involves a decision about how to judge the potential value to each party. Where there is uncertainty about value and costs partners prefer to progress on a stage by stage basis with relatively low commitments initially. Closer collaboration comes about with the development of trust and increasing mutual benefits under the right circumstances (Kay, 1993) .

## Conclusion and future work

Valuing technology is a strategic process with both suppliers' and acquirers' costs and benefits needing to be taken into account. For a technology supplier the main concern is to at least cover the incremental costs of development, production and supply either by a one-off sale of the technology or by transferring technology in the form of an ongoing collaboration arrangement. The immediate benefits to be derived from transfer in the form of financial returns should be set against the longer term strategic considerations and its associated commercial and technical aspects. For the technology acquirer on the other hand the main concern is about reducing immediate costs and maximising future benefit. An assessment of the technology's contribution towards achieving the acquirer's commercial and strategic targets as well as its own capability to absorb the technology are essential requirements. Target costing (Brausch 1994) and value engineering methods (Shillito and De Marle 1992) may be extended for the purpose of the analysis.

In many cases, suppliers and the acquirers may both be uncertain about the latter's capability to absorb the technology and the market conditions for end-products. Therefore, in determining the mode of technology transfer, participants will take into account the distribution of costs, risks and benefits. Previous investigations of UK machine tool manufacturers indicated that many companies deal with such uncertainties by adopting a phased approach starting with technology transfer within a limited form of collaboration, such as providing technology through a licence agreement, and proceed to closer collaboration if the initial stage is successful and trust develops between the two parties.

As noted earlier the value of technology is affected by the actual or potential threat from competing technologies and barriers against entry into target markets. The implications of competition for the value of technology will be represented by the substitute value within the overall model framework. Barriers against entry favour technology transfer as a means of entry into a market as opposed to direct exports. However the actual mode of technology transfer (e.g. one-off sale, licensing, co-production agreements and so on) may differ depending on the context and company strategy. The latter will be affected by objective considerations such as costs, competition and market entry barriers as well as subjective perceptions and judgmental factors.

Specific features of technology should also be considered in assessing its value. The technology to be transferred may often incorporate knowledge and capabilities, developed by the enterprise, which cannot be easily transferred. The supplier may also not wish to transfer such knowledge and capabilities as they may be crucial to its own competitive advantage unless a solid long-term strategic alliance is established. Suppliers and acquirers may have different perceptions on the compatibility of some parts of the  technology in the local market.  The feasibility of collaboration, capability to conduct the operation and transfer arrangement therefore all need to be considered in technology valuation.

The future work includes quantifying the components of transfer value, determining and assessing  the components of transfer value, comparing technology attributes with their costs, and analysing the influence of perceptions and judgmental factors.

The research ream will carry out further case study investigations within the machine tool sector in both the UK and China as well as studying users of machine tools in China. Three categories of user have been identified for purpose of analysis: i) foreign owned companies and joint ventures, ii) Chinese companies using foreign technology, and iii) traditional Chinese enterprises. The purpose of the investigations into users is to gather information from which the 'transfer value' component will be developed. Apart from case studies, three questionnaire surveys are also to be conducted: i) among Chinese machine tool manufacturers, ii) among users in China, and iii) among UK machine tool manufacturers.  Survey data will be analysed for the purpose of refining the framework.

## References

Baker N R and Freeland W H (1975) "Recent Advances In R&D Benefit Measurement and Project Selection Method" Management Science, 21(10).

Bennett D J, Vaidya K G, Zhao, H Y and Wang X M (1996) "Transferring Technology to China: Supplier Perceptions & Acquirer Expectations", Aston Business School Research Institute, Research Paper Series RP9614, Birmingham, UK.

Bennett D J, Vaidya K G, Zhao, H Y and Wang X M (1997) "Technology Transfer to the China Machine Tool Industry: The Need for a Technology Valuation Model", Industry and Education, 11 (1).

Bohn R E (1994) "Measuring and Managing Technological Knowledge", Sloan Management Review, Fall.

Brausch J M (1994) "Target Costing for Profit Enhancement", Management Accounting, November.

Bruijn E J and Jia X F (1993) "Transferring Technology to China by Means of Joint Ventures", Research Technology Management, Jan-Feb.

Hymer S H (1976) The International Operations of National Firms, Lexington Books Lexington, Mass.

Kaplinsky R (1990) "Technology Transfer, Adaptation and Generation: A Framework for Evaluation", In Chatterji M (Eds) Technology Transfer In the Developing Countries, The Macmillan Press, London.

Kay J (1993) "Foundations of Corporate Success", Oxford University Press, Oxford.

Roessner J D and Porter A L (1990) "Achieving Technology-based Competitiveness in Developing Countries" In Chatterji M (Eds) Technology Transfer In the Developing Countries, The Macmillan Press, London.

Shillito M L and De Marle D J (1992) Value: Its measurement, Design and Management, John Wiley & Sons Inc, New York.

Sounder W E and Mandakovic T (1986) "R&D Project Selection Models - The Dawn of A New Era", Research Management, 29 (4).

Teece D J (1982) "Transaction Cost Economics and The Multinational Enterprise", University of Reading Discussion Paper in International Investment and Business Studies, No 66, Reading, UK.

# EXPERT SYSTEMS IN PRODUCTION INTEGRATED MANAGEMENT: RESULTS OF THREE STUDIES

## 015

Miguel Angel SASTRE CASTILLO
Jose Ignacio LOPEZ SANCHEZ
Luis Eugenio CARRETERO DIAZ
*Departamento de Organización de Empresas*
*Universidad Complutense de Madrid*

## 1.- Introduction

In order to maintain their competitiveness, companies feel compelled to adopt productivity increasing measures. Yet, they cannot relinquish the flexibility their production cycles need in order to improve their response, and thus, their positioning in the market.

To achieve this, companies must combine these two seemingly opposed principles. Thanks to new technological advances, this combination is already a working reality in some companies[1]. It is made possible today by the implementation of Computer Integrated Manufacturing (CIM) and Artificial Intelligence (AI) techniques, fundamentally by means of Expert Systems (EESS) and robotics.

Depending on how these (AI/CIM) techniques contribute to automation, their immediate effects are an increase in productivity and cost reductions. Yet also, the system's flexibility allows for easier adaptation and, as a result, an increased ability to generate value, in other words, competitiveness is improved.

We have analyzed three studies[2] to identify the possible benefits or advantages, as well as the inconveniences, that this type of techniques may bring to the companies, specifically in the production field. Although the scope of the studies and their approach differ from one to the other, their joint contribution can be of unquestionable value in order to understand a little better the importance of Expert Systems within the production system.

## 2.- Computer Integrated Manufacturing and Expert Systems

Computer Integrated Manufacturing (CIM) is a way of, directly or indirectly, coordinating all the elements involved in the production process: Computer Aided Manufacturing (CAM), Computer Aided Design (CAD), Computer Aided Production (CAP), etc., in order to achieve the strategical objectives set by the company's management (Hitomi, 1994).

The CIM concept might be one of the hardest to define. This is due mainly to the different approaches taken by the studious of this acronym. Some authors believe that CIM is a software package sold on the market. Others look for the integration of computer and automation technologies only, and exclusively, within the area of production. For others, CIM is a production technique that automates the whole company, a state-of-the-art technology, a business concept, etc. We can state that CIM is all of this, and more.

CIM is not a product that can be acquired on the market, it is rather a philosophy aimed at obtaining objectives (Weston, 1994). Unlike convencional automation projects (flexible manufacturing systems, numerical control machines, robots, etc.), CIM is a complex and long-term project because, apart from the technical structures, it is necessary to also consider the organizing ones (Rowlinson, Procter and Hassard, 1994).

So, CIM must be a part of the company's strategy that contributes to improving its competitiveness. It is company specific and should respond to the markets requirements by means of specific technical and economic objectives (Thomas and Wainwright, 1994).

Artificial Intelligence is a science and a technology that deals with the comprehension of intelligence and the design of intelligent machines. These machines are those that present characteristics normally associated with human understanding such as reasoning, written and spoken language comprehension, decision making, et al. (Valle, Barbera, and Ros, 1984).

Within AI, Expert Systems constitute the most important field of study. We can define them as computer systems designed to collect and register both, the aspects of the human expert which are necessary for decision making in order to ease problem solving in specific domains, and the expert's behaviour when faced with such situations. One of these areas, production, is the our object of study in this article. The main reason for the use of this technique can be found in the type of problems that must be solved. Situations that, although repetitive, are not completely structured because, even if the problem happens again, the circumstances surrounding it might vary.

## 3.- Areas In Which Expert Systems Can Be Applied Within Production

Although there are many areas in which Expert System prototypes can be developed (ES) -as many as problems or domains can be identified- in practice these techniques have been shown to be more applicable to structured and semi-structured problems.

Rao and Lingaraj (1988) classify the areas focusing on two dimensions: on one hand the temporary horizon (that they identify as tactical or strategic) in which they will have to be developed; on the other hand, depending on the function that the decisions to be adopted represent: operation management (production, programming, quality, etc.) or resources (machines, personnel, etc.).

In Figure 1 we see the four quarters that result from this classification. The numbers between parenthesis indicate those areas that can be moved from one quarter to another, focusing solely on the temporary horizon. It all depends on the implication of, and the frequency with which, such decisions are made. The maintenance function could be transferred to the first quarter, and the design of posts to the third quarter, depending on how wide a meaning we want to attach to the words.

As far as the areas of implementation go, Rao and Lingaraj (1988) in their work mention that companies rarely adopt decisions concerning plant distribution (layout), post design and location. For this reason, efforts to develop Expert Systems in such areas are not important, economically speaking they would not be justified. However production programming (scheduling), capacity planning, product and process design, and maintenance are seen as the most promising areas for the application of Expert Systems within the production field.

| | | Application Orientation | |
|---|---|---|---|
| | | Strategic | Tactical |
| Application Emphasis | Operations | 2<br><br>Aggregate Planning (1)<br>Forecasting (1) | Scheduling 1<br>Capacity Planning (2)<br>Layout<br>Process and Product Desing (2)<br>Quality Control<br>Job Design |
| | Resources | 3<br>Location | Inventory Control 4<br>Maintenance and Realiability |

Figure 1. Two-dimensional classification of Production/Operations Management applications (Rao y Lingaraj, 1988)

For Meyer (1990, p. 308) there are three main areas in which Expert Systems are applied, diagnosis, process planning and production programming. In project EP932 (Meyer, 1990 pp. 305-314), as we will later comment, 55 knowledge-based systems are developed, tested and implemented in the functions of production planning, quality control and maintenance. The distribution amongst each of the areas is enlightening, almost half of the systems, 49%, are established in the production planning area, 18% in the maintenance area, and 7% in that of quality control. So 74% of the systems were developed in one sole area. The remaining 26% belong to more than one area (see Figure 2). This fact shows that there is no significant percentage of Expert Systems that might be favoured by the benefits of knowledge integration. Work is done in well delimited domains to solve specific problems.

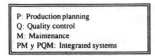

P: Production planning
Q: Quality control
M: Maintenance
PM y PQM: Integrated systems

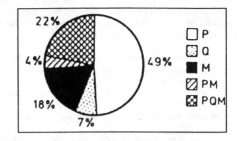

Figure 2. Result by function area (Meyer, 1990).

On the other hand, the European Auerbach report (Chip, 1989, pp. 80-81) recognizes six categories as a result of the study the most regularly used Expert Systems in industry. Most applications are included in any one of them: diagnosis and interpretation of data, planning and programming, design, process monitoring, simulation and prediction, and intelligent tutoring.

Of all the 46 areas in which Seai Tech. Publ. (1990) classifies the world's knowledge-based systems[3], of the 10 first only 3 directly affect the object of our study (see Figure 3).

| Ranking | AREA | % |
|---------|------|---|
| 2 | Diagnosis and Maintenance | 8,5 |
| 6 | Production Planning and Management | 3,8 |
| 7 | CAD/CAM/CIM | 3,3 |

Figure 3. Areas of aplication (production) of the EESS in the world

However, this study forecasts an important change within the next few years in the areas with the best perspectives for the application of knowledge-based systems. Thus, from among the ten first areas, 5 fall completely within the production field, ousting medicine from first place and substituting it with diagnosis and maintenance (Figure 4).

| Ranking | AREA | Valuation |
|---------|------|-----------|
| 1 | Diagnosis and Maintenance | 8,7 |
| 3 | Ingineering | 8,0 |
| 4 | CAD/CAM | 8,0 |
| 6 | Flow-Shop Process | 7,2 |
| 7 | Job-Shop Process | 7,2 |

Figure 4. Areas with the best perspectives for the application of EESS (production area)

The evolution is clear, the growth potential of Expert Systems, due to the type of problems they aim to address within the field of production, is a reality taking place in many countries while in Spain its still taking its time. Nevertheless, there seems to be a certain consensus among different AI experts which will result in a notable advance of Expert Systems within production, "a great effort will be devoted during the next few years to implementing Expert Systems within the production methods, to develop, firstly, tasks of interpretation, diagnosis, planning, configuration, monitoring, and control, prediction and acquisition of knowledge" (Andrés Puente 1993, p. 21).

## 4.- The Potential Benefits of Applying Expert Systems to Production

We often find, in specialized literature, news concerning the benefits that some Expert Systems bring to their respective domains, specifically within the production field[4]. This is not so when failures occurring while developing some of them are concerned. The benefits, such as the ones we have already identified, tend to increase productivity, but at the same time make the productive process much more flexible through a more fluid information flow. Their origin stems many times from a cost reduction, accompanied by an increase in the operativeness of the system, brought along by reduced execution times.

Although production systems might be a promising area for the development of Expert Systems, and many companies have already installed them, there is very little information available on use of Expert Systems within production from a business standpoint, much less than from the technical perspective. "An atmosphere of secrecy and privacy has surrounded the development of production directed Expert Systems within private organizations. Although these private organizations are developing Expert Systems, literature contains very little empirical information on their application and implications" (Byrd, 1993, p. 119).

Thus, we can identify three types of complementary reasons, all clearly defined albeit not mutually excluding, under which the main benefits that justify the implementation of Expert Systems and of other AI techniques in a specific domain (CIM) may be grouped (López Sánchez, 1995): those based on the need for **automation**, those based on **competitive factors** and finally, those motivated by the **type of problems** that must be solved and, thus, the type of decisions that must be adopted within the production system itself, as well as in the company as a whole. Knowledge-based systems add a new dimension to problem solving within the CIM field that other types of techniques did not contemplate: **knowledge**.

It is difficult to pinpoint what advantages or inconveniences are generated by the implementation of Expert Systems in an integrated production environment. This is not only due to how unknown they are, but to how hard it is to quantify them. Moreover, many of these, the company's image, the personnel's morale, the consistency in decision making, the increase in client satisfaction, etc. are **intangible**. For these reasons, the identification and later valuation of benefits is based on the opinions of experts and users from the companies that have implemented them. It is difficult to find perfectly quantified data comparing the conditions before and after their implementation.

Meyer[5] (1990) and Byrd[6] (1993) identify and value the advantages and inconveniences of implementing Expert Systems within the production field. The first one achieves it by studying the development, test and implementation of 55 knowledge-based systems within the functions of production planning, quality control and maintenance. He identifies the qualitative benefits (not measurable in monetary terms) and the quantitative ones (measurable in monetary terms) that result from the application of AI techniques within a CIM environment. He also studies the organization levels at which these techniques are used and the types of products that they turn out (standard, prototypes, internar exploitation and bought products). Concerning the analysis of the benefits that the aforementioned systems bring the companies, Meyer's work gathers the criteria that have been submitted to the different organizations in which Expert Systems have been implemented for valuation.

Eleven criteria for valuating the qualitative benefits have been describes. These are detailed in Figure 5. The criteria are classified according to the importance their impact on the companies. The company's image is the one with the most impact, whilst the product variety is given the last place. The order of the criteria is the same as the one in the bar graph presented in Figure 6.

| Number | CRITERION | EXPLANATIONS |
|---|---|---|
| 1 | Company image | Customers´s view of the company and its reputation |
| 2 | Production schedule flexibility | Adaptability of scheduling to real situations and their dynamic conditions |
| 3 | Labour morale | Job satisfaction due to shifts in skills |
| 4 | Internal communications | Communication between departaments |
| 5 | Product quality | Standard of quality of finished products |
| 6 | Response to change | Response to changes in the external environment (market demand) |
| 7 | Risk | Uncertainty when making high level decisions |
| 8 | External communications | Communication with the suppliers and the customers |
| 9 | Product innovation | Supporing product development by feedback of information from production and quality control |
| 10 | Safety | Prevention of accidents |
| 11 | Product variety | Range of products that can be made |

Figure 5. Criteria selected for the qualitative value analysis (Meyer, 1990).

The analysis of the results is presented in a bar graph where each of the three areas described above - production planning, maintenance, and quality control- are grouped under each criterion. The maximum possible value for each criterion, resulting form the sum of the three areas, is 33. The closer we get to this figure the greater the impact of this criterion will be on the company[7] (Figure 6).

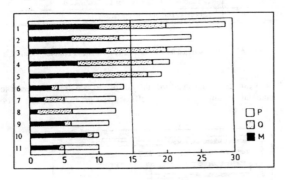

Figure 6. Qualitative benefits (Meyer, 1990).

The relative valuation analysis per each criterion of the different areas is interesting. For example, worker's morale is benefited more in the areas of maintenance and quality control, than in production planning. It can be due to the greater contact workers have with the former areas, because planning might be taking place at a higher level (for example the workshop chief) and thus its benefit is not evident to the workers.

Within the five first criteria, we highlight the place obtained by the improvement of the company's image: first. Note that it has approximately the same impact in the three areas dealt with. It can be said that the improvement of the company's image is a direct result of the implementation of Expert Systems. The second criterion is the improvement in the production planning's adaptation to changing situations. In other words, an increase in the flexibility of the production system, not as much in the variety of products, as in route assignment, machine loading, posts, etc.

Twenty criterion have been describes under quantitative benefits (Figure 7). Some of them are valuated through the cost reductions they bring to their respective entries. Valuation by criterion and area ranges from 1 to 20 (1 being the non-existence of benefits). The maximum value per criterion is 60 (the sum of all three areas). The absolute value depends on the value identified in that scale. Just as with qualitative benefits, the order in which the aforementioned criteria appear reflect how important the impact of each of them is.

| Number | CRITERION | EXPLANATIONS |
|---|---|---|
| 1 | Productivity | Utilization levels of all resources |
| 2 | Production throughput | Amount of production per unit of time |
| 3 | Scrap | Amount of waste in the manufacturing systems |
| 4 | Labour | Staffing on the shop floor clerical and the other office staff |
| 5 | Financial management | Cash flow and general financial health |
| 6 | Work in process (WIP) | Materials, parts, components and subassemblies waiting to be processed |
| 7 | Flow time | Time needed to produce a finished product from the first operation to dispatch |
| 8 | Order delay | Number of orders delivered late |
| 9 | Market share | Proportion of the total market demand for products supplied |
| 10 | Materials handling | Equipement meeded to move materials and products around the site and the customers |
| 11 | Training | staff training |
| 12 | Finished goods | Stocks of finished products awaiting shipment |
| 13 | Capital | Assets held on the factory site |
| 14 | Tools | Utilization of machine tools |
| 15 | Customer support | Dealing with customer enquiries and complaints |

| 16 | Reworks | Parts, components and products that require remaking or repairing |
|----|---------|----------------------------------------------------------------------|
| 17 | Floor space | Floor area required for production |
| 18 | Equipment life | Life of equipment needed to build products, depending on the type of processing |
| 19 | Raw materials | Raw materials purchased or parts subcontracted |
| 20 | Energy consumption | Total energy consumed in the factory |

Figure 7. Criteria selected for the quantitative value analysis (Meyer, 1990).

In Figure 8, you can see the result of the analysis of the said criteria relevant to the three areas of performance. We highlight the ranking's top two: efficacy and productivity, this last one being the most balanced of all in all three areas.

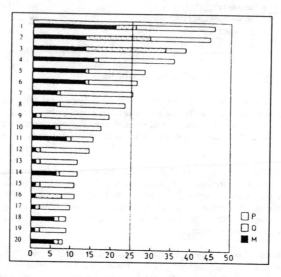

Figure 8. Quantitative benefits (Meyer, 1990).

Byrd (1993), unlike Meyer, does not study any particular system and tries to reflect the opinion of 74 Knowledge Engineers specialized in production from private companies, by means of a survey (Figure 9). Among the issues dealt with we find: the important points to follow to successfully implement an Expert System; how and what are the Expert Systems being used for; what are the motivations behind the development of successful Expert Systems; identification and valuation of the benefits brought along by Expert Systems; the effects of Expert Systems on end users; and, what are the most commonly employed knowledge acquisition techniques.

| BENEFIT | Mean (0-5) | PROBLEM | Mean (0-5) |
|---------|-----------|---------|-----------|
| More consistency in decision making | 3,72 | Lower job satisfaction | 4,25 |
| Improved productivity | 3,56 | Decline in job attractiveness of end-user | 4,15 |
| More timely business reporting and decisions | 2,95 | Sabotage on the part of user | 4,05 |
| Workers free to do more creative work | 2,95 | EESS seen as dehumanizing | 4.01 |
| Improved competitiveness and market share | 2,92 | Increase in mental work load of end-user | 3,95 |
| More accurate business reporting and decisions | 2,76 | Deskilling of personnel | 3,92 |
| Reductions of workers doing rutine tasks | 2,39 | Role of human in decision-making process ambiguous | 3,88 |
| More educations and training accomplished | 2,26 | Over-reliance on EESS for final decisions | 3,69 |
| Reduction in operations personnel | 1,78 | Explanations of recommendations of EESS non sufficient | 3,57 |

80

| Easier access to computer networks | 1.71 | Lack of trust by users in EESS solutions | 3.50 |

Figure 9. Benefits and Problems of the EESS implementations (Byrd, 1993)

Among the most important contributions of Expert Systems to the aforementioned domain are the growth of the company's image, more flexibility to production programming, and the dramatical increase of consistency in the decision making process and all of that without renouncing the system's efficiency and productivity.

It is important to note from Meyer's study (1990) the lack of Expert Systems on the market because, of the 55 systems studied, 89% are either not functioning (47% are prototypes) or, if they are (products exploited internally account for 42%), the amount of companies (generally from the same group) that benefit from these techniques is small. This situation is very similar to the one found in Spain where not very many Expert Systems are sold as products. The majority of them are developed and used inhouse.

## 5.- Result of a Study of Spanish Companies that Develop Expert Systems Within the CIM Context.

The difficulty encountered when determining the amount of CIM Expert Systems that exist in Spain is mainly due to the fact that most of the applications are custom-made. Oftentimes its the large companies' own research departments who are most active in the development of AI solutions. Even more so than the software companies who dedicate themselves to this technology.

If the situation does not change, few companies will have the possibility of acquiring such tools. This will undoubtedly affect the necessary cost reductions of the system. As a result, analysts cite two situations that are beginning to develop in Spain: a clear tendency of substituting custom-made applications (which are presently the majority) for the development of standard solutions; and, secondly, the appearance of small companies targeting specific niches or market segments. These small companies stem mainly from the great industrial, computer or telecommunications groups (Rubio, 1993).

The study we discuss next, was undertaken because of the existing lack of research on Expert Systems in the production field (the CIM concept) within the national context. This derives from the fact that there are not very many national reports available in Spain. Our intention was to reveal the opinion of some of the experts concerning the ideas we maintain all throughout this work. We did this by sending out a survey to the twenty companies that develop these technologies in Spain (López Sánchez, 1997).

All the companies surveyed answered affirmatively to the question about the development of Expert Systems in any of their production areas. From this we can derive the existence of products which are undoubtedly not known, or that companies do not disclose. The datum concerning the type of applications used (custom-made or standard) is interesting: 70% of the companies surveyed develop more than half of their applications (Expert Systems/CIM) to suit to their own needs. These applications are normally produced on some of the best known development tools.

On the other hand, all companies act as consultants on this type of applications. A reason for this policy lies in the ignorance among the companies in relation to this kind of software which, not being convencional, needs more support from its developers.

The analysis of the possible areas of applicability of these systems, as gathered from the answers received, is reflected in Figure 10, even though valuation (from 0 to 10) of each of the areas differs from one company to the next[8]. What is important is that we can be sure that companies are clearly willing to bet on this type of technology.

There seems to be a certain consensus as to which areas lack possibilities or are less favourable for the application of Expert systems, among them: laboratory management, data set up and acquisition and Electronic Data Interchange (EDI). As far as the rest of them go, there are disparate opinions, but we can assure that the most requested ones are those which tradicional studies done in other countries describe: finite capacity programming (scheduling), process simulation and plant distribution, management and quality control, logistics and distribution, production control and management, and maintenance.

| AREAS | Mean | Std. Dev. |
|---|---|---|
| MAP and Maintenance | 8.10 | 0.70 |
| Production Control and Management | 8.00 | 0.89 |
| Logistics and Distribution | 7.90 | 0.94 |
| Scheduling | 7.90 | 0.83 |
| Process Simulate and Layout | 7.60 | 1.11 |
| Administration | 7.00 | 1.00 |
| Quality Control | 7.00 | 1.18 |
| CAD/CAM/CAE | 6.20 | 0.98 |
| Automate Storage | 6.10 | 0.70 |
| Electronic Data Interchange | 4.20 | 0.60 |
| Data Capture | 4.20 | 1.17 |
| Laboratory Management | 3.10 | 0.70 |

Figure 10. Valuation of EESS implementation in the production areas

The time required to implement an application does not exceed a year in any of the companies surveyed: ninety percent achieves it in between 6 months and a year, the remaining 10% in less than 6 months. This time period depends basically on the companies' experts ability and the degree of understanding between the Knowledge Engineers and them.

Product cost calculations are not easy to make due to the high component added by the producing company, the cost of the tool, that is usually set at around 6.000 ECUs. The amount of hours worked, auxiliary systems, in-house developments, etc. must be then added to this price tag. Nevertheless, 90% of the time their cost was never below 31.000 ECUs. The system's estimated average cost (for custom-made applications once implemented) can be estimated at around 62.000 ECUs.

One hundred percent of the companies employ Digital's VAX computers and personal computers (the IBM compatible type) as the necessary platform for the systems. However, in 80% of the cases they can be run on personal computers housing Intel 486 or similar processors, with 8 Mb of RAM and a Hard Disc capacity of around 80 Mb; and under the normally used operating systems (MSDOS, Windows or UNIX).

As to the market at which the companies aim their products, it is convenient to note that among the type of company we surveyed -large computer groups or companies belonging to them (public or private)- approximately 90% of their market is national and the remaining 10% European. International orders (excluding Europe) are not meaningful. The companies not included in the aforementioned group (which amount to around 60%), operate basically within regional markets.

A similar behaviour can be detected with respect to which type of companies they aim their products at. Large computer groups aim their products towards other large companies more than 80% of the time, without dismissing small companies. On the other hand, regional companies supply their applications 80% of the time to small and middle-sized companies within their business area.

All the companies surveyed considered that they have more than 75% client loyalty. This percentage is simply a guideline because many companies only answered positively without specifying a percentage. Also, all of the companies maintain a client Help-Line service to which their clients can address any type of consultation. Specially those related to doubts stemming from solutions recommended by the system, Knowledge Representation, the inference process, etc.

They all answered positively to the question of what their policy concerning cooperation with other companies, universities and research centres is. Many of them maybe because of image concerns -but it can be stated that, in general terms, they feel proud of having one. Some 30% of the companies participate in some kind of Research and Development programme (Eureka, Marco, etc.) though they do not specify what the project consists of, or what domain it is aimed at.

As far as the generic strategies of each of the companies is concerned, their answers are totally unanimous: product differentiation. They all consider quality and brand image to be fundamental because these are the factors that guarantee old client loyalty, as well as the ones that attract new ones. We consider this is due to the high percentage of existing custommade applications relative to the total amount of applications they all have developed.

Concerning the companies' situation regarding their competition, we must highlight the production costs entry as an interesting datum: a full 90% of them consider it to be bad. None other entry, by any of the companies, is considered so. Since there is a large amount of dispersion we will not analyze them one by one, but we can say that there are signs of a sound situation vis-a-vis their competitors. All companies consider that the current competitive situation, valuated by the intensity of the five known competitive forces, is high or very high, with the exception of the threat of substitute products which is considered meaningless.

After having analyzed the data, our opinion is that, according to investigators, Expert Systems offer the companies important advantages (Figure 11). These advantages can be translated as an increase in productivity and an improvement in management of the whole productive process in general. Nevertheless, in this study we have not analyzed the quantitative valuation that the mentioned advantages contribute to the companies which implement them. Our study simply shows the favourable opinion that a series of experts have concerning the possible repercussions of these techniques.

Regarding possible problems (Figure 12), two of them stand out from all the rest: the high investment volume (high cost) and the unawareness of the system's potential benefits. These two problems are the basic cause of the low number of Expert Systems implemented within our companies. We should maybe comment that in many cases it is not only that companies do not know their potential benefits, but that they are unaware of the existence of Artificial Intelligence techniques and that these can be implemented within their activities.

| ADVANTAGE | Mean (0-10) | Std. Dev. |
|---|---|---|
| Scheduling improve | 8,90 | 0,54 |
| Increase in productivity | 8,40 | 1,02 |
| Reduction of supervision | 8,10 | 0,83 |
| Improvement on product quality | 8,00 | 1,18 |
| Increase of customer's satisfaction | 8,00 | 1,00 |
| Improvement on management | 7,60 | 0,92 |
| Integration sinergy | 7,50 | 1,20 |
| Reduction of breakdowns | 7,50 | 0,92 |
| Reduction of marketing cycle | 7,50 | 1,12 |
| Operations Flexibility | 7,40 | 1,20 |
| Reduction of losses | 7,40 | 0,92 |
| Increase of product fiability | 7,30 | 1,27 |
| Increase of labour morale | 7,30 | 1,55 |
| Reduction of stocks | 7,20 | 1,25 |
| Reduction of labour force | 6,80 | 0,98 |
| Increase of security | 6,70 | 1,00 |
| Reduction of transport costs | 5,80 | 1,72 |
| Reduction of suppliers | 3,80 | 1,08 |

Figure 11. Advantages of the EESS/CIM to the companies

| PROBLEM | Mean (0-10) | Std. Dev. |
|---|---|---|
| High investment volume | 8,30 | 0,90 |
| Unawareness of the system's benefit | 8,30 | 0,78 |
| Human factor | 5,50 | 1,20 |
| Training of team | 4,50 | 1,50 |
| Integration difficulty | 4,20 | 1,25 |
| Lack of appropiate software | 4,10 | 1,70 |
| Operation costs (maintenance, supervision...) | 3,20 | 0,87 |

Figure 12. Companies problems in the EESS/CIM implementation

All those surveyed consider that the sales volumes of Expert Systems/CIM will increase in Spain, although it will happen at a slow growth rate -a maximum 10% annual rate. This is contrary to the expectations set by some AI experts who, as was said before, forecast an important growth in Western Europe[9].

However, the situation of Spanish companies with respect to their European counterparts is seen under a favourable light by 90% of those surveyed. Through personal contacts we have been able to gather the following impression: our Knowledge Engineers feel proud of their high technical qualification in comparison to our European Community partners, as well as with respect to other countries of the world.

Finally, 70% of those surveyed respond that they do not consider the implementation of Expert Systems/CIM more expensive than other applications; the remaining 30% does consider them more expensive. This datum might indicate that although Expert System/CIM applications are not more expensive than the rest -which does not mean that they are not costly- the main problem probably lies basically in the unawareness f both their existence and their potential benefits as we have seen in Figure 12.

## 6.- Conclusions

We have analyzed three studies from different global locations (United States, Europe and Spain). Despite their different orientations, the general conclusions extracted from them confirm how relevant Artificial Intelligence Techniques are to the field of production within the CIM context. Specifically the use of Expert Systems.

Although there are many areas in which Expert System prototypes can be developed -as many as problems or domains we might be able to identify- practice has demonstrated that semistructured problems are the ones to which these types of techniques can best respond. Situations that, although repetitive cannot be considere completely structured because, even though the problem shows up again, the circumstances that surround it can vary (maintenance, production management and control, logistics and distribution, programming, process simulation, etc.).

According to the companies that manufacture them, the most important contributions of Expert Systems to the production field are their ability to add flexibility to production programming, and the way in which they substantially increase the consistency of the decision making process -all of this without relinquishing the production system's efficiency and productivity. However, the amount of companies using this type of technology is evident, yet moderate, and is experiencing no spectacular increases. The reasons being how little known they are and their high cost.

Companies will gradually implement them, but only to ease the solution of partial and clearly specific problems. The next step will be to totally integrase them within the production system, with the rest of the automation systems, as a connective technology that finally achieves the total operation of the productive system, with less and less intervention by the human operative.

## References

- AJMAL, A. (1994).- "Intelligent Knowledge Based Expert Inventory Control System for Computer Integrated Manufacturing". *Computers & Industrial Engineering*, Iss. 1-4, vol. 7, pp. 173-175.
- ANDRES PUENTE, E. (1993).- "Automática, Robots y Robótica". *Desarrollo Tecnológico*, Núm.4, pp. 19-21.
- BROWNE, J. (Ed.)(1989).- "Knowledge Based Production Management Systems". North-Holland, Amsterdam.
- BYRD, T.A. (1993).- "Expert Systems in Production and Operatios Management: Results of a Survey". *Interfaces*, vol. 23, Iss. 2, pp. 118-129.
- CENTRO DE TRANSFERENCIA TECNOLOGICA DE INGENIERIA DEL CONOCIMIENTO (CETTICO) (1992).- "Directorio de Empresas de Ingenieria del Conocimiento". Facultad de Informática, Universidad Politécnica de Madrid, Madrid.
- CHATURVEDI, A.R. (1993).- "FMS Scheduling and Control: Learning to Achieve Multiple Goals", *Expert Systems with Applications*, Vol. 6, July-September, pp. 267-286.
- CHIP (1989).- "Cómo Desarrollar Sistemas Expertos", *Chip*, núm. 93, pp. 71-89.
- CIMWORLD (1992).- "Guía'92 del Software CIM en España". IDG Communications, Madrid.
- DE LA FUENTE, D. and PINO, R. (1993).- "Ventajas Competitivas de la Utilización de Nuevas Herramientas en la Gestión de la Producción", paper presented to III Congreso Nacional de la Asociación Científica de Economía y Dirección de la Empresa (ACEDE), Valencia, Spain, 12-14 septiembre.
- FRY, T.D.; PHILIPOOM, P.R. and SWIEGART, J.R. (1993).- "A Comparison of Two Intelligent Scheduling Systems for Flexible Manufacturing Systems", *Expert Systems with Applications*, Vol. 6, July-September, pp.299-308.
- GHIASEDDIN, N.; MATTA, K. and SINHA, D. (1990).- "The Design of an Expert System for Inventory Control", *Expert Systems with Applications*, vol. 1, Iss. 4, pp. 359-366.
- GIL, M.A.; DURO, R. and GINER, F. (1994).- "La Implantación y el Impacto de las Nuevas Tecnologías de la Información en la Empresa Española. Una Primera Aproximación a partir de un Cuestionario". *Esic-Market*, núm. 83, pp. 81-91.

- GUPTA, T. and GHOSH, B.K. (1988).- "A Survey of Expert Systems in Manufacturing and Process Planning", *Computers in Industry*, vol. 11, pp. 195-204.
- HITOMI, K. (1994).- "Automation-Its Concept and a Short History", *Technovation*, Vol. 14, Iss. 2, pp. 121-128.
- HOOKS, K.; RABELO, L. and VELASCO, T. (1995).- "An Expert System Framework for a CIM based Quality Inspection System", *Computers & Industrial Engineering*, vol. 29, Iss. 1-4, pp. 159-163.
- KANET, J.J. and ADELSBERGER, H.H. (1987).- "Expert Systems in Production Scheduling", *European Journal of Operational Research*, vol. 29, pp. 51-59.
- KERR, R.M. and EBSARY, R.V. (1988).- "Implementation of an Expert System for Production Scheduling", *European Journal of Operational Research*, vol. 33, pp. 17-29.
- KUSIAK, A. (Ed.) (1988).- "Artificial Intelligence: Implications for CIM", Springer, Berlin.
- KUSIAK, A. (Ed.) (1992).- "Intelligent Design and Manufacturing", John Wiley & Sons, New York.
- KUSIAK, A and CHEN, M. (1988).- "Expert Systems for Planning and Scheduling Manufacturing Systems", *European Journal of Operational Research*, vol. 34, Iss. 2, pp. 113-130.
- LOPEZ SANCHEZ, J.I. (1995).- "La Implantación de Técnicas de Inteligencia Artificial en un Entorno Integrado de Producción. Estudio del Software CIM en España". *Revista de Economía Industrial*, núm. 303, tercer trimestre, 1995, pp. 77-94.
- LOPEZ SANCHEZ, J.I. (1997).- "La Incorporación de los Sistemas Expertos en el Contexto CIM: Estudio de la Situación Española". *Organización y Dirección-CEPADE*, núm. 19.
- MELLICHAMP, J.M. and WAHAB, A.F.A. (1987).- "An Expert Systems for FMS Design", *Simulation*, vol. 45, Iss. 51, pp 201-208.
- MELLICHAMP, J.M.; KWON, O. and WAHAB, A.F.A. (1990).- "FMS Designer: and Expert Systems for Flexible Manufacturing Systems Design", *International Journal of Operations Research*, vol. 28, Iss. 11, pp 2013-2024.
- MERTENS, P. and KANET, JJ. (1986).- "Expert Systems in Production and Operations Management: An Assessment", *Journal of Operations Management*, Vol. 6, Iss. 4, pp. 393-404.
- MEYER, R.J..(1987).- "AI and Expert Systems: In Pursuit of CIM", *CIM Technology*, February 1987, pp. 15-26.
- MEYER, W (Ed.) (1990).- "Final Report EP 932/FB 722-90", Philips Forschungs-laboratorium GmbH, Hamburgo.
- MEYER, W. (1990).- "Expert Systems in Factory Management: Knowledge-Based CIM", Ellis Horwood, Chichester, West Sussex.
- RAO, H.R. and LINGARAJ, B.P. (1988).- "Expert Systems in Production and Operations Management: Classification and Prospects", *Interfaces*, Vol. 18, Iss. 6, pp. 80-91.
- ROWLINSON, M.; PROCTER, S. and HASSARD, J. (1994).- "CIM and the Process of Innovation: Integrating the Organization of Production", *International Journal of Production Economics*, vol. 34, Iss. 3, pp. 359-369.
- RUBIO, G.G. (1993).- "La Inteligencia Artificial se vuelve más Discreta pero también más Efectiva", *La Gaceta de los Negocios*, 08-12-93, p. 25.
- SANCHEZ TOMAS, A. (1993).- "Sistemas Expertos en Contabilidad de Gestión", *Técnica Contable*, núm. 540, pp. 787-799.
- SEAI TECH. PUBL. (1990).- "Expert Systems'90", SEAI Technical Publications, Madison, Georgia.
- SVIOKLA, J.J. (1990).- "An Examination of the Impact of Expert System on the Firm: The Case of XCON", *MIS Quarterly*, vol. 44, Iss.2, pp. 127-140.
- THOMAS, P. and WAINWRIGHT, D. (1994).- "Gaining the Benefits of Integrated Manufacturing Technology-Just Who Benefits and How?", *International Journal of Production Economics*, vol. 34. Iss. 3, pp. 371-381.
- TURBAN, E. and SEPEHRI, M. (1986).- "Applications of Decision Support and Expert Systems in Flexible Manufacturing Systems", *Journal of Operations Management*, Vol. 6, Iss. 4, pp. 433-448.
- VALLE, R.; BARBERA, J. and ROS, F. (Ed.) (1984).- "Inteligencia Artificial. Introdución y Situación en España", Fundesco, Madrid.
- WESTON, F.C. (1994).- "Three Dimensions of CIM", *Production & Inventory Management Journal*, vol. 35, Iss. 1, pp. 59-61.

Notes

1. Gil, Duró and Giner (1994), in their research work "La implantación y el impacto de las nuevas tecnologías de la información en la empresa española. Una primera aproximación a partir de un cuestionario" (The implementation and impact of the new information technologies in Spanish companies. A first approach based on an survey), reveal that one de main motivations for the implementation of these technologies is the desire to improve competitiveness by means of cost reductions and an increase in productivity. In fact, from among all the functional areas of the business, the area of production is the most affected by technology. This is not only due to the large quantities invested in it, but to its strategical importance.

2. From the three studies analyzed, the one that makes reference to the Spanish situation is ours. Its origin can be traced to the conclusion reached by the precompetitive Group Research Project of the Universidad Complutense de Madrid "Metodología de implementación de los sistemas expertos aplicados a la gestión empresarial" (Methodolgy of the implementation of expert systems as applied to business management), Madrid, 1991.

3. The rating table can be found in the aforementioned reference. In it each one's share in regard to the total is specified. Note that rating is never done solely in the production field.

4. Some references in which benefits are described, and even different Expert Systems within the production field analyzed, are: Kusiak and Chen (1988); Rao and Lingaraj (1988); Meyer (1987); Cimworld (1992); Kusiak (ed.) (1988); Kusiak (ed.) (1992); Browne (ed.) (1989); Sviokla (1990); Kanet and Adelsberger (1987); Kerr and Ebsary (1988); Ghiaseddin, Matta and Sinha (1990); Mertens and Kanet (1986); Turban and Sepehri (1986); Mellichamp and Wahab (1987); Mellichamp, Kwon and Wahab (1990); Meyer (1990); Gupta and Ghosh (1988); De la Fuente and Pino (1993); Sánchez Tomás (1993); Fry, Philipoom and Swiegart (1993); Chaturvedi (1993); Ajmal (1994) and Hooks, Rabelo and Velasco (1995).

5. The study commented is the European Community's so called project EP932, Knowledge-based realtime supervision in CIM, from ESPRIT (European Estrategic Programme for R&D in Information Technology) (Meyer, 1990, pp. 305-314).

6. To analyze all the results obtained by the mentioned research in detail you can consult his work "Expert Systems in Production and Operation Management: Results of a Survey" (Byrd, 1993).

7. The procedure followed for criterion valuation is that known as the ranking method. Four levels of incidence are identified for every criterion in each one of the 55 systems: none, low, medium, high. The total benefit of each criterion is proportional to the number and magnitude of the individual benefit levels registered by each criterion. In this way the highest value that a criterion can reach, by area, is 11 (Meyer, 1990, p. 311).

8. Opinions many times vary depending on the area in which they have been developing their conventional applications, as well as the size of the manufacturing group.

9. The Artificial Intelligence market's growth ratio in Europe is estimated to be somewhere near 100% for the period of 1992-1995 ( a sales volume of between 520 and 1.286 Million ECUs) (Rubio, 1993).

# 016

## TIME-AUTO TRAINING THE MANAGEMENT OF TECHNOLOGY WITHIN AUTOMOTIVE COMPONENT SMES: AN INNOVATING VOCATIONAL TRAINING PROGRAMME

Author:
CHANARON Jean-Jacques,Professor
CNRS-ESC Grenoble
BP 123
38003 GRENOBLE CEDEX 01
FRANCE
Tel:        +33-4-76-70 60 39
Fax:        +33-4-76-70 61 39
Email:      chanaron@esc-grenoble.fr

Co-authors:
B. Chapelet and Guy Sarrey
Groupe ESC Grenoble
BP 123, 38003 Grenoble Cedex 01, France
Tel:        +33-4-76 70 60 39
Fax:        +33-4-76 70 61 39

## ABSTRACT

The paper will present the main characteristices and results of a European Union funded project under the Leonardo Da Vinci Programme dealing with training managers of European small and medium size automotive component suppliers to the Management of Technology (MOT). This project, so-called TIME-AUTO, is organised as a « club » or a consortium of SMEs and is expected to be a very innovative training programme based on a mixture of self-diagnosis, traditional lecturing on the state-of-the-art in MOT and seminars to exchange best practices and experiences.

The paper will deal with three main topics:

1° The background and rationale, the objectives, the targets (i.e. the firms and people to be trained), the consortium of partners - enterprises, training institution, - the expected final products and the evaluation process;

2° The analysis of the training needs of small and medium size automotive component suppliers (first or second rank to OEMs) in Europe;

3° The content and organisation of the training modules designed for a pilot training session;

4° A general reflexion on the future of such appraoch and more particularly about the potential opportunities of dissemination within the automotive industry as a whole or to other industries.

Key words: Management of Technology, Automobile, Training

# 017

# Increasing the Speed of Knowledge Transfer at the Interface of Corporate Research and Divisional Product Development

L.F.G. Thurlings
PHILIPS
Eindhoven, The Netherlands

## ABSTRACT

The study reported here builds on two former studies, one dealing with the general trends in R & D and the other probing the fundamentals of knowledge transfer at the interface of the Philips' corporate research laboratories and the productdivisions.
In up-stream innovation, i.e. the product creation in the pre-concept phase, the inter-expert verbal communication process appears to be dominant. This process with direct personal contact precedes documented knowledge transfer and facilitates the transfer of tacit knowledge, which is a prerequisite for the speed of the transfer process. Incremental innovation requires limited adaptations and extensions to the existing network; in discontinuous innovation the network has to be newly established. Network creation, i.e. inter-personal networking among potential participants in a new product creation process, seems to be the fundamental process for success in discontinuous innovation. The higher the order of the depth of the network, the faster the speed of innovation. Entrepreneurial scientists, following the tune of the trends in R & D, seek contacts downstream far beyond their usual contacts and earlier than strictly needed for their scientific research, thus obeying the laws of tacit knowledge transfer. The same laws hold at higher abstraction levels of innovation: at management level, the networking of departments and projects; at executive level, the networking of businesses all along the value chain. Successful innovation requires a synchronous development of networks at all three levels.

## KEYWORDS

knowledge transfer, knowledge management, technology transfer, networking, communication, transition management, project management, process management, product creation, tacit knowledge

## INTRODUCTION

Changing market conditions, faster technological developments and increased competition nowadays forces companies to improve their innovative power drastically. This trend may be on going for some time, but it seems to accelerate in recent years (1). The demands that are put on the strategy development process, product development process improvement, the alignment of technological resources and so on, are now so strong that a gradual process improvement is not sufficient anymore. What counts is how quickly the company is improving as a whole (2) and the role of the technical professional (3). For the R & D units of the organization this often implies (4):improving the technology transfer from research to the development organization, accelerating time-to-market for new products and processes, and institutionalizing cross-functional participation. Answers to these problems are often sought in an adaptation of the organization structure (5). However, considering the knowledge transfer processes (6),(7), professional personal network creation seems to be much more effective. In this paper we shall present the most important characteristics of this interface, and how to manage the knowledge transfer process.

THE INTERFACE

A 'corporate research' organisation may be expected to focus on research activities only. However, in daily practice, a wide range of activities is on the agenda: fundamental research, applied research, pre-development and product development, see also Fig.1. 'Fundamental research' explores the principal behavior often far beyond the limits that are believed to be of practical use. 'Research' tries to understand the functioning of materials, methods and mechanisms within defined combinations of limitations.
'Pre-development' focusses on evaluating alternative product options, within the limitations as defined by 'research'. 'Product development' selects the most favorable product option and generates the instructions for the supply chain. Although the main stream of knowledge transfer flows from 'fundamental research' to 'development', knowledge also meanders between equivalent stages (for instance from research to research). The apparently chaotic flows are, however, quite structured as becomes evident when the LIS-model is applied (8). It shows the place of the innovation-units in the value chain and thus the interrelation of supply processes and innovation processes.

| | Fund.Res. | Research | Pre-Dev. | Development |
|---|---|---|---|---|
| output | scientific knowledge | applicability conditions | product options proven | instructions for production |
| complexity | discovery | invention | innovation | consolidation |
| time horizon | beyond known horizons | shifting the horizon | within defined horizons | scheduled |
| recognition | scientific authority | creation of industrial property | scouting new products | product creation |

Fig. 1. Main characteristics of the four stages of innovation.

Another factor, often misunderstood, is the time dimension of technology development. Certain technologies, as for instance a new IC (Integrated Circuit) production process, take much more time than other technologies -as for instance

the design of the IC itself. Basically, this throughput time depends on the complexity of the technology. If the complexity is low, often a single designer can do the job. If the complexity is high, many more experts from different disciplines become involved.
In the example of the IC production process, the latter consists of a series of production steps. However, most of these steps influence to a certain extend the other production steps. If you alter one step, you are immediately involved in collaboration with the 'owners' of the other production steps.

The same holds for complex products. If a certain property of the product, or a component or unit is independent of the other parts of that product (by simple interfacing, or by standardization), the complexity is low (for instance, the power supply in a TV set). If however the interrelation affects many other properties or components, the complexity is high (for instance the antenna signal receiver of a TV). Higher complexity here also leads to the involvement of other experts.

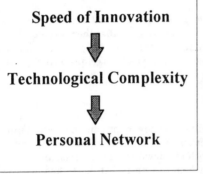

**Speed of Innovation**

⬇

**Technological Complexity**

⬇

**Personal Network**

Fig.2. The time dependence of technology relates topersonal networking

Apart from product- and production process complexity, the organizational complexity has an impact on the time dimension of technology development. It may hamper the network development in the former two. It may also influence the network development along the value chain (since almost any business is a link in a chain of businesses). From these observations it is concluded that *network development* is the true foundation of high speed innovation.

TRANSITION KNOWLEDGE MANAGEMENT
If there are formal organizational borders at the interfaces of the innovation stages (fundamental research - research, research - predevelopment, etc.) as is often the case in practice, then the flow of innovative information looks like a cascade. At each interface special attention is paid to the knowledge transfer problems. The structure of the formal interfaces brings about that people working in one stage regard the people in the succeeding stage as representative of the rest of the chain. Transition management concentrates on one transition at the time. However, as we shall see hereafter, this has only a limited impact. True network management considers many transitions at the same time. Though, *single transition management* could be, when well designed, a first step into the direction of *network management*.
As a result of our studies in the Philips' innovation organization (1, 6), we have met a number of approaches that strongly tie the cascade, see Fig.3. The studies

revealed that the stronger the transfer of needs (up-stream), the more effective the (down-stream) of technology. The figure shows where the different approaches are more, and where less effective.

a. *posting down-stream*
.Posting an expert down-stream (with the project) is a favorable method for successful technology transfer. The up-stream knowledge is at hand when the new technology has to be implemented. The down-stream experts are coached in a direct way. The imperfections of the new technology are revealed through direct observation of the up-stream experts. And, if fundamental problems arise, they can be transferred instantaneously in up-stream direction. Also, the up-stream experts become acquainted with the down-stream 'rules-of-the-game', which makes future transfers easier.
A disadvantage may be that up-stream innovations are slowed down by the frequent absence of the experts. Another disadvantage is that there are no incentives for down-stream experts and management to 'swim up-stream', i.e. to take notice of new technologies themselves since the experts come down anyway.

b.*posting up-stream*
Posting up-stream is an excellent method to steer the up-stream innovation into the right direction. Up-stream experts get response on their ideas directly and the investigations carried out together with the down-stream experts, are instantaneously linked to the application from the start. By this method, more than in any other approach, the experts constitute a "one brain" as they work together.
Posting up-stream is often perceived by the down-stream experts as a challenge (and as a break from their scheduled and busy life). Since the down-stream

| Management methods | fR — R | R — prD | prD — D |
|---|---|---|---|
| posting  down-stream | 0 | + | + |
| posting up-stream | + | ++ | ++ |
| job-rotation down-stream | 0 | + | + |
| job-rotation up-stream | + | ++ | + |
| double task experts | 0 | - - | ++ |
| transition management | + | ++ | + |

Fig. 3. Effectiveness of thr various transfer management approaches

organization has to decide on the manpower allocation, the organizational commitment to the transfer of technology is high.

A disadvantage is certainly that up-stream experts are not obliged to move down-stream to take notice of the down-stream circumstances since the down-stream experts will transport the new technology.

If posting up-stream is the only method, the usual 'ivory-tower' image of the up-stream organization will not change.

*c.job rotation down-stream*
Whereas in the foregoing situations the expert is posted temporarily, in the following he takes a job in the down-stream organization. In this way a very effective interlink is ensured, if the new position is related in some way to the up-stream transition. New scientific knowledge flows down-stream.

After some time however, the direct benefits weaken, and methods like the ones above have to be implemented as well.

*d.job rotation up-stream*
Up-stream job rotation has the positive effect of counter balancing "wild" innovation forces with application oriented forces. If a significant number of down-stream experts have taken jobs up-stream, innovation is steered into the right direction from the start. The up-stream organization will acquire a co-operative image.

As with the method 'posting up-stream', a disadvantage may be that the up-stream experts may not be encouraged to move down-stream. This could even create a larger psychological distance since the up-stream organization now has all the experience and skills in-house.

*e.double-task experts*
In the foregoing approaches an expert works either up-stream or down-stream. But, of course, mixed models are practiced as well. In this case an expert then works on an up-stream investigation and on a down-stream design. This way of transition-coupling can be extremely effective if both tasks are related by content and do not have conflicting priorities.

*f. transition management*
However, it is much more effective to change the management responsibility long before the actual transfer. If a down-stream projectmanager is also responsible for up-stream activities, it will leverage the application orientation, and accelerate the technology transfer.

On the other hand, in the case of complex, revolutionary, technologies it is much more effective to let the up-stream projectleader be responsible until the transfer has really reached the down-stream phase.

A special form of transition management is the one where a manager has a line-management responsibility in the up-stream organization, as well as in the down-stream organization.

# NETWORK MANAGEMENT

In the above, the innovation process is outlined as a more or less linear flow of information through the linked organizations. And especially if the organizations are positioned in a certain stage of the 'cascade', the characteristics of the transitions can be defined properly. However, the organizational reality is much more complex. One organization is often not only involved in just one stage of the innovation process (for instance: the research organisation is involved in the whole range of activities, from fundamental research to product development). Mostly, innovation is a matter of a whole series of businesses, all dealing with certain parts of the application ( a model to deal with this complexity is explained in Ref. 8.).

Our study on 'Trends in R & D', see Ref. 1., indicates that the profession of the employee in R & D is drastically changing. They may have had a technical focus only, but nowadays he must acquire a profound understanding of the market and the application also. Since these aspects are often beyond the daily horizon, and because of the mentioned linkage of businesses, he *has to develop a personal network down along the innovation cascade and beyond.*

As a result of the studies of Nonaka (9) we know that in up-stream innovation the knowledge transfer processes are predominantly tacit-to-tacit knowledge transfer processes. Experts, especially in the up-stream stages of innovation, have a strong drive to create, to develop new tacit knowledge themselves. This desire, which is inherent to professionalism, must be respected and management must deal with this as *if it were a fundamental law.* If not, the receiving expert will start anew, and thus suffer from the NIH (not-invented-here) syndrome. Networks thus have to be created and managed according to a number of specific rules. The most important ones will be treated here.

## 1. Verbal, face-to-face, expert communication is the dominant part in communication in up-stream knowledge transfer

Up-stream experts explore and create tacit knowledge. By the communication with down-stream experts their knowledge creation process is agitated and steered in the right direction. Since down-stream experts have equal rights to explore and create new knowledge, they have to collaborate from an early stage. The new knowledge is often hardly explicit (for instance the taste of a new liqueur).

## 2. Documented communication is of importance to make the knowledge explicit, but verbal communication precedes the documented communication

Although the major part of the transfer is a verbal knowledge transfer process, the experts use written documents for communication as well. These are, however, merely written expressions of the mind at that moment (formula's, graphs, drawings). Detailed documents are produced and transferred much later, but then the essentials of the technology are already understood.

## 3.The speed of innovation is dependent on the depth of the expert's network. The higher the order of the depth, the faster the innovation

To develop the tacit knowledge in the right direction, the up-stream expert has to understand the context of the down-stream expert. But it is tricky for him to regard the down-stream expert as a representative of the down-stream network. The information may be heavily filtered and adapted. Therefore he should seek higher order contacts deep down the line, down the value chain. The deeper he comes in that network, see Fig.4, the better focused to the application will his contribution to the innovation be.

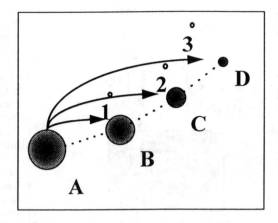

Fig.4. The higher the order of the depth of the network, the higher the speed of innovation.

**4. The speed of innovation is often hampered by the difference in perspective the participants in the newly developing network have about the quality of that network.**
Once the network is in operation there is still no guarantee that the knowledge transfer proceeds smoothly. Missing links in communication are the major cause of hampering innovation processes, as well as misconceptions of one another's views. These misconceptions can easily be revealed and be judged on its real value, see (4).

**5. In revolutionary innovation the network does not exist yet. In evolutionary innovation the network is in place - but needs adaptations and extensions.**
Technological innovation means that new technologies are used to create (new) products. In revolutionary innovation the technology has never existed before, thus new experts come in to scene and create a brand new network. Incremental innovation of existing products only slightly changes the current network of experts.

**6. Networks have a layered structure, reflecting the hierarchical layers**
Networks develop in horizontal layers (more or less), reflecting the hierarchical structure of organizations. The creation and maintenance of these networks must be carried out synchronized; The upper-layer networks should develop before networks at lower hierchical levels do..

**7. Networks have a chain structure, reflecting the ordering along the value chain**

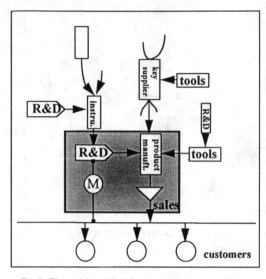

Businesses are in most cases a link in a longer chain of businesses (the value chain). The R & D units are located along such a chain, their specific position depending on their specific task, see Fig.5 (see also ref. 8). Since a major part of the innovation initiatives stems from the R & D units, these units along the same value chain must have a good understanding of each other's technology and views on the future. Experts in the same technical area may have contacts via their technical professional networks (congresses). Experts from neighboring technologies may need some encouragement to meet and exchange information. But if that happens through the units of one and the same value chain, the speed of innovation increases drastically.

Fig. 5. The position of R & D units along the value chain.

CONCLUSION

As a result of two former studies we found that the broader perspective of the employee in R & D urges him to develop his personal networks. Networking in his own technical discipline is not sufficient anymore. Networking along the innovation cascade is a first prerequisite, with special attention to cross-layer networking. However, truly effective networking can only be established once he starts to develop his network in the businesses along the value chain. The classic professional networks may be used to network the R & D units along the value chain.

REFERENCES

1. "Trends in managing industrial innovation- First insights from a field survey", L.F.G. Thurlings and K. Debackere, Research.Technology Management, Vol. 39, No. 4, July - August 1996, pp. 13 - 14.
2. "The high performance business:Accelerating performance improvement", P.R. Nayak, E.Drazen, G. Kaster, AD. Little Prism, First Quarter 1992.
3. "Developing technology with R&D customers", A.M. Pawlak, Research.Technology Management, September-October 1996, pp.44 - 47.
4. "Benchmarking R & D productivity", I.Krause and J.Lin, Planning Review, January - February 1993, pp. 16 - 21.

5. "Aligning technology with business strategy", A.N. Chester, Research.Technology Management, January-February 1994, pp. 25 - 32.
6. "Testing in-company technology transfer processes", IAMOT, Proceedings of the Fifth International Conference on Technology Management, Miami, February 1996, pp. 712 - 721.
7. "Improving the R&D productio interface in industrial companies", E. Vasconcellos, IEEE transactions on Engineering Management, Vol. 41, No. 3, p. 315.
8. "The landscape of Innovation and Supply: A graphical model for visualising the interrelationship between the innovation functions and the supply chain", L. Thurlings, IEMC 1996 Conference Vancouver (IEEE/ International Conference on Engineering andTechnology Management), Proceedings, August 1996, pp. 678 - 682.
9. "The knowledge creation company", I.Nonaka, Harvard Business Review, November - Decenber 1991, pp. 96 - 104.

## BIOGRAPHICAL NOTE

The author has joint Philips in 1975 and has had several positions in research, product development and training. He has published a number of articles in the field of technology and innovation management. He is currently responsible for the Technology and Innovation Management trainingprogram of the Philips company.

# 018

## IS THE NET-VIRTUAL-FIRM ALWAYS VIRTUOUS? SOME EMPIRICAL EVIDENCE FROM AIRCRAFT JET ENGINES

Author:
Prof. Massimo PAOLI, Scuola Superiore S.Anna,
Via Carducci 40,
I-65100 PISA
Italy
Tel:        +39-50-883326
Fax:        +39-50-883210
Universita' 'G. D'Annunzio', Viale Pindaro, 42, PESCARA
Italy
Tel:        +39-85-4537604.

Co-author:
Andrea Prencipe
Science Policy Research Unit (SPRU)
Sussex University, Mantell Building
Falmer Brighton BN1 9RF
England
Tel:        +44- 1273 686758
Fax:        +44-1273 685865
Email:      a.prencipe@sussex.ac.uk

## ABSTRACT

In this paper we claim that decisions to hollow out companies and to move towards virtual corporations fall far short of being 'useful' in some industrial sectors. Indeed, we argue that the high degree of systemic content of the products belonging to such sectors have particular implications for their development and manufacturing. The paper consists of three main sections.

The first part points out that the main strategic problem for those companies developing product-systems, labeled system companies, lies in the effort to master the evolutionary dynamics of the product itself. We argue that system companies should maintain in-house those knowledge bases regarded crucial for the integration of the product-system if they want to master such evolutionary dynamics. Knowledge bases, in fact, should be regarded as 'generative contexts'of innovations, and therefore, possible alternatives of the product-systems dynamics. In the light of this, contracting out R&D (and /or manufacturing) activities means losing cognitive activities and ability to introduce innovations.

The second part of the paper shows the results of the empirical study based on the analysis of US patents granted to some system companies in the jet engine sector, between 1969 and 1994. Our attempt is to analyse breadth, length, and dynamics of technical fields relevant to the development, manufacturing and integration of the jet engine, by using US patents as proxy measure.

In the third part we draw some conclusions based on the empirical evidence. Specifically, we argue that presciptions suggesting companies hive off R&D (and/or manufacturing) activities and move towards the virtual corporations might turn out to be extremely 'harmful' for those companies developing product-systems. We revisit, therefore, the vertical integration and related outsourcing strategies issues, claiming that the ability to 'control' the evolution of the product-system is rooted in the technological competencies developed and accumulated in-house over time.

KEYWORDS: product-systems, system companies, virtual corporations, knowledge bases, jet engine.

Oral presentation

# 019

Unstructuring Incompetence: Problems of Contracting, Trust and the Development of the Channel Tunnel

Audley Genus, Brunel University, Uxbridge, U.K.

## Abstract

This paper examines aspects of the contractual relationship among the principal actors in the development of the Channel Tunnel. Based on interviews with key participants and a wealth of public and semi-public documentary data, the paper presents a case study illustrating the interconnectedness of contractual form, process and trust, and the management and performance of complex, large-scale technological projects. Theoretically, the research is informed by a cross-disciplinary approach taking in contributions to the management of complexity and inter-firm relationships associated with the markets and hierarchies debate in economics and in organisation theory and research on the management of scale from the technology policy and project management literatures. More specifically, the paper builds upon Stinchcombe's findings that: a) contrary to the Williamsonian view contracts between firms are employed in the practice of administering complex undertakings (i.e. rather than 'hierarchy'); but that b) to enable such contracting to perform effectively, 'hierarchical' features are devised by the parties in a bid to 'structure' their joint 'incompetence' at managing the unknowns and unknowables of complex projects, and of selecting appropriate contract forms. In the case of the Channel Tunnel development the nature of the various contractual arrangements is described. An evaluation of the extent and quality of hierarchical aspects of the contractual relationship between Eurotunnel, TML (the principal constructing contractor), financial, governmental and other organisations is conducted. This is carried out in terms of the ease or difficulty experienced in managing changes in design specification, monitoring work that was executed, or in resolving disputes over the interpretation of contractor performance criteria, for example. Ultimately, the paper points up the extent to which differing expectations from the project, adversarial contractual relations and lack of trust between the client and the main contractor (against a background of 'fast track development') contributed to problems of cost-effectively designing, constructing and coordinating Channel Tunnel technology. The conclusion serves to indicate how and why hierarchical elements of contracts may exacerbate 'incompetence' in the management of complex or large-scale technology projects, rather than to 'structure' it, to the detriment of overall project performance.

# Introduction

The Channel Tunnel was opened on 6 May, 1994 and all four services offered by Eurotunnel and the national railway companies (Le Shuttle passenger and freight services, Eurostar, and the freight train service) had commenced operation by the end of that year. The development of the Channel Tunnel now in existence was far from the first proposed scheme for a fixed link between Britain and continental Europe. Ideas for a tunnel under the English Channel date back to at least 1802 and no less than 26 other proposed schemes were rejected between the time of the plan put before Napolean and the late 1970s (Vickerman,1994). The development of the current fixed link can be traced back to 1978 when a mini-railway tunnel was proposed by the French and British national railway companies and to 1984 when the Channel Tunnel Group was set up by a number of British banks and building companies (namely: Balfour Beatty, Costain, Tarmac, Taylor Woodrow, George Wimpey, National Westminster Bank, Midland Bank, with Morgan Grenfell and Robert Fleming as merchant bank advisers to the Group). A similar group called Francemanche SA was also established and together CTG-FM submitted a proposal, in October 1985, for a twin bored rail tunnel scheme, following an Invitation to Promoters issued by the British and French Governments in February that year. In February 1986, the British and the French signed the Treaty of Canterbury which gave intergovernmental sanction for a fixed link. This was subsequently ratified in July 1987. The Concession to design, construct and operate the fixed link was awarded to CTG-FM on 14 March 1986. Two important organisational developments occurred later in 1986. First, the building companies that had been involved in CTG-FM withdrew from this group to form the Anglo-French joint venture TransManche Link.

TML was awarded the contract to design and build and commission the Channel Tunnel on 15 May, 1986. Secondly, the Eurotunnel Group, comprising Eurotunnel SA and Eurotunnel PLC, was floated on the London and Paris stock exchanges. CTG-FM had started to structure the two companies in early 1986 in readiness for flotation and they had been incorporated in September 1986 (and had existed 'on paper' since April, 1986). However, it was not until October, 1986 when the delayed Equity 2 share issue was made that Eurotunnel acquired a 'mind of its own'. This was due to a requirement of the issue that the entry of the investment institutions was conditional on the promoters of the project, the building companies and the banks, giving up control of Eurotunnel, so permitting an independent majority on its board (Benard and Morton, 1989). This was nearly nine months after the award of the Concession to CTG-FM and five months after TML was awarded the Construction Contract. The Equity 3 flotation brought together the various agreements, legislation and contracts plus the marketing and equity package and took place on 'Impact Day', 16 November, 1987, just a month after the global stock exchange crash that was 'Black Monday' and which could have undone the whole thing (Benard and Morton, 1989).

The difficulties that have plagued the development of the project are near-legendary. As this paragraph is being written the Channel Tunnel is closed, following a fire near the French end of the link on November 18, 1996. A complex knit of technical, organisational, financial, and policy -related factors has contributed to delays in construction and in the date by which all four services offered through the Tunnel became fully operational. The latter represented an eighteen month slippage in the project schedule. The estimated total costs of development (construction plus financing in 1994 prices) have increased from £ 7 billion in 1987 to £ 12.5 billion in 1998.

Since flotation the finanical survival of Eurotunnel has been in question, and Mrs. Thatcher had emphasised that this was to be a privately-financed scheme and that there were to be no government subsidies for the project.There have been prolonged negotiations about the restructuring of the Group's £ 9 billion debt with the 220 banks that have provided 80% of Eurotunnel's financing.

A detailed analysis of the relationship between policy-making, the scale and control of Channel Tunnel technology development and the micro-economic performance of the project has beem presented elsewhere (Genus, 1996). An important element of this concerns the implications for the management of the project of relations between Eurotunnel and TML.These relations are treated to a more in-depth analysis here and so provide the focal point for this paper.

Theoretically, the starting point for the research concerns the need to consider how well the transactions costs approach deals with mixed/hybrid modes of organising economic activity, as distinct from a preoccupation with the polar opposite modes of 'markets' and 'hierarchies' identified by Williamson (1975). Williamson's own thoughts on the selection of mixed modes of economic organisation are framed, as in his specification of the factors influencing the choice of market or hierarchy, by an understanding of certain behavioural assumptions and critical factors which explain how transactions differ (Williamson, 1993). So, the pure market solution may be ruled out where there is bounded rationality and hence incomplete contracting, 'opportunistic' behaviour on the part of contractors which renders contracts as 'naive' and sanctions or safeguards necessarily built into trading relationships, and where assets have highly specialised, non-redeployable uses. The conjunction of asset specific investment and incomplete (though 'safeguarded') contracts suggests the bilateral dependence of the parties and their identity becomes critical, where in the neo-classical market transaction it would not matter. This is the realm of either the mixed/hybrid mode or hierarchical mode of organisation, depending on the depth or severity of the conditions. Williamson (1993) considers bilateral dependency to greatly complicate 'the intertemporal governance of contractual relations'.

To the extent that costs of transacting (writing, monitoring or executing contracts) are exacerbated by operating either spot market trading or, say, subcontracting in the conditions described above, an organisation will choose 'hierarchy' and so integrate the transaction within its boundaries. However, the question is posed as to why a large integrated firm cannot do everything a collection of small firms can do, if this is the way that the complexity and inefficiencies of contracting promoted by bounded rationality, asset specificity *inter alia* are best ameliorated. An explanation is made by reference to the notion of 'selective intervention', which refers to the replication of the market by the integrated organisation in all respects except where hierarchical control is the source of expected net gains (Williamson, 1992). Selective intervention is likely to break down where there is a loss of 'incentive intensity' within the integrated organisation, where assets are 'dissipated', or through what Williamson (1992) refers to as an 'added latititude for politicking'. Other, non-integrated modes may be more efficient.

The approach taken by Stinchcombe and Heimer (1985) to explaining mixed modes of organisation proceeds from the observation that in practice contracts are employed to govern large scale projects where, according to a raw application of the Williamsonian approach, 'the market' should operate with difficulty and hierarchy ought to be found instead. However, all is not what is seems with these contracts. Stinchcombe and Heimer consider what it is about such contracts which may enable them to work in situations where they ought, in theory, to be found wanting. They resolve that hierarchical elements may be found in contracts administering the conduct of large-scale projects. Three principal reasons are given to explain why these administrative provisions are written into contracts. First, one may identify the need to control for uncertainties connected to the specifications required by the client. These uncertainties may arise where different design possibilities are being explored or out of changing regulatory or competitive circumstances, for example. Secondly, there may be cost uncertainties, which also need to be controlled for. These might be linked to the nature of the market for specialised assets, or unforeseen (or unforeseeable) technical difficulties. And, thirdly, there may be problems of observing and monitoring performance of activities stipulated in the contracts governing the project. These then are conditions where 'ideal' market transacting will be inoperable and where there will be a need to develop certain hierarchical structures to mitigate the incompetence of parties involved in a large-scale project.

The work of Williamson on transactions costs focuses on the economics of exchange, indeed some would say that the appeal to contractual imagery and the emphasis on the role of opportunism in shaping inter-organisational relations are overemphasised (Kay, 1992). The Stinchcombe and Heimer work draws our attention towards contracting as a matter of social exchange and relations albeit that the hierarchical social structures they discuss are considered to be constructed out of 'contracts between legally equal corporate bargaining agents in a market' (Stinchcombe and Heimer, 1985: 122).

Other treatments of organisational and inter-firm relations have helped to develop the social exchange approach to understanding modes of organising complex activities, with greater attention paid to the significance of mutuality and trust to facilitating such relationships with benefits to effciency. Questions of cooperation, control and efficiency feature in Ouchi's work, for example, wherein the 'problem of organisation' is addressed. Essentially, any collective entity which has an economic goal will need to find mechanisms for controlling efficiently the diversity of individuals which it employs. 'Left to their own devices' such individuals may pursue goals which only partially overlap with those of others within the organisation and their efforts may be uncoordinated (Ouchi, 1980). Different combinations of goal incongruence and performance ambiguity suggest alternative conditions where three basic types of control and coordination mechanism may operate with differential efficiency. Hence 'markets' may be efficient when performance ambiguity is low and goal incongruence high. Secondly, 'bureaucracies' will be efficient where both goal incongruence and performance ambiguity are relatively high. And finally, 'clans' will be efficient where goal incongruence is low and performance ambiguity is high.

Jarillo (1988) considers four modes (or prototypes) of organising economic activity which are determined by two variables: the legal form of organisation (i.e. whether a formal hierarchy exists or whether the parties maintain their separate identities); and the kind of relationship that the parties enjoy. In short, the latter variable refers to the degree of goal congruence or inseparability of returns that characterises inter-firm relationships, and Jarillo employs a distinction between zero-sum (competitive) and non zero-sum (cooperative) games to capture in short hand the fundamental approaches that may be taken by the parties.

The four modes are thus defined. Firstly, bureaucracy, where the legal form is the hierarchical organisation and the antagonistic employee-management relationship reflective of a zero-sum game. Secondly, 'clans', a term which Jarillo borrows from Ouchi and considers to be closest to Williamson's notion of 'hierarchy' i.e. 'long term relationships, carried out through non-specified contracts within the formal environment of an organization'. That this relationship is characterised as a non zero-sum game may be seen as reflective of the importance of trust and fairness to the interactions of organisational participants. Thirdly, the 'classic market' is identified as a mode where, as in the Williamsonian view, many separate organisational entities interact through 'spot' transactions. Fourthly, the final mode specified by Jarillo is that of the 'strategic network'. Here, the 'hub' firm has 'especial' relationships with other firms in the network. Of particular relevance to this paper is the notion that 'these relationships have most of the characteristics of a 'hierarchical' relationship: relatively unstructured tasks, long-term point of view, relatively unspecified contracts' (Jarillo, 1988: 34). Further, the relationships in a strategic network are considered to have all the characteristics of 'investments', since having the know-how of dealing with a particular supplier, for example, rather than a new one carries a degree of 'asset specificity'. However, the contracting parties maintain their separate identities. They remain independent organisations 'with few or no points of contact along their many dimensions' (Jarillo, 1988: 34).

To examine aspects of contracting and hierarchy in the case of Channel Tunnel development six taped interviews were conducted with senior members of Eurotunnel and TML, a member of the Disputes Panel and a senior academic who has researched European and regional transport policy and economics. Interviews were between ninety minutes and two hours in duration. In addition, telephone interviews were conducted with individuals having a project management or contract

negotiation role in three subcontracting firms on the project, and a mailed questionnaire

completed and returned by a senior projects executive at Eurotunnel. Unfortunately, forty other

potential interviewees who were approached declined to take part in the study.

The remainder of the paper is organised as follows. The next, second, section outlines briefly the

nature of the hierarchical structures of contracts identified by Stinchcombe and Heimer. In the

third section, a comparison is made between these conceptualised hierarchical mechanisms and

the nature of such structures as may be identified in the contractual arrangements pertaining to

the development of the Channel Tunnel. As this section proceeds, the effectiveness of the

structures is considered in the context of client-contractor (and also other inter-organisational)

relationships relevant to the conduct of contracting and work on the Channel Tunnel. The

preceding paragraphs suggest that appealing to mutuality or goal congruence, the existence of

a long-term orientation, and the significance of trust to inter-organisational relationships, may

enable some insight into such interactions as relate to the Channel Tunnel case. The conclusion

reconsiders the work and findings of the paper with these latter points and the relevance of a

transactions cost approach to understanding inter-firm relations in mind.

## Contracts as Hierarchical Documents

According to Stinchcombe and Heimer, where hierarchical elements are provided for in

contracts for work on large-scale projects, five 'structures' may be defined. These are:

- command structures and authority systems

- dispute resolution procedures

- incentive systems

- standard operating procedures

- pricing of variations in performances (of the contractor) (Stinchcombe and Heimer, 1985: 158).

Command structures and authority systems refer to the administrative provisions in contracts pertaining to the recognition of changes in specification and compensation as binding on the parties. At issue, here, is the extent to which the consequences of changing the contract (such as the contractor bearing the risks of the change) are specified *ex ante* by the authority assuming the right to make the changes in question(noting that the authorising entity may not always be the 'client'). With regard to incentive systems, the primary issue concerns the relative merits of alternative contractual mechanisms for rewarding or penalising performance of activities and for apportioning the risks or benefits of performance between the client and the contractor. More specifically, one may consider the incentive effects of, say, fixed price compared to cost-plus contracts. It is interesting to note the view that 'to preserve maximum flexibility, the client should reserve the right to change the incentive system as conditions change' (Stinchcombe and Heimer, 1985: 125). The suggestion is of a support role played by incentive systems to client authority systems and of potential adverse implications for performance if the client does not or cannot reserve the right to change incentives.

The existence of standard operating procedures may indicate an attempt by the client to ascertain that the contractor is playing by the rules of the game as much as representing any attempt to monitor the performance of work. For example, the creation of elaborate document paper trails may be rather less about the substantive data contained in the documents than they are about the contractor's adherence to procedure. This is not deny that the establishment of routines will not serve more tangible functions, such as to enable the speed and efficiency with which inter-organisational matters are processed, or for dealing with work scheduling, quality control, or accidents and emergencies (Stinchcombe and Heimer, 1985).

Dispute resolution procedures are seen by Stinchcombe and Heimer as ways in which the parties air and resolve differences about the interpretation and performance of the contract, such that they may be thought of as 'grievance procedures'. It is noted that in the British construction sector, contracts nominate a neutral professional engineer who resolves all disputes between client contractor bit provide for appeals against that engineer's decisions to a named body for binding arbitration (Stinchcombe and Heimer, 1985:125). Although such disputes may be brought before an external court of appeal, the purpose of dispute procedures internal to the contract is to prevent their development 'into expensive and disruptive legal battles' (Stinchcombe and Heimer, 1985: 126). Finally, the fifth hierarchical element that may be present in contracts entails the pricing of variations in the performance of the contractor. In this paper, the issue of pricing performance variations is addressed in tandem with the matter of the incentive effects of the different mechanisms for rewarding the work of the contractor, as mentioned earlier.

**Unstructured Incompetence and Hierarchical Elements of Channel Tunnel Contracting**

*Command structures and authority systems*

To analyse that aspect of inter-organisational relations connected to the right to specify or alter the nature of work governed by contracts between the actors in the Channel tunnel development, is to address the central area of difficulty in the conduct of the project. A past co-chairman of Eurotunnel, Sir Alastair Morton, has referred to the 'polo mint' structure of the contractual arrangements. Morton emphasises the implications of not having a viable client in place at the time when the contrator, TML, and the banking consortium which provided most of the funding for the project were establishing the Construction Contract (Morton, 1995).

The choice of one overall contract to govern the various tunnelling, fixed equipment and rolling stock-related activities may be seen as having much to do with the influence of the bank's wish for a single document which would identify a sole focus of responsibility for the completion of the project, TML. From another perspective, the selection of a single contract may be taken as being indicative of TML's concern to retain control over the full spread of activities, even in areas such as the procurement of rolling stock where it had little experience. The view has been expressed that the nub of this concern was that the client might seek to take work away from TML under a different contractual regime (Eurotunnel lawyer, interview). Either way, the option to adopt another arrangement such as separate contracts for different aspects of the work, rather than a single 'design and build' document, did not find favour.

The belated arrival of Eurotunnel was accompanied by attempts by the newly-formed client to amend aspects of the Construction Contract that had been written without them. However, a significant factor in the process of amending or renegotiating the contract was the attitude of TML regarding the 'ownership' of the project and the role of the client. In short:
'...TML always believed that this project was theirs and that Eurotunnel was Johnny-come-lately...Eurotunnel's role should be...to pay TML's monthly bills, give the nod on design

development, and no more than that. Anything more than that was perceived by TML as being ET interfering' (Eurotunnel lawyer, interview).

In essence, there was no interest for the contractor to create a client in the formative stages of the project, while the bid for the Channel Tunnel Concession was being prepared. Nor would it have been in TML's interest for there to be anything other than a weak client once the bid had been prepared and the Concession won (Kirkland, 1995).

Authority to make changes in design specification was a major source of contention between Eurotunnel and TML, although the client was not the only subject of the contractor's dissatisfaction. The focal point of the conflict was the concept of 'optimisation', as found in clauses underpinning the Construction Contract which referred to the best balance that could be achieved between capital costs and operating costs. Agreement on these optimisation clauses involved the reassessment of the outline design that had been included the proposal that had won the concession from the British and French Governments in March,1986. Unfortunately, however, the split between capital costs and operating costs referred to by the notion of optimisation mirrored a situation where TML bore the capital costs and Eurotunnel the operating costs of the Channel Tunnel. As such the two parties had quite divergent interests, which translated into quite different views as to how to interpret and to operationalise 'optimisation'. This was compounded by two factors. One was the ambiguous nature of the relevant clauses, in any case. The clauses which were seen by one TML interviewee as 'the incoherent result of compromise reached during negotiations'. Another was time since:

'[the concept of optimisation] did not allow for the fact that six months had already been knocked off an already tight project programme and during the CC (Construction Contract) negotiations. There was therefore little time left in an already crowded crucial front-end design phase for such a complex task, which would require the closest co-operation between the new operator and the contractor at the very time when a host of other priorities would be pressing for attention' (TML project manager, interview).

Another view of this links insufficient attention to project definition to the need for the contractor and the funding banks, which were the promoters of the project, prior to the birth of Eurotunnel, to make returns to their investment as quick as possible.

A view from inside Eurotunnel of optimisation, at least in terms of the mechanical and engineering work on the terminals and fixed equipment, was that TML did well from the relevant clauses.

Hence:

'TML banged on at length about the optimisation in terms of the lump sum (work). We did an analysis in-house to find out whether or not there was any truth in this..[we]...look[ed] at the Construction Contract [and] what it was that TML was obliged to deliver and what it is that...we're going to get. The answer showed that ET was actually going to get, in performance terms, a lot less than [was] proposed in the contract...certainly we weren't getting anything...which exceeded the Construction Contract's performance requirements so that our perception is that there is a lot of myth surrounding this whole idea of ET wanting an optimised thing up here and TML providing an optimised thing down there...If you actually look at the project as built and its performance, you weren't getting much more than the Construction Contract, in fact you're getting less' (Eurotunnel lawyer, interview).

By contrast, the view from within TML was that Eurotunnel was attempting to upgrade design specification beyond what had been agreed in the Construction Contract and, moreover, trying to get the contractor to pay for design changes insisted upon by the IGC ('Intergovernmental Commission', the authority responsible for the public safety aspects of the development project). According to a TML project manager:

'we had priced the lump sum based on the concession design...but when more and more features were introduced under the subjective and manipulated term 'optimisation', which had serious cost implications and disrupted the programme, then the question is 'Who pays for the changes?' We believed it should be ET.' (Interview).

One of the areas where intervention by the IGC generated complaint from TML concerned the width of the pedestrian doors to a passenger train. Here, there were delays in deciding on an option to widen these doors from 600mm to 700mm, a change which would have cost £5.8 million at that point. To try to keep up with schedule TML went ahead with the manufacturing of the trains. However, sometime later the IGC decided that there 600mm doors were unacceptable; implementing the revised door option incurred a nine month delay and added a further £45 million to costs which the contractor would have to bear.

One might expect some dissatisfaction from the contractor about this but a member of the Disputes Panel has also pointed to an undermining of the authority of the IGC in that whilst safety was doubtless a serious and important matter:

'[the IGC] had a lot of power without responsibility...I am quite sure that a lot of the additional cost...could have been mitigated'(interview).

There are other aspects of the authority issue which relate both to the resolution of disputes between Eurotunnel and TML, which is discussed in the next sub-section, and to the monitoring of contract activities by bodies such as the Maitre d'Oeuvre and the Project Implementation Division. The latter is addressed below, in the sub-section on standard operating procedures.

*Disputes resolution procedures*

There was a Disputes Panel set up to resolve contractual disagreements between Eurotunnel and TML. This comprised four members, three from a technical, engineering background and a commercial lawyer who acted as Chair (Disputes Panel member, interview). As mentioned above the subject of optimisation proved to be a major source of conflict between the parties with the quite different interpretations of what the concept meant reflecting the different foci of concern of client and contractor. Moreover, disputed claims have been traced back to lack of preparation linked to the rush to get development underway during 1986 and 1987. For example, the cost target stipulated in the contract for tunnelling work was based on an analysis of the ground conditions which was found to be quite inadequate, rendering the target cost set, and the sharing of the costs for failure to meet the target, a bitter point of dispute between Eurotunnel and TML. This is not to say that one might not expect inaccuracies in this type of activity. Rather, the point is about spending a little extra time at the beginning of a project on ensuring that analyses of this type, which may be critical to rewarding performance according to contract conditions, can at least serve as useful 'reference points' (Disputes Panel member, interview).

The degree of antagonism between Eurotunnel and TML has been expressed by a member of the Disputes Panel who considers what he refers to as the 'American approach' to resolving disputes, whereby the parties:

'see a little bit of a problem coming and...immediately arm [themselves] with all the lawyers [that they] can find and it is fought out on that basis...the more the lawyers appear on the scene, the more they persuade you that your case is strong and [that] that's how to do it' (interview).

This adversarial approach is not at all one of 'partnering' where the parties sit down and more calmly try to sort out matters on the basis of 'getting the engineering right' and then working out 'who pays for this', to the mutual satisfaction of client and contractor.

In addition, a mutual approach is not facilitated where little problems are allowed to escalate before the disputes procedure 'kicks in'. Thus in the Channel Tunnel case study the Disputes Panel were not able to deal with disputes as they arose, they were seen by the parties as a forum for resolving major disagreements. In this way relatively small problems tended to fester into intractable conflicts (Disputes Panel member, interview).

The lump sum contract became the subject of protracted conflict in October, 1989 when TML claimed an additional £380 million from Eurotunnel in recompense for costs incurred in changes in design and specification ordered, in part, by the InterGovernmental Commission. In its role of technical auditor, the Maitre d'Oeuvre (MdO) oversight group produced in, December 1989, an independent assessment of costs which supported Eurotunnel's overall estimate of costs for the work (a total of £1.48 billion). This decision was not a binding ruling, contractually, but was not received by TML as representing any proper indication of out-turn costs of the work to be done. The matter was brought before arbitration to be settled and a partial deal worked out which was sufficient to persuade the banks to provide enough funding to Eurotunnel to keep the project going for another four months, by which time there was to be a final settlement between Eurotunnel and TML. This settlement left much of the core of the lump sum disagreement unresolved but changes were made to the target works and procurement contracts (see below). It was agreed that there would be further arbitration on the matter of the lump sum costs which won a promise of interim funding from the banks. In addition, Eurotunnel agreed to downgrade the specification of the lump sum work by reducing the speed of the trains to 130 kph, so reducing the heat generated in the tunnel and the expense of the ventilation system (Anderson and Roskrow, 1994).

However, the denouement of the 1990 renegotiations was not without further twists. Even the deal just mentioned was not promptly signed by TML. A key factor in their refusal to sign was the role of Sir. Alistair Morton whose actions and publicised comments, for example about the 'poor productivity' of U.K. compared to French construction work on either side of the tunnel, were seen as central to the deteriorating relationship between the senior management of both parties. (Interestingly, there was a restriction in the Contract on the ability of TML to make public statements about the project). Essentially, TML, or at least TML senior managers including chief negotiator Peter Costain, who had complained of demotivating and unconstructive remarks by Morton in the latter's briefings to the press, wanted Morton out. Without TML's signature on the deal the banks would not pay, although, of course, this could rebound on TML who would not get paid by Eurotunnel. TML did get management changes at Eurotunnel as they had hoped. The only trouble was rather than Morton being moved out of the picture as might have been implied by his vacation of the co-chair, he slipped into a new position of deputy chairman and chief executive, which if anything seemed a stronger position than before. In addition to not signing the agreement, TML recommenced legal proceedings against Eurotunnel in the French courts, still in January 1990, for non-payment of their monthly account, where the ruling was that the now nearly bankrupt Eurotunnel were to pay the contractor £60 million as its monthly payment. An intervention by the Governor of the Bank of England during February 1990 helped to break the deadlock and resulted in the signed deal and the appointment of John Neerhout as project chief executive at Eurotunnel, although the lump sum disagreement was to linger on. Morton remained as chief executive and then, until recently, co-chairman of the Eurotunnel Group (Anderson and Roskrow, 1994).

A further partial resolution of the lump sum conflict came in July 1993 and was the culmination of another lengthy process of bitter negotiation and tactical delays in work by the contractor and in payment by the client which held up completion of the project. In short, Eurotunnel would pay TML an advance of £235 million in return for the contractor hitting a number of deadlines so as enable handover of the project to the client in December, 1993 and eventual opening in March, 1994. This allowed for resolution of the contractors funding problem and for Eurotunnel to set its sights on testing and the day when revenues would eventually flow into its coffers. It was not, however, any substantive settlement of the fixed equipment claim by TML. The centrepiece of this second phase of the dispute over the lump sum contract was TML's 'global claim' for £1.27 billion from Eurotunnel for the fixed equipment plus a £60 million management fee. This was at odds with the lump sum contract which stipulated that claims, rather than being global, should be costed item by item and was in effect a strategy of converting the lump sum into a cost-plus contract. Basically, the contractor's view was that:

'Eurotunnel had, with the IGC, started to impose so many innovative requirements upon the specification for the M&E [work]...that the lump sum should be disregarded and the whole thing converted to a cost plus basis' (Eurotunnel lawyer, interview).

(As an aside and quite topically on this issue, Eurotunnel had argued with the IGC safety authority about its open-sided design for the HGV shuttles. Where the latter had been concerned about the possibility of an uncontrollable fire being spread because of the fanning of flames by air flowing through the sides of an open designed wagon, Eurotunnel pointed to the 'astronomical' costs of closing in the wagon trains that were already in construction (Anderson and Roskrow, 1994: 153). Indeed, the boast has been made that Eurotunnel were ordering freight shuttles at a saving of 60% on the price of their original freight shuttles, which were to be to the client's own design and needed less in the way of maintenance (Eurotunnel, 1995).

In March, 1992 a Disputes Panel ruling on the global claim stated that the lump sum should remain but that 'reasonable and proper' costings of work affected by design changes should be made. Further, the Disputes Panel was willing to fix rates for aspects of the work which TML and Eurotunnel could not agree upon. Controversially, the Disputes Panel also ordered Eurotunnel to triple its monthly payment to TML for the fixed equipment work, starting from April 1992. These rulings were seen as beyond the remit of the Disputes Panel by Eurotunnel. The authority of the panel to make such ruling was challenged and reference was made to the International Chamber of Commerce in Brussels for arbitration. Their eventual ruling was clear on the matter of Eurotunnel's extra monthly payment to TML for lump sum work: the Disputes

Panel had overstepped its powers under the contract. However, in allowing TML to go to the panel to fix costs but declaring that the panel should not make decisions on these which might subsequently be overturned in arbitration, the ambiguity of the message that the ICC was sending only served to exacerbate relations between client and contractor, both of which issued their own interpretations of the ruling.

Although relations were often difficult much of the disputes between Eurotunnel and TML were dealt with at the Disputes Panel or arbitration. There was, however, increasing recourse to the courts during the course of the project, in the matter of whether TML could stop work on the tunnel's cooling system, for example. Here, the cooling system was seen by TML as a key part of the project which had had to be totally redesigned incurring an extra 50% in costs (to £130 million). It was thus symbolic of the general difficulties of work on the project and, in late 1991,TML decided to stop work until it was paid extra for the additional work beyond the original contract. Eurotunnel went to the High Court for an injunction against the stoppage of work, which it won in November, 1991. In January 1992, TML won an overturn of this ruling at the Court of Appeal which Eurotunnel then challenged with an appeal to the House of Lords. Their ruling was in favour of TML.

*Incentive systems and variations in performance*
Briefly, there were three principal mechanisms governing the reward of performance of Channel Tunnel development activities: a target cost mechanism related to tunnelling work; there was a lump sum arrangement pertaining to work involving fixed mechanical and electrical equipment, including signalling; and a cost-plus element of the Construction Contract compensated the

contractor for the purchase of rolling stock. As far as the choice of these mechanisms is concerned it has been argued that the target cost arrangement was appropriate since it was felt that 'the ground conditions had been relatively well mapped' (Eurotunnel lawyer, interview). Thus it was considered to safe to set a target cost that TML could achieve; one which would provide a bonus to contractor based on the expectation that there would be an underrunning of cost.

One basis of the lump sum mechanism seemed to be a similar optimism, this time about the definition of the technology that was to be employed regarding the fixed equipment. The need on the part of the funding banks for a degree of certainty concerning their exposure to the financial risks of development has also been cited as an important factor pertaining to the choice of the lump sum for the M&E works. The cost-plus mechanism may be seen as a way of attending to TML's concerns about procuring rolling stock when the expertise of the companies within the consortium was more to do with civil engineering and the M&E work than in transport and trains. At the same time this arrangement allowed the banks to retain a single focus of responsibility for the conduct of project as a whole. Hence the view of the banks was that 'it was far better to have one person [at] whom you could point the finger at' (Eurotunnel lawyer, interview), even if this meant that TML were charged with the responsibility of delivering something at which they were not expert. It also helps to explain why there was not separate contracting for different aspects of the work.

The allocation of the risks and benefits of development between the parties varied according to the contractual mechanism in question. Thus the target works saw the greater balance of the risk of cost overruns above target cost borne by Eurotunnel. On the lump sum the risks lay with the contractor once there were additional costs over and above those estimates on which the contract was based. Where at first there was a degree of optimism about controlling costs within the lump sum, it was not long before this aspect of the Construction Contract became the subject of additional claims for cost by the contractor. These were such that it has been claimed that TML actively sought to subvert the whole philosophy of the lump sum and to get it converted to a cost-plus arrangement (Eurotunnel lawyer, interview). The procurement of rolling stock carried little risk to the contractor whose costs were reimbursed and who received a set percentage fee for this work, (although TML still bore overall responsibility post-contract for the performance of the equipment). Essentially, though, Eurotunnel was left with most of the financial cost risks of procurement.

At this juncture it is interesting to consider Stinchcombe and Heimer's point relating to the client possessing the right to change incentives as conditions change. Clearly, the backdrop to changes in the various aspects of the Construction Contract was most visibly marked by the burgeoning costs of development of the Channel Tunnel project. For example, work on tunnelling has been estimated at an outturn of more than 75% above the 1987 figure for costs. Of the lump sum works, terminals have been the subject of increases of over 25% above the 1987 level of cost, whereas there has been a near doubling of the estimated costs of fixed equipment since then. Estimated procurement costs for rolling stock have more than trebled since 1987. Altogether, the total estimated cost for construction activities has increased by two-thirds of the 1987 estimate, to more than £7 billion (in 1994 prices). Finally, projected to 1998, the costs of financing will have doubled in comparison to the 1987 estimate, leaving the total (1998) costs of the project as a whole over 75% above the 1987 estimate at £12.5 billion (Genus 1996).


The target cost provision has been viewed as the one 'which worked least disastrously' of the three contractual mechanisms in the Construction Contract (Eurotunnel lawyer, interview). There was some disagreement between Eurotunnel and TML over the sharing of costs linked to the overruns mentioned above. These had stemmed largely from the ground conditions being much wetter than was anticipated, necessitating shut down and redesign of some of the tunnel boring machines. In short, Eurotunnel were responsible for 70% of the overrun costs in the 1987 contract, while TML were to bear the other 30%, subject to a cap of 6% of the total cost of tunnelling. Part of the 1990 contract renegotiations was driven therefore by Eurotunnel's need to redress the allocation of risks in this area. Fundamentally, this was realised in the removal of the 6% cap so that TML was subsequently to bear 30% of overruns on the target works occuring above the threshold of £1.58 billion for which Eurotunnel were responsible.


The lump sum and the procurement mechanisms were both ineffective though for different reasons. The notion that the technology and costs referred to in the lump sum agreement could be set in advance with confidence has been considered as 'frankly naive' in retrospect (Eurotunnel financial adviser, interview). As it was the additional unforeseen costs were such that TML tried to overturn the lump sum and pushed for a cost-plus mechanism for compensating for the costs of constructing the terminals and the M&E works. TML's claim for £380 million from Eurotunnel for the cost of making variations in design specification in order to satisfy the IGC/SA was a major source of dispute that has already been discussed above..

Basically, the choice of mechanism for rewarding the procurement of rolling stock appeared to have little to do with giving TML an incentive to minimise costs, as discussed above. Rather, the extent to which the procurement contract was devised so as to allow TML to avoid cost risks underpinned the stipulation that Eurotunnel would bear the costs of the rolling stock that was purchased while TML would receive a handling fee of 11.5% of such costs. The view from within Eurotunnel was that the contractors 'were getting an excessive amount for the work that they were doing' (Eurotunnel financial adviser, interview). So this was another aspect of the 1990 renegotiations driven by Eurotunnel's wish to redraw the balance of risks. This time the parties agreed to a capping of the fee for the procurement of rolling stock.

*Standard operating procedures*

Standard operating procedures which appear most critical to the management of the Channel Tunnel project include those relating to the monitoring or auditing of work. Within Eurotunnel it was felt that the greatest supervisory influence on the contractor lay in the development of a hands-on, independent role for a project manager. It was felt that the client enjoyed adequate rights to audit the target work but insufficient rights to audit procurement activities, for example, but that having these rights in principle should not be confused with the capability to exercise them in practice.

So, for the procurement contract there was no specific auditing team and more generally, the auditing team for monitoring the target activities was considered to be too small to audit effectively (Eurotunnel lawyer, interview). The problems of auditing were exacerbated by aspects of the contractor's cost control systems. Most notably, the view has been expressed that there were several different philosophies underpinning approaches to cost control and analysing cost data. These philosophies have been said to stem from the fact that, on the British side for example, TML comprised a joint venture of five different partner firms. The difficulties inherent in all this were such that there was 'still a problem in terms of getting a proper system of cost control in place even up to mid/late 1989' which made any attempt by Eurotunnel to audit effectively even more troublesome than iot might have been otherwise (Eurotunnel lawyer, interview).

The above helps to explain the willingness of Eurotunnel to develop closer contacts with sub-contractors on the procurement activities, a matter which became a key source of friction with TML.(There was also some direct contact with sub-contractors on lump sum [e.g. signalling] work which incurred TML disapproval though arguably to a lesser degree). The motivation for these moves by the client to get 'closer to the sub-contractor' may be considered in terms of the perceived need to fill a vacuum of control over the specialist equipment suppliers of rolling stock with which TML had sub-contracted, remembering that TML had little expertise in rolling stock procurement.

More specifically, the role of the Maitre d'Oeuvre (MdO) as a project manager was questioned at Eurotunnel. The MdO organisation was set up with a remit to manage the Construction Contract between TML and Eurotunnel. As indicated earlier, the original role envisaged for Eurotunnel was as an operator in waiting. Eurotunnel was to approve design 'on the nod' under Clause 7 of the Construction Contract and pay TML's bills *inter alia*. Ultimate approval for design was the MdO's responsibility, as was supervision of health and safety at work issues connected to the development and assuring the banks and the two national governments of the overall quality of the system. The MdO was to provide a quarterly report on the progress of ongoing activities.

The need for Eurotunnel to agree the results of optimisation studies with TML provides one avenue for addressing the movement of the MdO sideways and Eurotunnel into a more direct management relationship with TML and sub-contractors on the Construction Contract. The Construction Contract included a requirement that the contractor do optimisation studies which analysed the life cycle costs of the project and which would indicate the balance between capital and operating/maintenance costs. Clearly, a source of opportunism existed here where the capital expenditure of the contractor could be reduced by minimising the design of what was provided, whilst leaving higher operating costs for the client to bear. This from Eurotunnel's point of view was an area where they clearly needed to be involved directly, although some input from the MdO would still be required (Eurotunnel financial adviser, interview).

Effecting this closer scrutiny of development was the objective underlying the setting up of the Project Implementation Division by Eurotunnel in March 1988. The PID represented Eurotunnel's main project management interface with TML and comprised engineers and managers from Eurotunnel and engineering firms such as Bechtel, W.S. Atkins, Sir William Halcrow and SETEC. Its principal roles were to monitor design and construction costs and schedules, to co-ordinate between Eurotunnel, TML, and other external agencies, and to prepare monthly reports on costs and progress for Eurotunnel project and general management and for the purposes of keeping the funding banks informed. The latter was especally important bearing in mind the Banks' tight reporting requirements for a group such as Eurotunnel with cash inflows still yet to be received on such a major project (Ridley, 1989).

The composition of the PID was initially relatively small with 35 staff being seconded from the American firm Bechtel, which had a reputation for being a construction 'troubleshooter'. Where this number was considered to be insufficient by Eurotunnel to perform the required task, the later growth of the PID to 350 staff was enough for it to be dubbed the 'shadow contractor' by TML (Anderson and Roskrow, 1994). (Also, much of its expertise was drawn from the same employing organisations as the staff of the MdO.) The claim by TML was that the PID was creating extra work and cost through the need by the contractor to attend to the mass of correspondence it generated and by duplicating functions of the contractor and the Maitre d'Oeuvre.

## Conclusion

This paper has identified aspects of inter-organisational relations underlying difficulties of managing the Channel Tunnel project. Fundamentally, the 'polo mint' nature of decision-making relating to the Channel Tunnel Concession and the Construction Contract has facilitated neither client-contractor relations nor the conduct of such a large-scale development. The absence and weakness of the client during the formative stages of the project and the choice of a single 'design and build' contract are put into perspective by considering TML's sense of ownership of the project, especially bearing in mind the role played by TML's constituent building contractors in putting forward the winning proposal for a fixed tunnel link when part of CTG-FM. In addition, it is necessary to recognise the wishes of the funding banks for a focal point of responsibility for the overall realisation of the Tunnel, when considering why the Construction Contract was not split by activity. Another view of the choice of the seven-year design and build Construction Contract is that such an option would help to reduce the long lead time which *inter alia* typifies large-scale technology projects and so improve the prospects for attracting financing. However, a contrary standpoint is that such a contract, as employed on the Channel Tunnel project, left too many unresolved design and other issues to be attended to during construction, making it hazardous to estimate project costs and, indeed, exacerbating lead time (Benard and Morton, 1989).

The interpretation of the Construction Contract was clear a major source of contention between Eurotunnel and TML linked to the very different expectations and objectives each party had of the project. The parties may have been bilaterally dependent on each other but one could hardly describe relations between them, overall and at critical junctures, as being cooperative, reflective of mutuality and trustful. It is not appropriate to adopt too categorical a stance with regard to the generalisation of findings from a study such as this where the project in question may be seen as unique. Further, it is not possible to make any informed comment about the relative performance of different modes of organising (since neither pure market nor pure hierarchy alternatives have applied). However, the Channel Tunnel may be said to possess the characteristics that major technological projects have been shown to share, and on this basis a general message regarding inter-organisational relations and the management of scale may be advanced. Thus where the development of large-scale technology is involved, a shortfall in the more positive characteristics of inter-organisational relations may have serious implications for the effectiveness of project management. In terms of the direct concerns of this paper, this may mean that the operation of administrative or hierarchical provisions within contracts (as relate to the administering of design changes, dispute resolution, and monitoring and rewarding performance) is likely to be painful. To the extent that their operation is so troubled, the designing of hierarchical elements into contracts may be said serve to *unstructure* the incompetence of contracting parties in their joint management of uncertain or complex large-scale technology projects rather than to structure it.

## References

Anderson, G. and Roskrow, B. (1994), *The Channel Tunnel Story*, E&FN Spon, London.

Benard A and Morton, Sir A. (1989), 'The Private Sector Financing of the Channel Tunnel' in Institution of Civil Engineering, *Channel Tunnel*, Thomas Telford, London.

Disputes Panel member, *taped interview* (1996).

Eurotunnel. (1995) *Progress Report*, Eurotunnel, London and Paris.

Eurotunnel financial adviser, *taped interview* (1996).

Eurotunnel legal team member, *taped interview* (1996).

Genus, A. (1996) 'Managing Large-scale Technology and Inter-organisational Relations: the Case of the Channel Tunnel', *in preparation.*

Jarillo, J.C. (1988) 'On Strategic Networks', *Strategic Management Journal*, **9**, pp. 31-41.

Kay, N.M. (1992) 'Markets, False Hierarchies and the Evolution of the Modern Corporation', *Journal of Economic Behavior and Organizations*, **17**, pp. 315-333.

Kirkland, C. (1995) 'The Channel Tunnel - Lessons Learned', *Tunnelling and Underground Space Technology*, **10**, pp. 5-6.

Morton, Sir A. *(1995) Transcript of Speech to EC Banks in the City*, London, 20 October.

Ouchi, W. (1980) 'Markets, Bureaucracies and Clans', *Administrative Science Quarterly*, **25**, pp. 129-142.

Ridley, T.M. (1989) 'The Role of Eurotunnel', in Institution of Civil Engineers, *Channel Tunnel*, Thomas Telford, London.

Stinchcombe, A.L. and Heimer, C.A. (eds.) (1985) *Organisation Theory and Project Management*, Norwegian University Press, Oslo.

TML project manager, *taped interview* (1996).

TML project manager, *taped interview* (1996).

Vickerman, R. (1994) *The Channel Tunnel: The Case for Private Sector Provision of Public Infrastructure?* The Channel Tunnel Research Unit, Kent University.

Williamson, O.E. (1975) *Markets and Hierarchies: Analysis and Anti-trust Implications*, Free Press, New York.

Williamson, O.E. (1992) 'Markets, Hierarchies and the Modern Corporation', *Journal of Economic Behaviour and Organization*, **17**, pp. 335-352

Williamson, O.E. (1993) 'The Logic of Economic Organisation' in O.E. Williamson and S.G. Winter (eds.), *The Nature of the Firm: Origins, Evolution and Development*, Oxford University Press, New York

# 020

# INTEGRATING BUSINESS STRATEGY AND COMPETENCE DEVELOPMENT

Author:
Anders Drejer, Associate Professor, Ph.D.
Aalborg University
Department of Production
Fibigerstraede 16
DK-9220 Aalborg East
Denmark

Tel: +45 9815 4211 - 3009
Fax: +45 9815 3030
e-mail: i9AnD@iprod.auc.dk

## ABSTRACT

In order to create prosperity, business and work opportinities through technology management, it is necessary to know how to integrate business strategy (externally directed strategy) and technology management. This paper, therefore, attempts to answer to questions:

1) How can integration of business strategy and technology management be defined and understood?
2) How can methods for such integration be ordered and applied?

In order to answer these questions, case studies of four Danish firms are presented. The case studies aim at uncovering how and why the four firms work on integrating their business strategy and technology management - and which methods and models the firms apply. Furthermore, a literature review is presented.

Based on the case studies and literature review, a model for ways to integrate business strategy and technology management is proposed along with a definition of this kind of integration. Integration is divided into three different kinds of integration: a) integration of different aspects (or disciplines), integration of different activities, and integration of different time horizons. It is demonstrated how the case firms in actual cases apply the three kinds of integration in different manners in different situation. This leads to a contingency view of integration.

Furthermore, the model makes is possible to order existing methods for achieving integration and to discuss the process in which the methods are to be applied. The existing methods have been ordered according to a set of issues formulated for each kind of integration and stored in a software application developed for use in industrial practice.

Finally, conclusions will be drawn and implications for further research will be discussed.

Keywords: Integration, business strategy, technology development

# 021

# Felix H.A. Janszen

# Computer simulation of the innovation and product creation process

*Key words: strategic management of technology, technological innovation, systems dynamics, computer simulation*

Erasmus Universiteit Rotterdam
Rotterdam School of Management
P.O. Box 1738
3000 DR ROTTERDAM
THE NETHERLANDS
Tel. +31 10 4082008
Fax. +31 10 2120549
E-mail: fjanszen@fac.fbk.eur.nl

Topic letter: I
Category number: 1
This paper is suitable for oral presentation only

# Computer simulation of the innovation
# and product creation process

*Felix H.A. Janszen*

**Abstract**
For management of innovation to be effective, it is relevant to obtain insight into the complex process of innovation. However, the dynamics of the innovation process is essentially non-linear, making extrapolation from one situation to another hazardous. This paper presents a computer simulation model of the innovation process, based on system dynamics . This model can simulate and analyse the performance of various competitive strategies. It is argued that these computer simulation models can be used both as a basic research tool for formulating research questions and as a management tool for supporting scenario-based planning and management learning in strategic management of technology.

Key words: strategic management of technology, technological innovation, systems dynamics, computer simulation.

## 1. Introduction
Nowadays innovation is perceived as one of the most important means for companies to improve their market position. However, the dynamics of the innovation process is essentially non-linear, making it hard to manage and the results of the process difficult to predict. In the last two decades the knowledge over non-linear processes has increased dramatically. It is now recognised that most processes in nature shows non-linear dynamics and the appearance of linear processes is more an exception than a rule. Non-linear dynamics of processes have been identified through the development of chaos theory, catastrophe theory and complexity theory in mathematics (Nicolis 1995; Peitgen et al 1992). All these theories are based upon coupled differential equations, representing negative and positive feedback loops, to describe the process. The systems, these processes occur in, are named complex systems. The application of complex systems to industrial environments and organisational dynamics has been confirmed by several authors (Senge 1990; Stacey 1995). The non-linear characteristic of the R&D process has already been recognised for more than a decade and has been incorporated in flow diagrams of the R&D processes (e.g. Kline and Rosenberg (1986) and Rothwell (1990).
Only few publications deal with the non-linear character of the innovation process although the existence is widely recognised among scholars. New types of instruments are yet to be developed for innovation and strategic management,.
In this paper a system dynamics model of the innovation process will be described. It may generate a better understanding of the negative and positive feedback mechanisms involved in this process. This model may also be used to create a variety of scenarios supporting the strategic management of technology.

## 2. Computer model of the innovation process
An important heuristic in computer modelling is to start as simple as possible and try to include only the essential elements in the model. Therefore I started to define a minimal system of innovation that included only the most essential elements necessary in innovation.. To this minimal model one by one additional environmental elements were added. In total twelve variants were studied.
The minimal model constitutes two companies and customers who buy a product on the market The companies compete with each other on product quality, price of the product and time to market. The customers look for value for money. They compare the quality/price ratio of both products and choose the highest one. Both companies develop a new product based upon one new technology. The R&D

process of the companies consists of applied research, product development and market research. The computer model of the R&D process is based on the conceptual model as developed by Janszen (1994).
In figure 1 this minimum model of the innovation system is presented schematically.

Figure 1 *Schematic model of minimal system of innovation.*

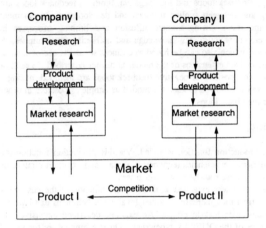

In making this computer model I have made use of the software tool Ithink of High Performance Systems. One of the basic building blocks of the models constructed in this study is the logistic curve, which can be represented with the following formula: $dx/dt = M.A.x(1-x/L)$.
In this formula x represents knowledge, t is time, M, A and L are constants. M and A determine the rate of development and L determines the limit for development of x. In My formula M represents the methodologies and skills used in the product creation process and A represents the activity allocated to this process.
The logistic curve, in the form of the well known S-shaped curve, represents the outcome of the different phases of the product creation process. Outcomes of applied research, product development and market research processes are knowledge (x) about technology, design of the product (determining product quality) and customer knowledge respectively. The coupling of the different phases of the product creation process are mathematically expressed by coupling of the different logistic curves of the individual phases. Coupling of the logistic curves is achieved by using the variable x, the outcome of the phases, as constant in the logistic function of the other phase. For example the limit ($L_p$) of the product development phase is determined by the embodied technologies ($x_t$). The methodologies ($M_t$) in the logistic formula of the applied research phase is (partly) determined by development of the underlying science base ($x_s$).
The formula for market penetration can also be represented by a logistic curve.
The size of the market (L), the companies compete on, is determined by the sum of the perceived added value of the products. The companies penetrate the market (m) via a diffusion process following a logistic curve, $dm/dt = D(1-m/L)$.
The diffusion constant of this logistic curve (D) is influenced by the ratios of the customer values of the products. The customer value is determined as quality(Q)/price(P). The diffusion constant for product 1 is therefore expressed as $Q_1.P_2/Q_2.P_1$. In the basic model the price is fixed during the whole

process. The limit of the market or the potential market in My model is a function of the sum of the product qualities, i.e. sum($P_1+P_2$). In My model dm/dt cannot become negative. Customers can change from one product to the other. This substitution depends on the ratio of the difference of the customer values of the products. In My model the constant E, rate of exit, for product 1 is expressed as $dE/dt=(P_1-P_2)/P_1*(Q_2-Q_1)/Q_1$ ($dE/dt>=0$). In the annex the model is presented via the set of corresponding equations.

In this model six positive, reinforcing, feedback loops and four negative, limiting, feedback loops are present, i.e. reinforcing loops during and between applied research and development, development and market (research) and reinforcing loops during market diffusion and limiting processes in diminishing technology, product development, customer knowledge and marketing opportunities. A number of other positive feedback loops, which also can be found in business situations are omitted in the basic model. These are included in various extensions of the model as further described. In each of these model variants, only one or two extra positive or negative feedback loops are included making a total of 12 model variants. This approach is followed to keep the models as simple as possible in order to be able to study the effects of these feed back loops.

Below these variants are described shortly:

1. Static and dynamic efficiency. A production function is added. Via this production function the company could obtain static and dynamic efficiencies (economies of scale and experience curve or learning by doing) . These efficiencies were translated in lower prices.
2. Customer learning by using. The model was extended with a learning function of the customers (learning by using). This learning effect may increase customer loyalty and heightens exit barriers of the customers and stimulates customer lock-in effects. An example described extensively in literature (Redmond 1991) is the case of the QUERTY typewriters. Other examples are the use of computer software packages, DOS, windows and the Apple OS or the prescription of medicines by physicians.
3. Complementary products. The existence of complementary products, as is the case with computer hardware and software, VCR hardware and software, products that require special equipment or accessories for equipment that add new functionality's or improve existing functionality's.
4. Public aversion. After market introduction public aversion starts to increase. Examples are, use of addictive drugs, cigarette smoking or other products that may damage health or has an deleterious impact on the environment.
5. Public acceptance. After market introduction an initial public aversion changes into public acceptance. Examples are, new means of steam traction in the last century, television sets in the fifties and the introduction of the contraceptives in the sixties. A present day example may be the application of biotechnology to food.
6. Common network. The efficacy of the product is dependent upon an external network. The networks growth depends on the intensity of usage of the product. Examples of such networks are, the energy distribution network, the information highway, transport networks or a distribution network.
7. Complementary network. The building up of company specific distribution networks. Examples are dealer networks.
8. Lock-in technology. The product is dependent upon another supporting product or process technology. During development this dependency becomes greater (technological lock in), which hampers further development. Examples are, dependency of product technologies on process technologies, dependency on material technologies.
9. Supporting technology. The product is dependent upon the development of another supporting technology. Examples are again dependency of product technology on R&D technologies or instrumentality's (Janszen 1994; Rosenberg 1982), process technologies or on material technologies as is the case for I.C.'s, and other high technologies.

10. Supporting scientific development. The development of the technology is dependent on scientific developments. Numerous examples are found in the development of new medicines.
11. Governmental requirements. The presence of governmental requirements on product development. Examples are found in the development of pharmaceuticals, food and aeroplanes.
12. Governmental subsidies. The government subsidises technological development. Examples are found in Europe and North America.

In each of these adaptations the standard model remained unchanged and the variations were added successively[1].

Some of the model variations represent an additional negative, inhibiting, feedback loop, others represent additional positive, reinforcing, feedback loops.
All these additions are regarded as structural additions, whose parameters are out of company control.
In each simulation experiment I started with a comparison of the evolution of the market shares of both companies, by equalising the parameters of both companies. In this case each company obtain an equal market share. Then, in subsequent runs the strategies of the companies are varied and the market share of each company is measured after a certain period. The strategy of the company is determined by changing those parameters that are under the control of the companies, like price, choice of technology, allocation of resources, integration between the various R&D phases In this study these parameters are labelled "strategic parameters". The remaining parameters of the model, such as product preferences of the customers are defined as "structural parameters".
In the simulation experiments four types of company strategies are investigated. In these strategies the components time to market, product quality and price play different roles. Below the scenario's with the different strategies of the companies are summerised:
a. Scenario 1: In a control simulation the companies follow identical strategies.
b. Scenario 2: In a second situation one company (company II) has exchanged speed for product quality, by choosing for a more advanced technology. The development of this more advanced technology however takes more time.
c. Scenario 3: In a third situation product qualities are similar, but one company (company I) is slightly faster by better integration of the R&D process.
d. Scenario 4: In a fourth situation one company (company I) follow a price strategy versus a quality strategy.

### 3. Results of computer simulation studies
In all cases where the two companies followed identical strategies (scenario 1) both companies obtained exactly the same market share. In the simulations of various model variants this scenario was taken as a control, proving that the model was symmetrical with regard to structural parameters and that all strategic parameters had equal values.
In figure 2 a and b the results of the evolution of market shares of company I and II are presented under scenario 2. In figure 2a the evolution of the market shares is given under the basic conditions in the minimal computer model. In this case company I first comes on the market with his product. However after some time it looses market share because company II enters the market with a better product. In figure 2b customer learning takes place. In that case customers become locked in and the substitution of product I by product II takes longer.

---

[1] The equations of all the computer models described in this paper are available on request.

Figure 2 a/b *Evolution of market shares of company I and II in the basic computer model[2] in case of better technology but slower development by company II (scenario 2)*

Figure 2a       *Scenario 2 in the basic computer model*

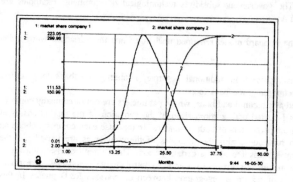

Figure 2b       *Scenario 2 in case of learning by doing by customers*

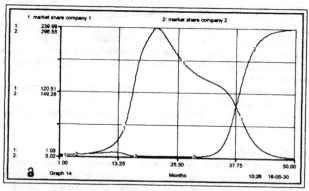

The evolution of the market shares of both companies are rather easily understandable. In most cases market equilibrium is reached after a relatively limited number of iteration periods.

In table 1 the results of the simulations in the twelve variant models including the minimal model as control are presented. In the table only the results of the three strategies, e.g. scenario's no. 2, 3, and 4, are given. In the table in each case two results are given, namely, the marketshare in arbitrary units of company I and company II. The absolute numbers of the arbitrary units are given instead of percentages because the limit of product quality was not always reached (building up of public aversion, technological lock in effects) or sometimes the market became bigger because of higher product qualities (supporting scientific developments, supporting technologies). The sum of the market

---

[2] In the figure at the horizontal axis time is represented in periods(months) and at the vertical axis the outcome of the simulation is represented, i.e. market share of company I and company II. Also the cumulated sales are presented at the vertical axis. The number in the curves indicate which variable is presented by the curve. The maximum level of the curve is presented at the top of the vertical axis. All curves reach the maximum in the figure, representing however different values.

shares in the same model varies, but under different scenario's were not always equal. This also indicates that not in all cases equilibrium was reached after the chosen time of 50 periods. This indicates that the information obtained by the simulations is richer than can be presented in the table. Therefore, when necessary the whole evolution of market shares are presented.

In a number of modelvariants company I, the company that competed on time to market, obtained the total market under all three scenario's. This occurred in the situation of existence of static and dynamic efficiency, complementary products and complementary networks. In all these circumstances positive feedback loops exist in the market giving the product that is first on the market an advantage. In the case of learning by using there exists also a positive, reinforcing, feedback loop in the market resulting in a customer lock in effect. It is expected that this will result in a larger market share of the company that is first on the market, i.e. company I. This is not shown by the results presented in table 2. Comparison of the evolution curves demonstrate, that the exit barrier has increased in the case of learning by using, resulting in a slower change in market shares.

Table 2 *Accumulated sales and market shares of company I and II respectively. The figures represent the market shares in arbitrary units, at the left side company ! and at the right side company II.*

## Market shares company I/company II

| | Scenario 2<br>Company II: better technology, slower development | Scenario 3<br>Company I: better integration | Scenario 4<br>Company I: better integration, lower price<br>Company II: better technology, slower development |
|---|---|---|---|
| Standard | 0/300 | 146/104 | 185/0 |
| Statistic/dynamic efficiency | 300/0 | 237/13 | 300/0 |
| Customer learning by using | 0/300 | 160/180 | 150/0 |
| Complementary products | 320/0 | 249/0 | 320/0 |
| Public aversion | 0/53 | 72/69 | 0/21 |
| Public acceptance | 0/300 | 130/119 | 0/214 |
| Common network | 0/300 | 136/113 | 250/0 |
| Complementary network | 300/0 | 215/0 | 300/0 |
| Lock-in technology | 100/145 | 154/97 | 200/0 |
| Supporting technology | 320/60 | 298/151 | 450/0 |
| Supporting scientific development | 0/499 | 270/179 | 450/0 |
| Governmental requirements | 0/300 | 129/123 | 200/0 |
| Governmental subsidies | 0/300 | 133/116 | 0/297 |

This table shows an evolution that one expects in cases of increased customer exit barriers. The effect on market share is transient. The barrier of exit increases with longer time advantage and stronger customer experience. Sensitivity analysis demonstrates this (data not shown).
In a number of model variants product quality seems to be more important compared to the basic situation. In these variants both in strategy no. 2 and no. 4 company II has the highest market share. This is the case in the public aversion and public acceptance model variants. This result can be easily understood. In both cases a follower strategy seems more appropriate.

In a number of cases, the relative position of the companies on the market has not changed compared with the basic situation. This is the case with the model variants common networks, supporting scientific developments and governmental requirements. These effects seem to be competition neutral. It only changes the rate of market formation and market penetration. In the variant model in which governmental subsidies are involved, the relative position is changed in scenario no 4. Governmental subsidies for R&D therefore stimulate the higher product quality and gives company II an advantage.

In these simulation experiments I have studied only a certain set of the structural and strategic model parameters. It will be evident, that the effect of the variations depend upon the given parameters. For example by changing the parameters of the effect of "learning by using" on market exit, I can adjust the influence of "learning by using" to higher or lower levels.

In figure 3 I have performed the analysis on the strategic parameters in the basic model and compared this to the outcome of this sensitivity analysis of the model with complementary products and of the model with static and dynamic efficiency. The strategic parameters, that have been varied over speed of development of company I and product quality of company II. In the figure the quality and speed are expressed as a percentage of product quality and speed of development of the other company.

Figure 3. *Space map of strategic parameters. Horizontal performance of technology of company II as % of technology of company I, and vertical speed of development of company I as % of speed of company II. On the left side of the curves company one posses occupy total market, right of the lines company II occupies total market.*

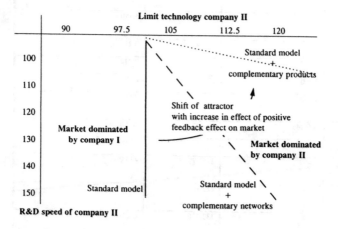

In figure 3 it is demonstrated, that in the basic model speed can not compensate for product quality. However in the model with market reinforcing loops and lock-in effects speed can overcome product quality. In these experiments complementary products had the strongest effect. This strong effect depends however on the type of coupling between the two. It may be expected that the effect will be less, when coupling is less tight. Examples are auto accessories, where only additional functionality is added, and the complementary products are not essential for the functionality in contrast to the case of computer hardware and software.
In conclusion it can be remarked that for full evaluation of the models both structural and strategic parameters must be varied.

## 4. Conclusions and discussion

Time to market seemed to be associated with these types of mechanisms. When on the market a positive feedback loop was present, time to market became important for gaining market share.
Static and dynamic efficiency resulted in lower price stimulating market penetration. Higher market penetration resulted in bigger static and dynamic efficiencies and again a reinforcing process in the market was present. Similar situations were found in the variant with complementary networks (dealer network) or learning by using effects of customers.
These results make clear that time to market under certain conditions is more important than in other situations. This is an important result in contrast with part of the literature, that does not make these nuances.

A number of structural characteristics of the innovation system were found that were competition neutral. These influenced the market as a whole, made it more or less attractive, but did not affect competitive strategy. Governmental policies belonged to this class. This may be the objective of governmental policies. This result indicates that this class of computer models may also be of interest to government to test its technology and industry policies against its objectives.
From the above results it can be concluded that computer modelling is a valuable instrument and complementary to the verbal and graphic models. They make it possible to refine research questions and test hypothesis on consistency before being tested empirically. They also help management to test its propositions about competition and markets before acting. They help researchers to understand best practices and learn about the contingencies of these practices. I believe that computer modelling deserves a place in the armatarium of the basic researcher, the applied researcher, the consultant and the manager.

## References

Janszen, F.H.A., (1994), R&D management and the role of the primary process in Research and Development, In: Management of Technology V, T.M.-Khalil and B.A. Bayraktar (ed.), Industrial Engineering and Management Press, Norcross, Georgia, pp. 434-443.

Kline, S.J., Rosenberg, N. (1986), An overview of innovation, In: National Academy of engineering, The positive sum strategy: Harnessing technology for economic growth. The National Academy Press, Washington D.C.

Nicolis, G., Prigogine, I., (1994), The fourth European Framework program and research on complex systems, paper on: The university. Facing up its European responsibilities, Pisa, 23-26 November.

Nicolis, G. (1995), Introduction to non-linear science, Cambridge University Press, Cambridge.

Peitgen, H.O., Jurgens H., Saupe D., (1992), Chaos and fractals. New frontiers of science, Springer Verlag, New York.

Porter, A., Roper A.T., Mason T.W., Rossini F.A. and Banks J. (1991), Forecasting and management of technology, Wiley series in engineering & technology management, John Wiley & Sons, Inc., New York.

Redmond, W.H., (1991), When technologies compete: the role of externalities in non-linear market response, Journal of Product and Innovation Management, Vol.8, pp.170-183.

Rothwell, R. (1992), Successful industrial innovation: critical factors for the 1990's, R&D Management, Vol.22, pp.221-239.

Senge, P.M., (1990), The fifth discipline. The art & Practice of the learning organization, Currency Doubleday, New York.

Stacey, R.D., (1995), The science of complexity: an alternative perspective for strategic change processes, Strategic Management Journal, Vol.16, pp.447-495.

# 022

**Author:**  Dr. Éric Alsène
Associate Professor
Département de mathématiques et de génie industriel
École Polytechnique
C.P. 6079, Succ. Centre-Ville
Montréal, Québec
CANADA H3C 3A7

Telephone: (514) 340-4622
Fax: (514) 340-4173
E-mail: eric.alsene@mailsrv.polymtl.ca

**Co-author:**  Sara Limam
Research Associate
Département de mathématiques et de génie industriel
École Polytechnique
C.P. 6079, Succ. Centre-Ville
Montréal, Québec
CANADA H3C 3A7

**Title of paper:**  A METHOD FOR MEASURING THE DEGREE
OF COMPUTER INTEGRATION OF AN ENTERPRISE

**Key Words:**  Computer technology - Enterprise integration -
Measurement techniques

**Topic:**  B. Enterprise integration and integrated information systems

**Categories:**  1. Theoritical
2. Experimental

**Presentation:**  a) Oral presentation only

## A METHOD FOR MEASURING THE DEGREE
## OF COMPUTER INTEGRATION OF AN ENTERPRISE


### INTRODUCTION

Information technology appears increasingly to be a substitute for organizational means of integrating an enterprise, such as direct supervision or the standardization of work processes (Twigg et al., 1992; Petrie, 1992; Mintzberg, 1979). Computer systems make possible the sharing and exchange of data which bring the various functions of the enterprise closer together.

There is agreement among numerous authors about the benefits of computer integration of the enterprise (Petrie, 1992; ESPRIT Consortium AMICE, 1993; Sheridan, 1994; East, 1994). Curiously enough, no method exists which would enable true measurement of the degree of computer integration achieved by enterprises (Working Group 3 of ICEIMT Workshop IV, 1992). For example, Gibert (1989) proposes calculating the degree of integration of production workshops based on the number of functions integrated by means of computer technology, but recognizes that the task may prove to be difficult in the absence of a precise nomenclature of the functions involved in manufacturing[1].

Such a situation becomes a problem if we intend to strategically use computer systems as a means for integrating the enterprise. If, for example, the degree of computer integration in a given enterprise remains unknown, how is it possible to establish objectives for this enterprise in the matter of computer integration and to verify later whether or not these objectives have been achieved?

This paper is an attempt to provide a remedy for this situation. Proposed here is an original definition of the degree of computer integration of an enterprise, and a concrete method for calculating it. The paper also reports the results of a test conducted in a medium-sized Canadian manufacturing enterprise, which is a subsidiary of a multinational firm.

### PRELIMINARY DEFINITIONS

Three notions on which our proposal is based must first be explained. These notions are: functional unit, informational activity and integrating system.

#### Functional unit

By "functional unit", we mean any part of an administrative unit which groups together individuals who fulfil more or less the same function.

An enterprise is composed essentially of two types of functional units: 1) "management units", including an "executive unit" and "supervisory units"; and 2) "basic units".

The executive unit comprises the executives and senior managers of the enterprise (CEO, vice-presidents, etc.), as well as non-management personnel who report directly to them and help

---

[1]   The scales occasionally put forward in the literature may appear to be a worthwile alternative, since they propose the direct classification of enterprises in terms of their "level" of integration (cf. Gupta and Somers, 1993; Carl and Judd, 1994). It is far from established, however, that the suggested categories are valid, or even operative.

them carry out their functions (secretaries, assistants, etc.).

The supervisory units are composed of middle-managers who belong to the same hierarchical line (down from the executive unit), as well as non-management personnel who report directly to them and help them carry out their functions (secretaries, assistants, etc.) - with the condition that these middle-managers supervise people other than these non-management individuals[2].

Finally, the basic units are composed of:
- either employees at the lower end of the hierarchy who are under the supervision of the same manager, and whose job does not consist in helping this manager to carry out his or her functions;
- or employees at the lower end of the hierarchy whose job is to help their supervisor to carry out his or her functions, as well as this supervisor, when he or she supervises only these employees.

## Informational activity

By "informational activity", we essentially mean one of the following:
- an activity aimed at obtaining data, information, instructions, etc. in order to accomplish other activities - for example, an employee who attends an informational meeting, or a foreman who checks the work of his or her subordinates;
- an activity aimed at putting data, charts, information, orders, etc. at the disposal of other individuals (within or outside the enterprise) to accomplish their own activities - for example, a technician who telephones a colleague with the results of an analysis, or an engineer who designs a product;
- an activity which contributes directly to putting data, charts, information, orders, etc. at the disposal of other individuals (within or outside the enterprise) to accomplish their own activities - for example, a clerk who collects and distributes mail, or a computer scientist who develops an application.

Having said this, we can also consider as an informational activity an activity aimed at, or contributing to, ensuring that machines or instruments are fed with signals for their operation (for example, a worker who operates the control system of an NC machine).

## Integrating system

By "integrating system", we mean a computer system which is used jointly by members of different functional units.

The term "computer system" in the above definition refers to a system which provides human beings with one or more information processing applications, or information editing applications[3]. It should be noted that this system can be a simple system with - so to speak -

---

[2]  In other words, a "manager" who has no one under his or her supervision other than a secretary and an assistant cannot be considered as belonging to a supervisory unit.

[3]  In other words, a computer system may be a CAD/CAM system, a decision-support system, a production control system, a personnel management system or a database inquiry system; but not, in general, an operating system, a LAN management system or a database management system; or a pure communications system, such as an electronic mail system or an EDI system.

only one module, a complex system composed of a number of different modules, or a metasystem composed of various systems designed as separate entities and interrelated by means of connecting artifacts (interfaces, common databases, intelligent agents, etc.).

A computer system is said to be used "jointly" when there is an exchange, a sharing or a pooling of data (in the broad sense, which includes texts, graphs, etc.) among the users while the system is in use.

The "use" of a system includes any system manipulation (interaction, operation, etc.), and can be both direct and indirect. In indirect use, the user is not in contact with the system, but rather "uses" the system through a direct user (as, for example, in the case of the vice-president who studies a report which she has requested from a manager and which the manager has produced with the aid of the point-of-sale management system that he regularly uses).

## DEFINITION OF THE DEGREE OF COMPUTER INTEGRATION OF AN ENTERPRISE

We propose to view the degree of computer integration of an enterprise as the propensity of its various functional units to use integrating systems to accomplish the informational part of their activities.

Indeed, if there is any computer integration in an enterprise, then certain informational activities, at a minimum, are being run, or supported, by computer systems. It would be difficult to imagine computer integration of an enterprise based on activities other than informational ones - that is, based on non-informational activities (such as distribution of supplies, assembly of a product, housekeeping, etc.).

Furthermore, for computer integration to occur, some of the computer systems involved must be integrating systems. If none of the systems used is an integrating system, this would mean that all computerized informational activities taking place in each functional unit are accomplished without the computerized exchange, sharing or pooling of data with other functional units. If this were the case, it would be virtually impossible to talk about bringing the various functions of the enterprise closer together through the intermediary of computer technology.

Finally, it is clear that the more the informational activities in each functional unit are accomplished with the aid of one or more integrating systems, the more links there are among the various functions of the enterprise, and therefore the more the enterprise is integrated through computer technology. Furthermore, it is clear that an enterprise is totally integrated by computer technology when all the informational activities in all the functional units are accomplished by, or with the aid of, integrating systems[4]. Indeed, the total number of functional units constitutes an exhaustive partition of the enterprise, as opposed to traditional administrative units, which

---

[4] It must be pointed out, however, that this eventuality is a highly improbable one, because: 1) it is far from a given that technology will one day run or support all the informational activities in enterprises; and 2) the use of computer technology for processing and editing information does not necessarily exhaust the range of informational activities under way in enterprises (communication from one individual to another, for example).

cover only a part of the structure of the enterprise[5].

Technically speaking, we propose the following: If we call the contribution (C) of each functional unit to the degree of computer integration of the enterprise the ratio between the time (TS) spent to use integrating systems and the time (TA) devoted to informational activities in this unit, then the degree (D) of computer integration of the enterprise will be understood as the arithmetic mean of the contributions of the set (N) of functional units (i) which make up the enterprise.

$$D = \frac{\sum C_i}{N} \quad for\ i=1\ to\ N,\ \ with\ C_i = \frac{TS_i}{TA_i}$$

The degree of computer integration of an enterprise is thus a value falling between 0 and 1. It should be emphasized that this value may not remain unchanged over a period of non-investment in information technology: if, during such a period, an enterprise develops new informational activities or revises its organizational structure, then its degree of computer integration may change.

## METHOD FOR MEASURING THE DEGREE OF COMPUTER INTEGRATION OF AN ENTERPRISE

Because the notions on which our definition of the degree of computer integration of an enterprise is based are either new or have not been very well explored, we also propose a method which will aid in the determination of the degree of computer integration of a given enterprise. This method comprises four major steps and a number of sub-steps.

### Step 1: Inventory of functional units

#### 1.1. Establishment of the organizational structure
This step is based on the most recent organizational charts of the enterprise. These organizational charts must, if the case presents itself, be completed by adding those individuals who do not appear on them, but who form an integral part of the enterprise (consultants and trainees who have been in place for some time, recruits, etc.). Vacant positions must not be removed, except if it is clear that they will never be filled, or will not be filled for a very long time. The baseline we recommend is the enterprise as it would look like if all its "useful" personnel were in place at the time of the study.

#### 1.2 Identification of functional units
Once the organizational structure of the enterprise is known, the functional units are identified, based on the definitions given above. First, the executive unit is delineated, followed by the supervisory units. There are as many supervisory units as there are managers under the

---

[5] Departments, for example, have above them, at a minimum, the president of the enterprise, and possibly all kinds of managerial and vice-presidential positions as well.

direct supervision of the executive unit. Finally, the lower end of the hierarchy is studied in order to obtain the basic units. It should be noted, however, that the exact composition of the supervisory units and the basic units is not known until some verification has been carried out: for instance, it must be remembered that, if a manager only supervises employees whose job is to help him or her carry out his or her functions (secretaries, assistants, etc.), then this manager and his or her subordinates belong to a basic unit rather than to a supervisory unit.

It should also be noted that, if certain individuals work for more than one department, then they must be "shared" among the functional units concerned in accordance with the amount of time they spend in each. In this way, strict partitioning of the enterprise is maintained.

Having said this, we must add that such a partitioning may be a virtual one, since vacant positions may have been taken into account in the preceding step. Incidentally, it is even possible for a functional unit to be "empty" - to have no personnel at all.

## Step 2: Inventory of the integrating systems used in each functional unit

### 2.1 Enumeration of computer systems

Computer systems are enumerated by consulting the lists of systems and applications made up by the systems department of the enterprise, and also by asking the members of each functional unit about the systems and applications they use. The computer specialists are rarely aware of all the software that the employees of the enterprise use, except in cases where all the workstations are terminals or networked microcomputers without hard disks.

During this investigative work, it is also important to find out from each employee, for each application used by the employee, if he or she is the only individual manipulating the data that he or she manipulates, or if others manipulate either some or all of the data as well - and if they do so via the same application or via other applications. In the latter case, the application(s) in question, and the user(s) involved, are noted.

This work can be time-consuming, depending on the size of the enterprise. It is not always necessary to question all the personnel in the enterprise, however. A secretary, for example, can often answer on behalf of his or her boss, and one employee can be the spokesperson for his or her colleagues if they are all fulfilling the same functions. It is sometimes even possible to distribute a questionnaire on the subject to the personnel in certain functional units.

### 2.2 Identification of integrating systems

The next step is to classify each system (or application) used in each functional unit on the basis of information obtained during the preceding step. The following five elementary - but not mutually exclusive - situations serve as a reference in performing this task:

1. System A is used non-jointly by one or more users in unit X (without any exchange, sharing or pooling of data).
2. System A is used jointly by users in unit X only (without any exchange, sharing or pooling of data with users in other units).
3. System A is used by one or more users in unit X jointly with one or more users in unit Y (with exchange, sharing or pooling of data with users in unit Y).
4. System A is interrelated with system B, and this combined system is used jointly by users in unit X only.

5. System A is interrelated with system B, and this combined system is used jointly by one or more users of unit X and by one or more users of unit Y respectively.

If, for a given system in a given functional unit, only situations 1, 2 and 4 exist, then the system is considered to be "non-integrating" with respect to that unit. If, by contrast, situations 3 or 5 exist, then the system is considered to be an "integrating" system with respect to that unit. In other words, we propose that a system be considered as an integrating system at the functional unit level as soon as one member of this unit uses it, either alone or interrelated with other systems, jointly with users of other functional units[6].

In this way, a list of the integrating systems - or components of integrating systems - used in each functional unit is gradually generated. This list may be incomplete, however, as it is sometimes impossible, even indirectly, to collect information about certain vacant positions.

## Step 3: Study of the informational activities carried out in each functional unit

### 3.1 Collection of data on informational activities

The best way to obtain data on the informational activities carried out in each functional unit would seem to be to ask each employee in each functional unit to fill in a questionnaire on a confidential basis.

We recommend that this questionnaire include three questions: the first on the average length of the work week (including work done in the home, business travel, etc.); the second on the percentage of the work week devoted to informational activities; and the third on the time spent per week in using each of the integrating systems.

Of course, these questions must be presented in such a way that any employee in the enterprise will be able to answer them. For instance, definitions, examples, etc. can be provided, tools can be distributed to enable employees to practice responding to the questionnaire, or assistance can be offered to employees to enable them complete it.

It is also important to design a version of the questionnaire for each functional unit, which includes only the integrating systems that concern its employees. In this way, the feeling on the part of employees that they are being excluded from the development of computer technology in their enterprise can be avoided. An additional benefit of this approach - since each questionnaire is anonymous - is that it offers the possibility of subsequently compiling the data per functional unit.

Finally, if some individuals are absent during distribution of the questionnaire (position vacant, long vacation, etc.), we suggest, whenever possible, asking people whose work is similar or who know the work of these individuals well enough to respond in their place.

### 3.2 Calculation of the time devoted to informational activities

Once the number of hours worked per week and the proportion of time devoted to informational activities by each individual in each functional unit are known, the time devoted

---

6    We are aware that this baseline may represent a significant bias for subsequent calculations (overestimation of the degree of computer integration). We could probably have removed the problem by increasing the degree of sophistication of the procedure, but we did not do so since we judged that the method was cumbersome enough as it was.

per week to informational activities in each unit can be calculated. First, the time devoted by each individual to informational activities is determined, and then the times obtained are totaled with respect to each unit.

In the case where information with regard to one or more individuals in a functional unit is lacking (substitutes not found, questionnaires not returned, etc.), we propose attributing to the individual or individuals in question the mean result obtained for the unit - using the data successfully obtained up to that point. And if some information is lacking for all the individuals making up a functional unit, we suggest extrapolating proportionally the result obtained for the most similar, or least different, unit[7].

### 3.3 Calculation of the time of utilization of the integrating systems

In addition, as we know the time of utilization of each integrating system in each functional unit by each individual, we can calculate the time of utilization per week of the integrating systems in each unit. First, the total time spent by each individual in using the integrating systems is determined, followed by the total time spent in each unit. The same extrapolation procedure as discussed previously for missing information is recommended.

### Step 4: Determination of the degree of computer integration of the enterprise

#### 4.1 Calculation of the contribution of each functional unit to the degree of computer integration

Once the time devoted to informational activities in each functional unit per week and the time of utilization of the integrating systems in each unit per week have been calculated, the contribution of each functional unit to the degree of computer integration of the enterprise can be determined. This contribution is simply the ratio of the second result to the first.

#### 4.2 Calculation of the degree of computer integration

Having completed the preceding step, it remains only to calculate the degree of computer integration of the enterprise. This figure is obtained, in conformity with the definition given above, by taking the arithmetic mean of the contributions of all the functional units that make up the enterprise.

### TEST IN AN ENTERPRISE

In 1995-96, we tested the method presented here in a medium-sized Canadian manufacturing enterprise operating in the fluid technology domain. At the time, this enterprise managed 15 branches across Canada and was one of the many subsidiaries of a multinational firm. Its staff at the end of the study numbered 78 (including one employee on sick leave). Three positions were temporarily vacant. The virtual staff of the enterprise thus numbered 81.

---

[7]   Clearly, such approximations are undesirable; however, it would be unreasonable to suggest that they could be avoided altogether.

As it turned out, the enterprise was made up of some 21 functional units, 6 of which were management units and 15 of which were basic units (Table 1). Two of these, the Human Resources supervisory unit (no. IV) and the Products A basic unit (no. 9), had a null staff: they had only one position, which was vacant. The staff of two others, the Control (no. II) and Operations (no. VI) supervisory units, were fractions: one executive secretary sometimes worked for one unit and sometimes for the other.

Table 1. The functional units in the enterprise under study

| Types of functional units | Functional units | No. | Actual staff | Virtual staff |
|---|---|---|---|---|
| Management units | Executive | I | 2 | 2 |
| | Control | II | 6.5 | 6.5 |
| | Marketing | III | 9 | 9 |
| | Human Resources | IV | 0 | 1 |
| | Quality | V | 2 | 2 |
| | Operations | VI | 3.5 | 3.5 |
| Basic units | Information Systems | 1 | 3 | 3 |
| | Information Systems Support | 2 | 3 | 3 |
| | Accounting and Billing | 3 | 4 | 4 |
| | Accounts Payable | 4 | 2 | 2 |
| | Credit | 5 | 1 | 2 |
| | Engineering | 6 | 4 | 4 |
| | Drafting | 7 | 3 | 3 |
| | Marketing Coordination | 8 | 2 | 2 |
| | Products A | 9 | 0 | 1 |
| | Products B | 10 | 2 | 2 |
| | Communications | 11 | 1 | 1 |
| | Human Resources | 12 | 3 | 3 |
| | Quality | 13 | 1 | 1 |
| | Materials | 14 | 4 | 4 |
| | Operations and Services | 15 | 22 | 22 |
| TOTAL | | | 78 | 81 |

In terms of information technology, no fewer than 63 systems and applications were in use in the enterprise. A large system was running on an AS-400 minicomputer, and the remaining systems and applications were running on networked microcomputers. It was determined that 15 of these systems functioned as an integrating system - or as a component of an integrating system - for at least one functional unit (Table 2). It was not possible, however, to collect information for the person on sick leave (unit 14) and for one of the vacant positions (unit 9).

As recommended, a questionnaire on the informational work practices was distributed to all personnel present in the enterprise. In addition, we were able to ask someone to respond for an absent individual - in this case, the Human Resources Coordinator, for the Director of Human Resources (unit IV), who had just left the enterprise. Only four questionnaires, all concerning unit 15 (Operations and Services), were not returned. This means that data were collected with regard to 74 of the 81 employees making up the virtual staff of the enterprise (or 91% of this staff).

The results of the compilation of these data and of the correlative extrapolations for the time devoted to informational activities and the time spent using the integrating systems in each of the

| Computer systems | I | II | III | IV | V | VI | 1 | 2 | 3 | 4 | 5 | 6 | 7 | 8 | 9 | 10 | 11 | 12 | 13 | 14 | 15 |
|---|---|---|---|---|---|---|---|---|---|---|---|---|---|---|---|---|---|---|---|---|---|
| AS-400 | x | x | x | x | x | x | x | x | x | x | x | x | x | x |  | x | x | x | x | x | x |
| ACCESS |  |  |  |  |  |  | x |  |  |  |  |  |  |  |  |  |  |  |  |  |  |
| AIR CANADA | x | x |  |  |  |  |  |  |  |  |  |  |  |  |  |  |  |  |  |  |  |
| AUTOCAD |  | x |  |  |  |  |  |  |  |  |  | x |  | x |  |  |  |  |  |  |  |
| CREDITEL |  | x |  |  |  |  |  |  |  |  |  | x |  |  |  |  |  |  |  |  |  |
| D & B |  | x |  |  |  |  |  |  |  |  |  | x |  |  |  |  |  |  |  |  |  |
| DBASE |  |  |  | x |  |  |  |  |  |  |  |  |  |  |  |  |  |  |  |  | x |
| EXCEL | x | x | x | x | x | x |  |  | x | x | x | x |  | x |  | x | x | x | x | x |  |
| EXECUVIEW | x | x |  |  |  |  | x | x |  |  |  |  |  |  |  |  |  |  |  |  |  |
| FDC |  |  |  |  |  |  | x |  |  |  |  |  |  |  |  |  |  |  |  |  |  |
| FLYPS |  | x |  |  |  |  |  |  |  |  |  |  | x |  |  | x |  |  |  |  |  |
| QUOTATION |  | x |  |  |  |  |  |  |  |  |  |  |  | x |  |  |  |  |  |  |  |
| SHOWCASE |  | x |  |  |  |  |  |  |  |  |  |  |  |  |  |  |  |  |  |  |  |
| SMT TEXT |  | x |  |  |  |  |  |  | x |  |  | x |  |  |  |  |  |  |  |  |  |
| WORD | x | x | x | x | x | x | x |  | x | x | x | x |  | x |  | x | x | x | x | x |  |

functional units of the enterprise appear in Table 3. The extrapolations affected four functional units in total: in units 5 and 14 (1 person absent) and in unit 15 (4 questionnaires not returned), the extrapolation was performed on the basis of the respective internal mean obtained; in unit 9 (1 person absent, this person making up the whole unit), the extrapolation was performed on the basis of the mean obtained in unit 10 - since unit 9 (Products A) normally accomplishes more or less the same type of activities as unit 10 (Products B).

Table 3. Calculation of contributions of functional units to the degree of computer integration of the enterprise under study

| Functional units | Time devoted to informational activities (hours per week) | Time of use of integrating systems (hours per week) | Contributions to the degree of computer integration of the enterprise |
|---|---|---|---|
| Unit I | 31.00 | 23.00 | 0.742 |
| Unit II | 194.08 | 129.00 | 0.665 |
| Unit III | 342.49 | 135.99 | 0.397 |
| Unit IV | 32.00 | 2.00 | 0.063 |
| Unit V | 60.75 | 14.25 | 0.235 |
| Unit VI | 112.80 | 84.00 | 0.745 |
| Unit 1 | 115.00 | 15.50 | 0.135 |
| Unit 2 | 80.25 | 22.00 | 0.274 |
| Unit 3 | 109.99 | 103.00 | 0.937 |
| Unit 4 | 58.10 | 53.75 | 0.925 |
| Unit 5 | 70.00 | 22.50 | 0.321 |
| Unit 6 | 127.60 | 51.50 | 0.404 |
| Unit 7 | 100.00 | 99.00 | 0.990 |
| Unit 8 | 75.50 | 66.50 | 0.881 |
| Unit 9 | 34.90 | 12.00 | 0.344 |
| Unit 10 | 69.80 | 24.00 | 0.344 |
| Unit 11 | 33.73 | 1.08 | 0.032 |
| Unit 12 | 98.75 | 28.00 | 0.284 |
| Unit 13 | 36.00 | 12.00 | 0.333 |
| Unit 14 | 121.90 | 79.92 | 0.656 |
| Unit 15 | 267.64 | 101.44 | 0.379 |

The above results made it possible to calculate the contribution of each functional unit to the degree of computer integration of the enterprise (cf. Table 3 again), and finally the degree of computer integration of the enterprise. We arrived at a value of 0.480 for this enterprise.

## CONCLUSION

Since we arrived at a value for the degree of computer integration of the enterprise under study and succeeded in completing the recommended sequence of steps, and did so without major difficulty, we can conclude that the test we carried out was a success. In other words, the method that we propose for measuring the degree of computer integration of the enterprise has some validity, and the underlying definition some operative quality, unlike the very rare suggestions that have been made in the literature.

It is clear, however, that the value obtained is not completely accurate. This value is the result of a certain number of approximations (designating a system as an "integrating system" when at least one individual in a functional unit uses it, extrapolating the results when information is missing). In addition, the value is based on perceptions and not on objective measures.

Moreover, the test was carried out in only one enterprise, and this enterprise was a medium-sized one. Until other tests have been conducted in other enterprises, particularly large ones, we must be careful. At this point, it is almost certain that the larger the enterprise, the more numerous the cases of missing information will be, and the more approximate the value of the degree of computer integration of the enterprise.

It seems reasonable to assume, nonetheless, that strategic decision-makers would prefer to have at their disposal an approximate value of the degree of computer integration of their enterprise than not to have any value at all, as is currently the case.

## REFERENCES

Carl, E.J. and Judd, J.L. (1994) "Bridging Product Data Management Systems for Effective Enterprise Integration," *Industrial Engineering*, vol.26, no.12, pp.18-21.

East, S. (1994) *Systems Integration: A Management Guide for Manufacturing Engineers*, London, McGraw-Hill.

ESPRIT Consortium AMICE (eds.) (1993) *CIMOSA: Open System Architecture for CIM*, 2nd, Revised and Extended Edition, Berlin, Springer-Verlag.

Gibert, M. (1989) *L'intégration des systèmes de production: le cas des ateliers d'usinage*, Lyon, Presses Universitaires de Lyon.

Gupta, Y.P. and Somers, T.M. (1993) "Factory Automation and Integration of Business Functions," *Journal of Manufacturing Systems*, vol.12, no.1, pp.15-23.

Mintzberg, H. (1979) *The Structuring of Organizations*, Englewood Cliffs, Prentice-Hall.

Petrie, C.J. (ed.) (1992) *Enterprise Integration Modeling: Proceedings of the First International Conference*, Cambridge, MIT Press.

Sheridan, J.H. (1994) "EI: The Next Plateau," *Industry Week*, vol.243, no.12, pp.30-38.

Twigg, D., Voss, C.A. and Winch, G.M. (1992) "Implementing Integrating Technologies: Developing Managerial Integration for CAD/CAM," *International Journal of Operations and Production Management*, vol.12, nos.7/8, pp.76-91.

Working Group 3 of ICEIMT Workshop IV (1992) "Enterprise Metrics: Evaluation of Investments towards Integration," in Petrie, C.J. (ed.) *Enterprise Integration Modeling: Proceedings of the First International Conference*, Cambridge, MIT Press, pp.90-98.

# 023

## SIXTH INTERNATIONAL CONFERENCE ON MOT 1997

### Gothenburg, Sweden

### June 25 - 28, 1997

Name: Roberto Del Rio Soto

Company: PEMEX-Refinacion
Mexico City

Title of Paper: A New Approach to Corporate and Technology Strategy

While more than three decades have passed since strategy became a subject of interest and study in the business as well as in the academic sphere, it has been possibly no more than 20 years since its linkage with technology emerged as a serious topic. Nowadays, it is a well recognized fact that technology is a vital force driving the firm's competitive strategy. However, the majority of literature about the strategic management of technology and R&D is only focused on partial issues of its overall context and scope.

A new integral and dynamic model is proposed for analyzing the complex interrelationships of technology and R&D strategies with the firm's internal climate, and the external forces of the environment. The substance of this framework is that technology and R&D strategies are built upon distinctive capabilities or core competences through a continuous organizational learning process within the corporation.

# A New Approach to Corporate and Technology Strategy

## 1.0 Introduction

There is no doubt that almost all firms have in recent years become more conscious of the critical role of technology in strategic decisions, and the necessity to integrate technology strategy into the strategic management process of corporations. In this context, technology has increasingly been perceived as a significant asset which plays an essential role in deciding the competitive position and the economic outcome of firms (Abernathy, Clark and Kantrow, 1983; Porter, 1980, 1983, 1985; Burgelman and Maidique, 1988). However, the technological behaviour of firms and their corporate strategies were often regarded as separate issues. It was only during the past decade that technology has been seen as both a main element for competition and, more specifically, as a vital resource that must be managed in a strategic manner (Kantrow, 1980; Abell, 1980; Maidique and Patch, 1982; Horwitch, 1986; Dodgson, 1989). For Porter (1983), technology is among the most important factors that determines the rules of competition. For Horwitch (1986), technology is a key part of modern strategic management.

Despite the increasing importance of technology as a critical resource in modern corporations, there is no technology strategy model which allows us to study and analyse the influence of technology inside the corporation in a coherent, integral, and comprehensive way. To put it differently, although firms are attempting to manage technology strategically, there is as yet no consensus on the essentials of a technology strategy framework. This paper argues that the conceptualization of technology strategy is still incomplete, mainly because the specialized literature relating to this topic has approached it up till now only in an oblique and partial manner.

The present paper develops a new model for discussing and analysing technology strategy. This is an integral and dynamic framework, whose general structure is presented in Figure 1 on page 3.

First of all, we have to explain what we mean by an 'integral and dynamic' framework. Because the words integral and integration are easy and ambiguous words, to us, integration is not merely the better linking of one thing with another, but also the way of looking at a whole system in order to analyse it in a broader perspective. In other words, our model is integral because it attempts to link the influences of the external forces with the internal climate of a firm, focusing upon the challenge of defining an appropriate technology strategy for a corporation. In this sense, our view of integration agrees with Whiston's notion (1991, p. 3) of organisational integration, when he asserts that there are three main clusters of integrative loops in a firm: internal linkages, external links which society imposes upon the firm (legislation, regulations, etc.) and external links which the firm directs towards society but feeds back into itself (R&D strategy, product portfolio, etc.). On the other hand, our model is dynamic because it is built upon a continuous assessment of changing environments, both external and internal. Therefore, the new framework proposed for technology strategy is not static in time or in context; it must adapt itself to the changing circumstances that surround its atmosphere.

At this stage, it is worth mentioning three principal ideas that underlie this new framework. The first is that technology and R&D strategies must be embedded in corporate strategy; in other words, technology strategy must be congruent and coherent with corporate objectives and direction. A second key idea is that the identification and development of distinctive capabilities is a device for developing an appropriate technology strategy. A third key idea is that only through the persistent practice of an organisational learning process can a firm achieve complete competitiveness.

In short, the concept depicted in Figure 1 is that technology strategy is based on developing distinctive capabilities through an organisational learning process. The overall system is shaped by both external forces in the environment and the internal climate of the firm. These factors together define the company's strategic behaviour in the short and the long-term. Each of these factors will be briefly addressed in the following sections.

## 1.1 Technology and R&D Strategies Embedded In Corporate Strategy

This article argues that the most successful firms, strategically, are those that are conscious of where they are and of what lies ahead, those that understand their environment and those that seek to attain and maintain competitive advantage over long periods of time. A firm has to be looking for ways of adapting to change in terms of marketing, technology, and also financial structure.

Taking into consideration the definitions of corporate strategy and technology strategy adopted in this paper, what follows is that technology (including R&D) strategy must be a key component of corporate strategy. In other words, the goals and direction of technology and R&D strategies must be consistent and congruent with the corporate direction and scope of the firm

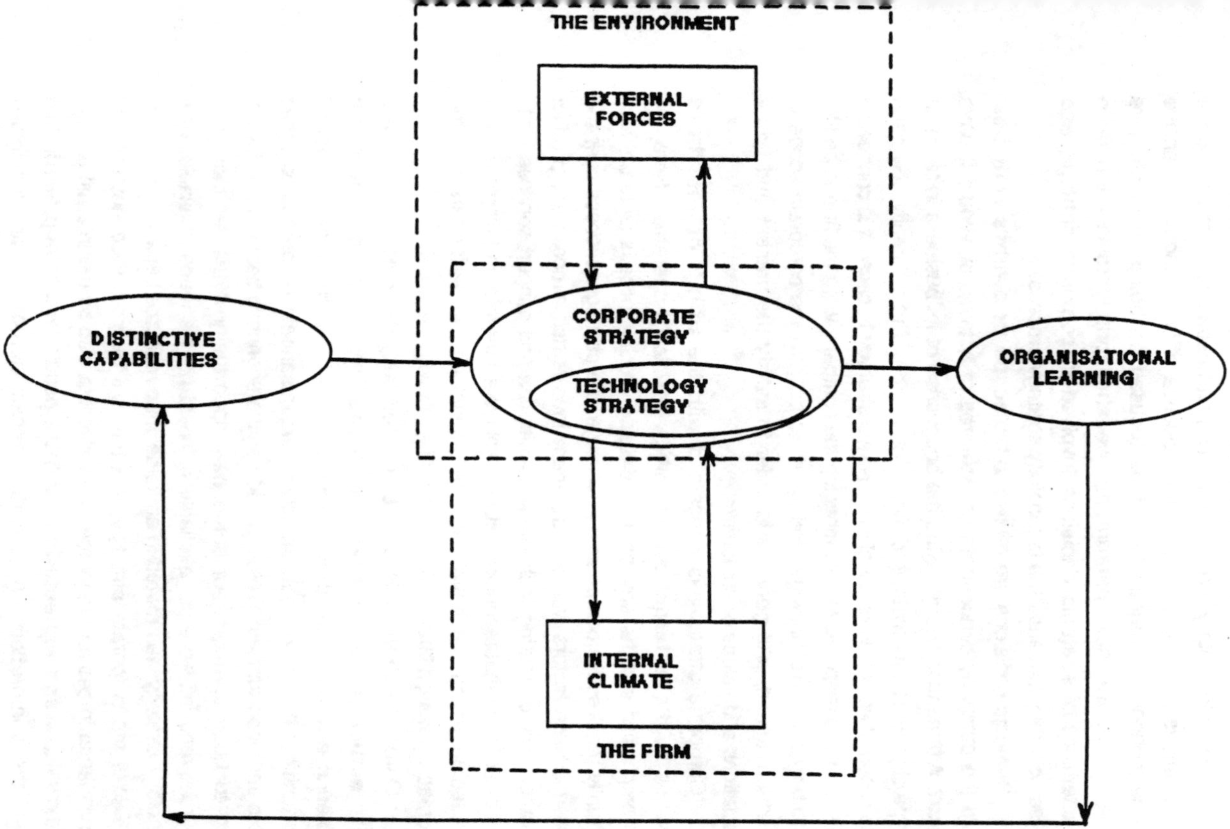

FIG. 5-1 INTEGRAL AND DYNAMIC FRAMEWORK FOR TECHNOLOGY STRATEGY

in the long run. We cannot conceive (viz approve of) a technology strategy that is not complementary with the firm's corporate strategy. For instance, if the company is pursuing the corporate objective of becoming a D-intensive firm, the technology strategy cannot be focused on being an R-intensive company. In the next paragraphs, we shall briefly review the main characteristics of strategic decisions involved in corporate strategy, and analyse how they influence the technology strategy process.

Strategic decisions are related to the **scope of a firm's activities**: should the company concentrate on one area of activity, or should it have several? A firm must clearly define the boundaries of its business in terms of the type of products, markets, and modes of service. Put differently, the issue of the scope of activity is cardinal to corporate strategy because it is connected with what those responsible for managing the company want the firm to be like and to be about. Technology strategy must support the corporate scope in products, markets, and services in order to satisfy the present and future expectations and values of customers.

Corporate strategy is concerned with the **fitting of the firm's activities to the external environment** in which it operates. Here, we must emphasize that the environment dictates crucial success factors that a firm really requires for competitive advantage and strategic success over the long-term. Such factors will vary, but many involve risk, process and product innovation, manufacturing technology, distribution and support services. It is within this context that technology strategy plays a key role, in being aware of those factors which can have a greater impact on the performance of the corporation (Twiss, 1992).

Corporate strategy is also concerned with the **matching of the firm's activities to its resource capability**. It is not only about countering environmental threats and taking advantage of environmental opportunities; it is also about matching organisational resources to these threats and opportunities. There would be little economic benefit for a firm in trying to take advantage of some new opportunity if the technological resources required were not available or could not be made available, or if technology strategy was rooted in an inadequate resource base.

Yet the corporate strategy of a firm will be perturbed not only by environmental forces and resource availability, but also by the internal climate - by the **values and expectations** of those people who have power in and around the corporation. In a certain sense, corporate and technology strategies can be thought of as a reflection of the attitudes and beliefs of those who have most influence on the firm (who are often not technologists).

Corporate strategic decisions are likely to modify the **long-term direction of a firm**. This is one of the main aspects of strategic management, or strategy itself, which is concerned with the establishment of a clear direction for the corporation and a means of getting there, and which needs the creation of strong competitive positions. In a way, this determines the long-term structure and activities of the firm. As we have already indicated, obviously, technology strategy must follow the direction defined by corporate strategy.

Our argument in this paper is consistent with what has been pointed out by other authors. For example, Porter (1983) stressed that:

"The starting point for a framework for analyzing technological strategies must be a broader concept of overall competitive strategy. Competitive strategy is an integrated set of policies in each functional activity of the firm that aims to create a sustainable competitive advantage. **Technological strategy is but one element of an overall competitive strategy**, and thus must be consistent with and reinforced by the actions of other functional departments" (Porter, 1983, in Burgelman and Maidique (eds.), p. 217 - emphasis added).

## 1.2 External Forces - The Environment

Several authors have defined strategy in terms of the relationship between a firm and its environment. Ansoff (1984) identifies strategy as: "The positioning and relating of the organization to its environment in a way which will assure its continued success and make it secure from surprises".

A firm exists in the context of a complex economic, political, commercial, technological, social and cultural world. This environment changes and is more complex for some companies than for others. Since strategy is concerned with the position a business takes in connection with its environment, an understanding of the environment's effects on a firm is of prime importance to corporate strategic analysis. The historical and environmental effects on a firm must be considered, as well as the present effects and the expected changes in environmental variables. This represents a paramount task because the range of environmental variables is so immense. Many of those variables will give rise to **opportunities** of some kind, and many exert **threats** upon the organisation (Johnson and Scholes, 1993; Twiss, 1992).

There are several external forces present in the environment that can influence the performance of a firm (Thompson, 1993). **Economic conditions** affect how easy or how difficult it is to be successful and profitable at any time because they upset both capital availability and cost, and also market demand.

But economic conditions are modified by **government policy**; equally, they are a significant influence on government decisions. There are diverse ways, however, that government decisions will modify firms both directly and indirectly as they provide both opportunities and threats.

Whilst economic conditions and government policy are closely related, they both affect a number of other environmental forces which can alter the circumstances of corporations. **Capital markets** determine the conditions for alternative types of funding for companies; they can be subject to government controls, and they will be guided by prevailing economic conditions.

The **labour market** reflects the availability of particular skills at national and regional levels; it is influenced by training, which in turn can be affected by government. Labour costs will be altered by inflation and by general trends in other industries, and also by the role and power of trade unions.

**Technology** in one sense can be part of both the firm and the industry, as it is used for the creation of competitive advantage. Nevertheless, technology external to the industry can also be captured and used, and this can again be affected by government support and encouragement. Technological breakthroughs can engender new industries which might prove a threat to existing corporations whose products or services might be rendered redundant, and those organisations which might be altered in this manner should be alert to such a possibility. Equally, new technology could provide a useful input, perhaps in production, but its purchase will in turn demand funding and possibly employee training before it can be utilized.

The **social and cultural forces** which encapsulate demand and tastes, both of which vary with fashion and disposable income, and general changes can again provide both opportunities and threats for particular organisations. Threats to existing products might be increasing due to demographic changes in the structure of population; also opportunities for differentiation and market segmentation might be appearing.

There are other powerful forces which may modify the strategic process in any firm in a significant way. For some manufacturing and service businesses, the strongest force will be **customers**; for others it may be **competition**. Under certain circumstances, **suppliers** can be critical.

Duncan (1972) argues that the environment is more uncertain the more complex or the more dynamic it is. Dynamism can be enhanced by a number of factors. Rapid technological change involving either products, processes or uses will mean that changes are probably likely to occur quickly and that corporations must stay aware of the activities of their suppliers and potential suppliers, along with their customers and competitors. An environment is complex where the forces and the changes involving them are difficult to understand. Quite often, complexity and dynamism occur together. Technology-based industries are an excellent example of this. With the growth and application of more and more sophisticated technology, there is an increasing move towards this condition of greatest uncertainty. The electronics industry, airlines and the computer industry are all in, or moving to, this dynamic and complex situation. A multinational firm may, as a corporate body, also be in a complex condition because of its diversity, while different operating companies within it face varying degrees of dynamism and complexity.

So far, the concern has been with broad aspects of the environment. However, for most firms, there is a set of external factors which are more immediate, and which they are possibly able to influence directly by their own actions. This is the immediate or competitive environment, and the concern here is with the factors which directly affect the capability of a firm to position itself more or less effectively against its rivals.

A firm is only one of a number of competitors in an industry; and to a greater or lesser degree these competitors will be affected by the decisions, competitive strategies and innovations of the others. These interdependences are critical and consequently strategic decisions should always include some assessment of their possible reaction. Equally a firm should seek to be fully conscious of what its competitors are doing at any one time.

Moreover, the industry to which a firm belongs will be tied to, and dependent on, other industries: businesses from which it buys supplies, and businesses to which it markets products and services. In essence, this is related to the 'five forces' model proposed by Porter (1980), which determines industry profitability.

The necessity of understanding the external forces of the environment is connected with a difficult problem, as we have shown in this section. In short, the importance of this lies in the fact that **the formulation of strategy is concerned with matching the firm's capabilities to its environment.**

### 1.3 Internal Climate - Resources and Values

For the aims of this paper, the term 'internal climate' is taken to mean the environment inside a firm, which involves not only the different kinds of **resources** available in the organisation, but also its **culture** and **values**. Just as there are external pressures on the firm and its choice of strategies, so there are internal influences.

The previous section has underlined the significance of matching the firm's strategy to the external environment within which the organisation is operating. However, any firm must pursue a strategy which it is capable of sustaining. Therefore this section is concerned with understanding a firm's strategic capability, and the ways in which the analysis of resources, plus a fuller comprehension of culture and values can contribute to this understanding.

One way of thinking about the strategic capability of a firm is to consider its **strengths** and **weaknesses**. These strengths and weaknesses may be identified by taking into account the resource areas of a business such as its physical plant, its R&D laboratory, its management, its financial structure, its marketing system and its products (Twiss, 1992).

Some authors (Wernerfelt, 1984; Collis, 1991) have observed that traditional methods of strategic analysis have overemphasized the external environment as the dominant factor in strategy formulation. They have argued that in many circumstances resource-based strategies would provide a better focus for strategy formulation. This requires a good understanding of the strategic capability of the firm, which in turn is supported in a profound resource analysis and an assessment of the distinctive capabilities or core competences which have been built up through the implementation of the company's old strategies, or which need to be developed to confront competition in future.

There are broad issues of capability which are appropriate to the firm as a whole. These are largely concerned with the overall balance of resources and the mix of activities. There are also assessments to be made of the quantity and quality of each principal resource area, such as machinery, processes, buildings and people. Nevertheless, a main argument of this paper is that the strategic capability of any firm is essentially determined by the separate activities which it undertakes in research, development, designing, manufacturing, marketing, delivering and supporting its products or services. It is an awareness of those activities with added value and the links between them which is vital when assessing strategic capability. These factors must usually be assessed relative to competitors.

However, the concern about a firm's resource profile is not only confined to strategic analysis. It should also be a crucial determinant during strategic choice, helping to identify directions which best match the firm's distinctive capabilities. In addition, the resources of a firm are not confined to those which it 'owns'. Strategic capability is substantially affected by resources outside the corporation which are an integral part of the chain of activities between the product or service design, through manufacturing and marketing to the use of the product or service by customers. This is closely linked with the value chain model developed by Porter (1985).

It has been stressed by Thompson (1993) that, if one wished to assert that a firm was being managed effectively from a strategic viewpoint, one would have to show, firstly, that its top managers appreciated fully the dynamics, opportunities and threats present in their competitive environment, and that they were paying due regard to wider societal issues; and, secondly, that the firm's resources were being managed strategically, considering its strengths and weaknesses, and that the firm was taking advantage of its opportunities. Key success factors and distinctive capabilities would be matched. **This will not just happen, it needs to be managed**. Furthermore, potential new opportunities need to be sought and resources developed. Still more, it is critical that the values of the corporation match the needs of the environment and the key success factors. After all, it is the values and culture which determine whether the environment and resources are currently matched, and whether they stay congruent with changing circumstances.

Pümpin (1987) proposes the term 'strategic excellence positions' (SEPs) to describe "capabilities which enable an organization to produce better-than-average results over the longer term compared with its competitors". In this sense, SEPs suggest that firms value the points of view of customers and develop the capabilities required to meet these needs. Furthermore, they are perceived by their customers to be a superior competitor because of their skills and accomplishments. Firms should seek to develop competitive advantage and achieve a strategic excellence position for each product and service. In this context, the overall congruence between the environment and its resources and values then depends upon these SEPs together with any corporate benefits derived from linkages and interrelationships.

None the less, the identification and development of SEPs and the overall congruence between the environment, resources and values take time to be developed, and require that all the functional areas within the firm recognize which factors are most important to customers. Once it has been achieved, it cannot be assumed that success in the long run is guaranteed. Situations change, and in this way, new opportunities emerge (Abell, 1978).

The culture, values and norms of behaviour influence the formulation, implementation, and execution of corporate and technology strategies, as well as the management of change in the corporation. The established culture, which is normally slow and difficult to change, is very significant in strategic decision-making that involves critical changes of direction. The established culture also assists in determining the freedom and the willingness or reluctance of managers to make changes as they detect opportunities and threats.

We emphasize that corporate and technology strategies in a firm can only be analysed in an effective manner, and understood, if top management appreciates the basic culture and values that affect the main strategic elements of the process. Corporate and technology strategies cannot be implemented successfully without due consideration to culture.

Altogether, a concern with the environment, the resources, the values, the expectations and the objectives within the cultural and political framework of the firm supplies the basis for the corporate and technology strategic analysis of an organisation.

## 1.4 Distinctive Capabilities

Capabilities are regarded distinctive if they differentiate a firm strategically. The notion is not new. Some authors have named them core or organisational competences (Prahalad and Hamel, 1990; Hayes, Wheelwright and Clark, 1988), others have used such terms as firm-specific competences (Pavitt, 1991), resource deployments (Hofer and Schendel, 1978) and invisible assets (Itami and Roehl, 1987).

The strategic importance of capabilities has been debated for decades, stimulated by such research as Rumelt's (1974) discovery that, of nine diversification strategies, the two that were built on an existing skill or resource base in the organisation were associated with the highest performance. Later on, Mitchell's (1989) observation that industry-specific capabilities expanded the probability a company could exploit a new technology within that industry, has confirmed the early work. More recently, Patel and Pavitt (1994) have claimed that "firm-specific technological competencies are major factors explaining why firms are different, how they change over time, and whether or not they are capable of remaining competitive". In this context, at any given point in a firm's history, distinctive capabilities are evolving, and corporate survival depends upon managing that evolution in a successful manner.

Many authors often assume that descriptors of distinctive capabilities such as 'core', 'unique', difficult to imitate', or 'superior to competition' render the term self-explanatory, especially if reference is also made to 'resource deployment' or 'skills'. Only a few authors involve activities such as 'collective learning' and explain how competence is and is not cultivated (Prahalad and Hamel, 1990). Perhaps one of the clearest definitions of distinctive capabilities or core competences is that provided by Teece et al. (1990, p.28): "A core competence is a set of differentiated skills, complementary assets, and routines that provide the basis for a firm's competitive capacities and sustainable advantage in a particular business". Teece et al. (1990) go on to emphasize that the competitive advantage of a particular firm is a function of its underlying core competences, and its relationship with customers and suppliers.

Leonard-Barton (1992) adopts a knowledge-based perspective of the firm and defines a core or distinctive capability as the knowledge set that distinguishes and provides a competitive advantage. For her, there are four dimensions to this knowledge set. Its content is embodied in (1) employee knowledge and skills embedded in (2) technical systems. The processes of knowledge creation and control are guided by (3) managerial systems. The fourth dimension includes (4) the values and norms associated with the various types of embodied and embedded knowledge, and with the processes of knowledge creation and control.

When researchers in the strategy-field talk of distinctive capabilities they almost immediately turn to the question of how to build them. For example, as Prahalad and Hamel (1990, p. 81) stressed: "In the long run, competitiveness derives from an ability to build, at lower cost and more speedily than competitors, the core competencies that spawn unanticipated products". This is evidently significant, and most distinctive capabilities have, in some sense or another, been developed by the corporations which hold them nowadays. However, the attempt to establish distinctive capabilities confronts its own version of wish-driven strategy. The fact of building distinctive capabilities must be a task of unusual difficulty because, if it were not, the capability would soon cease to be distinctive. This assumption is confirmed by Miyazaki (1993, p. 296), who in studying the dynamics of competence building in European and Japanese firms in the optoelectronics industry, concludes that "competence building is a painstaking and long process, entailing uncertainty and trial and error, and it requires continuous learning".

Therefore the emphasis in our model will be more on the definition and identification of distinctive capabilities than on their formation. Although we recognize that it is possible to generate distinctive capabilities, successful corporations are more often based on exploiting those capabilities which they already possess. These capabilities may emerge from their history, or from their technological trajectories or from their geographic location, or they may be capabilities that the firms have already established in related markets or industries. **Corporate and technology strategies start with an understanding of what these distinctive capabilities are.**

For Prahalad and Hamel (1990, pp. 83-84), there are at least three criteria that can be applied to identify distinctive capabilities or core competences in a firm: (1) a core competence must provide potential access to a broad variety of markets; (2) a core competence should make an important contribution to the perceived customer benefits of the final product; and (3) a core competence should be difficult for competitors to imitate.

A capability can only be distinctive if it has originated from a characteristic which other companies lack. However, it is not enough for that characteristic to be distinctive. It is also essential for it to be sustainable and appropriable. A distinctive capability is sustainable only if it is persistent over long periods of time. A distinctive capability is appropriable only if it exclusively, or mainly, benefits the firm which possesses it. Frequently the benefits of a distinctive capability are appropriated instead by employees, by customers, or by competitors. Under these circumstances, there are relatively few kinds of distinctive capability which satisfy these conditions of sustainability and appropriability (Kay, 1993).

For Kay (1993), there are three distinctive capabilities which recur in any analysis of the performance of successful firms: innovation, architecture, and reputation. Innovation is an obvious source of distinctive capability, but it is less often a sustainable or appropriable source because successful innovation almost immediately attracts imitation. Architecture is a system of relationships within the corporation, or between the corporation and its suppliers and customers, or both. Reputation is, in a certain sense, a kind of architecture but it is so widespread, and so prominent that it is best to consider it as a distinct source of competitive advantage. Easier to maintain than to create, reputation meets the imperative conditions for sustainability. Kay (1993) emphasizes that a distinctive capability becomes a competitive advantage when it is applied in an industry and brought to a market.

In addition, for the purposes of our model, we need to take into account the technological distinctive capabilities that a technology strategy must identify and develop. A technological distinctive capability can be defined as the change-creating technical capacity in a corporation. To put it differently, it is a bundle of skills assisting the firm to react to technological opportunities, to assimilate them into its core capabilities, by combining a stream of technologies and diverse functional specialism, and by profiting from synergies across divisions of the organisation (Miyazaki, 1993).

In a few words, the importance of distinctive capabilities lies in the fact that they must be an essential element of corporate and technology strategies. **Relevant strategy must not be a proclamation of corporate aspirations, but it must be based on the distinctive capabilities of the individual organisation.**

## 1.5 Organisational Learning

The heterogeneous notion of learning has been present in the industrial organisational literature for a long time. For instance, in Cyert and March's (1963) view of the firm, learning is a key feature; they state that "a theory of a long-term behaviour in organisations must contain a theory of how organisations learn, unlearn, and re-learn".

It has also been acknowledged that there exists a strong 'learning curve' associated with production activity. Arrow (1962) characterized the learning that comes from developing increasing skill in manufacturing as 'learning by doing', which results in the reduction of real labour costs per unit of production. Since the 1970s, the Boston Consulting Group and others have subsequently elaborated the concept of improvement by 'learning by experience' in ways that embody improvements in production processes, management systems, distribution, sales, advertising, worker training and motivation. Rosenberg (1982), based on his study of the aircraft industry, has introduced a different kind of learning process, 'learning by using', distinguishing between learning that is 'internal' and learning that is 'external' to the production process.

Maidique and Zirger (1985), in an extensive study concerned with the success and failure of new products in the electronics industry, found another type of external learning: 'learning by failure', which resulted in the development of new market approaches, new product concepts, and new technological alternatives based on the failure of one or more earlier attempts. They also considered that 'learning by failure' has another dimension which concerns organisational development. Here, a failure serves to identify weak links in the organisation and to inoculate strong parts of the firm against the same failure pattern.

In a stimulating paper, Pavitt (1991) claims that 'corporations are purposive organisations' and that three main features emerge from the analysis of the firm-specific learning process in large firms: first, sources of learning are very diverse, and their relative importance will vary according to the nature of the core competences of the firm; second, learning is a collective activity requiring frequent communication amongst specialists and functions; and third, R&D laboratories and other technical functions in the firm are necessary and centrally important components in nearly all the dimensions of learning (Pavitt, pp. 46-47).

Pavitt's (1991) viewpoint is shared by Teece *et al.* (1992), who state that learning has several fundamental characteristics: (1) learning involves organisational as well as individual skills; (2) learning processes are intrinsically social and collective phenomena; and (3) learning requires common codes of communication and coordinated search procedures.

In a fresh and different outlook of the learning organisation, Whiston (1995, p. 3) stresses that "learning (and skills) are intimately concerned with **Information flow**, decision procedures...Learning is dependent upon sensing, encoding and organising a flow of **Incoming** information, perceiving patterns, and decoding upon appropriate responses, actions, judgements; which is in essence **outflowing** information" (original emphasis).

In their book, *An Evolutionary Theory of Economic Change*, Nelson and Winter (1982) proposed that firms which work effectively can be understood in terms of practised organisational routines, which define lower-order organisational skills, and how these are coordinated, and higher-order decision procedures for choosing what is to be done at lower levels. The conceptualization of a hierarchy of organisational routines is the fundamental building block under Nelson and Winter's notion of core organisational capabilities. According to Pavitt (1991), 'routines' embody 'firm-specific competences', and their adaptation and change in the light of experience and further information is 'learning'.

Hayes, Wheelwright and Clark (1988, pp. 24-25) emphasized that:
"World class...companies dislike being dependent on outside organizations for expertise. They want to grow their own people, equipment, and systems, but also they respect the capabilities of others...They place great emphasis on R&D, experimentation, training, and the building of general organizational capabilities. They continually push at the margins of their expertise, trying on every front to be a bit better than before. Standards, to them, are

ephemeral-milestones on the road to perfection, **They strive to be dynamic, learning companies**" (emphasis added).

The technological literature has been inclined to focus on learning in manufacturing and post-manufacturing, rather than on R&D, and has rather narrowly concentrated on the learning that emerges as a 'natural' result of accumulated experience, as was recognized by Dodgson (1991). However, Rosenberg (1982) not only addressed 'learning by using' and 'learning by doing', but he also described 'learning in R&D' as a learning process in the generation of new technologies.

Dodgson (1991) has distinguished between two kinds of search activities or learning processes: tactical and strategic. For him, tactical learning has an immediate problem-solving nature, whilst strategic learning goes beyond immediate issues and involves firms developing skills and competences which provide the basis for future projects.

We agree with Dodgson's (1991) conception of technological learning as an integration of three broad types of learning: search, accumulation and diffusion, and review. Search encompasses seeking knowledge; search activities may be strategic or tactical. Accumulation of know-how again has both strategic and tactical elements. Learning about a tactical problem should be accumulated and diffused within the firm so as to anticipate repetition of search activities. Learning about strategic issues should be accumulated and diffused to inform future strategic plans and departures in different parts of the firm. A significant feature of learning is to review what the firm knows. Furthermore, an attribute of review learning is learning from failures or mistakes (Dodgson, pp. 112-113).

So far we have analysed several points of view about the concept of 'organisational learning' which have been developed in a partial and incomplete manner. However, for the principal aims of our framework for studying technology strategy, where organisational learning is a vital element of this model, we need to consider a more holistic or integral approach on what a 'learning organisation' must mean. In this context, we adopt Garvin's (1993, p. 80) definition:

> "A learning organization is **an organization skilled at creating, acquiring, and transferring knowledge, and at modifying its behavior** to reflect new knowledge and insights" (emphasis added).

We also concur with Garvin's (1993) opinion that learning organisations must be skilled at five main activities: systematic problem-solving, experimentation with new approaches, learning from their own experience and past history, learning from the experiences and best practices of others, and transferring knowledge quickly and efficiently throughout the organisation.

We can add that a learning organisation is not built from one day to another, it implies a firm's commitment to systematic effort over long periods of time. Moreover, it requires that the firm's environment is conducive to learning. **Organisational learning is a meaningful process, on which distinctive capabilities are developed and nurtured.** In this way, organisational learning becomes a cardinal issue for firms seeking to achieve and sustain a competitive advantage.

## 1.6 Conclusions

We have proposed an **integral and dynamic framework for analysing and studying technology strategy.** It is integral because it considers both external and internal forces to the firm, taking them account in a broader perspective. It is dynamic because it is not static in time or context. Corporate and technology strategies have life cycles, and strategies which prove to be effective today, will not always remain so tomorrow.

**Our model is built upon five main elements:** firstly, technology strategy embedded in corporate strategy; secondly, the external forces of the environment; thirdly, the internal climate of the organisation; fourthly, the identification, accumulation and development of distinctive capabilities; and fifthly, the organisational learning process which supports the system by encouraging the formation of distinctive capabilities.

We have emphasized that **in our new framework:** first, technology strategy must be a vital component of corporate strategy, following its objectives and direction through long periods of time; second, the external forces of the environment influence the corporate and technology strategies, which are precisely concerned with matching the firm's capabilities to its environment; third, not only the environment, but also the values, expectations and objectives within the cultural and political climate of the organisation provide the basis for the analysis of corporate and technology strategies; fourth, meaningful corporate and technology strategies must be based on the firm's distinctive capabilities; and fifth, organisational learning is a significant process to identify and develop distinctive capabilities.

# REFERENCES

Abell, D.F. (1978), 'Strategic Windows', *Journal of Marketing*, vol. 42, July.

Abell, D.F. (1980), *Defining the Business*, Prentice-Hall, Englewood Cliffs, NJ.

Abernathy, W.J., Clark, K.B. and Kantrow, M.A. (1983), *Industrial Renaissance. Producing a Competitive Future for America*, Basic Books, New York.

Ansoff, H.I. (1984), *Implanting Strategic Management*, Prentice-Hall Int., Englewood Cliffs, NJ.

Arrow, K. (1962), 'The Economic Implications of Learning by Doing', *Review of Economic Studies*, June.

Burgelman,R.A. and Maidique, M.A. (1988), *Strategic Management of Technology and Innovation*, Irwin, Homewood, Ill.

Collis, D.J. (1991), 'A Resource-Based Analysis of Global Competition', *Strategic Management Journal*, vol. 12, Summer, pp. 49-68.

Cyert, R.M.and March, J.G. (1963), *A Behavioural Theory of the Firm*, Prentice-Hall, New York.

Dodgson, M. (1989), *Technology Strategy and the Firm: Management and Public Policy*, Longman, Harlow, Essex.

Dodgson, M. (1991), *The Management of Technological Learning*, De Gruyter, Berlin.

Duncan, R. (1972), 'Characteristics of Organizational Environments and Perceived Environmental Uncertainty', *Administrative Science Quarterly*, pp. 313-327.

Garvin, D.A. (1993), 'Building the Learning Organization', *Harvard Business Review*, July-August, pp. 78-91.

Hayes, R.H., Wheelwright, S.C. and Clark, K.B. (1988), *Dynamic Manufacturing: Creating the Learning Organization*, The Free Press, New York.

Hofer, C.W. and Schendel, D. (1978), *Strategy Formulation: Analytical Concepts*, West Publishing Co., St. Paul, Minnesota.

Horwitch, M. (ed.) (1986), *Technology in the Modern Corporation*, Pergamon Press, New York.

Itami, H. and Roel, T. (1987), *Mobilizing Invisible Assets*, Harvard University Press, Cambridge, MA.

Johnson,G. and Scholes, K. (1993), *Exploring Corporate Strategy*, Prentice-Hall, Cambridge.

Kantrow, A.M. (1980), 'The Strategy Technology Connection', *Harvard Business Review*, July-August, pp. 6-21.

Kay, J. (1993), *Foundations of Corporate Success*, Oxford University Press, New York.

Leonard-Barton, D. (1992), 'Core Capabilities and Core Rigidities: A Paradox in Managing New Product Development', *Strategic Management Journal*, vol. 13, pp. 111-125.

Maidique, M.A. and Patch, P. (1982), 'Corporate Strategy and Technological Policy', in M.L. Tushman and W.L. Moore (eds.), *Readings in the Management of Innovation*, Pitman, Boston, MA, pp. 273-285.

Maidique, M.A. and Zirger, B.J. (1985), 'The New Product Learning Cycle', *Research Policy*, vol. 14, no. 6, pp. 299-313.

Mitchell, W. (1989), 'Whether and When? Probability and Timing of Incumbents', *Administrative Science Quarterly*, vol. 34, pp. 208-230.

Miyazaki, K. (1993), *The Dynamics of Competence Building in European and Japanese Firms: The Case of Optoelectronics*, D Phil. Thesis, SPRU, University of Sussex.

Nelson, R. and Winter, S. (1982), *An Evolutionary Theory of Economic Change*, Belknap-Harvard, Cambridge, MA.

Patel, P. and Pavitt, K. (1994), *Technological Competencies in the World's Largest Firms: Characteristics, Constraints and Scope for Managerial Choice*, STEEP Discussion Paper No. 13, SPRU, University of Sussex.

Pavitt, K. (1991), 'Key Characteristics of the Large Innovating Firm', *British Journal of Management*, vol. 2, pp. 41-50.

Porter, M.E. (1980), *Competitive Strategy*, The Free Press, London.

Porter, M.E. (1983), 'The Technological Dimension of Competitive Strategy', *Research on Technological Innovation, Management and Policy*, vol. 1, JAI Press, London.

Porter, M.E. (1985), *Competitive Advantage*, The Free Press, London.

Prahalad, C.K. and Hamel, G. (1990), 'The Core Competence of the Corporation', *Harvard Business Review*, May-June, pp. 79-91.

Pümpin, C. (1987), *The Essence of Corporate Strategy*, Gower.

Rosenberg, N. (1982), *Inside the Black Box, Technology and Economics*, Cambridge University Press, Cambridge.

Rumelt, R.P. (1974), *Strategy, Structure and Economic Performance*, Harvard Business School Press, Boston, MA.

Teece, D.J., Pisano,G. and Shuen,A. (1990), *Firm Capabilities, Resources, and the Concept of Strategy*, CCC Working Paper No. 90-8, University of California at Berkeley.

Teece, D.J., Rumelt, R., Dosi, G, and Winter, S. (1992), *Understanding Corporate Coherence: Theory and Evidence*, CCC Working Paper, Center for Research in Management, University of California at Berkeley.

Thompson, J.L. (1993), *Strategic Management - Awareness and Change*, Chapman & Hall, London.

Twiss, B. (1992), *Managing Technological Innovation*, Pitman Publishing, London.

Wernerfelt, B. (1984), 'A Resource-Based View of the Firm', *Strategic Management Journal*, vol. 5, pp. 171-180.

Whiston, T.G. (1991), *Managerial and Organisational Integration*, Springer-Verlag, Germany.

Whiston, T.G. (1995), 'The Learning Organisation', Chapter 17 in G. Gaynor (ed.), *McGraw Hill Handbook of Technology Management*, (forthcoming).

# 024

# COVER SHEET

Author:
George P. Lewett,
Director, Office of Technology Innovation

U. S. Department of Commerce
National Institute of Standards and Technology
820 West Diamond Avenue, Room 264
Gaithersburg, MD 20878-0001
Phone: (301) 975-5504
Fax: (301) 975-3839
E-mail: George.Lewett@nist.gov

Title:
TECHNOLOGY EVALUATION
A Key Element In Technology Transfer And Commercialization

Keywords:
Technology Transfer; Commercialization, Technology Evaluation,
Technology Innovation

Topic: H
Category: 2

Suitable for either Oral or Poster Presentation

# TECHNOLOGY EVALUATION
## A Key Element In Technology Transfer And Commercialization

## Introduction

In 1975 the National Institute of Standards and Technology (NIST) established a technology evaluation service designed to pay particular attention to the needs of individual inventors and small companies. The service was established in response to a directive in legislation which addressed the energy crisis of 1973, therefore it was limited to evaluating "energy-related" inventions. In 1977 a seed capital fund and other provisions were put in place by the Department of Energy (DOE) to support development of inventions recommended by the NIST evaluation service. It had become clear that the evaluation process in place would generate a continuous flow of worthwhile innovations from the diverse population it served.

In 1980 the Oak Ridge National Laboratory (ORNL) initiated a continuing project to measure the impact of the joint NIST-DOE evaluation-support program by surveying and tracking the recommended and supported technologies. The results, together with comprehensive performance statistics from the evaluation process, document operation of a system which should be of considerable interest to those involved in technology-based economic development.

The joint NIST-DOE effort is known as the Energy-Related Inventions Program (ERIP). The intent of this paper is not, however, to provide details of its operation or its successes. Rather, we wish to point out characteristics of its operation and aspects of its experience, which may be of interest to those engaged in other programs aimed at technology-based economic development. First, however, we need to describe ERIP operation.

## The ERIP Evaluation-Support System

The evaluation process was designed to meet the needs of individuals and small businesses unfamiliar not only with government procurement but also with technical proposal presentation. There are no formal procurement periods or rigid application requirements. An evaluation request can be submitted at any time; the evaluation system operates continuously. Subject area is limited only by the requirement that commercialization of the invention should have a significant direct or indirect impact on energy use or supply. Proposal preparation can be informal, and individual or company credentials need not be a part.

An evaluation request is first reviewed to determine acceptability for evaluation; about 50 percent of all submissions are rejected, not accepted, largely because of poor or inadequate presentation. After a submission is accepted, evaluation addresses technical and commercial feasibility, as well as energy impact. A first stage evaluation serves as a technical screening to surface "promising" inventions, rejecting 90 percent of those accepted, most often due to lack of technical or commercial advantage over competition. A second-stage evaluation addresses the "promising" invention in depth; about one-half of these are recommended to DOE for support.

Since 1975, NIST has processed over 33,000 evaluation requests, accepting and evaluating about 16,000, and recommending over 700 to DOE for support. In current operation, an average of 2-3 recommendations are forwarded to DOE each month.

Each formal NIST report to DOE justifies the recommendation in terms of technical feasibility, commercial potential, and energy conservation or supply potential. The report also provides a benchmark as to where the invention stands in the product development process and indicates the nature of remaining development required. A copy of the formal bound report is furnished to the individual inventor or company, and quite frequently serves as a valuable means for obtaining private sector support; in effect the recommendation from NIST establishes credibility.

The NIST evaluation addresses commercial feasibility only to the extent of determining whether the invention is likely to have an "edge" over its competition, either technically or economically. As an aid to planning, DOE has found more definitive market studies to be of significant value. Therefore on receipt of a recommendation, DOE contracts for a detailed market study, which is then provided to the recommendee as input to commercialization planning.

Inventors and small companies recommended by NIST are considered as potential grant applicants who probably lack experience in "grantsmanship" and in product development. Therefore, initial DOE contact is aimed at assisting the recommendee to plan and document development/commercialization requirements further. A key feature in this process is participation in a standardized 4-day Commercialization Planning Workshop (CPW).

The DOE sponsors 3-4 CPWs each year, providing for the attendance of 10-12 recommendees at each, all expenses covered. A "faculty" of 6 - 8 is assembled, practitioners or experts in such topics as licensing, new product development, finance, marketing, and entrepreneurship. With much one-on-one interaction with the faculty, the recommendees are encouraged and guided in development of a plan encompassing both technical and business development. The plan then is utilized as the basis for a grant application; grants average $80K - $100K. In addition to the market study, the CPW educational experience, and the grant, DOE also provides networking and brokering services, all aimed at maximizing the probability of successful commercialization

Metrics on ERIP are extensive. Since inception NIST has maintained computerized records and manual files that track every submission. Inventions are submitted principally by individuals and companies of less than 20 employees, although company size ranges up to 500 employees; universities also make use of the program. The inventions are very diverse in subject area, level of technology, and stage of development.

The ORNL staff and their private sector consultants have documented the progress of most of the recommended and supported cases, and have generated a series of reports and research papers (see References). The findings to date show that about 25 percent of the cases have been successfully commercialized, generating significant energy and economic benefits.

## A Model for Use in Technology-based Economic Development

Conversion of technology into new, marketable products is a key element in the formation of many small firms and is an essential activity if firms are to grow and maintain competitiveness. In the conversion process, evaluation and support are common functions which are performed in any case of product development. There is always an evaluation and an investment of time, money, and other resources as determined by the results of the evaluation.

Large companies routinely organize and formalize the process by which they develop new products. However, small companies need to access external means of evaluation and support. ERIP experience provides a basis for designing a system to provide and facilitate such access in the interests of community economic development.

The most significant finding from ERIP experience, relative to technology-based economic development, is that the number (proportion) of successes (companies formed, products launched, etc) is predictable as the outcome of the continuous process pictured in Figure 1 below.

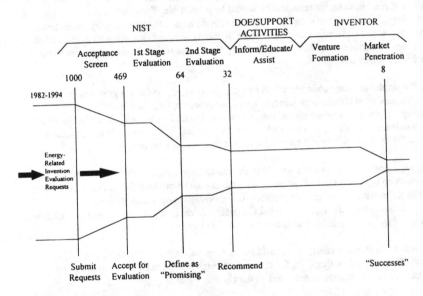

Figure 1. ERIP As A Model Of The Innovation Process (Results per 1000 evaluation requests)

Several conditions are important in process definition for prediction at the level shown in figure 1:

(1) Input should be random in time, depending only on the inventor's arrival at a point in the developmental process when external participation is necessary in his/her opinion. In ERIP, there are no solicitation periods or other stimuli to participate at a particular time.

Evaluation should be provided as a public service, available for use at the time needed by a person or company. This also implies that technical scope should be as wide as possible. One major benefit of this to a sponsoring government agency is that the resulting development is truly driven by industry or the market. In conventional technology development or commercialization programs, specification of proposal requirements and the timing of requests for proposals may result in developments which do not meet market needs.

(2) Evaluation and recommendation should be based on intrinsic merit, and not affected by overall input quality in the particular period. Intrinsic merit is determined by comparison with what the new item will replace or compete with, given that the item is technically feasible. Recommendation should be based on the extent to which the evaluated invention, or new product concept, promises to be better technically or economically. The decision to invest needs to be separate from the decision to recommend. The evaluation is solely intended to provide a basis for an investment decision. Relative merit is addressed by the investor whether comparing with other recommendations or with what is already in the marketplace.

(3) Evaluation results should be fed back to the inventor with as much detail as possible. Rebuttal and resubmission for reevaluation should be permissible, if not encouraged. The intent is to enable improvement of the invention and/or to provide a basis for a decision by the inventor whether to abandon or to continue development. It should be noted that some 20 percent of all ERIP recommendations were initially rejected, improved, and resubmitted one or more times before final recommendation.

Again, the emphasis is on public service and on the objective of providing a practical means to make full use of what should be considered a national resource, i.e., the creativity and entrepreneurial drive of a select part of the general population. Providing for qualified feedback and reevaluation is, in effect, a form of education and training for those who have some basic capability for activities which can have great impact on a nation's economy.

(4) Input volume needs to be at a level high enough to ensure significant output numbers. In a process with an expected yield of 2-4 percent , input should be on the order of 800-1,000. Lower input is likely to result in undesirable pressure on the evaluation operation to "find" recommendable items. Low input also results in inefficiencies since minimum evaluation staff size is determined by technical subject area scope rather than volume.

In taking steps to increase input, care should be taken to maintain or increase input quality. Outreach efforts should be designed, for example, to reach new patentees, researchers, and engineering firms that engage in new product development efforts.

(5) The support process needs to be multi-faceted. That is, financial assistance alone is not sufficient. Support by DOE in the ERIP emphasizes the need to inform and educate the individual inventor/entrepreneur or small company principal. The basic information provided in the NIST recommendation report (technical problem areas, developmental status, etc.) is only a beginning point.

Considerable attention needs to be paid to the qualifications of the individuals involved. While the evaluation focuses on the technology, the support process must address the "people" problems. The Commercialization Planning Workshops, described earlier, provide for this through the one-on-one interviews between "faculty" member and recommendee which yield a recommended commercialization strategy geared to the individual case.

## The Evaluator as a Decision-Maker

The typical workload of inventions evaluated under ERIP is diverse in terms of subject area and technical level of sophistication. Use of consultant experts was seen to be essential from the beginning. However, it quickly became clear that decisions could not be made solely on the basis of the consultant opinions. In spite of careful consultant selections their opinions were not always sufficient for decision, did not always agree, and at times had technical deficiencies.

The ERIP findings were consistent with other studies of peer review systems, which indicate the need for interpretation and integration of reviews by a decision-maker. The evaluation concept which developed therefore emphasized a distinction between the evaluator (staff) and the reviewer (consultant). The active NIST consultant network now comprises over 400 experts who are paid for their services in accordance with their standard fees.

The staff evaluator utilizes the consultant network as a primary source of information on the characteristics and potential of the inventions he evaluates. However, the evaluator is not required to justify or even base his conclusions on the consultant input. His responsibility as decision-maker is absolute, recognizing that the information gathered is always limited, uncertainty is always present, and the judgement of a competent trained engineer is best suited to the decision function. The staff evaluator acts as a well-informed "gatekeeper," to pass or not pass an invention on to the next stage of evaluation, solely on the basis of his/her judgement.

Consultants are instructed to be liberal in their reviews, i.e., to emphasize the positive , particularly in first stage evaluation. Of course, factual deficiencies are to be identified, but generally the idea is to minimize the probability of "missing the good invention." The reviews are unstructured, with no scoring or numerical rating, although the consultant is asked to make an overall statement on merit. While consultant identities are kept confidential, consultant comments are passed back to the inventor at the discretion of the evaluator.

Figure 2 summarizes consultant statements on invention merit versus staff evaluator decisions. In first-stage evaluation each consultant is requested to comment and make a recommendation for "Support" or "No Support" of the invention. It should be noted that opinions on a given invention are solicited independently from one or more consultants until the staff evaluator feels that he has sufficient information to make a decision to pass the information into second-stage evaluation or not. The tabulation shows that decision may require as many as 4 consultant reviews.

In Figure 2a consultant recommendations are tabulated for those inventions in first-stage evaluation which were eventually recommended to DOE for support. The number 139 under column 1 and in row 1 indicates that in 139 cases, 1 consultant recommended "Support" and another "No Support." The number 49 under column 2 and in row 1 indicates that in 20 cases, 2 consultants recommended "Support" and 1 consultant recommended "No Support."

From Figure 2a it is seen that, while agreement among or between consultants is frequent, disagreement is also frequent. They were unanimous for Support in about half the cases (51.8 percent), and unanimous against 13.4 percent of the time. The latter figure (13.4 percent) is of particular interest. It means that 13.4 percent of the recommendations were made solely on the basis of staff evaluator judgement, i.e., if the process were governed by consultants, 86 recommendations would not have been made.

In Figure 2b the consultant opinions for inventions which were turned down in first-stage evaluation are tabulated. Again, frequent disagreement is also clear. Here, however, unanimity occurred 83.6 percent of the time with respect to Non-Support, and 1.5 percent of the time with respect to Support.

Generally, it seems that consultants find it easier to say "No--(don't support)" than "Yes," based largely on the unanimity differences in Figures 2a and 2b. However, the principal point of interest is the significance of the staff evaluator's role as decision-maker. Clearly, if decisions were made by vote or other means, a great many recommendations would probably not have been made to DOE, and a significant number of those turned down by the staff evaluator would have been recommended.

It was noted earlier that about 25 percent of NIST-recommended inventions are expected to be "successes." Figure 2c provides the data for recommendations found to be successes by ORNL after DOE support. The first-stage consultant opinions on these recommendations, although the number of cases is small, seem to show basically the same pattern as depicted in Figure 2a. Of particular interest is the marginal total showing consultants to be unanimously negative in 17.0 percent of the cases. The conclusion is that "good" inventions are not always recognized.

That use of a "gatekeeper," i.e., one informed decision-maker, makes such a difference is not too surprising. We anticipated this somewhat by ruling early against committee-type decision-making.

Technology Diffusion

The originating legislation mentioned in the introduction, the Energy Research and Development Act of 1974 was enacted for the purpose of developing new energy technologies. Major programs were initiated, targeting development in such topical areas as solar energy, combustion engines, and industrial processes. Such technology development is typically carried out by professional engineers and scientists with appropriate educational and experimental backgrounds. The results of their efforts are applied in new products and processes which in most cases were visualized as end objectives of the targeted R&D, i.e., as first applications of the developed technology. Further product development, however, is generally not carried out by the same engineers and scientists who developed the basic technology.

A principal stimulus to Congress in directing the NIST technology evaluation service was the input of suggestions from the general technical public on new applications of existing technologies. This population included people in a wide variety of occupations, with diverse educational backgrounds and experience, frequently lacking the technical and business credentials which would inspire confidence in their technology development and commercialization capabilities. The subject areas, technical sophistication, and stages of development of their

Number of Consultants Who Said Support in Each Case

| Number of Consultants Who Said "No Support" In Each Case | | 0 | 1 | 2 | 3 | Inventions | Percentage |
|---|---|---|---|---|---|---|---|
| Number of | 0 | - * | 139 | 182 | 13 | 334 | 51.8 |
| Consultants | 1 | 31 | 139 | 49 | 2 | 221 | 34.3 |
| Who Said | 2 | 49 | 26 | 3 | | 78 | 12.1 |
| "No Support" | 3 | 5 | 5 | | | 10 | 1.6 |
| In Each Case | 4 | 1 | | | | 1 | 0.2 |
| Total Inventions | | 86 | 309 | 234 | 15 | 644 | |
| Percentage | | 13.4 | 48.0 | 36.3 | 2.3 | | 100.0 |

(a) All Inventions Recommended

Number of Consultants Who Said Support in Each Case

| Number of Consultants Who Said "No Support" In Each Case | | 0 | 1 | 2 | 3 | Inventions | Percentage |
|---|---|---|---|---|---|---|---|
| Number of | 0 | - * | 159 | 163 | 10 | 332 | 2.3 |
| Consultants | 1 | 3340 | 1625 | 112 | 3 | 5080 | 36.7 |
| Who Said | 2 | 7262 | 470 | 24 | | 7756 | 56.0 |
| "No Support" | 3 | 578 | 55 | | | 633 | 4.6 |
| In Each Case | 4 | 50 | | | | 50 | 0.4 |
| Total Inventions | | 11230 | 2309 | 299 | 13 | 13851 | |
| Percentage | | 81.1 | 16.6 | 2.2 | 0.1 | | 100.0 |

(b) Inventions Rejected After 1st Stage

Number of Consultants Who Said Support in Each Case

| Number of Consultants Who Said "No Support" In Each Case | | 0 | 1 | 2 | 3 | Inventions | Percentage |
|---|---|---|---|---|---|---|---|
| Number of | 0 | - * | 15 | 9 | | 24 | 51.1 |
| Consultants | 1 | 1 | 9 | 3 | | 13 | 27.7 |
| Who Said | 2 | 7 | 2 | | | 9 | 19.1 |
| "No Support" | 3 | | 1 | | | 1 | 2.1 |
| In Each Case | 4 | | | | | | |
| Total Inventions | | 8 | 27 | 12 | | 47 | |
| Percentage | | 17.0 | 57.5 | 25.5 | | | 100.0 |

(c) 50 "Most Successful" Recommended Inventions

* 59, 65, and 3 Cases respectively in (a), (b), and (c) without consultant input

Figure 2. Tabulation of Consultant Opinions in First-Stage Evaluation

inventions were likewise diverse. For the most part, the inventions or new product ideas submitted then, and now, are the result of applying existing technology rather than developing new technology.

The diffusion of technology has been widely studied as a sociological phenomenon, as the way in which technology is fully exploited in terms of societal benefits. Dissemination of information on technology and its applications is clearly essential if it is to be more widely applied. Advances in information technology, and the resulting improved communications, are a positive stimulus to diffusion. However, the nature of the NIST evaluation service, as noted in the preceding paragraph, and the way it has operated suggest that it also acts as a mechanism to accelerate diffusion.

The "open appeal" feature of the evaluation service, mentioned before, provides for reconsideration, reapplication, and reevaluation, as often as requested by the inventor. The result over time has been a significant increase in the yield of inventions recommended, on the order of 25 percent.The data of Figure 3 show the extent and results of appeals. Note that the numbers represent specific inventions not the number of actual appeals; for example, in a given case rejected in first stage and appealed, the inventor may have appealed and the invention reevaluated several times before final rejection or advancement into second stage.

| Dispositions | Acceptance Screen | First Stage | Second Stage |
|---|---|---|---|
| Originally Rejected | 17118 | 13932 | 921 |
| Appealed | 2058 | 3008 | 341 |
| Disposition: | | | |
| Rejected - Acceptance Screen | 1632 | | |
| - First Stage | 397 | 2691 | |
| - Second Stage | 14 | 142 | 278 |
| Still in Process | 8 | 75 | 12 |
| Recommended | 7 | 100 | 51 |

Figure 3. ERIP Open Appeal Statistics (1975-1996)

In appealed cases the inventor usually engages in dialogue, written or oral, with the staff evaluator, increasing and elaborating on the information fed back in the reports furnished with the rejection letter. In effect, the staff evaluator acts as a "sounding board" for the inventor to test and develop his concepts of technology application. The inventor is then able to correct errors and his technical understanding, and advance his product development effort.

It needs to be emphasized that the staff evaluator always closely coordinates with and uses the input of the private sector consultants involved in the evaluation. Direct contact between consultant and inventor is not permitted in first stage evaluation. Nevertheless the inventor gets the full benefit of the consultant's comments through the staff evaluator. The evaluation service thus acts in a management capacity to ensure effective use of the private sector consultant population by inventors and small business; consultants are paid at their going rates.

Almost by definition, technology diffusion is accomplished by those who have not participated in the original development effort and who tend not to be as technically strong. The diffusers tend to bring other capabilities and knowledge to bear which are essential to application, and thus to diffusion. Providing them with a technical resource seems a logical and appropriate means to increase technology application and accelerate diffusion.

Final Remarks

The intent of this paper is to call attention to a body of information and data of potential value to those dealing with the complexities of technology-based economic development. The notion of providing technology evaluation as a public service, in order to accelerate technology diffusion, is presented as having proven value in terms of the economic and societal benefits which are realized through technology commercialization. The proven value is documented as described and detailed in the publications listed as References.

References

Braid, Jr., R. B., M. A. Brown, S. M. Cohn, C. A. Franchuk, C. G. Rizy, and C. R. Wilson. 1996. *The Energy-Related Inventions Program: A Continuation of Demonstrated Benefits to the Inventor Community.* Oak Ridge, Tennessee: Oak Ridge National Laboratory, ORNL/CON-429.

Brown, M. A., C. R. Curlee, and S. R. Elliott. 1994. "Evaluating Technology Innovation Programs: The Use of Comparison Groups to Identify Impacts," *Research Policy*, forthcoming.

Brown, M. A., C. R. Wilson. 1993. "R&D Spinoffs: Serendipity vs. A Managed Process," *Journal of Technology Transfer*, 18 (3-4): 5-15.

Brown, M. A., S. M. Cohn, C. A. Franchuk, D. Jones, and C. R. Wilson. 1992. *The Economic, Energy, and Environmental Impacts of the Energy-Related Inventions Program.* Oak Ridge, Tennessee: Oak Ridge National Laboratory, ORNL/CON-381.

Brown, M. A., and S. A. Snell. 1988. *The Energy-Related Inventions Program: An Assessment of Recent Commercial Progress.* Oak Ridge, Tennessee: Oak Ridge National Laboratory, ORNL/CON-252, October.

Brown, M. A., J. A. Morell, S. A. Snell, E. J. Soderstrom, and W. Friggle. 1987. *Evaluation of the Energy-Related Inventions Program: An Empirical Analysis of 204 Inventions.* Oak Ridge, Tennessee: Oak Ridge National Laboratory, ORNL/CON-225, March.

Brown, M. A., C. R. Wilson. 1990. *The Energy-Related Inventions Program: Commercial Progress of Participants Through 1988.* Oak Ridge, Tennessee: Oak Ridge National Laboratory, ORNL/CON-301, May.

Brown, M. A., C. R. Wilson, and C. A. Franchuk. 1991. *The Energy-Related Inventions Program: A Decade of Commercial Progress.* Oak Ridge, Tennessee: Oak Ridge National Laboratory, ORNL/CON-339, December.

Rorke, M. L., and H. C. Livesay. 1986. *A Longitudinal Examination of the Energy-Related Inventions Program.* Rockville, Maryland: Mohawk Research Corporation.

# 025

## COMPETITIVE ANALYSIS FURTHER UPSTREAM: SHIFTING THE FOCUS OF ANALYSIS OF A JAPANESE MULTINATIONAL

Author:
Dr. Clement K. Wang
Dept. of Business Policy
National University of Singapore
10 Kent Ridge Crescent
Singapore 119260
Tel:        +65-772-3154
Fax:        +65-773-5016

Co-author:
Dr. Paul Guild
Dept. of Management Sciences
University of Waterloo
Waterloo, Ontario
N2L 3G1
Canada
Tel:        +1-519-888-4802
Fax:        +1-519-888-4884

## ABSTRACT

A firm enjoys competitive advantage when it can master and exploit its competencies (whether technological or not) to a greater degree relative to its competitors. In this paper a comparison is made between a common product-oriented (fruit-level) perspective and a competence-based (root-level) approach to inter-firm competition. The knowledge gained in analyzing and anticipating the actions of rival firms, known as competitive intelligence, can be used by decision makers to formulate strategy to outmaneuver and outperform other firms
Competitive analysis undertaken in many firms has a tendency to overemphasize the fruit-level source of rival firms' competitiveness such as end products, market share and financial indicators. While information contained) at the product-oriented perspective helps to generate a picture of how well a rival firm is presently competing, the analysis solely at this level may fail to capture that firm's intent and possible future direction. Since analysis needs strategic import to the decision makers, the focus must not only he directed toward a rival's present position but also postulate where and how that firm will advance in the future. To accomplish the latter focus, competitive analysis must reveal the strategic impacts of competitors. In other words, in order to answer the where and how questions, one must probe into what fundamental factors a rival firm is exploiting, to enable that firm to derive superior economic performance.

An external analysis of a technology-based firm in Japan from both the fruit- and root-levels were presented to its own R&D personnel. The respondents were asked to evaluate the information content from the two levels along the following dimensions: significance (trivial or insightful; usefulness (useful or not in assessing future directions); and detriment (disadvantaged or not if a competitor got hold of the information). As was expected, the information generated from a competence-based approach was more insightful, useful than that derived from the product-oriented perspective. In addition, if a firm had access to information derived from the former approach on a rival firm, then that rival firm could potentially be competitively disadvantaged.

Key Words: competitive intelligence, competence-based approach, strategy formulation

Oral Presentation

**Competitive Analysis Further Upstream: Shifting the Focus of Analysis of a Japanese Multinational**

**Introduction**

A firm enjoys competitive advantage when it can master and exploit its competencies (both technical and non-technical) to a greater degree, relative to its competitors, in contributing to perceived customer value. In this paper a comparison is made between a product-oriented (fruit-level) perspective and a competence-based (root-level) approach to competitive analysis in inter-firm competition. The knowledge gained in analyzing and anticipating the actions of rival firms, known as competitive intelligence (CI), can be used by decision makers to formulate strategy to outmaneuver and outperform other firms.

The process of competitive intelligence scanning, monitoring and analysis is expected to become a major concern of senior management in both product and service-based industries. To many, the unrelenting pace of technological advances might be considered as either a blessing or a curse. On the positive side, a firm might proactively exploit the benefits of rapid technological change by introducing new products and/or services. On the other side, firms which fail to capitalize on imminent technological change may face dire consequences in lost market share and growth, or worse, be unable to overcome entry barriers to new growth markets.

The survival and continued growth of many firms may depend on their abilities in studying the strategic moves of not only current business contenders but also emergent rivals that will vie for existing or new markets. These competing firms could either enlarge the current business domain or redefine the business scope of the particular sector. For instance, less visible competitors may quickly build a technological capability that could be a potential threat when turned to new markets (e.g., Netscape versus Microsoft). Furthermore, with increasing benefits from cooperative ventures, especially from transnational alliances, firms that could qualify as potential collaborators need to be carefully identified and screened for possible strategic partnerships.

The unpredictability of future competitive space has increased the awareness of firms to scan, monitor and analyze rival firms (direct and potential) and possible collaborators. However, much of the effort in current competitive analysis have focused on a firm's present position based on the assessment of its end-market indicators (such as products produced, markets entered and financial statements). We argue in this study that to increase strategic import to decision makers, analysis must go beyond the end product level (EPL). While knowledge derived from this level of analysis provides an indication of a firm's strength, this perspective is limited since end products may rapidly change especially under conditions of shrinking planning horizons. Consequently, analysis devoted exclusively at this level would fail to analyze a firm's fundamental root of competitiveness.

Furthermore, even the ephemeral view of a particular firm's strength gained would make it difficult for managers to postulate and be forewarned, where and how that firm will advance. To answer the *where* and *how* questions, we believe one must probe into *what* fundamental factors a competing (or collaborating) firm is growing and leveraging, to enable that firm to derive superior economic performance. This involves shifting the focus of analysis further upstream, from the end product level (EPL) to the competence level (CL), of the firm being analyzed. By focusing on what competencies firms posses and their abilities to deploy these competencies, one may infer a firm's competitive advantage. As Grant noted, "the resources and capabilities of a firm are the central considerations in formulating its strategy: they are the primary constants upon which a firm can establish its identity and frame its strategy, and they are the primary sources of the firm's profitability" (1991; p. 133).

The objective of the study is to gain a better understanding of the CI process in competitive analysis. More specifically, we seek to increase the effectiveness of CI to users (i.e., managers and decision makers) in its utilization to strategic decision making by comparing two approaches in the analysis of a technology-based Japanese multinational. The following section presents the EPL and CL approaches to competitive analysis. Hypotheses were developed and then tested in an on-site questionnaire study by thirty R&D personnel and managers in business planning. The results are highlighted and discussed in light of the findings. The paper concludes with managerial implications and insights concerning competitive analysis.

**Two Approaches**

Although competitive analysis is widely practiced, many firms have been disenchanted by their apparent inability to generate user-driven CI that can impact strategic decisions (Barndt, 1994). Consequently, competitive intelligence has not been able to respond to the needs and goals of decision makers and has therefore, not been effectively integrated into the decision making process (Weston, 1991). Information concerning a rival firm's tactical or operational issues, such as marketing strategies and sales tactics (cost position), may be useful at one level of analysis (Fuld, 1995). For formulating corporate strategy, however, competitive analysis must focus on intelligence that yields more of the rival firm's strategic orientation and intent.

Conventional scanning and monitoring of competitive information usually involves the assessment of a firm's visible manifestations, such as its end products, financial performance indicators, and market share. The main problem in looking at a firm solely in this way is that it fails to analyze the rival's fundamental root of competitiveness. As Quinn and Hilmer have stated, "products, even those with valuable legal protection, can be too easily back-engineered, duplicated, or replaced by substitutes" (1994; p. 45). According to Lei and Slocum, "a focus on products and prices rather than the underlying skills and competencies limits managers' options and strategic thinking" (1992; p. 91). Hence, to increase the strategic thinking derived from competitive analysis, it is imperative to understand how a rival firm competes by being "concerned with exploiting, developing and maintaining the sum total of the [rival] company's knowledge and abilities" (Ford, 1988; p. 85). In studying a competitor, the analysis should delve beneath the surface of a firm's end products to reveal the factors of competitiveness that enabled a firm to grow and profit in the marketplace.

This strategic approach regards firms as trees "growing" products and markets from its root competencies (Giget, 1988; Prahalad & Hamel, 1990). Using this analogy, a tree's root system can be viewed as the source of the competitiveness of a firm, and thus, is more enduring and persistent than the visible fruit-level manifestations. As a result of tracking merely the visible fruit-level and overlooking the root-level source of a firm's competitiveness, the emerging message may provide only an ephemeral view of the competitiveness of that firm. For example, it is possible to misread and therefore ignore potential entrants by looking just at the fruit-level and overlooking the root-level source of competitiveness of a firm. While fruit-level products will change (due to new product development within and potential replacement from rivals' substitutes without), the root system nurtures a firm's competencies and thus, is more enduring and less susceptible to short-term changes. This flaw of overemphasis on the visible manifestations while de-emphasizing the less visible but potentially more important manifestations of the origin of competitive advantage, can cause inaccurate managerial perceptions (Zahra & Chaples, 1993).

We advocate that the analysis should be conducted further upstream beyond the end product level (EPL). This approach shifts the analysis to the root competencies a firm is developing and exploiting. This 'deeper' level of analysis involves analyzing at the competence level (CL) of a firm, long before its manifestation in the end product market. This competence view is appealing in the context of competitive analysis since it centers on a firm's root-level source of competitiveness. Firms that can accumulate and exploit the most appropriate stocks of resources will likely experience superior performances (Collis & Montgomery, 1995). To develop strategic insights into firms (competitors or potential collaborators), competitive analysis should seek to uncover the factors these firms are leveraging to develop the competitive advantages their customers deem to be critical.

By concentrating on the root system as the basis of competitiveness, the direction of a firm might be inferred with greater confidence than looking at the fruit-level. Even when a firm moves into new markets, generally it is to leverage a discernible competitive advantage through existing or newly developed competencies. This trend is not surprising, since the leaves and fruit of a tree are engendered by absorbing the riches from the root system (organizational competencies). Interpreting organizational competencies assists competitive analysts to evaluate the future strategic opportunities of other firms. When a firm is developing strong roots in certain critical competencies, it emits subtle yet discernible signals that it is preserving and leveraging competitiveness in key areas into the future.

**Hypotheses**

Based on the previous discussion, three hypotheses were formulated. We hypothesized that the two levels of analysis, EPL and CL, will differ along three variables: significance, usefulness and detriment. The first hypothesis examined whether the results from CL analysis will be perceived as more insightful than from EPL. The second looked at whether the information derived from CL will be perceived as more useful in assessing a firm's future directions than from EPL. And the third investigated whether a firm will be more disadvantaged if its competitor were to conduct analysis using the CL approach.

Hypothesis 1: The information derived from CL analysis will be perceived as more insightful than information from EPL.

Hypothesis 2: The information derived from CL analysis will be perceived as more useful in assessing future directions than information from EPL.

Hypothesis 3: A firm will be more disadvantaged if its competitor were to conduct analysis using information derived from CL analysis than EPL alone.

**Methodology**

An external competitive analysis was conducted on a technology-based Japanese multinational corporation (disguised here as Firm A). More than fifteen databases and close to 200 non-electronic data sources were used to collect data on Firm A. Output from the scanning process reached several thousand of pages of data. Both English and Japanese sources were used. Comprehensive data ranging from patent records and organizational structure to industry trends were collected subject to the cost and time constraints. The collection was not once-for-all but iterative. During analysis, emerging patterns and conflicting indicators directed more focused searches.

Data analysis was aimed at two levels. First, analysis from the end product level (EPL) was conducted. Second, data were analyzed at the competence level (CL) to identify and interpret competencies that Firm A is developing, protecting, exploiting and renewing to establish competitive advantage over rivals. To preserve confidentiality of the results, only a general description of the findings is provided. Out of the eight competencies identified, two were commercialization know-how and environmental acuity. Firm A was found to be extremely adept at introducing waves of new products based on recognition and exploitation of proprietary technologies. Their research was organized according to mid- to long-term curiosity-driven programs and product-motivated applied development for specific applications. Over the years, Firm A has deliberately cultivated advanced technologies while avoiding simple ones, since sophisticated device and systems technologies can attract proposals for cross-licensing and cross-sales agreements or other cooperative ventures that are mutually beneficial. Environmental acuity in terms of ecological awareness and ecological assurance came up consistently in reference to materials, processes and new energy sources.

Thirty R&D personnel and business planning managers at Firm A heard a slide presentation, and were asked to answer three 7-point questions corresponding to the three variables for each slide, i.e., significance (1 = trivial to 7 = insightful); usefulness (1 = useful in assessing future directions to 7 = not useful in assessing future directions); and detriment (1 = extremely disadvantaged to 7 = not at all disadvantaged). The score of the EPL approach was averaged over six slides while the score for the CL approach corresponded to the average of four slides.

**Results**

Correlation matrices appear in Table 1 for the CL approach and in Table 2 for the EPL approach. Since the total sample was made up of two groups of respondents (21 from R&D and 9 from business planning), the scores from the three variables in CL and EPL were tested for potential differences. The result yielded no significant difference from the Man-Whitney U test. The Wilcoxon matched-pairs signed-rank test revealed a significant difference ($p < .001$) between the EPL and CL approaches with respect to all three variables. As was expected, the information generated from CL analysis was more insightful than that derived from EPL. The CL analysis was found to be more useful in assessing future directions of other firms. In addition, if a firm had access to information derived from CL analysis on a rival firm, then that rival firm could potentially be competitively disadvantaged. Therefore, Hypotheses 1 to 3 were supported.

Table 1

Spearman Correlation of Competence Level (CL) Approach [a]

| Variables | Mean | s.d. | 1 | 2 | 3 |
|---|---|---|---|---|---|
| 1 Significance | 5.32 | .78 | (.90) | | |
| 2 Usefulness [b] | 5.61 | .70 | .61*** | (.78) | |
| 3 Disadvantage [b] | 4.91 | 1.03 | .31* | .28[†] | (.79) |

[a] N = 30. Numbers in the parentheses on the diagonal are coefficient alpha reliabilities.
[b] These numbers were reverse coded in the questionnaire.

[†]   $p < .10$
[*]   $p < .05$
[**]   $p < .01$
[***]   $p < .001$

Table 2

Spearman Correlation of End Product Level (EPL) Approach [a]

| Variables | Mean | s.d. | 1 | 2 | 3 |
|---|---|---|---|---|---|
| 1 Significance | 3.73 | .84 | (.80) | | |
| 2 Usefulness [b] | 4.45 | .84 | .02 | (.70) | |
| 3 Disadvantage [b] | 2.76 | 1.10 | .33* | -.07 | (.75) |

[a] N = 30. Numbers in the parentheses on the diagonal are coefficient alpha reliabilities.
[b] These numbers were reverse coded in the questionnaire.

[†]   $p < .10$
[*]   $p < .05$
[**]   $p < .01$
[***]   $p < .001$

# Discussion

To increase the strategic thinking derived from competitive analysis, it is imperative to understand rival firms' inherent factors of competitiveness that enable them to develop strategic advantage. Analysis solely at the end product level may not adequately help decision makers to postulate and be forewarned, where and how other firms will advance. To overcome the propensity of competitive analysis toward evaluating only the more tangible and visible manifestations of a firm (i.e., EPL), this study sought to examine the view of competitive advantage emanating from the competence level of the firm being analyzed. The assumption here is that the foundational competence base which operates at the individual, group and organizational levels is the origin of a firm's long-term strategy in developing and sustaining competitive advantages.

The findings from the study show that analysis at the competence level and end product level of a Japanese multinational differed in terms of significance, usefulness and detriment. As was expected, the information from the CL approach was more insightful in content, and useful in assessing future directions of a firm than the EPL approach. In addition, if a firm had access to information derived from CL analysis on a rival firm, then that rival firm could potentially be competitively disadvantaged. Although the study clearly demonstrated some advantages of using the CL approach in competitive analysis, its actual cost in terms of resources (human, financial, etc.) was not determined. Elsewhere, a novel multidisciplinary team-based approach has been proposed to help accomplish this goal (Wang & Guild, 1995). Clearly, a more intensive effort is required to conduct CL analysis than with the EPL approach. Further investigation into the potential benefits and possible weaknesses need to be examined.

Armed with the insights gained from the competence level analysis, managers can better anticipate a range of potential threats and opportunities in strategic decision making. As stated at the outset, analyzing organizational competencies offers the potential for uncovering a firm's root-source competitiveness and hence, can be used to analyze that firm's future strategy and its intended actions. In other words, the analysis at the competence level can help decision makers to understand not only of a firm's competitive advantage today but also characterize the likely source of tomorrow's sustainable competitive advantage. When a firm's strategic moves based on its competencies have been adequately evaluated and understood, the intelligence picture should reveal options which could then be assimilated by managers and be imbedded in their decision making process. This is in agreement with Porter's contention that "gathering data is a waste of time unless they are used in formulating strategy" (Porter, 1980; p. 74).

In summary, there has been an increasing number of researchers who view firm differences based on the accumulation (or lack) of stocks of competencies. The premise underlying this study is that a competence level approach may be an appropriate perspective to link a firm's competitive analysis efforts to its strategy formulation. The present findings provide a first step in demonstrating the advantages of strategic import to competitive intelligence by shifting the focus of competitive analysis from the end product level approach to the competence level.

**References**

Barndt, W.D., Jr. (1994). *User-directed competitive intelligence*. Westport: Quorum Books.

Collis, D.J., & Montgomery, C.A. (1995). Competing on resources: strategy in the 1990s. *Harvard Business Review*, 73(4): 118-128.

Ford, D. (1988). Develop your technology strategy. *Long Range Planning*, 21(5): 85-95.

Fuld, L.M. (1995). *The new competitor intelligence*. New York: John Wiley & Sons.

Giget, M. (1988). The bonsai trees of Japanese industry. *Futures*, 20(2): 147-154.

Grant, R.M. (1991). The resource-based theory of competitive advantage: implications for strategy formulation. *California Management Review*, 33(3): 114-135.

Lei, D., & Slocum, J.W. (1992). Global strategy, competence-building and strategic alliances. *California Management Review*, 35(1): 81-97.

Porter, M. (1980). *Competitive strategy*. New York: The Free Press.

Prahalad, C.K., & Hamel, G. (1990). The core competence of the corporation. *Harvard Business Review,* 68(3): 79-91.

Quinn, J.B., & Hilmer, F.G. (1994). Strategic outsourcing. *Sloan Management Review,* 35(4): 43-55.

Wang, C.K., & Guild, P.D. (1995). The strategic use of organizational competencies and backcasting in competitive analysis. In L.W. Foster, (Ed.), *Advances in Applied Business Strategy,* Vol. 4, 33-56, Greenwich, CT: JAI Press.

Weston, D.M. (1991). Best practices in competitive analysis, *Business Intelligence Program,* SRI International Report No. 801.

Zahra, S.A., & Chaples, S.S. (1993). Blind spots in competitive analysis. *Academy of Management Executive,* 7(2): 7-28.

# 026

## UNIVERSITY AND INDUSTRY STRATEGIC PARTNERSHIPS TO LINK INNOVATION AND COMMERCIALIZATION: KEY FACTORS AND CASE STUDIES

Robert L. Swinth, Ph.D. and Catherine M. Bickle, M.A.
College of Business, Montana State University
Bozeman, MT 59717, U.S.A.

### ABSTRACT

University research centers and industry innovation managers seek to leverage their resources through strategic partnering. Yet, many of these alliances fail to lead to implementation of the university's innovations or competitive advantage for the firm. Others do result in commercialization. Why this variability in performance and what are the elements in successful relationships? In this research project several alliances between universities and firms were studied and the key factors in their relationships were identified. In accordance with theoretical arguments, eight factors in a university-industry strategic partnership were predicted to be necessary for the successful commercialization of innovations. In every case study investigated we found that the presence of all factors lead to successful performance, but the absence of one or more lead to failure to get the innovation introduced in the marketplace. The university-industry strategic partnerships that consciously managed such factors as having a joint competitive strategy, taking an interorganizational team approach, and identifying a technology with the potential for significant improvement over current practice/products were successful. Those that did not attend to such considerations failed.

### INTRODUCTION

Technology based firms are under major competitive pressure and need a ready, relatively low cost source of new technologies. At the same time, universities are struggling for new sources of research funding as governments cut back their sponsorship. Universities are also under increasing pressure to justify the relevance of their research activities to the larger community. This combination of influences has created a shared interest in strategic partnering between universities and industry. Yet, many of these alliances fail to lead to implementation of the university's innovations or competitive advantage for the firm, while others do result in commercialization [1]. Why this variability in performance and what are the elements in successful relationships?

### Bridging Innovation and Implementation

The transformation of research and marketplace needs into a business/ technology strategy is pivotal in bridging the two [2]. This technological development process and the issues affecting performance have been studied extensively [3-6]. From this literature a number

Acknowledgments: This work was supported by the College of Business and by the Center for Biofilm Engineering at Montana State University, a National Science Foundation-sponsored engineering research center (cooperative agreement EEC-8907039), and by a National Science Foundation, Management of Technology Program Grant (number DMI-9421477).

factors have emerged as generally important. Top management support; project leadership; the involvement of other key interests, such as suppliers and customers; etc., are all critical to success. When transformation extends across organizational boundaries, a new complexity is added, and special attention must be paid both to interorganizational relationship issues and commercialization issues.

## The University–Industry Strategic Partnership

Geisler [7] and Geisler and Furino [8] make a cogent case for the importance of university-industry cooperation in the emergence of new technologies. They suggest several factors that contribute to successful relationships. In this paper we consider these two streams of research on innovation, new product development, and university industry alliances, and seek to identify a set factors applicable to university-industry strategic partnering. We attempt to ascertain through several case studies whether such strategic partnering affects success in the implementation of innovations and the attainment of new product sales and profits.

## A MODEL FOR UNIVERSITY-INDUSTRY STRATEGIC PARTNERING

There are at least eight critical factors in successful relationships between university researchers and profitable firms marketing new technologies. See Figure 1. First, the bringing together of a commercial opportunity with a research idea requires the development of a cooperative effort. Five factors are essential to accomplish this. They include the presence of a university champion, a linkage between the university and industry, the presence of an industry champion, the successful allocation of risks and rewards, and the existence of a gap between current solutions and the proposed innovation. Secondly, the partners must have a good collaborative relationship. Two additional factors are necessary for this: a joint competitive strategy and a team approach with a systemic task perspective. Finally, the eighth factor, the implementation capacity of the industry partner, is needed for market success.

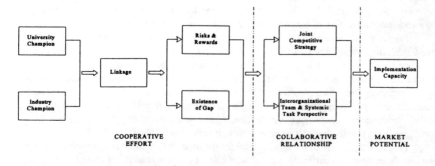

Figure 1. The university-industry strategic partnering model: from innovation to commercialization

## Factors Needed for a Cooperative Effort

*Factor 1: University Champion.* The university researcher must be generating ideas which have the potential for application. Much of the research generated by universities has no immediate commercial application [9], and university researchers are motivated by academia to become or to remain experts in their current research areas, rather than to develop new fields of expertise which could help develop commercially viable products. To generate marketable technology, there needs to be a champion working toward this goal from within the university.

*Factor 2: Linkage.* The second factor involves the formation of a link between university and industry. The importance of this linkage cannot be over-emphasized, as the integration of the industry's and the university's cultures and the two groups' ability to communicate [10] are central to the success of a joint venture. The organizational cultures, core competencies, technologies, management, and values of the two groups must be similar enough that the two groups can mesh together into an effective team. Leonard-Barton [11] shows the necessity of an alignment between the nature of a project and the organization attempting to complete it. The industry partner's flexibility toward changes in coordination and leadership [6] and ability to view innovation as a corporate-wide task [4] are key cultural components to the success of an industry-university strategic partnership.

*Factor 3: Industry Champion.* The third factor in the process centers around the characteristics of the industry champion. This person must see the application of the university research, or see how the research can be modified in order to be applicable. This entails overcoming tendencies to view university research as being too basic for commercial application [12]. The champion must also be willing to develop the link between opportunity and idea and follow it through whatever barriers lie ahead. In this regard, the industry champion is similar to Rothwell's [4] product champion. In order to be successful, the industry partner needs to be able to predict the market and sales potential for the product, assess the competition, and identify customer needs within existing markets [13,4] or create new markets for the technology [14]. This requires a strong marketing orientation, which must be coupled with industry experience and technological capability in order for the venture to be a success [15]. Considerable managerial skill is required to coordinate these efforts within the corporation and with the university. Success cannot be achieved without a long-term focus on the part of the company and an adequate allocation of corporate personnel to the project [16].

*Factor 4: Allocating Risks and Rewards.* Once the industry and university champions have linked, the allocation of financial risks and rewards must be addressed. The industry must be willing to assume the financial risks associated with new product development, and some sort of agreement needs to be reached with the university so that it receives some financial rewards without assuming risk. This requires that industry provide funding for the university to reward success, therefore ensuring that the university researchers are committed to implementation [17]. To date, "income from technology transfer (from universities) to industry has not made a significant impact on the budgets of major research universities" [18,1].

*Factor 5: Existence of a Gap.* In order for the product to achieve market success in the long run, there must be a sufficient gap between current solutions and the proposed innovation to overcome the inertia of the marketplace and enable the new product to gain a foothold.

**Factors Needed for a Collaborative Relationship**

*Factor 6: Joint Competitive Strategy.* The industry partner and the university must formulate a joint competitive strategy based on their coordinated efforts and shared financial rewards. Generally this strategy centers around shared information and expertise, with the university providing research expertise and industry providing market and application development expertise. The strategy must include both long-term goals for the adaptation of technology and interim goals which will increase industry's commitment to an ongoing relationship with the university [7,19].

*Factor 7: Team Approach/Systemic Task.* The industry partner and the university must take a team approach and view the task systemically. The relationship between the university and industry must extend beyond that of an employing company and a research contractor. Both the university and the industry settings must be seen as integrated parts of a systemic task, with teams meeting at both settings. The two organizations must evolve toward a high degree of overlap in knowledge, awareness, and interest. In order for this overlap to develop, each group must make an effort to learn each others' language and to document and distribute information adequately [10].

**Factors Needed for Market Success**

*Factor 8: Implementation Capacity.* Here, several related skills and commitments needed on the part of the industry partner are grouped together and considered as a whole. The industry partner must have adequate production facilities for the venture: ideally, the product will have been developed with the production process in mind [15]. Adequate market share [5] and sales experience [13] on the part of the industry partner are necessary for a successful implementation of any new product line. Finally, corporate funds must be made available to see the product through final development and production.

**Performance Measurement**

The implementation measure of performance is used in this study [20]. We assess performance in terms of whether or not the firm has commercialized the innovation.

**CASE STUDIES**

**Case 1: Engineering Consulting Firm with the Center for Biofilm Engineering (CBE) and the College of Business (COB) at Montana State University (MSU)**

*Company and University Background.* An interorganizational team from university and industry was formed in response to a request for proposals from the National Science Foundation. All three parties were interested in the opportunity: the engineering firm saw this as a chance to enter the biofilter industry, the COB saw an opportunity to study and build interorganizational teams and research and discover competitive strategies, the CBE could continue its research on biofilters and develop the steps needed to implement this technology. Initially, the team focused on doing a strategic analysis of the biofilter market and competition and on formulating a joint competitive strategy. Since the industry partner had no standing activity in biofilters, the team then examined entry alternatives. Two in particular were pursued, acquisition of an existing firm and in-house growth of expertise in biofilters. In the end the industry partner elected to not enter the market at this time.

*Factor 1: University Champion.* The corporate culture of the university was supportive: it was committed to strategic partnering and provided the prestige and empowerment necessary to those who were involved in the project.

*Factor 2: Linkage.* The CBE industry liaison and the industry partner made contact through the CBE's industrial associates program. When the NSF prospectus in environmentally manufacturing became available, the Colleges of Business and Engineering at Montana State University and the manager at the firm formed an alliance to produce new knowledge products as part of a grant from NSF.

*Factor 3: Industry Champion.* The corporate culture of the firm was somewhat supportive of a champion. It held those involved in the project in high prestige. But, key members seemed not to be empowered to implement this innovation in their firm. The industry partner recognized the contribution that can be made from research. Their clients' problems are often novel and there is a big gap between current approaches and the potentially best solution. Likewise, since the management of waste gases is driven by governmental regulation, it was important for the firm to be able to adopt to changes in requirements. The manager at this firm recognized these factors and saw the potential benefits of being able to bring on new technologies. He saw biofilters as one of the tools that could prove to be useful to an engineering consulting firm such as his.

*Factor 4: Allocating Risks and Rewards.* The university's financial contribution to the project was funded through the NSF grant and the support of the CBE and COB. The industry partner did not provide any financial support to the university, but was always ready to participate in joint meetings and discussions about the innovation. Any financial gain from the commercialization of biofilters by the industry partner would flow to the firm. MSU did not have any contractual agreements with the industry partner for sharing of risks and rewards.

*Factor 5: Existence of a Gap.* This was perhaps the most unclear issue in the partnership. The industry partner did not see a sufficiently large gap between currently used technologies and biofilters. They approached several clients to ask if they would like to have biofilters used at their plants, but none said that they would. The MSU partners thought they saw a potential market, but did not have the means to initiate commercialization.

*Factor 6: Joint Competitive Strategy.* The partners formed a closely linked strategy that appeared to be very promising. It would give the firm a competitive advantage in differentiating based on university credibility. And the university research partner would obtain a continuous stream of actual novel problems and the opportunity to find innovative solutions to them.

*Factor 7: Team Approach/Systemic Task.* Here as well, the COB, CBE, and industry partner put in major effort to work closely and to establish and maintain an effectively functioning interorganizational team. They also developed a task perspective that brought together the research, marketing and strategic dimensions into a common language. Students from COB and from CBE were involved and worked closely with the team leaders and each of the partners.

*Factor 8: Implementation Capacity.* The knowledge and skills of the people in both organizations were aligned with the innovation. While neither those in the university, nor those in the firm had specifically implemented a biofilter innovation before, all were familiar with the strategic, technical, and marketing issues. The university provided the resources in strategic analysis and the firm had the procedures for implementing innovations with its clients.

**Case 2: ILX Lightwave and MSU Physics**

*Company Background.* ILX Lightwave is a private company located in Bozeman, Montana, which manufactures laser diode controllers, laser measurement instruments (power meters), and fiber optic instrumentation. ILX's laser diode controllers help assess and control current levels entering into diodes and control temperatures. ILX has been working with Dr. John Carlsten of the Physics Department of Montana State University on the development of an external cavity diode laser.

*Factor 1: University Champion.* Dr. John Carlsten had not worked with diode lasers before he started his collaboration with ILX. In spite of this, he wanted to provide a way for his students to work on commercially viable technologies, and hoped he could establish some links with potential local employers as well. This alliance has been so successful for the university it has led the MSU physics department to establish the Optical Technology Center, whose mission is to establish additional collaborative projects with industry.

*Factor 2: Linkage.* ILX and MSU came together as a result of a casual conversation. The two groups have managed to create a flexible working relationship that allows the two cultures to mix together in joint training sessions and presentations of work in progress. Both groups have a view that innovation is a part of their culture. MSU needed to develop core competencies that are in line with those of ILX.

*Factor 3: Industry Champion.* ILX has consistently seen the benefits of working with a university, provided that the university was willing to move from being involved in basic research to more applied fields of study. The seed that was the source of the external cavity diode laser project came from ILX's focus on customer needs: they noticed that customers were asking for different laser frequencies than they had been in the past. This led to the idea for an economical laser that could be easily recalibrated, a solution that would be cheaper than those currently offered by the competition. ILX has maintained a long-term focus on this project, and expects to see the short-term benefits of several spin-off products in 1996.

*Factor 4: Allocating Risks and Rewards.* ILX contributes $50,000 annually to MSU to fund this research program, and Professor Carlsten has obtained matching fund to increase the budget to approximately $250,000. IF ILX makes a profit on products based on intellectual property rights owned by MSU, they will license the rights from MSU and pay royalty fees. Fifty percent of ILX's regular contributions to MSU can be applied to those fees.

*Factor 5: Existence of a Gap.* Other firms are currently offering products that implement the technology used in the external cavity diode laser, but in a different manner and at higher prices. ILX's competitors offer lasers that can be calibrated to any setting by the user, at prices ranging from $20,000 to $60,000. This price difference has created a significant gap between the value of the proposed innovation and the current market offering. ILX will offer lasers that are calibrated at the factory to any frequency the user desires, for a price of about $5,000.

*Factor 6: Joint Competitive Strategy.* In general, ILX has spotted market opportunities and pointed MSU in the right direction for their research efforts. MSU has pointed the way in terms of interim goals required for the development of the technology, and has created some spin-off products in the process. The external cavity diode laser project allows ILX to remain ahead of the competition on the experience curve and situates ILX as the low cost leader in the market.

*Factor 7: Team Approach/Systemic Task.* ILX and MSU has attempted to work together as a team by holding joint training sessions, research presentations, and brown bag lunches designed to inform each other of the progress made in research and trends that are developing within the industry. Student internships at ILX and senior projects involving technology applicable to ILX have been another factor in the two groups' joint research. In a recent development, ILX researchers are now able to work beside MSU researchers in the laboratory, something that was not possible in the past.

*Factor 8: Implementation Capacity.* ILX's strengths include its financial position, marketing position, and international distribution channels. Their weaknesses include limited core competencies in the new product lines and less market share in these new areas, and weak local support for the company's infrastructure, e.g., lack of local vendors for machine parts, inability to find local training for staff, difficulty locating engineers in the local area.

## Case 3: Phytotech and Rutgers University—Center for Agricultural Molecular Biology

*Company Background.* Phytotech, a private company located in Monmouth Junction, New Jersey, has developed a process for removing heavy metals from contaminated soil and water using plants. This technology can be used to clean sites contaminated with lead and other dangerous heavy metals or radioactive substances, including many Superfund cleanup sites. Customers for Phytotech's processes include private industry and governmental bodies, such as the EPA, which comprise the $12 billion per year hazardous waste remediation industry.

*Factor 1: University Champion.* In 1990, Ilya Raskin of Rutgers was exploring Russian literature from the 1960s regarding the reaction of plants which had absorbed the effects of radioactive fallout. This gave Raskin the idea of using plants to purposefully absorb waste contaminants.

. *Factor 2: Linkage.* Raskin made an invention disclosure to Rutgers, expecting them to want the rights to the process. Rutgers declined, so Raskin approached Burt Ensley, whom he had met when Ensley was renting lab space from Rutgers. Raskin inquired about his experience with the uptake of heavy metals, which led to a grant from the EPA for the development of the technology. Ensley believed that the technology was commercializable and patentable, so he provided the funds to patent the process. Phytotech was incorporated in April of 1994.

*Factor 3: Industry Champion.* Ensley saw the potential for Raskin's technology and used his expertise in raising capital to form a new company to develop the technology.

*Factor 4: Allocation of Risks and Rewards.* The ongoing research agreement between Phytotech and Raskin provides a 3 year, $1.1 million agreement allowing research from Raskin's laboratory to be licensed by Phytotech. The money is funded via venture capital. Researchers, including professors, post doctoral students, and graduate students have worked on the plant takeup process.

*Factor 5: Existence of a Gap.* Existing processes for remediation of sites contaminated with heavy metals include excavating, land fills, soil washing, "capping" the soil with a six inch layer of clay or concrete, solidification or vitrification (encasement in glass blocks), ion exchange, reverse osmosis, precipitation and flocculation (addition of chemicals causing metals to adhere to a surface scum). Phytotech's process provides a cleanup of equal quality to other technologies for a significantly lower price. Phytotech's technology's main disadvantage is that it can take up to three years to clean up a contaminated soil site, and that it will not treat contaminants that are more than two feet below the surface. The process will not treat high concentrations of contaminants. However, the technology is by far the most cost effective solution, costing from one-quarter to one-tenth the cost of any alternatives, with the exception of capping.

*Factor 6: Joint Competitive Strategy.* Phytotech's and Rutgers' joint strategy is to make Phytotech the low cost leader by using research to provide a higher quality service than alternative methods at a lower price and a higher margin. This competitive advantage from effectiveness and price is attainable through a stream of research insights that can be used to solve problems in implementation. And the higher margin can be used to support further research.

*Factor 7: Team Approach/Systemic Task.* The research scientist sets priorities for the group and identifies the key issues once the researchers explain their findings to him. Casual meetings are generally held once every two weeks, including social functions and jointly attended events. The relationship is very dynamic and free-flowing. Phytotech enjoys a collaborative relationship with all of the top scientists in the field, as the company is viewed as a technological leader.

*Factor 8: Implementation Capacity.* Phytotech's strengths include its financial position, management and finance experience, and public relations abilities. Their weaknesses include a very new sales staff, and a lack of sales in the market, resulting in no previous market share.

## PERFORMANCE

We have shown a correspondence between the presence of the factors and performance. In case 1, the gap was not seen as large and the industry partner did not make a financial contribution. See Figure 2. Here, the commercialization did not take place and there was not improved performance. In case 2 with ILX, all factors were present and their was improved performance. In case 3 with Phytotech, the commercialization is still in process and it is not known whether the firm has the implementation capacity. Needless to say, there is as of yet, no improved performance. Thus, these 8 factors are associated with performance. As is confirmed in the other brief studies shown in figure 2, all 8 need to be initiated for the firm to succeed. It is not enough to have a good idea. It is not enough to be strong in finding a market for a product. It is not enough to have a strong entrepreneur. Giving into the temptation for each of the interests to simply pursue their separate core competencies, will bring failure. They must approach product development as a process and help make the system come together, that is, see to it that all 8 factors are implemented.

| STRATEGIC PARTNERSHIP | INNOVATION | UNIVERSITY CHAMPION 1 | LINKAGE 2 | INDUSTRY CHAMPION 3 | RISKS AND REWARDS 4 | EXISTENCE OF A GAP 5 | JOINT COMPETITIVE STRATEGY 6 | TEAM APPROACH-SYSTEMIC TASK 7 | CAPACITY 8 | COMMERCIALIZATION EFFORT | PERFORMANCE |
|---|---|---|---|---|---|---|---|---|---|---|---|
| Montana State University (MSU) Engineering and Business, Industry | Biofilters by Center for Biofilm Engineering and others | Y | Y | Y | N | N | Y | Y | Y | No target found, new technology not commercialized | No |
| MSU Physics, ILX-Lightwave | Diode laser technology by several research and industrial groups | Y | Y | Y | Y | Y | Y | Y | Y | New products using new technologies | Success-market share gain with new products |
| Rutgers, Phytotech | Reuptake of heavy metals from contaminated sites by Rutgers and Phytotech | Y | Y | Y | Y | Y | Y | Y | ? | New products and processes developed, not yet in use | Yet to come to market |
| Brief studies (all performance failtures) of university-industry alliances lacking at least one of the factors | Corrosion Prevention | N |  |  |  |  |  |  |  |  | No |
| | Bacterial competition |  | N |  |  |  |  |  |  |  | No |
| | High nutrition food item |  |  | N |  |  |  |  |  |  | No |
| | Industrial water treatment |  |  |  | N |  |  |  |  |  | No |
| | Biofilm coupon |  |  |  |  | N |  |  |  |  | No |
| | Oil souring |  |  |  |  |  | N |  |  |  | No |
| | New plant hybrid |  |  |  |  |  |  | N |  |  | No |

Y = factor present;  N = factor absent

Figure 2.  Case studies of the relationship between presence of the eight factors and the commericalization of innovations.

# References

1. Feller, I. (1994). The university as an instrument of state and regional economic development: the rhetoric and reality of the U.S. experience. Manuscript, The Pennsylvania State University

2. Wheelwright, S., Clark K. (1996). Competing through development capability in a manufacturing based organization. In D. Aldridge and P. Swamidass (eds.) *Cross Functional Management of Technology.* Chicago: Irwin pp. 46-63.

3. Brown, S., Eisenhardt, K. (1995). Product development: past research, present findings, and future directions. *Academy of Management Review* 20(2):343-378.

4. Rothwell, R. (1992). Successful industrial innovation: critical factors for the 1990s. *R&D Management* 22(3):221-239.

5. Roure, J., Keeley, R. (1990). Predictors of success in new technology based ventures. *Journal of Business Venturing* 5:201-220.

6. Calantone, R., Vickery, S., Dröge, C. (1995). Business performance and strategic new product development activities: an empirical investigation. *Journal of Product Innovation Management* 12:214-223.

7. Geisler, E. (1993). On the important of university-industry-government cooperation: a global perspective. *International Journal of Technology Management* 8:435-438.

8. Geisler, E., Furino, A. (1993). University-industry-government cooperation: research horizons. *International Journal of Technology Management* 8:802-810.

9. Preston, J. (1993). Rescue the good ideas. *Chemtech*, April, pp. 8-11.

10. Roberts, S. (1991). Technology transfer: An opportunity for technical communicators. *Technical Communication*, Third Quarter, pp. 336-344.

11. Leonard-Barton, D. (1992). Core capabilities and core rigidities: a paradox in managing new product development. *Strategic Management Journal* 13:111-125.

12. Winton, K. (1987). The Edinburgh University link with industry. *Chemistry and Industry* 19:707-712.

13. Roberts, E. (1992). The success of high-technology firms: early technological and marketing influences. *Interfaces* 22(4):3-12.

14. Rowe, D. (1987). Science parks as an instrument for technology transfer. *Chemistry and Industry* 19:712-715.

15. Kumar, B. (1995). Partner-selection-criteria and Success of Technological Transfer: A Model Based on Learning Theory Applied to the Case of Indo-German Technical Collaborations. *Management International Review* 35:65-78.

16. Scott, W. (1994). Nuclear test facilities attract commercial ventures. *Aviation Week and Space Technology*, 7/18/94, pp. 77-78.

17. Dornheim, M. (1993). Public, private interests vie in cooperative research. *Aviation Week and Space Technology*, 11/8/93, p. 49.

18. Argynes, N., Liebeskind, J. (1996). Privatizing the intellectual commons: universities and the commercialization of biotechnology. Manuscript, University of Southern California.

19. Teja, A. (1989). University-industry research in thermophysical properties. *Chemical Engineering Progress* 85:20-23.

20. Dvir, D., Shenhar, A. (1992). Measuring the success of technology-based strategic business units. *Engineering Management Journal* 4:33-38.

# 027

# A RESEARCH ON THE NETWORK FORMATION FACTORS AND PERFORMANCE OF THE SMALL & MEDIUM ENTERPRISE IN TAIWAN

Author:
Benjamin J.C Yuan
Institute ofManagement of Technology,
National Chiao Tung University
1001 Ta Hsueh Rd, Hsinch, Taiwan 300
Tel:          +886-3-572-7657
Fax:          +886-3-572-7653
Email:        benjamin@cc.nctu. edu. tw

Co-author:
Tung-Pong Liang
Same address.

## ABSTRACT

High flexibility in management, sensitivity to market demand, and the ability to develop few but diversified new products are the characteristics of the small-to-medium businesses in Taiwan. However, threatened with international protectionism and the pressure of introducing industry technology, these small-medium businesses have insufficient capital and limited resources. If small-to-medium business, large corporate and research institutions can combine into a network, and build long-tern cooperation with mutual trust and commitment, they can share capability, market, technology, facilities and capital. They can support each other to conduct researches in new technology and new brands. Thus, small companies can turn disadvantages into advantages and maintain their competitive edge. This paper attempts to analyze how a network functions by studying the satellite system n the bicycle industry in Taiwan.

Here comes the conclusion derived from statistical analysis:

1.    The statistical data reveals that the number of staff and the capital available are enlarging. More than half of the companies interviewed believe that businesses can increase the use of network service to achieve the goal of the company.

2.    As the bicycle industry is export-oriented, the domestic network in marketing, sale and service gradually evolves. These is a potential relationship of supply and consumption among the members of the network. To meet the global demand, the companies must emphasize research and development and readapt strategies to produce value-added products.

3.    If companies want to pursue scale economies, the most suitable capital had better be between NT$10 million and NT$40 million, the number of staff be over 300, 50 that the rate of use can reach the maximum degree.

4.    As indicated in the pragmatic study, the factors contributed to the formation of industry network are as follow: (1)dependent on the scarce of resources( the complementary of resources);(2) to lower down the cost;(3)to learn through the function of network; and (4) to pursue scale economies.
5.    As for-general performance, "multi-activity development network," "work and logistics network" and "technological development network" are highly different in high and low performance. As for individual performance, "multi-activity network" "work and logistics network" and "scale economy network" are highly different in the satisfaction level of industry network and goal achievement.

# 028

# THE STUDY ON MODEL OF BUSINESS STRATEGIC ALLIANCE BY PRODUCT LIFE CYCLE

Author:
Benjamin J.C Yuan
Institute of Management of Technology
National Chiao Tung University
1001 Ta Hsueh Rd.,
Hsinch, Taiwan 300
Tel: +886-3-572-7657
Fax. +886-3-572-7653
Email: benjamin®cc.nctu. edu. tw

Co-author:
Joun-An Jou
Same address

## ABSTRACT

Recently, it becomes more and more popular for an enterprise to adapt "Strategic Alliance". Most firms expect to use this approach to create competitive advantage. The existence and nature of strategic alliance are on the basis of gaining benefit. However, it is very difficult for firms having a common perception about the model of alliance, due to the difficulty of balancing the gain and pay among the firms.
This study focuses on the model of strategic alliance by product life cycle. Then find out how to accomplish the strategic alliance during the different product life cycle stages among the firms for different purposes and needs. This study utilizes the methodology of "Business interview' and "Quality Function Deployment" to investigate a firm how to set its goal and purpose of alliance, find out the obstacles of alliance in process, and the relationship between the goal and success factors of alliance.

Keywords: Strategic alliance, Product life cycle, Quality Function Deployment

# 029

# A Case Study On Quality Control Certification Of Electronic Communication Companies In Taiwan

Benjamin J.C. Yuan & Todd Chang

Institute of Management of Technology, National Chiao Tung University

1001 Ta Hsueh Rd., Hsinchu, Taiwan 300

E-mail: benjamin@cc.nctu.edu.tw

Tel: (886-3)5725657

Fax: (886-3)5727653

## Abstract

This research uses experimental method to study an enterprise that after adapting ISO 9000 quality system, and compare its quality and operation performance with before adapting. Thus, we design a questionnaire to collect the desired information. Through the result of questionnaire, we analyze it by three directions. First, we try to find the variation of quality maturity by adapting ISO 9000. Then, we want to know the variation of internal and external benefits of gaining certification to ISO 9000. Finally, we use crosstabulation technique and expert interview, try to understand the context of its quality system operating, and if there exist some defects in a system. We will combine the survey result and the expertise then gives some suggestions for improve the system's operation. The results of this research also hope have some valuable advice and reference to relative company. That was seek certification to ISO 9000, of had been certificated but can not break through to higher quality level.

Keywords: ISO 9000, Quality system, Quality maturity, Internal and external benefits, Crosstabulation technique.

## 1. Introduction

ISO 9000 quality certification series has been greatly approved by nations all over the globe, since March, 1987. According to the survey made by Mobil Corp. [1], till March, 1995, 86 countries in total have passed the certification criteria of ISO 9000, and 95,467 manufacturers have enrolled in ISO 9000. From January, 1993 to March, 1995, the number of enrolled manufactures with ISO 9000 qualifications has rapidly grown 3.4 times. In brief, ISO 9000 certification is nowadays popular with the whole world.

According to studies both domestically and overseas [2] [3] [4] [5] [6], ISO 9000 indeed has benefited the enterprise world in many aspects. However, many people have different viewpoints concerning the performance of ISO 9000. For example, many manufacturers, in order to be qualified, cheat by bringing up false data. Besides, all relevant research emphasizes how to obtain the certification [2] [8] [9]; it hardly mentions how to maintain and improve the system after being ISO 9000 certified. In view of this, this study, via empirical methods, aims to depict the promotion of ISO 9000 and its influence on the enterprising world. Finally it will further discuss the maintenance and improvement of ISO 9000 series.

## 2. Research Approach

In this study, empirical itself, questionnaires are carefully designed with reference to domestic as well as overseas literature and reports. With an effort to increase the credibility of the questionnaires, this study will back up the results by the real figures of the case company.

### 2.1 Data Collection

This study adopts both domestic and overseas literature and surveys.

### 2.2 Choosing the Study Case

According to National Cheng Kung University [10], among those ISO 9000 certifiedcompanies in various fields, electronic communication and electrical engineering companies outnumber the rest. Seeing that, this study selects the first ISO 9001 certified electronic communication company as the research target. In September, 1992, this company was certified by SGS YARSLEY ISO 9001, England.

### 2.3 Choice of the Interviewees

In our stratified random sampling, we divide the population (the whole staff of the case study company) into several groups. That is, we random-sample evenly groups with different positions and years of experience from all departments. As a result, it shows that the category of department, position, and years of experience respectively take 25% of the population, exactly as what we anticipated earlier in designing the questionnaire.

### 2.4 Questionnaire Design

This questionnaire is composed of two major parts:

1. Quality Measurement: Via Crosby's assessment table, the quality change of case companies before and after ISO 9000 certification.

2. Effectiveness Assessment: Based on domestic and overseas literature, the questionnaire is designed to assess how quality upgrading, after ISO 9000 certification, affects an enterprise in all aspects. As for the measurement scale, the first part adopts nominal scale; the second part adopts Likert 7 point scale. And opposite adjectives and even intervals are applied in terms of approach.

# 3. Research Results and Analysis

## 3.1 Survey Report

The target of our questionnaire survey are the employees of the case company, who make one-fourth population of the whole staff. In total 159 questionnaires are distributed, and 106 are back; the recovery rate is 66.7%, which is highly positive. Among these 106 questionnaires, there are cases that the statistic figures are lower than 10; this is because the interviewees refuse to answer some questions or even skip them carefully. 36 people, 34% of those who give back their questionnaires, are surveyed concerning quality performance both before and after the application of ISO 9000.Regarding the content of the questionnaire, there are two parts: quality measurement and effectiveness assessment before and after the certification of ISO 9000. Now let's make an analysis by means of arithmetic average, range, standard deviation, and percentage as follows:

### 3.1.1 Quality Assessment

This section makes reference mainly to a quality assessment table in Crosby's "Quality without Tears" [11], which aims at offering a simple assessment approach to understand as well as facilitate an organization's progress in quality control. Therefore, in this study we assess the case company by means of this table, to see whether there is progress in quality after ISO 9000 certification. This table categorizes the quality control procedures as five stages, which are assessed by six different items. The scores are calculated as follows: 1st Stage: 1 point; 2nd stage: 2 point, and so on. And the higher total score means better quality control. As far as this section is concerned, there are two assessment objectives: the quality change after ISO 9000 certification ( the interviewees are limited to those who also survey the quality status before ISO 9000 certification.) and the performance of current quality control. ( All interviewees are involved in this aspect.) As a result, see table1, the total average before ISO 9000 is applied is 1.969, and that after ISO 9000 is 2.915; it grows by 0.946. Among all these six assessment items, the progress of the quality cost in terms of the business volume percentage seems to be the least obvious; it only grows by 0.572. The last but one in our progress ranking is company attitude toward quality; it grows by 0.801. As to the degree of progress of the rest, there is not much difference. Provided the samples of all the respondents, the total average of the six items is 2.629. What worthy of mention is that the total average is always lower than that derived from the interviewees who survey both before and after ISO 9000 certification. The difference in total average is: 2.915 - 2.629 = 0.286. This somewhat means that old employees have higher 2.916 confidence in their company quality.

With reference to Crosby's assessment table, the average between 1.0 and 1.9 represents "Uncertainty Stage"; and the average between 2.0 and 2.9 symbolizes "Awakening Stage"; that between 3.0 and 3.9, between 4.0 and 4.9, are regarded as "Enlightenment Stage" and "Certainty Stage" respectively. Finally, the average represents "Certainty Stage". In terms of these stages, the quality performance before ISO 9000 certification can be viewed as a stage between Uncertainty and Awakening. However, after ISO 9000 certification, the quality performance has made a step forward; i.e. it has reached "Enlightenment Stage".

Obviously it is a long way from the Uncertainty Stage to the Certainty Stage. Nevertheless, management executives would find great pleasure in striving all the way.

Table 1: Assessment Table Of Items Of Quality Performance

| Recognition Attitude | Average before Application | Average after Application | Average after ISO 9000 by the Interviewees Surveyed before ISO 9000 | Average Deviation of the Same Samples before & after ISO 9000 |
|---|---|---|---|---|
| Recognition Attitude | 2.270 | 3.095 | 3.243 | 0.973 |
| Importance of Quality Control | 1.857 | 2.667 | 3.000 | 1.143 |
| Problem Solution | 1.444 | 2.288 | 2.571 | 1.127 |
| Percentage of Quality Cost | 1.714 | 2.097 | 2.286 | 0.572 |
| Quality Improvement Activities | 2.167 | 2.886 | 3.167 | 1.000 |
| Quality cognizance | 2.361 | 2.743 | 3.222 | 0.861 |
| Total Average | 1.969 | 2.629 | 2.915 | 0.946 |

### 3.1.2 Effectiveness Assessment Before & After ISO 9000 Certification

In this section, the statistics approach is the same as the previous. The number of valid samples in the item of "Increase employees' productivity" is 105, because one interviewee didn't answer it. For the rest items, the number of valid samples is 36 before ISO 9000, and 106 after ISO 9000. And all the results are shown by the average of each item as well as the deviation average. We make a ranking table of assessment after ISO 9000 and the deviation value as well, so as to compare employees' satisfaction toward all survey items after ISO 9000.

The average of the 106 valid samples stand for the ranking of satisfaction degree of all effectiveness items. The first five worst in ranking are respectively; 1. decrease stock 2. lower design change frequency and better coordinate all departments 3. increase profit 4. clarify the responsibilities among departments 5. strengthen employees' loyalty. As for the first five which progress the best, they are in order as follows: 1. Boost company's and brand's reputation 2. better computerization 3. better document control 4. boost quality ideal 5. expand overseas market. And according to the average deviation, i.e. the value showing the progress degree, the number of valid samples before and after ISO 9000 is always 36.

The statistics shows the first five items which progress the least are: 1. increase profit 2. better coordinate all departments 3. shorten market introduction time 4. expand overseas market 5. lower design change frequency 5. decrease stock. And the first five with the most progress are: 1. better document control 2. fugirization management 3. boost company's and brand's reputation 4. expand overseas market 5. decrease product deficiency rate. In the following sections, we are going to go into details.

#### 3.1.2.1 Interaction of Beneficial Circulation

In the above effectiveness assessment, the first five in the ranking of satisfaction are as follows ( the overlapped ones are excluded ): boost company's and brand's reputation, better document control, increasecomputerization, expand overseas market, figurization management, decrease product deficiency rate, and boost quality consciousness. It is found that these seven items are closely related to each other.

#### 3.1.2.2 Analysis on Product Deficiency Rate and Internal Audits Defect Rate

Based on the case company's product deficiency rate and defect rate during the past five years. The defect rate in the ISO 9000 quality system are 81.21%,44.58%,40.59%,18.08% and 10.64% for 1992 to 1996,and product deficiency rates are 3.45%,4.24%,2.54%,0.86% and 0.13% for 1992 to 1996. At the first sight, we cannot see any relationship between these two rates, as the defect rate is the index of ISO 9000 fulfillment, and product deficiency rate shows the level of product quality.

### 3.1.2.3 Impact of External Environment

The last five in the ranking of satisfaction and progress include seven items with no overlapped ones: increase profit, lower design change frequency, decrease stock, shorten market introduction time, better department coordination, strengthen employees' loyalty, and clarify the responsibilities among departments.

Now let's examine these seven items one by one. First of all we will start with "lower design change frequency". In recent years, the case company's design change frequency is almost twice a day. After interviewing the authority concerned, we know that at present the peripheral industry of electronic & information field is undergoing rapid transformation, which causes the decrease in domestic demand. Under this circumstances, all manufacturers in this field are facing tremendous challenge; this can be seen from employee reduction and shutdown as well. As a whole, the high design change frequency is related to product strategies in response to the market construction change. While domestic demand is decreasing, the case company adopts larger product line strategy, i.e. developing more new models. And the new policy will certainly result in the high design change frequency.

As for stock and profit, they show the same problems as design change frequency. Its results of the operation of our case company in the recent years, coincide with the outcome of questionnaire. It is shown that the case company's profit rate is obviously declining; in 1997 it used to be 24.96%, but in 1995, it dropped to 5.61%. However, according to *Common Wealth Magazine* [12], the average profit rate of the information as well as communication industry is 4.7%, and this means that the profit rate of the case company is still above the average. In order to survive in this disadvantageous environment, the case company proposes several strategies. At a time of small market demand, they try to occupy the market by offering policy of "smaller profit but better sale" to customers. Indeed, the business volume grows; however, risk resulting
from market expansion also emerges, for example, increase of stock and decrease of profit. This exhibits that the operation of ISO 9000 system cannot change the external impact on the enterprise world. According to a foreign report [6], in the effectiveness assessment,

among the 477 ISO 9000 granted manufacturers, only 16% of them think ISO 9000 quality system would improve the profit rate, which ranks the eighth among the eight external effectiveness assessment items.

Regarding the employees' loyalty, ISO 9000 granted companies, as a whole, do not think much of ISO 9000's effect on this part [4], [5], [6]. In addition, Tim O'Brien's 477 interviewees also rank this item as the last; only 25% of them approve the contribution of ISO 9000 to employees' loyalty. All this means that employees' loyalty is influenced by the external environment, not by the application of ISO 9000; when a company is suffering depression, the index of employees' loyalty drops simultaneously.

Now, let's turn to look at "better department coordination" and "clarify the responsibility among departments". Our results show that these two items, which involve in how a company is organized, are not highly satisfactory. For further understanding, we need to analyze the case company's organization structure.

Under the General Manager, there are several similar departments are badly overlapped. For instance, Research & Development Department is divided into six parallel units; while Sales Department contains five parallel ones. Apparently, this kind of division is seriously against the criterion of ISO 9000. If similar duties cannot regulated under the same managing system, complexity in management as well as miscommunication among departments would thus occur. This can account for the low ranking of "better department coordination" and "clarify the responsibility among departments". Therefore, in order to raise the management efficiency among departments, first of all, the case company should rebuild its organization structure.

There is an interrelationship of the seven worst items in effectiveness assessment. The major causes of the problem lie in the change of the external environment and the organization construction, as explained below:

● Change of the External Environment

Due to the rapid decrease of domestic market demand, all manufacturers are forced to lower their product price, and this causes the low profit rate, of course. (However, our case study's profit rate, though unsatisfactory, is still above the average of the overall industry.) Besides, the market decrease also leads to the increase of stock. Needless to say, employees' loyalty is threatened. In order to survive in this transient competitive environment, the case study brings up multiple product line to lessen the risks of investment.

- **Inadequate Organization Design**

Inadequate organization design makes responsibilities among departments unclear and coordination among departments difficult. Both problems, along with various product models, cause the defects of products in mass production. Seeing that departmental interaction is far from smooth, the products in design have many flaws in function; sometimes, the feasibility of mass production is doubtful. Consequently, the design change frequency can not be lowered, and this explains why products cannot be introduced to market in a shorter time.

# 4. Conclusion and Suggestions

## 4.1 Conclusion

In the past, both buyers and suppliers spend lots of money and effort to establish an acceptable quality guarantee system so as to benefit both party. Hopefully, the birth of ISO 9000 quality system seems to have solved quality recognition problems which has lasted in the enterprise world for a long time. It contributes a lot especially to the international trade. Because of ISO 9000, there is no more "quality language barrier" among nations, and this greatly shortens international distance, making more business relations possible.

Being export-oriented, enterprises in Taiwan are required in pursuit of ISO 9000 certification in order to enter the international market. In addition to the advantage of getting more orders after being identified as ISO 9000 granted companies, they are advised to set up their own quality control system via the certification activity, so as to improve their current conditions.

The following sections are our conclusion and suggestions based on the previous research and survey.

### 4.1.1 Quality Assessment

This survey aims to, by means of Crobsy's quality control assessment table, comprehend the case company's progress of quality control system after adopting ISO 9000 certification. As a result, the company steps forward from "Awakening Stage" to "Enlightenment Stage", showing the positive influence of ISO 9000. However, there is still a long way to go; it needs to undergo "Wisdom Stage" and, furthermore, "Certainty Stage". In addition, among all the six survey items, the ratio of quality cost to business volume grows the least. Sad to say, most of the interviewees have no idea of the ratio; this reveals that notion of quality cost is not well instilled into them. As one knows, quality cost is the key point in the quality control system, because quality can only be assessed by figures before quality system reform starts.

## 4.1.2 External & Internal Effectiveness Assessment Before & After ISO 9000

The survey in this part is not limited to the range of quality; it extends to the overall management performance. To conclude, there are the following three facts:

1. In the past four years, the ISO 9000 system has rooted in all the departments of our case company. Under the constant supervision of the authority concerned, the defect rate drops year by year. The apparent achievements include better document control, figurization management, higher computerization, lower product deficiency rate, bigger overseas market, along with better brand reputation, stronger quality consciousness of employees, etc. Hopefully, the beneficial interaction has brought the case company much fruition.

2. On the other hand, it is found that in a time of depression the enterprise cannot but manage to improve the profit rate; as a result, stock increases. Quality control system, though not a means of making profit, can however consolidate profit making in circumstances of prosperity, because better product yield can not only reduce the cost loss due to the vain labor in process but also increase the product's competition capacity. Moreover, products of good quality makes customers confident in placing more orders. So in recent years the case company , though not in a highly profitable state, is among those few companies with growing business volume in this field. In addition to its excellent R & D capacity, the establishment of quality system and the high level of products have made valuable contributions.

3. Finally, an inadequate organization structure design would also lead to the inefficiency in quality system. The case company has divided similar departments into many parallel units with similar duties, however operating under different processes. As a result, complexity and budget waste arise, and what's more, departmental interaction becomes difficult and inconvenient. Seeing that, a quality control system can only be made good use of in coordination with proper organization structure.

# References

[1] ISO 9000 certifications worldwide: country-by-country break-down, ISO 9000 NEWS Vol. 4, No. 6, November/December 1995.

[2] Shu-ming Chen, "On Techniques and Difficulties on the Way to ISO 9000 Series Certification - a Case Study on Information & Electronics Industry".

[3] Fu-yan, Du, "On Domestic Experiences in Promoting ISO 9000", Institute of International Enterprise at National Cheng Kung University, 1995.

[4] J.L. Horner, "ISO 9000, the Growing Impact on International Trade", Quality Network, August, 95.

[5] Tim Eddy, Survey provides "snapshot" of ISO 9000 certification in 10 countries, ISO 9000 NEWS 4/1995.

[6] Tim O'Brien, Australian ISO 9000 survey reveals significant gains for certified organizations, ISO 9000 NEWS 6/1995.

[7] Shi-chang Ou, "Tendency of ISO 9000-Forged High Quality", Common Wealth Magazine, pp. 186 - 190, August, 1995.

[8] Jing-fen Yang, "Methodology of Taiwan Cable TV Business in Adopting ISO 9000 to Reinforce the Quality System", unpublished thesis, Institute of Industrial Engineering, National Tsing Hua University, June, 1995.

[9] Jiun-Shiung Huang, "On Current Promotion of ISO 9000 Series in Taiwan Manufacturing Industry", unpublished thesis, Institute of Industrial Engineering at National Chiao Tung University, June, 1994.

[10] David Hoyle, ISO 9000 Quality Systems Handbook-Second Edition, Butterworth-Heinemann Ltd, 1994.

[11] Philip B. Crosby, translated by Yi-fen Chen, "Quality without Tears", Common Wealth Series, June, 1988.

[12] Shi-chang Ou, "Information Chief Versus Industry Giant", Common Wealth Magazine Top 1000 Specials, June, 1996.

# 031

# Technology Commercialization in a Competence-based Perspective

Anders Paarup Nielsen, Ph.D.-Candidate
Department of Industrial Management and Engineering
Technical University of Denmark

## Abstract

Departing from the three major tasks within the management of technology this paper addresses the task which is concerned with technology commercialization. Technology commercialization is the organizational processes involved in the deployment and utilization of the technologies in the products offered. Technology commercialization is addressed from a competence based perspective and a number of competencies supporting the technology commercialization process are outlined. Furthermore, are the individual constituents of a competence described. The paper also addresses the role and significance of manufacturing competencies in the technology commercialization process and the way in which the these can be developed to a level where the technology commercialization process is efficiently supported. Furthermore, will the relation between the involvement of manufacturing in the technology commercialization process and the development of a manufacturing based competitive advantage be discussed.. The paper concludes with a discussion of the problems and challenges involved in the technology commercialization process from a manufacturing perspective.

## Introduction

At a highly aggregated level of analysis there are three major tasks within Management of Technology. The first of these tasks is concerned with the development and acquisition of technologies. This includes the management of the internal technology research and development activities as well as the management of the acquisition of technology from external sources through, i.e., alliances, research consortia, technology procurement, and joint ventures. These activities ensure that the technology portfolio of the company continuously is developed and maintained by adopting new technologies and improving existing technologies. The second task is concerned with the development of business and technology strategies in an integrated manner, thereby integrating technological considerations into the strategic planning process of the company. The activities within this task center on the management of the strategic planning process and are aimed at the exploitation of technologies (and competencies) in the market creation, thereby establishing the link between the market side and the technology side of the company. The activities carried out in connection with this task also ensures that the technology strategy is developed in accordance with the business strategy of the company. The third task is concerned with the commercialization of the technologies in the technology portfolio of the company. The technology management activities in connection with this task are focused on the management of the application and exploitation of technologies in the products (processes and services) offered by the company, thereby ensuring that the company is able to create value from its technology portfolio. This paper will focus on this third task and the role of competencies within the execution of this task. Special emphasis will be given to the deployment and exploitation of the of manufacturing technologies and competencies within the technology commercialization process.

In the following sections of this paper it will be attempted to describe and illustrate technology commercialization more closely this is followed by a discussion of the development of manufacturing competencies in relation to the technology commercialization process.

## Technology Commercialization

Technology commercialization is the activities and organizational processes within the company aimed at exploiting the technology portfolio in the products[1] offered by the company. According to (Mitchell & Singh 1996, p. 170) commercialization (of technologies) is the *".. process of acquiring ideas, augmenting them with complementary knowledge, developing and manufacturing saleable goods, and selling the goods in a market"*. Another perspective on technology commercialization has been offered by (Nevens et al. 1990, p. 156) who states that: *"Commercialization begins when a business identifies a way to use scientific or engineering advances to meet a market need. The process continues through design, development, manufacturing ramp-up, and marketing, and includes later efforts to improve the product."* Technology commercialization is thus concerned with the processes leading to the exploitation of technologies in products. This point of view is also found in (Howard & Guile 1992; Fildes 1990; Zahra et al. 1995) who all sees technology commercialization as the exploitation of technological knowledge in the creation of value and competitive advantage.

Technology commercialization is concerned with the organizational processes leading to the establishment of the connection between the technology portfolio of the company and the product portfolio of the company and thus the market. Technology commercialization is the organizational process by which different knowledge bases[2] are assembled and integrated to develop, manufacture, deliver a product embedding and utilizing a number of technologies.

Technology commercialization has two elements. The first element is concerned with the transfer of the technologies in the technology portfolio to the new product development activities. This transfer can also be concerned with the transfer of technological knowledge to the new product development processes, i.e., knowledge about constraints and possibilities within the manufacturing processes of the company. The new product development activities are the second element of the technology commercialization process. The new product development activities ensure the utilization of the technologies in the products offered by the company. The outcome of the technology commercialization process is the renewal or maintenance of the product portfolio. This is illustrated in figure 1 below. Figure 1 only represents a somewhat simplistic view on technology

---

[1] Products are perceived broadly to include processes as well as services offered by the company.
[2] The knowledge bases reside in the different functions of the company as well as in the company's external relations.

development and commercialization, as there will be numerous interactions and iterations between the different activities in an actual situation.

This paper will primarily be concerned with the problems involved in the transfer of technologies into the new product development process and the competencies needed to support the technology commercialization process. In relation to the transfer of technologies into the new product development process it should be emphasized that this transfer not only is concerned with the transfer of product technologies but also the transfer of manufacturing technologies (or technological possibilities, constraints, and considerations). This transfer is a prerequisite for the utilization of manufacturing technologies and competencies in the new product development process and thus for the development of a manufacturing based competitive advantage. The technology portfolio in figure 1 is also seen as representing the manufacturing technologies of the company.

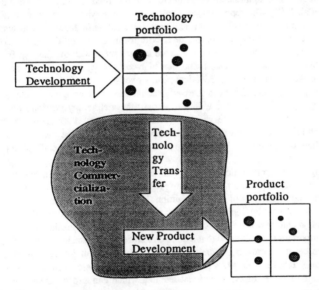

Figure 1: Technology commercialization as the link between the technology and the product portfolio.

## The significance of technology commercialization

Technology commercialization has gained importance as the relative stability of markets and technologies after the second World War has been replaced by a situation where markets and technologies are characterized by an ever increasing dynamic (Bettis & Hitt 1995). One of the major implications of this new competitive situation is that reliance on technological leadership through superior technology development skills in isolation is insufficient to ensure a sustainable competitive advantage. Companies will also need to focus and rely on the deployment and utilization of their technology portfolios. Examples from the VCR-industry (Rosenbloom & Cusumano 1987), medical equipment industry (Martin 1984), and the PC-industry (Rebello et al. 1996) clearly illustrate that it is not enough for a company to possess excellent technology development skills and be a technological leader in the industry to develop a sustainable competitive advantage. Companies need to nurture the ability to commercialize technologies as well as the ability to develop technologies. Technology Commercialization can thus be seen as the process by which the company harvests the fruits of its technology development and acquisition activities.

Spencer (1990) posits that many of the competitive problems facing US-companies can be ascribed to lack of managerial attention to and poor abilities in the technology commercialization process. The importance of the technology commercialization process has been captured by (Clark & Fujimoto 1991, p.4) who emphasized that: *"Competitive advantage accrues to firms that can bring technologies into the marketplace in a product that meets customer needs efficiently and in a timely manner."* The significance of technology commercialization has further been supported by (Nevens et al. 1990) who reported that industry leadership within a number of industries clearly depended on superior commercialization abilities. The success of Japanese and leading European and American companies can to some extent be attributed to well-developed competencies in technology commercialization. These findings are in agreement with the findings from a McKinsey study (Dumaine 1989) where it was found that high-technology products that are introduced six months late to the market will earn 33% less profits over 5 years. Abilities in the technology commercialization process have also been stressed in connection with core competencies, as one of the central managerial challenges is the ability to exploit the technology portfolio of the company in novel ways to create new competitive space (Prahalad & Hamel 1990; Hamel & Prahalad 1991). To accomplish this creation and thus to seize opportunities before the competition it is necessary to have excellent competencies that can support the technology commercialization process.

The technology commercialization process will also be an important contributor to corporate renewal, as every technology commercialization project is a possibility for the organization to extend and develop the competencies of the organization (Dougherty 1992; Leonard-Barton 1995), as the competencies of an organization only can be extended and developed through their active deployment in the organizational processes of the company. With regard to the development of competencies it is important to emphasize that a competence does not deteriorate through use as with the physical resources of a company as the competence only can be maintained and developed though its deployment (Prahalad 1993). As such the technology commercialization process can give rise to a considerable amount of organizational learning which can expand the repository of competencies in the organization, thereby enabling the company to maneuver more efficiently in the unstable and changing markets of today.

In the following sections of this paper the attention will be turned toward the competencies supporting and enabling the technology commercialization process. Special emphasis will be given to considerations related to manufacturing.

## Competencies needed to support the technology commercialization process

The success of the technology commercialization process will be dependent on the development and nurturing of a number of competencies in the company. At a highly aggregated level of analysis four different types of competencies contributing to or enabling the technology commercialization process can be identified. All of four types will directly or indirectly contribute to the success of the technology commercialization efforts. Three of the four competencies are seen as directly supporting the task within the management of technology that were outlined in the introduction of this paper. These competencies and their relation to the technology commercialization process are illustrated in figure 2.

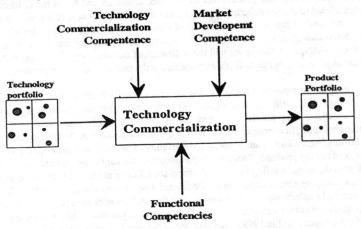

Figure 2: Competencies contributing to technology commercialization.

The first of these competencies is concerned with technology development and acquisition, which is an expression of the competencies needed to develop, renew, and maintain the currency of the company's technology portfolio. This competence is necessary for the company in order to successfully carry out the activities within the first task within the management of technology. This competence is not illustrated in figure 2 as it primarily is concerned with aspects concerning the development and maintenance of the technology portfolio. Secondly, a company will need to develop competencies in conceiving the exploitation of technologies in the development of new markets as well as the ability to conceive ways to exploit the existing technology portfolio to meet presently unmet customer demands. This competence emphasizes the company's ability to link market with technological opportunities and is concerned with the development of new streams of revenue and is necessary for the successful execution of the second task within the management of technology. Thirdly, the company will need competencies in managing the technology commercialization process it self. Included in this competence is the ability to coordinate and integrate the different functional competencies needed to achieve the efficient and effective development, manufacture, and delivery of the product embedding a technology. As such, this competence will be supporting the management of technology activities carried out in connection with the third task. The second and third type of competence are seen as controlling inputs to the technology commercialization process. The second competence addresses what technologies that should be commercialized and what customer needs that should be fulfilled whereas the third competence deals with the management of the commercialization activities. Finally, the company will also need strong functional competencies, i.e., manufacturing, marketing and product development competencies, which will enable the company to develop, manufacture, and deliver products, processes, and services to the customer in a timely and efficient manner.

The functional competencies are seen as inputs that can be deployed in the commercialization process. This paper will focus on connection between the manufacturing competencies and the technology commercialization process. An area of special interest will be on the utilization of the knowledge related to the manufacturing processes of the company in connection with the technology commercialization process. The utilization of manufacturing competencies within the technology commercialization process is one method whereby manufacturing can be used to create a competitive advantage. Furthermore, will the utilization of manufacturing in the technology commercialization process give rise to further enhancement the manufacturing competence.

Manufacturing technologies and competencies are for a number of reasons considered to be of great importance for the effectiveness and efficiency of the commercialization process and thus a number of success factors[3] related to the resulting products. Firstly, the manufacturing function is responsible for the physical embodiment of technologies in the products. As such, manufacturing is directly influencing the cost, quality, speed and reliability of delivery, and the responsiveness to the customer needs of the products. Second, a large amount of the capital investments of a company is located within the manufacturing function. As such, the efficient utilization of manufacturing technologies and competencies is important for the financial performance of the company. Thirdly, the development and implementation of new manufacturing technologies have (at least in theory) made it possible for companies to utilize manufacturing more proactively in the value creating activities of the company (Ettlie 1988). However, many companies have not yet exploited the full potential of these technological advances. Finally, manufacturing can be a major source of renewal in the company by, i.e., developing or initiating new streams of revenue. Furthermore, has it been recognized that manufacturing can be a very significant contributor to the competitiveness of the company and that manufacturing and manufacturing technologies and competencies in some cases form the basis for the business strategy of a company (cf. Hayes & Wheelwright 1984; Hayes & Pisano 1994).

Before addressing the problems and challenges involved in the efficient utilization of manufacturing in the technology commercialization process a brief discussion on the constituents of a competence. This discussion serves as an introduction to the problems involved in the exploitation and development of a manufacturing competence in the technology commercialization process.

## The constituents of a competence.

Competencies can in general be conceived as an expression of the capacity of a number of resources (i.e., technologies) to accomplish some task or activity. The resources can thus be conceived as the source of a company's competencies and the competencies can in turn be conceived as a potential source of competitive advantage (Prahalad & Hamel 1990; Grant 1991). As such,

---

[3] The important product related success factors of the technology commercialization process include: The speed or cycle-time of the process, the innovativeness of the products resulting from the process, the intensity or frequency of new product introductions, the timing of product introductions, and the cost and quality of the products.

the manufacturing competencies of the company can thus be seen as an expression of the manufacturing based competitive strengths of the company. For a competence to provide the company with a sustainable competitive advantage the competence needs to have two characteristics. Firstly, it should be valuable by contributing to the value creation in the company. Secondly, it should be difficult by competitors to imitate or substitute (Grant 1991).

The relation between technology and competence can be illustrated by decomposing a competence according to the contributing types of knowledge. A competence is constituted by three types of knowledge. The first is knowledge acquired within specific areas, such as a technology or a scientific discipline. Despite the importance of this knowledge, reliance on this type of knowledge will seldom be sufficient for a company to develop a sustainable competitive advantage. Companies have increasingly become skillful in copying technologies, thus quickly eroding the competitive advantage originating from the reliance on a single technology (Barney 1991; Clark 1989). This problem quickly leads to the second type of knowledge which focuses on the integration of these different areas of specific knowledge, a task that requires knowledge on how these knowledge areas interact and can be integrated to form a functioning system (i.e., a product) (Henderson & Cockburn 1994; Tushman & Rosenkopf 1992). This knowledge is often tacit and firm-specific and thus difficult to transfer or copy and the exploitation of this knowledge in the marketplace can render the company with a sustainable competitive advantage (Itami 1987). However, the development of new organizational knowledge is of little value if this knowledge is not used to create economical or commercial value for the company. This leads to the third type of knowledge which focuses on knowledge of how to exploit the preceding two types of knowledge in the creation of competitive advantage (Nevis et al. 1995; Leonard-Barton & Doyle 1996). This type of knowledge will be termed deployment knowledge.

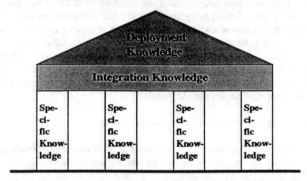

Figure 3. The constituents or elements of a competence.

The relation between the three types of knowledge is illustrated in figure 3. To develop a competence attention need to be paid to development and acquisition of all three types of knowledge.

An example of the three types of knowledge is concerned with the manufacturing system of a company and the knowledge needed within manufacturing. The specific knowledge can be seen as the individual pieces of equipment as this equipment can be seen as representing structured or embedded knowledge. The integration knowledge is concerned with the way the individual pieces of equipment can be integrated into a functioning manufacturing system that can accommodate the competitive priorities manufacturing should fulfill. Included within the integration knowledge is the knowledge embedded in the methodologies and software used to control the manufacturing function and coordinate the diverse pieces of equipment as well as the management skills involved in this integration. The development of specific and integrative knowledge is necessary for the manufacturing system to operate as required and expected. The deployment knowledge is concerned with the knowledge of how the specific and integrative knowledge within manufacturing can be deployed in the creation of competitive advantage. This does not only include the knowledge within manufacturing but also knowledge within other functions, thereby enabling that manufacturing can contribute to the value creation in the company.

The connection between the three types of knowledge can also be illustrated by looking at a Danish manufacturer of medical measurement equipment to human blood. The company commands approximately 35% of the world market for this type of medical equipment. In developing a piece of equipment the company draws on knowledge originating in a number of scientific or engineering disciplines. These disciplines include electro-chemical analysis, mechanical construction and fluid mechanics, design of electronics (hardware), software development, and design of user interfaces. The company can not be considered to be leading in any of these disciplines and parts of this knowledge are acquired through suppliers and consultants. The competitive advantage of the company originates from the knowledge the company over the years has developed within integration and deployment knowledge. There is among the employees a thorough understanding of and knowledge about the interfaces and interrelationships between the individual areas of specific knowledge. This integration knowledge enables the company to develop and manufacture products that are able to carry the desired analysis out quickly and with great precision. The knowledge on how to deploy this integrative and specific knowledge by having established well-developed understanding of the need the measurement equipment is going to fulfill forms the basis of the competitive advantage of the company. The development of all three types of knowledge has meant that the company for years have been highly competitive within the chosen niche by offering superior functionality and value to the customers. The company would not have been able to offer this without a well-developed deployment knowledge.

**Problems and challenges in technology commercialization**

The challenges involved in technology commercialization with regard to manufacturing is from a management of technology perspective to develop the deployment knowledge to a level where manufacturing can be exploited in the creation of a competitive advantage. This development of knowledge will require that organizational learning takes place both within manufacturing and within the new product development activities and that the resulting knowledge is transferred from project to project (Nobeoka & Cusumano 1995). The major way this knowledge can be developed is through the active involvement of manufacturing in the technology commercialization processes of the company, thereby enabling learning by experimentation (or by doing) to take place. The challenge from a technology commercialization perspective is to develop the deployment knowledge concerning manufacturing within the organization as a whole.

One way to develop this deployment knowledge is to utilize the organizational mechanisms enabling the integration between the different functions involved in the technology commercialization process. Integration can take on two forms interaction and collaboration (Kahn 1996)[4]. Interaction represents the structural and formal activities that should promote and encourage knowledge sharing among the different participants in the technology commercialization process. Included in this are the well-known methods from quality control, i.e., design reviews, house of quality as well as the use of cross-functional teams. Collaboration is concerned with the more unstructured and informal activities where people from different functions share knowledge and information. Both ways of integrating will be important. Interaction in isolation will not be sufficient to develop a shared understanding of the manufacturing potential in connection with the technology commercialization process. The development of this shared understanding will enable the development of the needed deployment knowledge which is a prerequisite for the utilization of manufacturing to create a competitive advantage. This deployment knowledge is developed through the tension between different "Thought Worlds" (Fiol 1994). The central managerial challenge will be to allow this creative tension to be established through the establishment of possibilities for collaboration throughout the technology commercialization process from the pre-project to the manufacturing phase (Adler 1995; Bessant et al. 1996).

The central challenge will be to manage the flows of knowledge from many diverse sources into the new product development process, integrating these streams of knowledge, and ensuring the effective utilization and exploitation of this knowledge throughout the entire commercialization process. This is only done by establishing extended possibilities for collaboration within the new product development process. Collaboration does not only mean utilizing the methods and tools from concurrent engineering, but also an emphasis on the development of a new mindset in the organization. A new mindset that will enable the free exchange of knowledge and information thus creating the needed redundancies that are necessary for the establishment of this new mindset (Nonake & Takeuchi 1995) and thus an efficient product innovation process, where the manufacturing competencies are exploited to their fullest and constantly is developed through their use.

**Conclusion and Summery.**

In this paper it has at a conceptual level been argued that the technology commercialization process is an important issue within technology management, as the technology commercialization process constitutes the link between the technology and product portfolios of the company. Furthermore has it been argued that a number of competencies are supporting or are being leveraged in connection with the technology commercialization process. A competence has three constituents and each of these needs to be developed. These constituents are (1) specific knowledge (2) integrative knowledge, and (3) deployment knowledge. The technology commercialization process can be a significant contributor to the development of this deployment knowledge and thus to develop a manufacturing based competitive advantage.

It has been emphasized that a company to develop a competence attention need to be paid to the development of all three kinds of knowledge. The technology commercialization process is con-

---

[4] Interaction and collaboration should rather be seen as the endpoints of a continuum.

sidered to be an important contributor to the development of the deployment knowledge, as the technology commercialization process is seen as one the occasions where learning from experimenting can take place, thereby developing this deployment knowledge. The organizational challenge is to develop and implement organizational form as well as a mindset that is conductive to collaboration, which is needed in the process of developing new organizational knowledge.

## References

Adler, P.S.: Interdepartmental Interdependence and Coordination: The case of the Design/ Manufacturing Interface, Organization Science, vol. 6 no. 2, Mar-Apr 1995, pp. 147-167.

Barney, J.: Firm Resources and Sustained Competitive advantage, Journal of Management, vol. 17 no. 1, 1991, pp: 99-120

Bessant, J., S. Caffyn & J. Gilbert: Learning to Manage Innovation, Technology Analysis and Strategic Manageement, vol. 8 no. 1, 1996, pp. 59-70.

Bettis, R.A. & M.A. Hitt: The New Competitive Landscape, Strategic Management Journal, vol. 16, Summer 1995 Special Issue, pp: 7-19

Clark, K.B.: What strategy can do for Technology, Harvard Business Review, Nov-Dec 1989, pp: 94-98

Clark, K.B. & T. Fujimoto: Product development performance - strategy, organization, and management in the World Auto Industry, Harvard Business School Press, Boston, Mass., 1991

Dumaine, B.: How Managers can succeed through Speed, Fortune, February 13, 1989, pp. 54-59.

Dougherty, D.: A practice-centered model of organizational renewal through product innovation, Strategic Management Journal, vol. 13 Special Issue), pp. 77-92, 1992

Ettlie, J.E: Taking charge of manufacturing - How companies are combining technological and organizational innova-tions to compete successfully, Jossey-Bass, San francisco, California, 1988.

Fildes, R.A.: Strategic Challenges in Commercializing Biotechnology, California Management Review, Spring 1990, pp: 63 72.

Fiol, C.M.: Thought Worlds Colliding: The role of Contradiction in Corporate Innovation Processes, Entrepreneurship Theory and Practice, Spring 1995, pp. 71-90.

Grant, R.M.: The Resource based Theory of competitive advantage: Implications for strategy Formulation, California Management Review, Spring 1991, pp: 114-135.

Hamel, G. & C.K. Prahalad: Corporate Imagination and Expeditionary Marketing, Harvard Business Review, July-August 1991, pp. 81-92.

Hayes, R.H. & G.P Pisano: Beyond World Class: The new manufacturing Strategy, Harvard Busines Review, Jan-Feb 1994, pp: 77-86

Hayes, R.H. & S.C. Wheelwright: Restoring our Competitive Advantage - Competing Through Manufacturing, John Wiley & Sons, New York, 1984

Henderson, R. & I. Cockburn: Measuring Competence? Exploring firm effects in pharmaceutical research, Strategic Man-agement Journal, vol. 15 Speical Issue, pp. 63-84, 1994

Howard, W.G. & B.R. Guile: Profiting from Innovation, The Free Press, New York, 1992

Itami, H.: Mobilizing Invisible Assets, Harvard University Press, Cambridge, Massachusetts, 1987

Kahn, K.B., 1996: Interdepartmental Integration: A Definition with Implications for Product Development Performance, Journal of Product Innovation Management, 1996, pp. 137-151

Leonard-Barton, D.: Wellsprings of Knowledge - Building and Sustaining the Sources of Innovation, Harvard Business School Press, Boston, Mass., 1995

Leonard-Barton, D. & J.L. Doyle: Commercializing Technology: Imaginative Understanding of User Needs, In: Rosen-bloom, R.S. & W.J. Spencer (eds): Engines of Innovation, Harvard Business School Press, Boston, Mass., pp. 177-207, 1996.

Martin, M.J.C.: Managing Technological Innovation & Entrepreneurship, Reston Publishing Company, Reston, Va., 1984

Mitchell, W. & K. Singh: Survival of Businesses using Collaborative Relationships to Commercialize Complex Goods, Strategic Management Journal, vol 17, 1996, pp. 169-195

Nevens, T.M., G.L Summe & B. Uttal: Commercializing Technology: What the best companies do, Harvard Business Review, may-june 1990, pp. 154-163.

Nevis, E.C., A.J. DiBella & J.M. Gould: Understanding Organizations as Learning Systems, Sloan Management Review, Winter 1995, pp: 73-85

Nobeoka, K. & M.A. Cusumano: Muliproject Strategy, Design Transfer, and Project Performance: A Survey of Auto-mobile Development Projects in the US and Japan, IEEE Transactions on Engineering Management, vol 42 no 4, pp. 397-409, 1995

Nonaka, I. & h. Takeuchi: The Knowledge Creating Company - How Japanese Companies create the Dynamics of Innovation, Oxford University Press, New York, 1995

Prahalad, C.K.: The role of Core competencies in the corporation, Research Technology Management, Nov-Dec 1993, pp. 40-47.

Prahalad, C.K. & G. Hamel: The core competence of the corporation, Harvard Business Review, May-June 1990, pp: 79-91

Rebello, K., P. Burrows & I. Sager: The fall of an American Icon, Business Week, february 5, 1996, pp. 34-42.

Rosenbloom, R.S. & M.A. Cusumano: Technological Pioneering and Competitive Advantage: The Birth of the VCR Industry, California Man-agement Review, Summer 1987, pp. 51-76.

Spencer, W.J.: Research to Product: A Major U.S. Challenge, California Management Review, Winter 1990, pp. 45-53.

Tushman, M.L. & L. Rosenkopf: Organizational Determinants of Technological Change: Toward a Sociology of Techno-logical Evolution, In: Staw, B.M. & L.L. Cummings (eds), Research in Organizational Behavior, vol 14, JAI Press Inc., Greenwich Connecticut, pp. 311-347, 1992.

Zahra, S.A., S. Nash & D.J. Bickford: Transforming technological pioneering into competitive advantage, Academy of Management Executive, 1995, vol 9 no 1, pp. 17-31.

# 032

# INTRODUCING ENVIRONMENTAL TECHNOLOGIES AND MANAGEMENT INTO UKRAINE

Author:
Dr. Dona T. Mularkey;
US Agency for International Development
Regional Mission for Ukraine, Belarus and Moldova, 19 Nyzhny
Val Street,
254071 Kyiv, Ukraine
Tel:       +380-44-462-5678
Fax:      +380-44-462-5834

Co-author: Mr. Ties van Kempen
CH2M Hill International Services, Inc.,
20 Esplanadna Street, 10th Floor,
252023 Kyiv, Ukraine;
Tel:       +380-44-220-1367
Fax:      +380-44-220-0242

## ABSTRACT

Ukraine is a country in transition from a communist-based centrally planned economy to a democratic-based market economy. Ukraine's environment is suffering from decades of unsustainable exploitation, unabated industrial pollution, nuclear fallout from the Chernobyl accident, mismanaged agricultural practices, and a large population. However, in the current transition climate economic and democratic objectives are a higher priority than environmental issues, in general. Because investment capital is scarce, enterprises must approach the introduction and management of technologies in a very conservative manner.

This paper describes two tasks of the Environmental Policy & Technology Project (EPT) sponsored by the U.S. Agency for International Development (USAID) and implemented by CH2M Hill International Services, Inc. in Ukraine which approaches environmental problems by supporting economic development and democratic objectives while improving environmental health and public services.

The first portion of this case study describes the work being implemented in the western Ukrainian city of Lviv in conjunction with the vodokanal, the local water utility. The vodokanal is working with multiple international donors to provide improved services to the city. Issues related to the capital infrastructure, general management, operations and maintenance, and the legal and regulatory environment of the vodokanal and approaches taken by the donors, including the introduction of new technologies, are discussed.

The second portion of the case study describes work being implemented in the eastern Ukrainian city of Donetsk related to industrial pollution and waste management. Much of the work involves the introduction of technical information and information technologies, the introduction of environmental economic principles, demonstration projects in waste reduction and recycling, new critical thinking approaches, and networking with US and foreign counterparts and experts.

Since this case study describes work currently in progress, a discussion is given on results to date and planned approaches for the future.

Key Words: economy in transition; industrial pollution; water utility; Ukraine; USAID

Oral presentation.

# 033

## OVERCOMING BARRIERS TO TECHNOLOGY TRANSFER FROM UNIVERSITIES AND PUBLIC LABORATORIES

(Key words: technology transfer, university patents, university research)
Suitable for oral presentation

Richard N. Cardozo
Chair, Carlson Entrepreneurship Program
Professor of Marketing
Carlson School of Management
University of Minnesota
Minneapolis, Minnesota 55455
612-624-5524
Fax: 612-626-8328
e-mail: rcardozo@csom.umn.edu

# ABSTRACT

Overcoming Barriers to Technology Transfer from Universities and Public Laboratories

The transfer to the private sector of technology developed with public support has broad appeal to funding agencies, elected officials, the public and many researchers themselves. Nonetheless, apart from dramatic examples like pyroceram and CAD-CAM, little evidence on the extent to which publically-funded technology has been commercialized is available. Reports to date suggest that most discoveries resulting from public grant funding have had little or no commercial impact.

To understand how much technology is transferred, and what opportunities might exist to improve the transfer rate and process, we reviewed pertinent literature, gathered documentation from and conducted interviews with more than 30 individuals involved in technology transfer from universities and public laboratories, and interviewed personnel in 19 companies that had licensed technology from a major research university.

Analysis of this material reveals that only a fraction of all research projects conducted within universities and public laboratories result in payments of royalties by a firm to which technology developed through the project has been licensed. Most royalty streams are modest, and few new jobs are created. Barriers to commercialization of technology occur at four transition points: (1) from research project to disclosure of invention, (2) from disclosure to patent, (3) from patent to license and (4) from license to royalties.

Existence of social networks linking inventors to licensees appears to be a necessary, but not sufficient, condition for transfer of technology both between and within organizations. In the absence of such connections, transfer becomes a daunting task.

Uncertainty surrounding the economic value of a new technology appears to be the principal barrier to transfer. If both the technology itself and the basis for developing that technology into a business were transferred, the efficacy of the transfer process might be improved.

# INTRODUCTION

University laboratories and federal laboratories together constitute a more than $40 billion research and development industry. Results from projects conducted in university and federal laboratories have been used to develop a broad variety of products -- pharmaceuticals, machine tools, cookware, software, agricultural products and many more (Leuthold et al 1994).

Universities' technology transfer offices seek to patent and license results from faculty and student research, both to generate income for their institutions and to contribute towards public well-being and economic development (Conyers 1993). Transfer of technology from the public to private sector presumably facilitates new business startups, growth of existing businesses and creation of new jobs (Matkin 1990, Parker and Zilberman 1993, Proctor 1993). New businesses, business growth and new jobs in turn create new social wealth. For example, a recent publication of the University of Minnesota reported that "...University research has contributed to the economic health of the state by creating more than 100,000 high quality jobs in the last 40 years." (Minnesota High Technology Council 1993)

In his first term, President Clinton proposed increased funding of technology, and transfer of that technology from federal laboratories to the private sector as a means of creating jobs. The initiative implied both that increased investment in technology would create economic value, and that there was an inventory of technology within federal laboratories that could -- and should -- be transferred to the private sector. Congress granted the National Institute of Standards and Technology (NIST) increased appropriations, and NIST has moved to expand its links to industry to facilitate transfer of federally-funded technology (Davis 1994; Graf, Mattson, Cardozo 1995).

Although the economic impact of technology transfer is thought to be substantial (e.g., Parker and Zilberman 1993), studies to document unambiguously the benefits and costs of wealth creation through technology transfer from university and government laboratories to private enterprises are lacking (Harmon et al, in press).

Anecdotal evidence suggests that many researchers are frustrated because their discoveries are not licensed or developed, that heads of technology transfer agencies face increasing pressure to transfer (license) more inventions, and that relatively few firms systematically "shop" universities and federal laboratories for technology (Conyers 1993, Harmon et al in press).

These observations prompt the following questions: (1) To what extent is technology now transferred? (2) What barriers impede the transfer of technology? (3) How, if at all, can those barriers be overcome to improve the process of technology transfer from universities and federal laboratories to private firms for commercialization?

# INTRODUCTION

University laboratories and federal laboratories together constitute a more than $40 billion research and development industry. Results from projects conducted in university and federal laboratories have been used to develop a broad variety of products -- pharmaceuticals, machine tools, cookware, software, agricultural products and many more (Leuthold et al 1994).

Universities' technology transfer offices seek to patent and license results from faculty and student research, both to generate income for their institutions and to contribute towards public well-being and economic development (Conyers 1993). Transfer of technology from the public to private sector presumably facilitates new business startups, growth of existing businesses and creation of new jobs (Matkin 1990, Parker and Zilberman 1993, Proctor 1993). New businesses, business growth and new jobs in turn create new social wealth. For example, a recent publication of the University of Minnesota reported that "...University research has contributed to the economic health of the state by creating more than 100,000 high quality jobs in the last 40 years." (Minnesota High Technology Council 1993)

In his first term, President Clinton proposed increased funding of technology, and transfer of that technology from federal laboratories to the private sector as a means of creating jobs. The initiative implied both that increased investment in technology would create economic value, and that there was an inventory of technology within federal laboratories that could -- and should -- be transferred to the private sector. Congress granted the National Institute of Standards and Technology (NIST) increased appropriations, and NIST has moved to expand its links to industry to facilitate transfer of federally-funded technology (Davis 1994; Graf, Mattson, Cardozo 1995).

Although the economic impact of technology transfer is thought to be substantial (e.g., Parker and Zilberman 1993), studies to document unambiguously the benefits and costs of wealth creation through technology transfer from university and government laboratories to private enterprises are lacking (Harmon et al, in press).

Anecdotal evidence suggests that many researchers are frustrated because their discoveries are not licensed or developed, that heads of technology transfer agencies face increasing pressure to transfer (license) more inventions, and that relatively few firms systematically "shop" universities and federal laboratories for technology (Conyers 1993, Harmon et al in press).

These observations prompt the following questions: (1) To what extent is technology now transferred? (2) What barriers impede the transfer of technology? (3) How, if at all, can those barriers be overcome to improve the process of technology transfer from universities and federal laboratories to private firms for commercialization?

# METHOD

To assess the extent to which technology is transferred, barriers to transfer and opportunities for improvement, personnel in the Carlson Center for Entrepreneurial Studies at the University of Minnesota reviewed literature on technology transfer, gathered documentation from and interviewed more than 30 individuals who had been involved in the transfer of technology from universities or public laboratories to for-profit firms, and interviewed personnel in 19 companies that had licensed technology from the University of Minnesota. These investigations took place from 1993 through 1995.

Data on numbers of projects, disclosures, patents and licenses come from both documents and interviews. The ideal method to track the numbers of projects that yield disclosures which produce patents that generate royalties is to enumerate all projects beginning in a particular year, and to identify their outcomes (in terms of disclosures, etc.) when final results are known, or at some specified date 7-10 years after the awarding of the grant. Because only about five percent of projects lead to disclosures, that approach would be costly and inefficient. Alternately, one might identify a set of disclosures made in a single year, and track their progress forward through the patenting and licensing process and backward to the grant date.

This second method, which was applied to two individual years, indicated that the time from disclosure to license took three to seven years. Disclosures typically occurred in the second or third years after the project began. This method revealed how many disclosures led to filings, filings to patents, and so on. But even this method proved time-consuming and inefficient.

A third approach is to assume that technology transfer from an established institution is a continuous process, which may be reliably sampled in any single year. In other words, one would assume that the ratio of projects to disclosures, disclosures to filings, etc., observed in any single year represented a fair sample of the behavior of the process over several years. The test of this assumption would be the similarity of results obtained from this sampling approach to results obtained through the second method described above.

A comparison of these two approaches revealed that intra-institutional variations in the numbers of disclosures, filings, patents and licenses in any one year was not substantial for two institutions from which data were available, save for known changes in practice. These changes involved becoming more selective in deciding which disclosures to file for patents. With or without adjustment for these changes in practice, annual sampling yielded virtually the same results as the exact tracking method for the two institutions (NIST and the University of Minnesota) from which comparative data were available.

The results reported in this paper reflect annual sampling data from more than a dozen institutions receiving research grants from public funds. Because the same data are not available from all institutions, numerical results are presented in summary form only. This summary should not be taken as a "benchmark;" rather, as an illustration of a typical (but not necessarily modal) outcome.

# RESULTS

We found that "technology transfer" involves a *sequence of events*, which refine the definitions of "technology" and "transfer." The sequence begins with the disclosure (transfer) to a patents and licensing office (or its equivalent) within an organization of an invention (technology) made by an individual or team of researchers working in that organization. After disclosure, that office decides whether or not to patent what has been disclosed. If the patent is granted (or likely to be), that office attempts to license (transfer) the rights to the use of a patented invention (technology) to another organization (typically a for-profit enterprise). If a license is negotiated, the licensee ordinarily attempts to develop a prototype product. If that effort is successful, the prototype (technology) may be taken from the R&D function and assigned (transferred) to the manufacturing function of a business unit, where a finished product will be produced for sale. Sale of the finished product typically triggers payments of royalties to the license holder, and constitutes the final event in the sequence. [Although sale from licensee to customer of a product based on the licensed technology does involve transfer, frameworks other than technology transfer (e.g., diffusion of innovations) appear more useful in understanding that phenomenon.]

This *sequence of events* includes four critical *transition points* at which barriers to transfer of technology or commercialization of inventions occur: (1) the transition from research project to disclosure of invention, (2) the transition from disclosure to patent, (3) the transition from patent to license, and (4) the transition from license to commercial sale and royalty stream. These transitions act like a series of dams, each trapping some technology and reducing the flow of technologies to the next.

Thus there are more research projects than disclosures, more disclosures than patents, more patents than licenses, and more licenses than royalty streams. Observations of activity in a single year of an illustrative mid-size research university or federal laboratory indicates that about 20 patents would be received. The ratio of projects undertaken to new royalty streams begun in that year is about 2,000 to one. Table 1 represents a composite, assembled from partial data from each of several institutions.

Table 1

Frequency of Technology Transfer Events in an Illustrative Year

| | | |
|---|---|---|
| • | Projects | 2,000 |
| • | Disclosures | 100 |
| • | Filings | 25 |
| • | Patents Received | 20 |
| • | New Licenses Signed | 3 |
| • | New Royalty Streams | 1 |

*Project to Disclosure*

Most projects do not yield disclosures because the projects were not intended to produce patentable inventions. "Projects" include, in the case of universities, hundreds of grants to fields in which no patentable inventions would be expected (e.g., social sciences [except perhaps for software]). In technical disciplines where inventions might be expected to be developed as a result of grant-supported activity, some research activities are directed towards understanding a process, rather than developing an invention. The percentage of projects that intended to produce an invention but failed to do so was considered low by those interviewed for this study.

In projects from which inventions do emerge, formal disclosures may not occur because the researcher or research team believes (a) that the invention includes no proprietary intellectual property, and therefore need not be disclosed; (b) that any intellectual rights belong to the sponsor, who is responsible for initiating disclosure and patent proceedings; or (c) that because the invention resulted from a federal grant, the invention rightly belongs in the public domain, into which it will be placed by dissemination through professional journals. Occasionally authors attempt to disclose their inventions to an internal patent/licensing authority after publication, when it's too late to initiate patent filing. Some researchers are simply unaware of disclosure and patent procedures. [Researchers employed by an institution are required by their institutions to report discoveries made in the course of their employment, whether funded with public monies or not; institutions, through their patent/licensing offices, have sole authority to apply for patent on behalf of the inventor and/or institution.]

Because the major reasons for failure to disclose, when disclosure is appropriate, reflect researchers' lack of understanding and misconceptions, many universities have offered seminars for grant recipients and developed informational packets for them. University technology transfer offices express some concern, however, that researchers most in need of such information are those least likely to attend seminars or study the information provided.

*Disclosure to Patent*

Most universities estimate that costs for filing a United States patent application approach $10,000; filings outside the United States may cost many times that amount. Because patent/licensing offices or their equivalents lack resources to patent every disclosure, they focus their efforts on those filings that (a) have clear economic promise, and (b) come from inventors who are willing to identify and help pursue prospective licensees. When inventors cannot identify prospective licensees, patent/licensing offices may estimate economic promise by consulting with the inventors themselves; and/or by having disclosures reviewed by student interns, technical specialists and businesspersons with experience in bringing new technology to market. If the estimate appears sufficiently promising, the patent/licensing office will likely pursue the patent application, with the intent to identify prospective licensees. Disclosures that appear likely to result soon in marketable products are far more likely to be pursued than those whose economic potential is less immediate and less certain.

These estimation procedures may be shortened if inventors identify likely licensees, whom the patent/licensing office may contact while the patent filing is in process. Estimation may be bypassed altogether if inventors bring qualified licensees to the office. In that case, a tentative licensing agreement may be negotiated contingent upon issuance of a patent.

Approximately one of every five patent applications does not result in the granting of a patent. Interviewees suggested that somewhere between one-third and two-thirds of the failures could be attributed to inventors' unwillingness to help refine the application; the balance reflected patent office rejections that the patent/licensing authority elected not to contest or pursue further.

*Patent to License*

Even when a patent is granted, if the inventor doesn't know a prospective licensee, successful transfer is unlikely to occur. Eight out of 10 licenses go to firms that employ people with whom the inventors are acquainted: former students, collaborators, professional colleagues or social acquaintances. Only about one license in 10 is negotiated between the inventor's organization and a previously unknown buyer. One license in 10 is granted to the inventors themselves, who establish a business (typically small) to commercialize the invention.

Even if the inventors are "networked" with prospective licensees, the latter may demur because of uncertainties associated with the technology for which transfer is proposed. If prospective licensees consider the patent unlikely to yield a marketable product within R&D time and dollar limits that the firm considers reasonable, a license is unlikely to be taken. Patents arising from basic research ordinarily face greater difficulty than those involving use of known methods to form new combinations of familiar components. Licenses are more likely to result when prototypes, or physical manifestations of the patented technology, are available.

Prospective licensees will not license an invention unless they believe that they can use the resulting product as a profitable addition to existing product lines or as the basis for a profitable new business. Firms may reject licenses because the investment required -- even though likely to be profitable -- appears greater than they can manage.

*License to Royalty Stream*

Not all licenses yield revenue (royalty) streams to the inventing organizations. Development work to turn the licensed invention into a product may be slowed down or postponed because of delays or difficulties in building a working prototype, or going from prototype to alpha test to beta test. If the "champion" of a product based on a license leaves the R&D function, development work may slow or halt.

Once a product is developed in R&D, it must be transferred to production and marketing. This transfer requires individuals in R&D to work with their counterparts in other business unit functions to effect the transfer. Good working relationships appear essential to successful transfer of the product based on the licensed technology.

Even if technical challenges are met and transfer is accomplished, the product may be delayed because the licensee's business priorities have changed, because the resources required to develop and to market the product based on the license are greater than originally foreseen, or because later-stage market analysis indicates substantially lower revenues than initially forecast.

When royalty streams do flow back to the inventing organization, those streams are ordinarily modest in size. Interviewees suggested that most licenses that produced royalties generated annual payments in the low or middle five figures. Almost all universities held only one or a few licenses that produced multimillion dollar revenue streams over the lives of the licenses.

Most licenses are taken for products that will constitute additions to existing businesses, additions that will require little additional wage and salary expenditure. Thus licensed technology typically creates little additional employment.

## DISCUSSION AND IMPLICATIONS

Two principal barriers inhibit transfer of technology at critical transition points: (1) lack of social networks and (2) economic uncertainty.

### Social Networks

Social networks that link inventors to individuals in licensee organizations, and span functional boundaries within licensing organizations, appear necessary to complete the transfer of technology. If an inventor cannot identify firms that might license his discovery, the patents/licensing authority faces a three-fold task. First, it must determine what type of product might be created from the invention. Second, it must identify firms that make and sell products in that class. Third, it must attempt to persuade one of those firms to license the proffered technology because a license would be profitable for the firm. These tasks are especially difficult for disclosures with unknown but conceivably wide-ranging applications. Small wonder that disclosures without links to licensees receive limited attention from patent/licensing offices, and that the process of seeking licensees is referred to as "technology salvage."

Both federal laboratories and universities have attempted to reduce this barrier in two ways. For example, NIST invites researchers from industry to work in its laboratories. When those researchers return to their companies, professional collegial linkages are in place. These relationships can facilitate subsequent transfers of technology. Many universities have comparable arrangements through which industry researchers work with faculty. Students and former colleagues who have entered the industrial community constitute a broad and durable network that facilitates transfer.

Another method used to foster university-industry networks is the requirement of some funding agencies (e.g., NSF) that grant applications for certain programs show evidence of industry support for the proposed project. Presumably, if the project yields the results foreseen in the application, inventor-industry links necessary to commercialize discoveries made in the course of the grant will be in place.

To facilitate transfer from R&D to a business unit within the licensee firm, periodic involvement of the inventor and/or a business development or venturing specialist may help to build or strengthen internal networks, if such networks are not functioning effectively. The role of personnel from the licensor organization is twofold. First, those persons make contacts with multiple individuals in the licensee organization, bringing them together in varying size groups whenever appropriate, to ensure that the network linkages are in place. Second, individuals from the licensor organization offer technical help and business consultation as needed, to assist the licensee organization in overcoming roadblocks that could delay or stop commercialization and, hence, royalties to the licensor. This activity serves the interests of both licensee and licensor.

*Economic Uncertainty*

Economic uncertainty delays or blocks technology transfer because technology has value to, say, a manufacturer only to the extent that the manufacturer can harness the technology to create value for its own customers and shareholders. Put another way, licensees are buying not the technology, but a means of creating value for their customers and, by doing so, for themselves. Thus we should think of transferring not merely *technology*, but *business creation potential* (see also Kuchinsky 1996).

Disclosures with business creation potential sufficient to command a royalty stream that would cover patenting and licensing costs should be pursued to patent and license, respectively. The time value of money suggests that the timing of future royalties be discounted at the institution's cost of funds to calculate whether it is worthwhile to invest in patenting and licensing.

Business creation potential represents a combination of estimates of revenues from a proposed business, costs of generating those revenues and investment requirements. To make these estimates, one must specify a product-service combination that would be offered at a certain price to identified customers for particular applications. If prospective customers thought that offering/price combination represented better value than what they could currently obtain, some demand could be anticipated. The level of demand, in terms of numbers of units purchased per time period, could be estimated on the basis of products currently purchased to perform the function that the new product would perform, adjusted for differences between current products and the new one.

Demand levels for the proposed product depend not only on value created for the customer, but also on the extent to which the new offering is supported through customer (and perhaps reseller) education. These and other costs must be estimated in order to forecast profitability of the business to be created around the new technology.

Prospective licensees will need to estimate the investment needed in R&D, specialized equipment and working capital to produce and market the new product. They will compare this investment with forecast profits to compute return on investment in the new technology. They will also estimate the likelihood that revenues, costs and investment will occur as forecast. If the forecast is considered fairly certain, and investment requirements are modest, the new technology may appear to involve relatively little uncertainty or risk. Highly uncertain forecasts and/or large investment requirements are typically considered high risk. Like most investors, licensees ordinarily require higher returns for high risk projects than for lower risk projects.

Licensees will compare the return/risk relationship projected for a business based on the new technology with other opportunities they face, choosing return/risk combinations with which they feel comfortable. These calculations may not be articulated, or may be done as coarse approximations. But if the transferring agency wants to complete a licensing agreement, it would be well advised to think through the prospective licensee's requirements both to decide whether to pursue a disclosure to patent, and to determine the terms on which licenses should be negotiated.

One way to bring this "marketplace discipline" into the transfer process is to place disclosures in the hands of an organization that has economic incentive to develop, sell or license those disclosures; and whose income flows entirely from that process, without other institutional subsidy. Some universities now use variations of this approach. Meaningful comparisons of that approach with those of other institutions are not feasible with present data.

[If a disclosure lacked business creation potential, the inventor's organization would be unable to license it for a meaningful price, and therefore would have no incentive to spend up to $10,000 to apply for a patent. Such disclosures might be placed immediately in the public domain, or the rights written over to the inventor.]

## CONCLUSION

Only a limited number of discoveries from publicly-funded research projects are commercialized, principally because of lack of social networks through which transfer may occur and because of economic uncertainties surrounding the technology to be transferred. This paper proposes ways to build and maintain networks where needed, as well as an approach to dealing with economic uncertainty.

This approach involves thinking about transferring "business creation potential" instead of "technology." This distinction is not merely a semantic dress-up. Rather, it implies that a prototype business plan be transferred along with a physical prototype of product(s) employing the new technology.

Development of such prototype business plans has received far less attention in business literature than has development of physical prototyping in engineering literature. Thus considerable opportunity and payoff exist for development of "protoplans" in parallel with development of technology.

# REFERENCES

Conyers, Michelle (1993), *Technology Transfer at the University of Minnesota*, Carlson Center for Entrepreneurial Studies, University of Minnesota

Davis, Bob (1994), "An Old, Quiet Agency Has Suddenly Become a High-Tech Leader," *The Wall Street Journal*, April 5, 1994

Graf, Ernest, Bruce Mattson and Richard Cardozo (1995), *National Institute of Standards and Technology, Industrial Partnerships Program*, NIST, Division 222, Gaithersburg, MD

Harmon, Brian, Alexander Ardishvili, Richard Cardozo, Tait Elder, John Leuthold, Jon Parshall, Michael Raghian, Donald Smith (in press), "Mapping the University Technology Transfer Process," *Journal of Business Venturing*

Kuchinsky, Allan (1996), "Transferring More than Technology," *Communications of the ACM, September*

Leuthold, John, Jon Parshall, Michael Raghian, Donald Smith (1994), *How Does Technology Transfer?* Working Paper, Carlson Center for Entrepreneurial Studies, University of Minnesota, Minneapolis

Matkin, G. (1990), *Technology Transfer and the University*, New York: Macmillan

Minnesota High Technology Council (1993), *Products of an Unheralded Industry*, Minneapolis

Parker, D.D. and D. Zilberman (1993), "University Technology Transfers: Impacts on Local and US Economies", *Contemporary Policy Issues* 11(2):87-99

Proctor, P. (1993), "Universities Seek Role as Technology Transfer Catalysts," *Aviation Week and Space Technology* 139 (19): 55-56

# 034

**AUTHOR :** Narciso Perales
Universidad Complutense
Departamento de Organización de Empresas
Campus de Somosaguas MADRID 28233
ESPAÑA
34-1-3942505
email :nperales@bitmailer.net

**CO-AUTHOR :** Diego de Vicente
Universidad Complutense
Departamento de Organización de Empresas
Campus de Somosaguas MADRID 28233
ESPAÑA
34-1-3942505
email :dvicente@tsai.es

**TITLE :** Internet as a marketspace:
a descriptive framework through the virtual value chain

**KEYWORDS :** Internet, marketspace, digital markets

**TOPIC :** G. Methods in technology management
It fits also in H.2 and L.e

**CATEGORY :** 1. CONCEPTUAL ( Empirically tested)

**ORAL** presentation preferably

# Internet as a marketspace:
## a descriptive framework through the virtual value chain

## 1) Introduction :From bits to atoms, From marketplace to marketspace.

The global computer network, Internet, is probably one of the most impressive technology transfers in the late XX century. The aim of this research is to summarize a framework in order to explain how actual business developments manage this technology in the multimedia section of Internet, the World Wide Web (WWW). We have used the virtual value chain concept to elucidate the main characteristics of this new competitive environment.

Nicholas Negroponte (1991), director of the MIT Media Lab, explains in a very intuitive manner how IT changes everything upside down : *From Atoms to bits*. Business were established on trade basis (atoms interchanges) Information Technology permits information trade without physical trade (bits interchanges) :new virtual markets. That is the reason for the use of virtual implements in business. Digital environments can evoke material ones and sometimes are more efficient and make unnecessary to work with *atoms*.

This paper lay on this premise : It is feasible to develop new business trough Internet because bits makes unnecessary the movement of atoms. Nevertheless goods and services are exchanged somewhere, if it is a physical location then we call it marketplace. This is a basis concept of economy because marketplace defines how companies compete, which industries and which are the target markets. The *Marketspace* theory (RAYPORT ;SVIOKLA 1994) resolves the new scenario.

*Marketspace* describes the transition from physically defined markets to markets based in and controlled by information. In this transition, information does not merely add efficiency to the transaction; it adds value. In the *marketspace* is possible to avoid physical constraints as location and time. The storefront of a physical shop can not sell outside its village, a virtual shop can sell outside its country. The ubiquity is a capability of this new environment. Other characteristic is the open time , they are opened 24 hours a day, 365 days. There exist the so called Sviokla's rule of thumb for knowing when you're in a *marketspace*: "If you can't tell exactly where the transaction occurred, it happened in the *marketspace*."

*Marketspace* is beyond electronic data interchanges (EDI) systems because EDI's are systems business to business with the purpose of efficiency and flexibility, in the *marketspace* the links are between end consumer and business (BLOCH 1995), Yannis Bakos (1991) describes this new Electronic Markets as an evolution of the Electronic Links (EDI). *Marketspace* is available because the improvement of telematics. It exists in Online Information providers (America Online, Prodigy, Compuserve) and in Telematic Networks (French Minitel, Spanish Infovia...) and specially on Internet, the net of networks.

In the essay we analyze how companies can manage this technology. Fist, we study Internet as a digital market then as a new competitive environment, and afterwards using the virtual value chain technique we study the different business developments.

Perales N./Vicente D.

## 2) Internet as a Digital market : the Rubbing Grade.

The apparition of the digital markets changes not only the context and the infrastructure on which we compete, it also changes the content of the transaction. (RAYPORT; SVIOKLA ; 142)

- **Content** : The product is replaced by information about the product.
- **Context:** The transactions are make using different tools, we negotiate through a computer instead face-to-face.
- **Infrastructure** : The information highways replace the physical highways as a mean of transportation.

In the digital markets, the content, the context, and the infrastructure is been changed by the information technology, therefore new products appears for the new markets. For example, some telecommunications companies offers a virtual answering machine with the acquisition of a new telephone line. The answering machine is replaced by a new product, the voice-box, the characteristics and profitability of the physical answering machine have been replaced by another concept, keeping tele-messages.In this case there is not any physical item, we do not have to worry about the maintenance, in terms of microeconomics, we do and optimal use of our resources, there is no idle resources.

Internet can be studied in many ways, we want to focus on the Market vision. We are interested in the Internet as a New Market, with New Rules, New Products, and also New Economic behavior. To start with our analysis we need to introduce the figure 2.1. We call Traditional Markets those that exists on the material world, the *marketplace* named before, and Digital Markets those that appears in the virtual world, the *marketspace*.

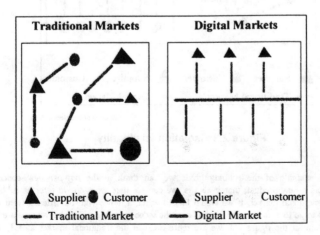

Source : own elaboration

**Figure 2.1 : Traditional & Virtual Markets.**

Perales N./Vicente D.

In the Traditional position, we know that we can create markets equaling Offer and Demand, these markets need to pass some physical tests, we are talking of geographic barriers, transaction costs, schedule differences, etc. In the Digital Markets we think that these problems can be solved. To analyze the difference between both markets, we have coined the term Rubbing Grade.

We understand **Rubbing Grade** as the effort required to move the market elements in search of market creation (Offer = Demand). In the figure 2.1 the rubbing effect is reflected, in the traditional market we need to assign resources in each market that we want to create in order to find a proper offer/demand, these economic resources are information costs, searching costs, contract costs, (transaction costs), opportunity costs ..., these all barriers makes difficult the creation of new markets. In the digital markets we can mitigate some of these costs thanks to the inner characteristics of this type of markets, as the ubiquity of the market. There is no rubbing grade, (at least it can be considered near to zero) we can move around the market without moving ourselves, we move our information, we move bits instead of atoms (NEGROPONTE, 1991).

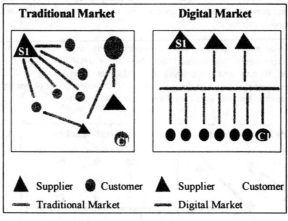

Figure 2.2 : Isolation *vs* ubiquity

As an example of the rubbing grade we can think in the *pay-per-view* concept, furthermore than a new product, that it also is, we can see here what do we refer as rubbing grade, in the traditional market, if we would like to watch a movie with our friends from our house, we need to go to a video-store , in this case the video-store is the Supplier and we are the Customer, looking at the figure 2.2, we are represented in the traditional market as C1, and Supplier as S1, as we can see, we are far away of the store, and also there could be other customers renting that film that we are interested of. So the rubbing grade to create a new market between us and the video-store is high enough to void these entertainment option and replace it

Perales N./Vicente D.

for a table game. By the other hand we have the digital market, in which we can get this film from our own house, without moving anything else that the remote buttons, furthermore, we can watch any film independently of how many people are watching the same film at the same time, it means that we have an unlimited and unscheduled supply. We can affirm that the higher the rubbing grade the lower probability of new market appearance.

If we look at the figure 2.2 we can find some peculiar facts. In the traditional market we can find isolated agents, it means, organizations that are for many reasons, difficult to reach, it means out of the market evolution, if we think about the geographic reasons we all know that we can find in our countries isolated areas, these isolation can be surpassed in a market without rubbing grade, the *cyber*market, of course we also need the physical market to transport the physical products or to establish eye contact, the latter is an important fact in the traditional culture.

## 3) Internet as a new competitive environment

Internet provides, as a competitive environment, not only multimedia capacities (images, sounds...) on different computer platforms but a universal system of communication between all the agents in a virtual market, almost potentially. There is no accurate surveys but there are some estimations in 86 millions of potential users around the world (Nettre 1996). These users are a very heterogeneous population, but without any kind of doubt, those millions of persons are all potential consumers.

The Web has made an efficient market in consumer goods likely, because it has dramatically lowered the cost of publishing information. Until recently, only large corporations or a few unusual individuals could reach a large audience. Through the web every company compete in the global market as a multinational. The web breaks down the communication barriers, geographic place and local time. Furthermore, the business developments in the web have ubiquity because virtual products possess the no rivalry consume faculty : More than one client can be using it at the same time with no loss on quality of the service[1].

The vast majority of the Internet developments give no direct revenues for the companies and Institutions. The objective is to publish information marketing products, brands and companies. This one is the reason for companies to invest money in web sites. But Internet technology permits a broad range of services. One important way to finance this services is selling advertisement space. At this moment Pay per view and subscription services are unaccustomed in the net

The web is a very flexible technology, manageable for a entire range of business developments. In our analysis of the virtual value chain we have categorized them under three streams : Marketing and Information, Distribution channel and New products. Each of them have peculiarities that we have tried to summarize in our VVC investigation.

The main problem in the web is to attract the client to the web site. This client comes to the virtual product by two ways : directly because he knows this web address before or by the use

---

[1] This point has been made as theoretical approach because in the reality there is a limit in the bandwidth of the network and in the processing capabity from the computer server provider of the virtual product.

of hypertext links from other web sites. Therefore, the marketing strategies for virtual products will have a double-face: outside and inside the web. A web site gives a technological image to the company, notwithstanding it is a good place to communicate with a potential or real client. This one is the reason for expend resources marketing web sites (by example in magazines advertisements).

The most important question analyzing the web technology as a competitive environment is to define the target that companies are competing for. In our humble opinion, Companies now are only competing to achieve users' critical mass. The Metcalfe's rule (The Economist 1996), hence that the value of a computer network can be expressed as the square of the users' number, is a reality for Internet business developments.

Virtual products and services have a peculiar attribute. The Critical Success Factor in this kind of business is to acquire a reliable image. This virtual developments are based in trust. Trust in the quality of the information given, as we will show in the next section. Trust in the reliability of the company, it is very easy and cheap to set a website but it is not so easy the commitment to conform the needs of a client. And finally trust in the security of link, security is a basic requirement in the Net (Michigan U. 1996). The expansion of the commerce through the net is limited by the lack of a secure way of payment. Nonetheless, now there are many efforts to solve this problem[2].

Some of the characteristics resumed in this paper are probably due to the fact that virtual products and services are now in the launch stage. Internet is able to be a new market, the first truly global. Today, market it is not the best adjective that fit with Internet.

## 4) Virtual value chain analysis

Rayport and Sviokla from Harvard University have a very attractive approach to the information economy. After they had specified in 94 the theory of *marketspace*, now they have defined the virtual value chain (RAYPORT ; SVIOKLA 1995). They think that companies uses IT first to visualize physical process in order to improve efficiency. The second step is to obtain mirroring capabilities and therefore make the process they use to do but trough IT. The last step is to obtain new relationships with the electronic links, new ways to create value or new customers. They have summarize the *Adding Value steps (IAVS)* in five points: Is possible to add value gathering the information, organizing it, selecting, synthesizing, or distributing it. These is a very clever way to analyze how our management of the information can add value to our products or can create new products.

Internet is interesting for users because it has produced network externalities. Internet has a unprecedented huge capability to accumulate data and Information (gather value step) and simultaneously has a user-friendly way to access information and therefore to distribute it to whom request a specific information (distribute adding value step). The sole access to Internt has a value because the large quantity Information that is free to access and the communication capabilities that Internet gives. The product and services in Internet are creating value because

---

[2] By example Secure exchange transactions (SET) or ecash implements.

they conform a implicit or explicit information demand. There are companies that their business is only to provide Internet access without any Information management.

We have employed the virtual value chain (VCC) concept in our analysis (210 companies sites)[3] reporting how companies in are using the Information Adding Value Steps : gather, organize, select , synthesize, distribute. We have classified the different strategic business approaches into three streams : Marketing and Information, Distribution Channel and New Products. This three categories condense nearly all the diversity of products and services that actually are operative in Internet at this moment (PERALES 96).

This VVC analysis is focused on the product and services that are developed within Internet, in the WWW. The Table 4.3 summarize our study reporting which IAVS and information capabilities are currently used for each kind of products.

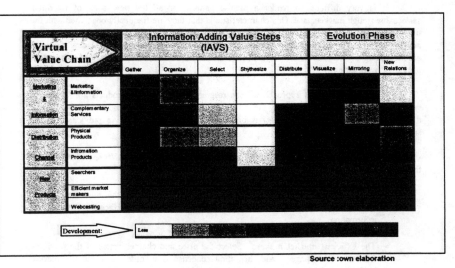

Source :own elaboration

Figure 4.3   Virtual value chain analysis

The main use of the WWW is as information channel. The WWW is a very appropriate method for marketing , to strengthen brand and corporate image. Multimedia interface and the gather capability of the web technology makes this employ of internet straightforward. This use of the Web deals intensively with the capability of gather information and to distribute it. The objective of this kind of developments is to use the information available now in a new media. As marketing tool, the web sites could be used as data-mines of the visitors, visualizing operations.

---

[3] The methodology we have used is not the the random sample . The rate of marketing services/ other products is aproximatly 10 to 1 an the bias of study would make it unuseful. We have analysed 70 web sites of each category.

Perales N./Vicente D.

The WWW is the perfect way to furnish more information to enhance customer service gathering, organizing and principally distributing the information to whom is allowed to request it creating new services in a new communication channel with the client.[4]

**Distribution channel** is a very evident apply of the marketspace, mirroring the usual physical operation in a multimedia on-line catalogue[5]. In order to attract clients this virtual shops could be grouped as a Internet mall. Outlets, Discount or auction houses are indeed concerned with the WWW because they have in it a worldwide potential market. This developments mainly gather and distribute information with no transformation. Moreover, the WWW allows to distribute directly through the net purely information products (software, encyclopedias, databases...) or intensive in information (e.g. financial services).This business are more touched with the information management and they gather, organize and select the information but indeed they add value distributing the information in a new manner.

It is very difficult to render a precise pattern for all the **new** sorts of **products** serviceable trough marketspace. One characteristic is that they are frequently concerned with the use of intelligent agents (softbots)[6] that exploit the IAVS and they are primary financed selling advertisements spaces rather than with subscription fees. The three principal new products are :Searching engines, Mediating players (Efficient market makers) and personalized information providers (webcasting).

In a transaction cost approach we can resume that this virtual products are successful when the transaction cost of obtaining the information (loss of quality, expenditure of time, price) directly through the market (Internet) is bigger the cost of their use (via publicity viewed, subscription or pay per view).

All this new products and services are intensive in the use of the IAVS specifically in the following ones :

- The **searching engines**[7] create value mainly organizing the huge amount of information in the net, selecting and having a user-friendly interface to access to this information.

- The **Efficient market makers**[8]. Select the price and characteristics of the products from the Web pages and then they condense it in order to avoid the market inefficiencies (essentially geographic or information asymmetries).This mediating agents are creating new links between producers and clients.

- The **webcasting**[9] services select and synthesize the information publish on the web or in the news to present to the user only the contents asked for.

---

[4] e.g. Drivers in computer and software industry, package information in mail express...
[5] mainly wear, books or computer products.
[6] Some rely more in human work (Yahoo by example, but it is a directory more than a searching engine)
[7] Yahoo, Infoseek, Altavista, Lycos, Magallan, Ole....
[8] by example Priceweb for computers, or Bargains fonder for CDs
[9] Pointcast, Crayon and the majority of on line services (Compuserve, America Online, MSN...)

# Conclusions

Internet is the first digital environment, from that experience is possible to obtain some insights that improve the management of other digital developments (television, radio...). There is a new way of doing business, there are new market opportunities, and also there are new requirements for the companies and the managers. This kinds of technologies whatever will be the product and the industry may give a competitive advantage because they are a efficient way to create value managing the information.

Internet is a technology that modify any of the classical three dimensions of a business (ABELL 1991) :Function ,Market, Technology. It is a radical new technology to serve matured business, It allows to access to new markets and besides that Internet creates new business opportunities. But, there is not only the arise of new markets, new products, new agents, the reason of the necessity of a modern economic analysis. It is the arise of a new competitive philosophy, we need to study a new culture based probably in the reliability of the markets. Companies will have to compete in a cuasi-perfect market, where only the contractor can break the equilibrium and take extraordinary profits.

We do not know where and how, but the *marketspace* is emerging from the inefficiencies of the marketplace. Nowadays, the digital markets play a complementary role of the traditional, but step by step this type of markets are weaving their own requirements, strategy, rules...

# References

ABELL (1980) : *Definiting the business*, Prentice Hall, Englewood Cliffs.

ANDREU, R ; RICART, J ; VALOR, J (1991) : *Estrategia y Sistemas de Información*, McGraw-Hill Madrid.

BAKOS,Y. (1991) : "Information links and electronic marketplaces: the role of interorganizational information systems in vertical markets.", *Journal of Management Information Systems*. Fall 1991, Vol 8, n° 2, pp.31-52

BLOCH M., PIGNEUR Y. ;SEGEV A. (1995) : "*on the road of electronic commerce- a Business value framework, Gaining competitive advantage and some research issues*". Electronic Publication http: //haas.berkeley.edu/bloch/docs/roadtoec/ec.htm.

HANDY, C (1995) :"Trust and the virtual organization." *Harvard Business Review*. May-June. Pp. 40-50

HOFFMANN D., NOVAK P., CHATTERJEE P. (1995) : "Commercial Scenarios for the Web: Opportunities and Challenges Electronic Commerce" *J CMC* Vol 1 N3.

Michigan University (1996) "*Hermes project*", electronic publication http ://www .michigan.edu/hermes.htm

Netree (1996) *"Internet Statistict updated on real time"* electronic publication http://www.netree.com/netbin/internetstats.

NEGROPONTE Nicholas (1991) : *Being Digital* , Alfred A Knopf, New York.

PERALES N. (1996) : *"vIrTual strategies :beyond markets and organizations"* , Procedures of the European Union COST Congress in management and new technologies, CSIC, Madrid 25-27 June 1996

QUELCH, J.A ; KLEIN, L.R (1996).: *"The Internet and International Marketing."* *Sloan Management Review*. Spring. Pp. 60-70

RAYPORT ,J.F ; SVIOKLA J.J (1995) : "Virtual value chain". *Harvard Business Review*. Nov.dec.

RAYPORT, J.F ; SVIOKLA, J.J (1994) : "Managing in the Marketspace". *Harvard Business Review*. November-December. Pp. 141-150.

RIGGINS, F.J ; MUKHOPADHYAY, T (1994) : "Interdependent Benefits from Interorganizational Systems : Opportunities for Business Partner Reengineering." *Journal of Management of Information Systems*. Fall 1994. Vol. 11, No 2, pp.37-57

The Economist (1996) : "The Economics of the Internet", *The Economist* Oct 19th 1996.

# 035

## FIRST AUTHOR

Isak Kruglianskas
Management Department
Faculty of Economics, Business Administration and Accountancy
University of São Paulo
Av. Prof. Luciano Gualberto, 908
05508-900 - São Paulo, SP, Brazil
Phone: 55.11.210-4640
Fax: 55-11.816-8044
e-mail: ikruglia@usp.br

## CO-AUTHOR

Haroldo Antonio Fernandes
Business Administrator
Faculty of Economics, Accountancy and Business Administration
Federal University of Rio Grande do Sul
Brazil
Phone: 55-51-480-7345
Fax: 55-51-480-7121
e-mail: hafernandes@nt.riocell.com.br

## TITLE

**MANAGING TO BECOME TECHNOLOGICALLY CLEAN AT A BRAZILIAN PULP AND PAPER PLANT**

**KEY WORDS:**

Process Technology Innovation
Environmental Technology Management
R&D Management
Pulp and Paper Sector
Clean Technology

**TOPICAL CATEGORY**

1, 3, Oral Presentation

# MANAGING TO BECOME TECHNOLOGICALLY CLEAN AT A BRAZILIAN PULP AND PAPER PLANT

## ABSTRACT

Among the main challenges which are being faced by most of the companies in the end of this century, the issue of sustainable development is one of the most defying to be faced by the enterprises. The search for clean technologies which provide processes and products environmentally responsible is in the top list of all companies which expect to be present in the next millennium. This paper presents the results of a research done within a big company which has gotten promising results according to its environmental performance. The results of the research suggest that for the companies which are strongly committed with the environmental matter it is fundamental a suitable insertion of the environmental management in the management of technology system. In the case studied, this referred insertion, associated with a corporate management approach based on the principles of "Total Quality" and a decided commitment and involvement of the high management of the company has shown to be a formula that is conducive to success.

## 1. INTRODUCTION

In the last twenty years the worry about the environment has increased significantly. The companies which expect to be present in the market in twenty years from now and which are elaborating realistic plans to materialize this expectancy are surely reformulating their technological priorities assigning to the environment conservation a bigger importance.

The search for more competitiveness, through efficiency gains as consequence of the reduction of loss, the so called eco-efficiency can't be obtained only by technological changes. The eco-efficiency requires, besides technological innovation, deep changes in the goals and in the assumptions which guide the behavior of the enterprise. Besides the introduction of new technology new management practices are needed. This perspective constitutes a rupture in relation with the conventional sense which prevail in the companies in relation to the relevance of the environmental and human aspects (Schmidheiny,1992).

Many examples of well-established companies have shown that there is a strong movement toward the search of technological changes with the purpose of improving their environmental performance (Kruglianskas,1995; Kruglianskas, 1996). Not only have these organizations shown the viability of these technological strategies, but also that these initiatives have made them more competitive - what is an stimulating and encouraging fact. While, for example, the production of chemical industries have more than duplicated since 1970 , the consume of energy per unit of production has reduced in 57% (OECD,1991). At Nippon Steel, each ton of steel produced in 1887 threw in the environment 75% less sulfur oxides and 90% less dust than in 1970. At Dow Chemical, the dangerous residual production was of 1 kilogram to each 1 kilogram of salable product in 1960; in the beginning of 1990 this equivalence turned to 1 kilogram of dangerous products to 1000 kilograms of salable products (Ehrenfeld,1991).

Even with all these gains of environmental efficiency , the global volumes of pollutant thrown in the planet are still increasing, specially in the North Hemisphere nations, overcoming the economical growth. In France, to each 1% of economical growth it is certified a 2% increasing in the number of products which are thrown in the environment (Chabason,1992) ; at the same time, the production of dangerous wastes is increasing 7,5% per year in the USA (Redington,1990).

The limits of economical growth are more and more being determined by the lack of safe absorption capacity of the nature and not by the scarcity of natural resources as the Report of the Club of Rome presumed in 1972 (Meadows et alli, 1972).The natural systems, aquatic, atmospheric and terrestrial are reaching their saturation limits in their capacity of assimilating the increasing volume of thrown materials.

Accordingly to Bennett (1993) many of the today's solid waste and pollution problems are being faced by rethinking old ways of manufacturing and packaging products. But in the near future new approaches of engineering and production will be required. That in turn will push R&D (Research and Development) in order to conceive new materials and production processes.

Being the pulp and paper industry, based on forests exploration, a sector of great expression in the world economy, with selling surpassing US$100 billion , its importance can't be under estimated. This industry has been very criticized by consumers and environmentalists because of the presumed pollution they are causing, under the allegation of bad forest management ( WBCSD,1996).

Considering the characteristics of this important industrial sector, the research done had as aim studying how to insert the Environmental Management of the enterprise in its Management of Technology in such way that this can benefit the eco-efficiency and the sustainability of the enterprise.

## 2. METHODOLOGY

The research was conducted using the case study approach. The case study is a research strategy that has shown very suitable for the study of the management process in organizations, specially when the questions are of the type "how" and "why" and the problem is related to contemporary events that are not controlled by the researcher (Yin, 1989).

The data gathering methodology was based on interview with executives of the company, based on a semi-structured script, that was sent in advance to the respondents. Were interviewed, personally by the researchers, six executives of different areas of the company, spending more than twenty hours in different opportunities. Besides the interviews were also gathered data from: folders of the enterprise, research reports and other type of publications. Accordingly to Yin (1989) the use of diversified sources of evidence favors the research validation.

## 3. DISCUSSION

Next are presented the analysis of the processed data. Initially it is described the context and profile of the studied enterprise and then are discussed some of the researched variables related with the processes of Management of Technology and of Environmental Management and finally some of the variables related with the Enterprise Performance.

### 3.1 - Enterprise Profile

RIOCELL is located in Guaiba County, in the metropolitan region of Porto Alegre, the capital of the State of Rio Grande do Sul, the southernmost state in Brazil. The company is located 30 km from the center of Porto Alegre (8 km as the crow flies), and is one of the largest companies in the State. RIOCELL today belongs to the IKPC Group – Klabin Paper and Cellulose Industries Inc. – the largest pulp and paper company in Latin America, with a strong presence in domestic and export markets. Figure 1 shows a simplified organizational chart of the IKPC Group.

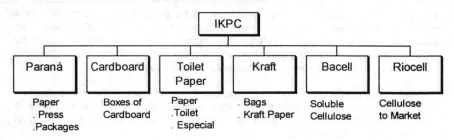

**Figure 1 - Organizational Chart of IKPC Corporation**

A very important characteristic of the Riocell is its management style. It is a very participating and lean system with few hierarchic levels. The organization chart of the company is shown in Figure 2.

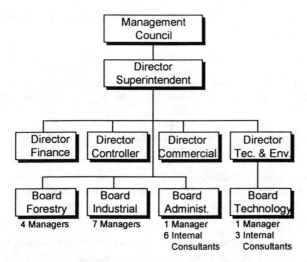

```
              ┌─────────────────┐
              │   Management    │
              │    Council      │
              └─────────────────┘
                      │
              ┌─────────────────┐
              │    Director     │
              │ Superintendent  │
              └─────────────────┘
                      │
     ┌────────┬───────┴───────┬────────┐
┌─────────┐┌─────────┐┌─────────┐┌─────────┐
│ Director ││ Director ││ Director ││ Director │
│ Finance  ││Controller││Commercial││Tec. & Env│
└─────────┘└─────────┘└─────────┘└─────────┘
     │                               │
┌─────────┐┌─────────┐┌─────────┐┌─────────┐
│  Board  ││  Board  ││  Board  ││  Board  │
│ Forestry││Industrial││Administ.││Technology│
└─────────┘└─────────┘└─────────┘└─────────┘
 4 Managers  7 Managers  1 Manager   1 Manager
                         6 Internal  3 Internal
                         Consultants Consultants
```

**Figure 2 - Organization Chart of Riocell**

The management is based on executive teams (boards), what is very original and innovative, and has shown, accordingly to the executives of the company, to be very effective for the dissemination of informations and to stimulate the involvement and the compromising of the company personnel. These executive teams meet regularly once a week to discuss and decide. This style of management was considered by all the interviewed executives as one of the critical factors for the success of the firm.

## 3.2 - Operations

When considering the operation of the company it can be broken down into two basic production processes. The process of production in the forestry or agricultural sectors, and the industrial production process.

- **Forestry Production**: While the technology employed in the forestry production process is similar in essence to that of other companies in the sector, it is worth mentioning some key differences between RIOCELL's practices and those of its competitors:

- Soil care and preparation: In 1988, RIOCELL eliminated the burning of forest waste prior to soil preparation. The burning of waste facilitates soil preparation operations because the ashes that result from burning are easily incorporated into the soil using light machinery. On the other hand, however, burning results in significant environmental impacts due to the emission of carbon dioxide into the atmosphere, degradation of the soil, loss of nutrients (especially nitrogen), and elimination of microfauna.

• Field debarking: This is one of the most interesting characteristics of RIOCELL's operations in comparison with those of other companies in the sector, especially those that produce pulp for sale. RIOCELL is the only one to have 100 percent of the debarking of the wood done in the field, and has practiced this since the start of operations in 1972.

- **Industrial Production:** The industrial unit is basically composed of three productive sectors.

1. The Fiber Line, where the wood is processed mechanically, chemically, and using heat, results in pulp for sale for the manufacture of paper, cellulose in solution for rayon, viscose, and cellophane, unbleached cellulose, as well as newsprint and writing paper, sold in the form of reams or rolls.

2. The Recapture of Chemical Products Line has the purpose of collecting the chemical reagents used in the digestion process for re-use, thereby reducing production costs and environmental impact. In March, 1990, RIOCELL installed a new unit for oxygen-based delignification, reducing even further its already low environmental impact.

3. The Utilities System, complements the other two mentioned above with the production of inputs (treated water, compressed air, steam and electricity, as well as the bleaching chemicals as well as with the treatment of industrial waste resulting from the production process.

### 3.3 - Management of Technology

In the past, the environmental management was the responsibility of a specific organizational unit, that acted in a more inspecting than guiding way. Nowadays, the management technology and the environmental management are strongly integrated in the scope of the same organizational unit - the DTA - Diretoria de Tecnologia e Ambiente (in english Directory of Technology and Environment).

One of the innovative characteristics of the DTA , according to the persons interviewed, is the use of a board to manage the units belonging to this Directory. This board is called UNITEC - Unidade de Tecnologia (in english Technology Unit). This board that is formed by four executives, respectively the manager of the group of laboratories (in number of 60); an internal consultant representing the organizational unit named "Environmental Technology" ,an internal consultant representing the organizational unit called "Process/Products" and an internal consultant representing the organizational unitnamed "Management of Technology" and also the organizational unit named CID (Central of Information and Documentation).

The attributions of DTA are typical of those encountered in a R&D - Research and Development unit, but showing a high concern with environmental issues. The Director of DTA has the responsibility of guiding , approving, following and mainly of stimulating the achievement of results according to the strategical priorities of the company. The management in a more tactical level is delegated to the UNITEC board. The activities in the DTA are performed through projects or straight technical assistance to the other areas of the company (trouble shooting) and collaboration in planning and other managerial activities.

UNITEC also gives support to other companies of IKPC and, more recently, is rendering services to external companies and organizations. These initiatives try to change UNITEC from a center of cost to a center of results through the capture of external resources-what is considerably original in terms of administration of in house R&D centers - reflecting the need of the company to reduce costs in order to be able to keep itself competitive in its market. This effort to change the R&D from a cost center to an auto-supported unit of business has been extremely favored by the creation of a "Technological Net" which integrates UNITEC through computer resources not only with other areas of Riocell , but also with other companies of Klabin Group, making UNITEC a link in this net (Morais,1994).This effort in reducing costs is complemented by intensifying the acquisition of external technical assistance through third party services (outsourcing), represented by universities, other research centers, external consultants and even other companies.

### 3.4 - Environmental Management

The nature of its productive process, its location (it is the only cellulose and paper Brazilian company which is very close to a big city) and its historical antecedents (which register the closing of the company for 100 days by environmental reasons in the 70's) made that the environmental matter has been constituting a great priority to Riocell.

The evidences about the concern to environmental issues can be seen clearly through its mission's announcement:

"Riocell must grow in Brazil and internationally producing and trading cellulose, paper and correlated products, satisfying the customer's expectancies, maximizing the return on investments, providing the increase of the international and external communities life standards, **preserving the environment**."

Besides this clear mention of the environmental matter, eleven principles about the company's behavior concerning the environment were established.

The interest and the initiatives in searching for a systematic improvement of technologies and procedures aiming the company's harmonization with the environment have produced concrete results. In November 1996, Riocell got its certificate in the "ISO 14001 System" completing its previous certification in the "ISO 9000 System" , and its participation -although it is not classified as a company in the chemical area-, in the "Responsible Care" program.

The environmental variable is already incorporated in all the company's different functional areas. As a consequence, for all the decisions and actions, considerations about the environmental aspects are taken. "Environmental Quality" is treated in a similar way as is the "Functional Quality". So not conforming to environmental standards means that the process or product is defective. This approach has permitted to deal with the environmental management in accordance with the principles of the TQM-Total Quality Management. Based on these assumptions it is seen in the company that the environmental issues are a responsibility of everyone and not only of any specific person or organizational unit.

One aspect to be highlighted is the fact that one of the UNITEC sectors is specifically concerned with the environmental technology. So, Riocell puts a highly skilled group of people to dedicate themselves specifically to the development of environmental technology. This strategy, from the company executive's point of view, has shown itself very effective. This group , besides developing technological projects with the purpose of improve environmentally the productive processes and of supporting other company areas concerning the daily operational problems, also has a very important role encompassing a set of responsibilities like: opportunity detector, executor and stimulator for Riocell participation in strategical programs in the environmental area. The conquest, by Riocell, of the ISO 14000 certification and the participation in the "Responsible Care Program" are examples of initiatives of this kind, for which the group has always counted , for its effective achievement, with the support and the stimulation of the DTA.

## 3.5 - Enterprise Performance

Riocell has shown to be a company of high performance and competitiveness. It is present not only in the domestic market, but also in the market abroad from where it get more than 50% of its revenues. Its market share is 6% at world level for bleached Eucalyptus cellulose.

When considering production costs Riocell has the lowest cost for the production of the raw material (wood available at the industrial plant floor) among all the Brazilian pulp exporting enterprises. The productivity of its human resources is the highest among the Brazilian enterprises, with a ratio of US$ 376,567/ woker in 1995 (Exame, 1996).

Relatively to the technical quality of the pulp produced by the company it can be said that Riocell has been able to achieve very good quality levels. For this reason the pulp furnished to the clients has been applied in the production of noble papers. One of the evidences of the good technical performance of Riocell's products is the high prices reached by them in the global market. Riocell is the enterprise that has the better economic price performance among its Brazilian competitors, what suggests that if the clients are ready to pay more for the cellulose they are buying this is a sign that the product has some differentiation that satisfies better their needs.

Finally when looking to the environmental performance of the firm it is worth-while to notice that it shows very low values for its liquid emissions of organo-chlorine (one of lowest in the world). It is one of the only two Brazilian enterprises certified by the ISO-14000 Norm. Among the Brazilian companies of the sector only Riocell uses a tertiary treatment for its liquid effluents, what permits the reduction of the color of the effluents, before delivering them to the river (Guaiba River). It is the sole company of the sector that operates a system for recovering solid wastes what permits the recycling of 99.8% of this kind of waste. Because of the restrictions imposed by the local regulatory entities, that are higher than those applied to the other enterprises of its sector in the rest of the country, or even abroad, Riocell has achieved levels of environmental performance that ranks it among the first of the set of Brazilian pulp exporting companies.

## 6. CONCLUSIONS

The research findings suggests that since the 70s there is a strong movement toward the introduction of deeply changes in the enterprises for the managerial practices related to the environmental factor. These changes originate from market increasing pressures, from manifestations of individuals and organizations in favor of the environment, from the implementation of new regulatory legal restrictions and technical norms. These induced changes as it should be expected are influencing significantly the way the Management of Technology is being exerted in the enterprises.

One of the aspects that is worthwhile to notice is the importance of the adoption of a style of management very participant at all levels and segments of the enterprise, specially in the area of management of technology. This style, when rooted in the principles of the TQM - Total Quality Management and strongly supported by the High Management, as is the case of Riocell, creates the appropriate context and culture that motivates the employees and the close suppliers to behave in such a way that permits the achievement of an environmental sustainability of the firm.

Accordingly to the research findings, another point to be noticed in order to reach high level of performance (specially in those firms very sensitive to environmental issues as all firms should be, and we believe will be in a near future) is the existence of someone or a group predominantly devoted to the environmental issues inside the R&D - Research and Development area, or the unit with major responsibilities for the Management of Technology. This sub-group of the technological area should be concerned not only with the technological aspects of the environment but also with the strategic issues related with the insertion of the company in programs for environmental certification and also with the effectiveness of the interfacing of its unit with the rest of the company organization.

The results of the research contribute to reinforce the propositions found in the literature (Schmidney, 1992) suggesting that for an effective environmental management it is essential that besides and suitable management of technology there must exist the support of the High Management providing orientation and stimulus.

Before ending this paper it must be recognized that the findings of this research can not be statistically generalized because it was based on a single case study. But it can be proposed an analytical generalization (Yin, 1989) in the sense that the insertion of the environmental management of the firm in the management of technology, in a context of Total Quality Management, is conducive to a high environmental and technological performance and contribute to the effectiveness of the enterprise.

## 7. REFERENCES

Bennet S. J., Freierman R., Stephen G.; Corporate Realities & Environmental Truths, John Wiley & Sons, Inc., 1993.

Chabason, L.; "Plan Vert Director", Speech at World Industry Conference on Environmental Management II, Roterdam, April 1991, quoted in Schmidheiny, S., Changing Course: A Global Business Perspective on Development and the Environment, MIT Prress, Cambridge Massachussets, 1992.

Ehrenfeld, J.R.; Technology and the Environment: A Map of Mobius, citado em Heaton G. et al.; Transforming Technology, Washington, D.C., World Resource Institute, 1991.

Exame, Maiores e Melhores em 1995, Editora Abril, Agosto, 1996.

Kruglianskas, I. - "Influência da Gestão Empresarial e Tecnoloógica no Desempenho Ambiental da Empresa: O Caso da Rhodia", in Anais do XIX Simpósio de Gestão da Inovação Tecnológica, outubro, São Paulo, 1996.

Kruglianskas, I., "Desenvolvimento Sustentável e Gestão Tecnológica na Empresa", in Vol. I dos Anais do III Encontro Nacional de Gestão Empresarial e Meio Ambiente, EAESP-FGV, São Paulo, 1995.

Meadows et al., The Limits to Growth, New York: Universe Books, 1972.

Morais, A. A., Fernandes, H. A. & Macadar, M.A., P&D na Empresa: Centralização, Descentralização e Terceirização, in Gestão da Inovação Tecnológica: Anais do XVIII Simpósio da Inovação Tecnológica, São Paulo, 1994.

OECD - Organization for Economic Cooperation and Development; Technology in Changing World, Paris, 1991.

Redington, D.B.; "Corporate Transition to Multimedia Waste Reduction", speech at EPA/IACT - International Conference on Pollution Prevention, Washington, D.C., Junho, 1990.

Schmideney, S. - Changing Course: a global business perspective on development and environment, MIT Press, 1992.

WBCSD - World Business Council for Sustainable Development, "Um futuro em transformação para o papel", versão resumida, 1996.

Yin, R., Case Study Research: Design and Methods, Sage Publications, Revised Edition, 1989.

RIOCELL 6 - 20/01/97 14:31- LA

# 036

Successive Assembly System Design Based on Disassembly of Products

Tomas Engström[a], Dan Jonsson[b] and Lars Medbo[a]
[a] Department of Transportation and Logistics, Chalmers University of Technology, S-412 96 Gothenburg, Sweden.
[b] Department of Sociology, Göteborg University, S-411 22 Gothenburg, Sweden.

ABSTRACT

This paper presents and illustrates some previously unpublished information about the design procedure of the defunct Volvo Uddevalla plant by highlighting some specific aspects of general interest. Namely our design procedure used in the form of work structuring principles and work structuring methods using disassembly of products combined with product information in order to, among other things, gain a holistic perception of product and work. The existence, as well as the application, of these methods within the Swedish automotive industry during the last decade underlines the engineering aspects of the actual design procedure.

The paper will report on experiences made in assembly system design through describing the design procedure used for work structuring using disassembly of products and taking advantage of the product information available. The experiences reported formed the platform for the design of e.g. the new Autonova plant ten years later, which has recently started operations in the same building as the Uddevalla plant.

## 1 INTRODUCTION

Since parallel flow assembly systems have more degrees of freedom than conventional line assembly systems, the design of parallel flow assembly systems is more demanding and requires a more elaborate theoretical foundation; a foundation not yet fully crystallised and communicated.

An important principle involved in the design of parallel flow assembly systems with long cycle time assembly work is that of structural congruence. In particular, this congruence might be formulated as a need for conformity between: (a) a <u>hierarchical product structuring scheme</u> used to describe the product as a structured aggregate of components; (b) a <u>hierarchical assembly structuring scheme</u> used to describe the assembly work as a structured aggregate of assembly operations; (c) the <u>intra-group work pattern</u>, i.e. the allocation of assembly operations to operators within each work group responsible for the assembly of a complete product and (d) the <u>layout and product flow pattern within each work-station system</u> responsible for the assembly of a complete product.

Due precisely to the requirement for structural congruence, the design of one structure has to take restrictions on other structures into account simultaneously, and the total design procedure is an iterative process rather than a linear process proceeding from the design of (a) to the design of (d). For analytical purposes, however, the design procedure may be regarded as starting with the design of a suitable assembly-oriented product structuring scheme (a).

Though an ideal design procedure of parallel flow assembly systems ought to be based on total congruence between (a), (b), (c) and (d), this paper will mainly report experiences on (a) and (b). Thus we only briefly sketch on (c) and (d) since these have been reported elsewhere (see Engström and Medbo 1994a; Engström et al. 1995). The methods we have developed and used to design the product and assembly structures will be discussed below, and will be illustrated mainly by data from the Volvo Uddevalla final assembly plant.

We shall be considering work in autonomous work groups, sometimes denoted "<u>collective working</u>" to emphasise the fact that operators in an assembly system work together on one or more products, having common responsibility for production output within a so-called <u>work-station system</u>.

The generality of the design procedure described below is underlined by the fact that the design procedures for final assembly reported here have been refined and used later by two of the authors for e.g. redesigning the Volvo Torslanda automobile plant in 1989 (a redesign which was never implemented; see Engström and Medbo 1994b), the Volvo truck plant Tuve in 1990, and the Autonova automobile plant in 1996. All these three cases used, or use, long cycle time parallel flow assembly systems. The last case is the reopened Volvo Uddevalla automobile plant operated as a joint venture between Volvo and Tom Walkingshaw Racing (TWR) denoted Autonova. This company has at the moment (end of 1996) just started production of exclusive coupés and convertibles by using some carry-over components from Volvo. A plant which for about one and a half year until this moment has manufactured the Volvo 850-model partly for training and running-in purposes.

## 2 USING PRODUCT DISASSEMBLY TO DESIGN AN ASSEMBLY-ORIENTED PRODUCT STRUCTURING SCHEME AND A CORRESPONDING ASSEMBLY WORK STRUCTURING SCHEME

### 2.1 Overview

To support long cycle time assembly work, there is a need for a reformed product perception using the product information already available in the form of the existing overall product structure. This product structure is mainly design and market oriented and based on the so-called function group register as described in e.g. Engström and Medbo (1993) and Engström, Jonsson and Medbo (1993), as well as on information available from the central product and process department as discussed below. This is an essential requirement since it facilitates the design procedure (i.e. reforming information already available) and promotes the introduction of e.g. new unorthodox materials feeding techniques (i.e. it is necessary for the function of the new assembly system to communicate with the overall product structure).

To design a hierarchical assembly-oriented product structuring scheme and a corresponding hierarchical assembly work structuring scheme we have during the last decade disassembled some automotive products, i.e. the Volvo 200-, 700- and 800-models, as well as the Volvo truck F-model. The methods used, in the case of the Volvo Uddevalla plant design procedure, were in many respects an interactive search process during a period of approximately 8 – 10 months engaging two of the authors who were involved not only in this activity.[1] This was in almost all respects a tedious manual process making notes by hand during the disassembly, using photocopy machines, basing different types of analysis on insufficient and often incomplete data printouts from the Volvo expertise, etc., as well as a search process for the right information and personal contacts within Volvo.

Though the process was time-consuming, it certainly resulted in the building-up of our own knowledge, as well as serving as a method for formalising practitioners knowledge. e.g. by having Volvo expertise continuously check our work by e.g. cross reading our registers describing product functions, explaining anachronisms, calling for specific documents required for the running in of the plant in the form of assembly instructions and variant specifications, etc.

The development of the assembly-oriented product structuring scheme and a corresponding assembly work structuring involved a constant change between the components from the disassembled products placed on the floor of an experimental workshop, production documents and data print-outs placed on large tables. The development work was practically performed by moving the physical components around, modifying photographs and drawings using scissors and glue to compose new documents including different types of product information, data print outs, etc. until we achieved a logical coherence between physical and logical descriptions verbally, as well as by illustrations of structuring principles successively crystallised during this process.

These structuring principles have proved to be generally applicable to most vehicles (as illustrated by photos in figure 4 and reported by Engström 1991). These structuring principles are based on five characteristics generic to all vehicles. As illustrated by the photos there is at least one obviously generic characteristic implying the existence of general structuring principles, i.e. the components distributed around a symmetrical axle running in the middle of the body, back to front. An organic symmetry where some components are symmetrical in pairs around the mid axle, while others appear only once, almost like a human body. In fact, automobiles and trucks, as well as most other automotive vehicles, show five generic characteristics or, symmetries, which form the basis of the work structuring; (1) similarity to the human body as mentioned above, (2) functions, (3) plus/minus relationships, (4) generativity and (5) diagonal symmetry.

The disassembled products laid out for long periods of time on our shop floor in our experimental workshop also served as illustrations of the production principles developed including the design of the materials feeding techniques, e.g. kitting fixtures, design of sub-system for kitting of small components in plastic bags, etc. The experimental workshop also served as a vital source of

---

[1] This procedure has later been speeded up considerably and further refined by the use of e.g. database programs, personal contacts with expertise within Volvo for the supply of product information on diskettes, printouts of specially required labels (see figure 3), etc. Thus, as was the case in the Autonova plant, making it possible to engage both operators and the plant´s engineers in the procedure, thereby bridging the practical gap between practitioners and researchers.

information for the management, Volvo expertise and qualified external visitors approved by Volvo during the period 1985 – 1991.

Very briefly described, in general terms, the design procedure used for work structuring contains four phases, denoted A – D, as described below. A procedure which of course can have different scopes according to e.g. vehicle model and the course of product variants.

Figure 1. Disassembled automobile used for design of an assembly system. The photograph is from the authors´ development work for the Autonova plant in 1995. This work essentially repeated the work done for the design of the Volvo Uddevalla plant ten years earlier.

## 2.2 Collecting information used in later stages (phase A)

This design phase mainly includes:

A.1 "collecting" the relevant product information in the form of Volvo product including e.g. so-called materials control codes complemented with information about suppliers, materials supply methods and quantities, weight, the need for or use of special packaging, etc.

A.2 "collecting" the correct translation of so-called variant codes into true product characteristics.

A.3 "collecting" correct component names and descriptions of product systems function including synonyms and homonyms.

A.4 "getting hold" of data files stating the assembly times for each detailed assembly task.

A.5 "getting hold" of an assembly sequence from specific plants or alternatively from some persons familiar with this sequence. The latter might prove to be difficult since overview of the detailed sequence neither was nor is within one specific practitioners knowledge.

"Collecting" the relevant product information in the case of Volvo automobiles requires among other things; (1) to have a diskette of the existing overall product structure containing components name, components position on the product, variant code, etc. and (2) to get hold of the detailed assembly instruction from the central product and process department, so-called process- and control instruction[2], as well as other types of relevant information.

Collecting the correct translation of variant codes and turning these codes into e.g. true real product characteristics, component names and product was (and still is) quite another matter within Volvo since some of the codes (e.g. type of market, type of emission system or type of chaise springing and dampening) are not related to product characteristics relevant on the shop floor. The reason for this is that these characteristics do not influence the product on the shop floor in a logical way. Therefore a deep knowledge of the product and product information is necessary to decode this information. The overall knowledge is not available at a single source within the company or promoted as a necessity since it is divided between numerous individuals.

The authors have therefore in all cases of application of this specific phase in the cases mentioned above been required to construct alphabetical registers and lexicons themselves based on workshop manuals, service instruction material, information process and control instructions, interviews, etc. Consequently, the term "collecting" certainly merits a separate paper.

Work in this phase, in the Uddevalla case, proved to be time-consuming since the product perception on the shop floor, as well as from the production engineering's point of view, proved far

---

[2] These assembly instructions contain, among other things, illustrations of the detailed assembly work.

too fragmented to even allow systematic disassembly of an automobile. Still less so while at the same time understanding which components were interconnected or related to other components due to product functions or true product variant characteristics. The knowledge is obviously present in the company mainly in the design department, but during the transformation of product information from the design department to the shop floor, both logic and information are deformed or lost (see Engström and Medbo 1993; Medbo 1994).

Note that the different engineering documents did not, and still do not, possess a coherent stringent vocabulary. Thus it was, and still is, extremely difficult to cross-read or get hold of the total mass of information available about product and manufacturing processes, which in fact has proved necessary in both the Volvo automobile and truck companies.

## 2.3 Preparing for disassembly (phase B)

This design phase mainly includes;

B.1 creating small cards describing the detailed assembly work (see figure 2).

B.2 creating labels comprising information from the product overall product structure, (see figure 5). These labels also contain information concerning the components suggested to belong to other types or groupings, i.e. the so-called final assembly functional groups (see section 2.4) or information, as to whether the same materials control code is used for one or more components fitted in different positions on the vehicle, as is the case for Volvo automobiles and trucks.

B.3 excluding all the small cards that are non-assembly relevant due to the scope and restrictions on the design procedure (e.g. excluding punching the identification number on the vehicle, automatic gluing of the windshield, work performed in the testing workshop after assembly, etc.).

B.4 grouping the small cards according to the suggested assembly sequence into suggested work modules, i.e. different levels of the detailed assembly sequence, depending on specific shop floor preconditions (se 2.4), forming the suggested intra-group work pattern.

During our design work in the case of the Autonova plant we were supported by having the Volvo overall product structure available on line, as was also the case in our work for the Volvo truck company, and we also used a database programs to support our work. An analysis data base composed of different Volvo data files including information such as size of materials containers, weight, suppliers, etc. was created for the Autonova plant design. This was unfortunately not the case during the early Uddevalla experiences.

Thus we could easily document the successive results from the disassembly work, as well as transfer the results for the total design of an assembly system, regarding among other things, material requirement, space utilisation for stored materials, etc. In fact, in the Autonova case the design procedure, as well as the starting-up of this plant, was based on this specific analysis data base.[3]

## 2.4 Disassembly and checking through assembly (phase C):

This design phase mainly includes:

C.1 successively disassembling the product guided by the suggested assembly sequence and the preliminary work modules represented by the grouping of the small cards. The cards are

---

[3] There are at least three explanations for the extremely time-consuming work to create a database related to the Volvo overall product structure based on disassembly, i.e. to designate the correct physical component to the "right administrative position" in the overall product structure. This is a reversed process to the ongoing work in a running plant to use the bills-of-materials (derived from the overall product structure) to trigger the materials to be delivered.

One reason is that in the original overall Volvo product structure the smallest identifiable unit (the so-called material control code) is equal to the materials address along the traditional assembly line. Thus identical components could be fitted at different positions on the product and it is time-consuming to identify and designate the components correctly.

Another reason is that the information systems within Volvo are not designed for this type of analysis. They have in fact been developed over the years into a complex conglomerate of information systems suited for steering a complex, constantly changing organisation there work moves around between manufacturing facilities, subassembly and final assembly stations, etc.

Finally, the product information and the product specifications are constantly changing (i.e. change orders) and the different files containing different product information are not synchronised. Therefore each existing local assembly plant transforms the overall Volvo product structure according to the specific assembly system design and the product variants manufactured (see e.g. Engström and Medbo 1993).

positioned on tables, sometimes divided by wooden lathes, in order to overview the component and allowing work modules to be redefined by regrouping small cards.

C.2 successively positioning the components on the floor dividing suggested work modules by the wooden lathes, including positioning the correct labels on or beside the respective component including correcting the analysis data base as the work goes on.

C.3 rechecking the disassembly and the analysis data base by guiding selected expertise through the disassembled components.

C.4 final rechecking by assembling the product.

The small card ought to be positioned on tables near the corresponding components. Any questions and assumptions must be noted on the small card or on white boards as the work goes on in order to systematically decompose the product. This makes it possible to have extra personnel assist the researchers by guiding the design phases described in this paper, thus speeding up the work. Or, as has been the case in Autonova, to let operators who were going to be responsible for specific work on the product perform the disassembly work.

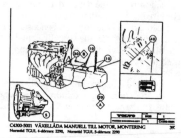

Figure 2. Small cards (approximately 14 x 10 centimetres) used for guiding the disassembly, as well as the subsequent assembly work. Illustrations of detailed work tasks on the cards were derived from the Volvo process and control instructions. These instructions contain illustrations of the work, name of the operations, etc. The cards have been composed by us to include assembly time required for a specific product variant and name of the work since the original document is quite extensive. The cards has also been complemented by us with sequence number in this case from 1 to 997 in order to be able to find the original card since some were prone to get lost during the design procedure, and since the result of the procedure might need to be updated later due to change orders. The method used to create these cards requires shrinking of the illustrations, transferring the name and function group codification (coded into the groups of components (coded 2 000 – 8 000) to the front page of the card since the original document contains front illustrations (1 – 10 pages), as well as a standardised form (1 – 40 pages in A4 format) comprising assembly sequence and materials required (component number, component name, variant codification, tools, torque, quality demand, etc.). The card shown above is from our work for the Autonova plant.

During this process we marked each component with the labels containing complete information from the existing overall product structure (see figure 5). We also sewed all small components together with the appropriate illustrations onto 21 large (220 x 120 cm) white sheets of paper[4]. This allowed the authors to acquire in-depth learning of the product, as well as to establish the interrelationship between the components and the existing overall product structure. We used illustrations reduced in size from those provided by the central product and process department (see figure 2), and we also constructed a new illustrations system as a contextual visual aid. This illustrations system contained several interrelated levels and used a standardised outline for normalising the illustrations. The vehicle is viewed diagonally from behind, as if entering an automobile on the driver's side, see Engström, Hedin and Medbo (1992).

Finally, the disassembled products are assembled or the analysis data base is used for mirroring yet another product which is assembled in order to verify the assembly-oriented product structuring scheme and a corresponding assembly work structuring scheme. The latter approach was performed for the design of the Autonova plant where the analyse data base was developed and refined during

---

[4] These paper sheets were also used by the new operators to learn the assembly work in the training workshop, as well as for the initial identification of the small components suited for packing in plastic bags. A unique materials feeding technique especially developed for the Uddevalla plant.

the manufacturing of the Volvo 850-model and later mirrored in and used for the manufacturing of the C70-model.

| | | |
|---|---|---|
| 94 82 10<br>bandklamma 45.<br>3730-1001<br>2<br>2.0 | GOLVMATTA,BLA     A 1   001<br>V FRAM<br>  1310002      8552010 011   1<br>. V-STYRD   GLES LUG BLA MAT<br>(GOLVBEKLADNAD<br>golvmatta främre V, V-styrd, lägnivå | PLUGG,SVART<br>FIXERING AV BOTTEN-<br>^SVALLARKABLAGE<br>LEDNING,BOTTENSVALLARE<br>16st   3760 010 515   1264326   011100<br>flera lägingar<br>V:2   C3760-5001   deladat   LB014<br>80<br>Mont.fas:      Delfas:      Delad med: |
| Label used in 1987 for disassembly used for the design of Volvo Uddevalla plant[5] | Label used in 1989 for disassembly used for the design of Volvo Torslanda plant[6] | Label used in 1995 for disassembly used for the design of Autonova plant[7] |

Figure 3. Example of different labels containing product information used for disassembly. These labels complement the small cards shown in figure 2, by having all information necessary to relate the label, which represents one component in the existing overall Volvo product structure, process engineering instructions, material supply information and selected reference plant processes. Thus it becomes possible to decompose e.g. one single product using its components as representative of all product variants. Practically the component, e.g. one seat, was removed from the automobile body according to the small card and the labels for all variants of seats were placed on or fitted to this specific seat. Thus, as has been the case in the Autonova plant design, the product information in the form of labels and small cards could be up to date, while the product decomposed could even be somewhat old. The planned rebuilding of the Volvo Torslanda plant referred to above was never implemented (see Engström and Medbo 1994b).

*

Note that the purpose of the design procedure could differ. For example in the Uddevalla case it was initially a question of finding a logical grouping of the components. Which in fact proved possible by some thinking and moving around of the components of a disassembled automobile on the shop floor of the experimental workshop.

As a result of this work to puzzle together the components on the shop floor, and by the aid of photos of the components taken in the experimental workshop, we recognised five final assembly functional groups. These groups were: (0) Doors; (1) Leads for electrics, air and water; (2) Drive line; (3) Sealing and decor and (4) Interior. The first group being subassembly work, while the other four were work on the automobile body. These groups of components imply not only a general classification applicable for automobiles – but also, and this is important, a classification based on five generic characteristics always present in all vehicles.

The detailed assembly work is then derived from this classification according to levels, where the highest level, depending on the specific assembly system designs is work modules. [8] That is, an

---

[5] These labels were used for our first work structuring. i.e. the disassembly was aimed at identifying a taxonomy, i.e. the final assembly functional groups, as well as the suggested detailed assembly sequence for the first automobiles assembled in Uddevalla. In this case a delimited number of specific product variants. Our knowledge of the merits of using existing product and process information was quite insufficient.

[6] These labels were used for disassembly comparing three specifically different product variants (denoted "A1", "B1" and "C1" on these labels) during a period when no formal product- and process information regarding parallel flow assembly system existed within Volvo. The Uddevalla plant was being designed using inferior information support since this system was under development and the responsibility for the information quality was not defined. This dissembly helped us conform the final assembly functional groups and their "variant tracks".

[7] These labels were used to guide the design, for all product variants, of the detailed intra-group work pattern, materials feeding techniques, analysis data base, etc., as well as to guid the unpacking and sorting of components delivered for the first 40 product variants manufactured in Autonova. The unpacking refined the analysis data base still further. Note that in this case the taxonomy was already known. We also directly during the disassembly, started to designate the right material control code to the correct assembly position on the automobile. This was performed by letting the components with the same material control code but different assembly positions have as many labels as number of positions chosen. Resulting in adapted material control codes through splitting of the original codes.

[8] The final assembly functional groups are intersected with work modules forming the intra-group work pattern for the "collective working" in the case of the Volvo Uddevalla plant. In this case the modules corresponded to the working position and the position of the automobile body. The modules were fitted in a so-called tilting device, which enabled the automobile body to be altered (e.g. the modules were denoted "tilt over" corresponding to assembly work on the upside of the vehicle as well as on a tilted automobile body)

overall taxonomy, in the form of the so-called final assembly functional groups was first stipulated, and different levels of the detailed assembly sequence, depending on specific shop floor preconditions (work group size, competence overlap within the group, ergonomic preferences, etc.) are later derived from this classification. This procedure allows, among other things, an implicit defined interrelation between materials and tools, work descriptions and other types of production documents and instructions on how to perform the assembly work in practice. Thus the technical and administrative preconditions on the shop floor facilitate the long cycle time work in order to reduce the individual learning time. In fact this prestructuring of information and materials is vital for long cycle time work.

In the case of the design of the Autonova plant ten years later, these groups were known, as well as the general structuring principles. Thereby work was primarily concentrated on a search for intra-group work patterns based on work modules and the creation of an analysis database to support the design and running in of the plant by serving as an instruction both for organising the materials for the first automobiles built and for the building of all other products manufactured until today.

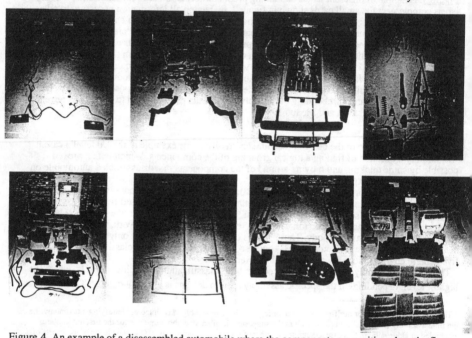

Figure 4. An example of a disassembled automobile where the components are positioned on the floor according to their position in the automobile body. Photographs from the Uddevalla experiences dated 1986 showing a Volvo 740-model. In this case the photographs correspond to 1/8 of an automobile, i.e. approximately 20 minutes cycle time where three operators were responsible for the assembly work. These photographs proved to be valuable for us when formulating and communicating work structuring principles as described above. Placing all eight photos of the disassembled automobile made it evident that a plant layout where 1/8 of an automobile was assembled in eight separate workshops in series would require enormous buffer volumes between assembly workshops or a constant shifting of operators according to time differences between product variants with different product designs. In fact, no congruence between the product structuring scheme and the assembly structuring scheme was possible to achieve until at least 1/4 of the automobile was overviewed.

2.5 Considering the effect of product variants (phase D)

This design phase mainly includes:

D.1 detailing the assembly information gained according to variance introduced by different product variants, product variants that are not necessary to disassemble since they could be grasped intellectually by the analysis data base and work performed in phase A. Thereby making it possible to generalise the hierarchical product structuring scheme and the hierarchical assembly structuring scheme to include all product variants through the identification of the so-called <u>variant tracks</u>.

D.2 identification of variant tracks corresponding to characteristics more or less obvious due to the choice of the final assembly functional groups. These tracks correspond to the need for e.g. overlapping competence between operators within or between work-station systems. i.e. these tracks may or may not call for extra work, as is evident from the table shown in figure 7.
9

D.3 grasping the differences in assembly work stipulated by a decomposed reference product variant in relation to product variants. This could be either by rough estimations or by taking advantage of available manufacturing process information. 10

This assembly time analysis according to D3 and illustrated in figure 5 also made use of the delimited time-and-motion studies performed in Uddevalla. During this period only a restricted number of product variants were manufactured. i.e. the delimited assembly times from the Uddevalla plant were compared to the assembly time gained through information from the central Volvo product and process department in order to check the reliability of the information. 11

## 2.6 Continued assembly system design

To summarise, the results from the analysis phases briefly described above are an assembly-oriented product structuring scheme and a corresponding assembly work structuring scheme necessary as an input for calculating production capacity considering e.g. assembly time constraints, i.e. the choice of capacity for the work-station system design in relation to the total assembly time stipulated by the product design and the targeted production capacity for the total plant.

The last procedures have been reported elsewhere in Engström and Medbo (1994a) and Engström et al. (1995). Briefly sketched, they contain design of the intra-group work pattern, the work-station system layout, the product flow pattern, the design materials feeding techniques, defining subassembly work tasks suitable for integration into the work-station system, etc. Thereby including, for example, the design of the overall layout of a specific assembly system, is quite an elaborate procedure. We have therefore delimited this specific paper to explaining some vital work structuring phases in the design procedure of assembly systems which we have utilised during the last decade. The assembly system design must of course include e.g. the choice of product flow pattern such as serial or parallel flow assembly systems, adapted to production capacity and assembly time

---

9 Regarding product variants these ought to be described in terms of characteristics which are always present in all product variants. Two such characteristics exist for all vehicles, (1) distinguishing groups of components, which is possible since a vehicle does not consist of one part alone (final assembly will of necessity always need to be described in terms of groups of material) and (2) generativity (gender), i.e. those components which have been assembled or are to be assembled imply characteristics of a specific vehicle. Therefore product variants may be described according to variant tracks at different levels A – E. Level A showing characteristics having their origin outside final assembly work, which becomes obvious when viewing e.g. the naked automobile body or the complete vehicle (i.e. colour, 4/5 doors, with or without sunroof etc.). Level B showing characteristics having their origin in large, synchronous sub-assemblies (i.e. power plant with fuel system, facia etc.). Level C showing characteristics which have their origin in a specific functional group but which overlap more than one group (i.e. ABS and ETC-systems). Level C showing characteristics which have their origin within a functional group but do not belong to any others (i.e. upholstery colour). Level D characteristics which are not generative at all (i.e. wheel embellishments). See Engström (1991).

10 In e.g. the Uddevalla case information from the central Volvo product and process department. Information in the form of time-and-motion studies specifying assembly times for specific detailed work tasks available for all product variants. Thus we did not e.g. need to disassemble more than two product variants in the case of Uddevalla and one in the case of the Autonova plant design.

11 Put diffently, there was a coherence between (1) the central times gained stipulating net assembly times (i.e. the minimum time required for one worker to assemble the complete product at full pace if tools and materials materialised in his hands at the precise moment required based on time-and-motion studies) gained through our work mapping and (2) the Uddevalla times gained locally through the Uddevalla engineers' time-and-motion studies based on the restricted number of product variants manufactured during this period.

constraints, that is production capacity targets and required assembly times for the product and product design considered.

| | Reference variant (%): | Variant 1 (%): | Variant 2 (%): | Variant 3 (%): | Variant 4 (%): | Variant 5 (%): | Variant 6 (%): |
|---|---|---|---|---|---|---|---|
| Type of variant:* | B230FS, 4D, | B230FS, 4D ABS-brakes | B230FS, 4D, Aircondition | B230FS, 4D, Sunroof | B230FS. 4D, | B230FT, 4D, | B230FT, 4D, ABS-brakes Aircondition Sunroof |
| Operator 1: | 25 | 0 | 12 | 0 | 0 | 0 | 17 |
| Operator 2: | 25 | 0 | 0 | 20 | 14 | 0 | 31 |
| Operator 3: | 25 | 0 | 1 | 16 | 0 | 0 | 21 |
| Operator 4: | 25 | 2 | 0 | 16 | 0 | 3 | 20 |
| Operator 5:* | +20 | 3 | 13 | 0 | 1 | 1 | 55 |

* Extremely brief description B230FS = 2.3 litre suction engine with injection, B230FT = 2.3 litre turbo engine with injection. 4D = four doors, 5D = five doors.
** This operator performed only subassembly work corresponding to 20 per cent extra in relation to the 100 per cent work on the automobile body, i.e. he was not fully balanced if the five operators performed "collective working".

Figure 5. Time spread in per cent of assembly work on the automobile body in comparison to disassembled reference product variant according to our design procedure performed for the Volvo Uddevalla plant design in 1987. In this case we assumed a distribution of the assembly work into four equal parts of an automobile which of course would not be possible to achieve in practice. The time given in the table was used for the design of different intra-group work patterns thereby assuming an ideal balancing of the work for the reference variant (Engström, Medbo and Tuhnberg 1987). The estimation of relevant assembly times for different product variants was a tedious work performed in the experimental workshop in Gothenburg by two of the authors of this paper based on our work mapping in the training workshop in Uddevalla (see Engström and Medbo 1994a) by coding every component according to variant code, as well as composing and decomposing detailed work tasks organised according to the function group register (coded into the groups of components 2 000 – 8 000).

3 CONCLUSIONS

This paper highlights some specific aspects of general interest of the story about the design and development of assembly system design within the Swedish automotive industry, namely the design procedure including work structuring principles used for several assembly system design cases. Thereby we will emphasise the importance of the technical aspects mostly neglected in the international debate concerning the socio-technical design approach where design processes tend to be regarded as mainly participative in nature.

In practice the work structuring phases in the design procedure reported above underline that the overview and detailed information required to structure the work in order to achieve an efficient assembly work, using parallel flow assembly systems with long cycle time assembly work, according to the need of the structural congruence required, is not possible to obtain from present "digitised" information about the product and work available within the automotive industry. It requires a combined design approach amalgamating "analogous" physical products and their components, as well as data from the overall product structure. By using the procedure described, it is possible to interrelate "shop floor reality", the present descriptions of the shop floor reality of both products and manufacturing processes and the future "shop floor reality" i.e. the assembly systems not yet designed.

From our point of view the design cases reported are not pure cultivation of participation as has been the international public profile of non-traditional Swedish assembly plants. Instead the plant design does include a true engineering approach, supported by established knowledge from social science (e.g. Karlsson 1978; Nilsson 1981). However, the true core of the plants might have been internationally misunderstood as a human relation approach further dimmed by terms like participation and humanisation - since the true engineering approach, certainly has been present in some cases, as described above.

Generally speaking, our experience from and involvement in the design of the Volvo Uddevalla plant in 1985 – 1988 and the Autonova plant ten years later, as well as several other assembly facilities, underlines the importance of transferring design procedures and design experiences between large industrial development projects. A responsibility which in the case concerning assembly system design, due to various circumstances, has come to be the role of the researchers.

REFERENCES:

Engström T (1991). "Future Assembly Work – Natural Grouping". Design for Everyone, Queinnec Y, Daniellou F (eds.), Taylor & Francis Ltd, London, Proceedings, Vol 2, pp 1317 – 1319.

Engström T, Hedin H, Medbo L (1992). "Design Analysis by means of Axonometric Hand–drawn Illustrations". The International Product Development Management Conference on New Approach to Development and Engineering, Brussels 1992. Proceedings, pp 147 – 157.

Engström T, Jonsson D, Medbo L (1993). "An Assembly–Oriented Product Description System as a Precondition for Efficient Manufacturing with Long Cycle Time Work". Productivity & Quality Management Frontiers – IV, Suthmanth D J, Edosomwan J A, Poupart R, Sink D S (eds.), Industrial Engineering and Management Press, Norcross, Georgia, pp 453 – 462.

Engström T, Jonsson D, Medbo P, Medbo L (1995). "Interrelation between Product Variant Codification and Assembly Work for Flexible Manufacturing in Autonomous Groups". International Journal of Material Processing Technology. Vol 52, pp 133 – 140.

Engström T, Medbo L (1994a). "Intra–group Work Patterns in Final Assembly of Motor Vehicles". Published in International Journal of Operations & Production Management, Vo. 14, No 3, pp 101 – 113.

Engström T, Medbo L (1994b). "Finns det en vidareutveckling av Volvos Uddevallafabrik?". Genomförande av förändring, Palmerud G (redaktör), Nordiska Ergonomisällskapets Årskonferens, Stenungsund, Proceedings pp 166 –1969 (in Swedish).

Engström T, Medbo L (1993). "Naturally Grouped Assembly Work and New Product Structures". International Journal of Technology Management, Vol 7, No 4/5, pp 302 – 313.

Engtröm T, Medbo L, Thunberg K (1987). "Sammanfattning av diskussioner kring förutsättningar för layoutval". Department of Transportation and Logistics, Chalmers University of Technology, Gothenburg (unpublished work report).

Karlsson U (1978). "Alternativa produktionssystem till lineproduktion, Department of Sociology, Gothenburg University, Gothenburg (PhD-thesis in Swedish).

Medbo L (1994). "Product and Process Descriptions Supporting Assembly in Long Cycle-Time Assembly". Department of Transportation and Logistics, Chalmers University of Technology, Gothenburg (licentiate thesis).

Nilsson L (1981). "Yrkesutbildning i nutidshistoriskt perspektiv". Pedagogiska Institutionen. Göteborgs Universitet, Göteborg (Ph.D. thesis in Swedish).

# 037

# Production Models and Social Contexts

Dan Jonsson[a], Tomas Engström[b] and Lars Medbo[b]

[a] Department of Sociology
Gothenburg University
S-411 22 Gothenburg, Sweden

[b] Department of Transportation and Logistics
Chalmers University of Technology
S-412 96 Gothenburg, Sweden

ABSTRACT

This paper discusses production models for final assembly in the automobile industry. Some issues and pitfalls in current production model discourse are briefly considered, and in this context a distinction between manufacturing models and broader industrial models is introduced. Drawing on this distinction, we discuss the Japanese "Lean production" as an industrial model and the impact of socio-economic and socio-cultural contexts on manufacturing models and industrial models.

Based on data on labour's share of value-added as related to value-added's share of sales, we argue that the competitive advantage of Japanese automobile manufacturers may be due rather to the strength of Japanese "Lean production" as an industrial model than to its efficiency as a manufacturing model. Specifically, assembly plant productivity and assembly plant practices do no warrant the amount of attention paid to them recently (e.g. by Womack et al. 1990), whereas, as our analysis implies, supplier relationships may be a key issue.

Additional factors that have to be taken into account in the current production model discourse are prevailing societal values such as the reputed Japanese "hardship mentality" and the corresponding values in "post-industrial" societies such as Sweden. For example, in the Swedish Uddevalla and Kalmar plants we found that the most important determinants of job satisfaction were perceived opportunity to exert influence over one's own work and whether one's work was perceived to be interesting, providing opportunities for personal growth. By contrast, workers' evaluation of the pay received, for example, was not a significant determinant of work satisfaction. Clearly, the manufacturing model used must agree with predominating societal values; for example, few assembly workers in the Uddevalla plant would probably have felt happy with traditional assembly line work.

The analysis in this paper indicates that it is more interesting to look for those conditions that allow big wage differentials between suppliers and assemblers to exist than to look for assembly plant practices that allow assembly plant man-hour counts to be reduced. In this connection, attention should be directed at the Japanese company union system and the core company – core employee alliance in the Japanese automobile industry.

1 . Introduction

During the last decade, management's search for profitability and other elements of business success seems to have taken a new turn. The business strategy perspective has been de-emphasized in favour of a production model perspective.

In the business strategy perspective, the design of manufacturing operations are regarded as involving a number of trade-offs between performance aspects, e.g. a trade-off between productivity and product quality. The choice of manufacturing strategy reflects the priority assigned to various performance aspects, e.g. whether productivity is given priority over product quality. The priorities and the manufacturing strategy chosen ideally depend, in turn, on the contingencies characterizing the current situation, including the type of products manufactured, the broad business strategy adopted by the company and its business environment. A manufacturing strategy that is appropriate in one context would be inappropriate in another context according to this line of thinking.

According to the current production model discourse, by contrast, manufacturing operations should be designed in accordance with a production model that tends to be regarded as generally applicable and superior in all respects. Trade-offs between different performance aspects are de-emphasized. For example, it is believed that there is no real contradiction between productivity and product quality; they can be improved simultaneously by applying appropriate production methods – that is, by emulating a universally valid production model. Thus, the precepts of "World Class Manufacturing" are presumably valid in all contexts.

Clark (1995) points out that the shift to a production model perspective has been inspired by Japanese manufacturers' market success during the seventies and eighties. This market success seemed to derive from a superior production competence rather than a clever choice of business strategy.

The management best-seller "The Machine that Changed the World" (Womack et al. 1990) explicitly linked the competitive advantage of Japanese automobile manufacturers to a specific production model pioneered by the Toyota Corporation, so-called "Lean production". A basic explanatory model proposed in this book is summarized in Figure 1 (Jonsson 1995).

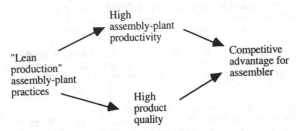

Figure 1. Summary of causal analysis of Japanese automobile assemblers' competitive advantage according to Womack et al. (1990).

As explained in some detail by Jonsson (1995), this explanatory model is unsatisfactory for several reasons. Most important in the present context is the fact that the model is incomplete. The point is that the assembly plant represents only the tip of the iceberg in the automobile industry. It is a great analytic mistake, therefore, to focus on assembly plant practices and performance, neglecting the broader industrial system "beneath the surface" and the relevant social context.

This paper may be viewed as an attempt to clarify, criticize and extend the current production model discourse, using the automobile industry as an illustration.

## 2. Some issues and pitfalls in the current production model discourse

The notion of a production model represents a theoretical abstraction from and simplification of actual industrial practices. It may be questioned whether such ex post schematizations and categorizations of complex, disparate and constantly changing industrial practices do really clarify issues. Some problems involved will be illustrated by the case of "Lean production" or "Toyotism" (cf. Boyer and Freyssenet 1995).

First, it has been questioned whether "Toyotism", and even more so "Lean production", is a well-defined, coherent model. "The Machine that Changed the World" praises "Lean production", but does not really define it. Also, there is no general consensus about what are the essential elements of "Toyotism". The fact that Toyota is now experimenting with new production practices, in particular at the Tahara IV and Kyushu plants (Nomura 1993, Benders 1994), highlights this lack of precision. Does this mean that Toyota is now using two production models simultaneously, or does it mean that one production model is changing into another one, or is this a change within the scope of the same production model?

Second, while Womack et al. (1990) contrast "Mass production" to "Lean production", others (e.g. Warnecke and Huser 1993) have seen more continuity than change. "Lean production", after all, retains key elements of traditional "Mass production" such as the paced assembly line, short cycle times, standardised work methods and a hierarchical organisation structure.

Third, there is a frequent confusion about levels of analysis in the current production model discourse, as suggested by some authors' change of vocabulary from "Lean production" to "Lean enterprise". The question is whether "Lean production" or "Toyotism" should (1) be regarded as a production model in the narrow sense, i.e. a schematization of assembly plant practices, or should (2) be understood as including design, component supply, marketing, finance etc. For example, Womack et al. (1990) vacillate between these two interpretations in a confusing manner.

To emphasize this important distinction between levels of analysis, production models in the narrow sense will be referred to as manufacturing models in the remainder of this paper, while production models in the broader sense will be referred to as industrial models.

Another significant problem in the current production model discourse is distinct from but related to the mainly conceptual problems just considered. This is the problem of causal misinterpretations of performance differences. Specifically, inter-firm differences with respect to physical and economic performance measures are frequently erroneously attributed to differences between manufacturing models rather than differences between products, differences between industrial models, differences between social contexts, etc.

In particular, the cost contribution of assembly plant man-hours is not sufficient to merit the amount of attention paid to them by Womack et al. (1990). In a Swedish final assembly plant recently studied, the labour costs amounted to less than 10 percent of the costs for materials alone. Even though labour costs for welding and painting of bodies have to be added to this figure, the labour costs in the assembly plant amounted to only about 5 percent of total production costs. Similarly, Mishina (1995) reports that in Toyota's Kentucky plant labour accounts for only 7 percent of manufacturing costs. These figures indicate that even if labour costs in the assembly plant are reduced dramatically, the resulting total cost reduction will be marginal, and this marginal cost reduction cannot reasonably account for the huge market success enjoyed by Japanese automobile manufacturers up to the early 1980s.

In a broader perspective, on the other hand, there are many significant elements of the total production costs that may favour Japanese automobile manufacturers. Especially during the 60s and 70s, the main expansion period for the Japanese automobile industry, lower domestic wages – especially among suppliers – also created a cost advantage. As late as 1980, Japanese labour costs in the motor vehicle sector were only 58 percent of those in the US (Williams et al. 1994). In 1989, Japanese motor industry firms with less than 100 employees – a category where the lower echelons of suppliers are found – paid wages equal to only 53 percent of those in the largest firms (Williams et al. 1994).

Ironically, statistical data suggest that the productivity in the Japanese motor vehicle industry was lower than that in the United States at least until the mid-1970s (Williams et al. 1994). Nevertheless, the Japanese share of the world motor vehicle market increased from 1.3 percent in 1960 to 18.1 percent in 1975. On the other hand, the Japanese share of the world motor vehicle market has not grown since about 1980, despite the productivity advantage presumably existing lately.

3.      "Lean production" as an industrial model

Observations such as those reported above suggest that the competitive advantage of Japanese automobile manufacturers may be due more to the strength of Japanese "Lean production" as an industrial model rather than its efficiency as a manufacturing model. As a further illustration of this theme, we shall consider some data on labour's share of value-added as deduced from company reports.

Company reports indicate that labour's share of value-added is smaller in Japanese automobile companies (Toyota, Mazda, Nissan and Honda) than in American and European companies. This could of course be interpreted as evidence of higher productivity in Japanese companies, i.e. evidence of superior performance of "Lean production" as a manufacturing model. Further analysis of the data shows, however, that labour's share of value-added is also strongly correlated with value-added's share of sales, and that these shares are smaller in Japanese automobile companies than in non-Japanese companies.

Figure 2 shows that for Japanese and non-Japanese automobile manufacturers alike, labour's share of value-added tends to decrease as value-added's share of sales decreases. Further analysis reveals that the correlation between the national affiliation of the automobile manufacturer and labour's share of value-added vanishes almost entirely when value-added's share of sales is kept constant. According to the path analysis in Figure 3, using the same data as in Figure 2, the national affiliation of the automobile manufacturer is not per se a significant determinant of labour's share of value-added. Figure 2 shows that for Japanese and non-Japanese automobile manufacturers alike, labour's share of value-added tends to decrease as value-added's share of sales decreases. Further analysis reveals that the correlation between the national affiliation of the automobile manufacturer and labour's share of value-added vanishes almost entirely when value-added's share of sales is kept constant. According to the path analysis in Figure 3, using the same data as in Figure 2, the national affiliation of the automobile manufacturer is not per se a significant determinant of labour's share of value-added.

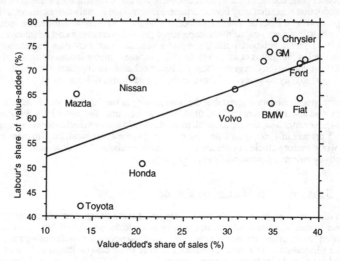

Figure 2. Plot of value-added's share of sales and labour's share of value-added for 13 automobile manufacturers. Mean values for a ten-year period (1981 – 1990). Source : Value-added's share of sales: Williams et al. (1994); labour's share of value-added: Williams et al. (1994).

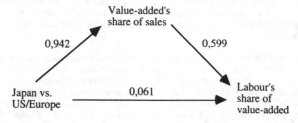

Figure 3. Path analysis based on correlations between (a) national affiliation of automobile company (Japan vs. US/Europe), (b) value-added's share of sales and (c) labour's share of value-added.

It may be asked, of course, why labour's share of value-added tends to decrease as value-added's share of sales decreases. This can be explained in substantial as well as mathematical terms.

The substantial explanation hinges on wage gradients in supplier networks. Cusumano (1985) estimates that Nissan and Toyota each controls roughly 200 subsidiaries and primary contractors, who in turn employ about 5 000 secondary subcontractors and some 30 000 tertiary subcontractors. Many secondary and tertiary subcontractors are quite small companies. As noted above, Japanese motor industry firms with less than 100 employees paid wages equal to only 53 percent of those in the largest firms in 1989. Cusumano (1985) points out that even the largest subsidiaries of Nissan and Toyota paid lower wages than the parent firms. During the fiscal year of 1989 the average monthly income in 15 of Nissan's major subsidiaries was only 81 percent of the wages at the parent company, while average monthly income in 10 of Toyota's major subsidiaries was only 79 percent of the wages at the parent company.

It seems safe to assume that the average ratio of supplier to assembler wages in the Japanese automobile industry did not exceed 70 percent. Furthermore, the 70 percent wage gradient has been reported to apply to Japanese automobile industry supplier networks in the United States (Kenney and Florida 1993). The bottom line is that, given this wage gradient, profits can be increased simply by moving work from the assembler to its suppliers, substituting cheap labour for expensive labour. And as profit's share of value-added increases, labour's share of value-added decreases.

Table 1 provides a numerical illustration of the fact that labour's share of value-added for the assembler tends to increase when relative wages in supplier firms increase. The hypothetical values in Table 1 reflect the assumptions (i) that cases (a) and (b) differ from cases (c) and (d) with regard to the extent of outsourcing and with regard to the margin between suppliers' sales revenues and labour costs, and (ii) that cases (a) and (c) differ from cases (b) and (d) with regard to the wage gradient, i.e. the relative wages among suppliers.

Table 1 also illustrates the fact that assemblers who rely extensively on outsourcing are more sensitive to increases in relative wages among supplier firms than assemblers who do more manufacturing in-house. For example, under the assumptions underlying Table 1, an increase of relative wages in supplier firms from 70 percent of that in the assembler firm to 100 percent leads to an increase of labour's share of value-added from 40 percent to 280 percent for an assembler where value-added's share of sales was initially 20 percent, compared to an increase of labour's share of value-added from 60 percent to 72 percent for an assembler where value-added's share of sales was initially 50 percent.

| CASE: | A | B | C | D |
|---|---|---|---|---|
| Sales, industrial system | 100.0 | 100.0 | 100.0 | 100.0 |
| Purchase, industrial system | 20.0 | 20.0 | 20.0 | 20.0 |
| Value-added, industrial system | 80.0 | 80.0 | 80.0 | 80.0 |
| Purchase, assembler | 80.0 | 97.1 | 50.0 | 58.6 |
| Value-added, assembler | 20.0 | 2.9 | 50.0 | 41.4 |
| Value-added, suppliers | 60.0 | 77.1 | 30.0 | 38.6 |
| Labour costs, assembler | 8.0 | 8.0 | 30.0 | 30.0 |
| Wage gradient, suppliers/assembler | 70% | 100% | 70% | 100% |
| Labour costs, suppliers | 40.0 | 57.1 | 20.0 | 28.6 |
| Value-added - labour costs, suppliers | 20.0 | 20.0 | 10.0 | 10.0 |
| Labour's share of value-added., assembler | 40% | 280% | 60% | 72% |

Table 1. Numerical illustration of the combined effect of extent of outsourcing and wage gradient in supplier network on labour's share of value-added for assembler.

The mathematical explanation of the association between value-added's share of sales and labour's share of value-added, on the other hand, hinges on the observation that when a component is outsourced and bought at cost price, the company's profit is (by definition) not reduced, but value-added is. As a consequence, profit's share of value-added is increased, and labour's share is decreased accordingly. The hypothetical values in Table 2 illustrate the fact that labour's share of value-added tends to decrease as value-added decreases, assuming that the assembler's profit does not change.

| CASE: | A | B |
|---|---|---|
| Sales, industrial system | 100.0 | 100.0 |
| Purchase, industrial system | 20.0 | 20.0 |
| Value-added, industrial system | 80.0 | 80.0 |
| Purchase, assembler | 80.0 | 50.0 |
| Value-added, assembler | 20.0 | 50.0 |
| Value-added, suppliers | 60.0 | 30.0 |
| Profit, assembler | 10.0 | 10.0 |
| Profit as share of value-added, assembler | 50% | 20% |
| Labour's share of value-added, assembler | <50% | <80% |

Table 2. Numerical illustration of the effect of extent of outsourcing at cost price on labour's share of value-added for assembler.

Note that the substantial and mathematical explanations of the fact that labour's share of value-added tends to decrease as value-added's share of sales decreases do not exclude each other. Whatever the explanation of the correlation observed, the argument above provides convincing proof that the entire supply chain must be taken into account when evaluating corporate performance. That is, the current production model discourse must be extended to consider the industrial model perspective.

It appears, then, that cause and effect are confounded in the causal model in Figure 1. Rather than being a main cause of competitive advantage, the apparent high productivity in Japanese assembly plants is to a large extent a result of extensive outsourcing. Competitive advantage derives from extensive outsourcing combined with low relative wages among suppliers rather than high assembly-plant productivity. It is also clear that outsourcing is driven by low relative wages in supplier companies.

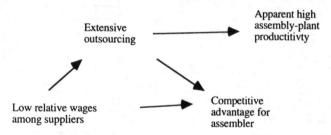

Figure 4. Summary of causal analysis of assembler's competitive advantage in the industrial model perspective.

It should also be noted that the quality of the end product depends to a large extent on the quality of the components assembled. Product quality may thus be due more to the achievements of the suppliers than those of the assembler, especially if extensive outsourcing is practised as in the Japanese automobile industry.

4.    Socio-economic and socio-cultural contexts

Yet another level of analysis, pertaining to socio-economic and socio-cultural contexts, should be introduced into the current production model discourse. For example, it may be argued that the growth of world market share for the Japanese auto industry does in part only reflect the phenomenal growth of its sheltered domestic market – the number of motor vehicles sold in Japan increased from some 200 000 in 1960 to about 7 000 000 in 1989.

Additional factors that have to be taken into account in the current production model discourse are prevailing societal values such as the reputed Japanese "hardship mentality" (Lillrank 1995) and the corresponding values in "post-industrial" societies such as Sweden.

By way of illustration, let us consider some of our data from the Volvo Uddevalla plant based on a "multi-disciplinary" questionnaire covering psychosocial and technical aspects. This questionnaire was distributed to the subjects during working hours. The subjects were randomly selected and they answered the questionnaire anonymously. The response rate was approximately 90 per cent. The total study included 97 employees including 64 assembly workers out of a total work force of 708 blue-collar and 108 white-collar employees.

Assembly workers were asked for an overall evaluation of their work and workplace, and also described these in a number of respects listed in Table 3. A multiple regression analysis revealed how important each of these dimensions was as a determinant of job satisfaction. As shown in Table 3, the most important determinants of job satisfaction was the perceived opportunity to exert influence over one's own work and whether one's work was perceived to be interesting and provide opportunities for personal growth. By contrast, workers' evaluation of the pay received, for example, was not a significant determinant of work satisfaction.

| INDEPENDENT VARIABLE: | Regression coefficient (β) | Standardised regression coefficient |
|---|---|---|
| Pay | 0.08 | 0.08 |
| Physical work environment | 0.03 | 0.02 |
| Chance to exert influence over one's own work | 0.23* | 0.28 |
| How well one is going along with one's work mates | 0.07 | 0.06 |
| Whether one's work is interesting and provides opportunities for personal growth | 0.34* | 0.45 |
| Whether something of value for others is produced | 0.04 | 0.04 |

Table 3. Regression coefficients, based on our data from the Volvo Uddevalla plant, indicating to what degree job satisfaction is affected by assessments of work and workplace in various respects. Regression coefficients marked with an asterisk (*) are statistically significant ($p<0,01$).

The Volvo Uddevalla plant might be suspected to represent an aberrant case in view of this plant's youth and its innovative design. A survey carried out by us at the older and more traditional Volvo Kalmar plant gave quite similar results, however. This survey was based on the same "multi-disciplinary" questionnaire as used at the Uddevalla plant (Engström, Jonsson, Johansson 1997). It was performed approximately one year after the Kalmar plant was closed down and included all former employees at the Kalmar plant. The questionnaire was distributed by mail and was returned by 344 employees, corresponding to a response rate of approximately 50 percent.

The only notable difference between the two plants in this regard was that how well one was going along with one's work mates tended to be more important as a determinant of job satisfaction in the Kalmar plant than in the Uddevalla plant (see Table 4).

| INDEPENDENT VARIABLE: | Regression coefficient (β) | Standardised regression coefficient |
|---|---|---|
| Pay | 0.02 | 0.02 |
| Physical work environment | -0.14 | -0.14 |
| Chance to exert influence over one's own work | 0.20* | 0.29* |
| How well one is going along with one's work mates | 0.23 | 0.16 |
| Whether one's work is interesting and provides opportunities for personal growth | 0.21* | 0.32* |
| Whether something of value for others is produced | 0.09 | 0.12 |

Table 4. Regression coefficients, based on our data from the Volvo Kalmar plant, indicating to what degree job satisfaction is affected by assessments of work and workplace in various respects. Regression coefficients marked with an asterisk (*) are statistically significant (p<0,01).

Given their preferences, few of the assembly workers in the Uddevalla plant would have felt happy with traditional assembly line work. On the other hand, it may be argued that assembly line work is more acceptable in Japan due to the above-mentioned "hard-ship mentality". At any rate, it is obvious that the current production model discourse and the choice of manufacturing model should take dominating societal values into account.

5. Conclusions

The analysis above indicates that it is more interesting to look for those conditions that allow big wage differentials between suppliers and assemblers to exist than to look for assembly plant practices that allow assembly plant man-hour counts to be reduced.

In this connection, the Japanese company union system is of considerable importance. Japanese unions are organized not by industry or trade but by company, and these company unions recruit white-collar as well as blue-collar employees. This system is more conducive to big wage differences between suppliers and assemblers than the industrial union system existing elsewhere, where employees in assembler and supplier companies to a large extent belong to the same union, such as the Svenska Metallindustriarbetareförbundet in Sweden or I.G. Metall in Germany.

The company union system with its close ties between employers and employees is not necessarily a manifestation of Japanese culture, though. Indeed, an industrial union within the automobile industry, the Zenji, was formed in 1947, but it was dissolved in 1954 after being defeated in a fierce labour market conflict involving Nissan, Toyota and Isuzu. Cusumano (1985) comments:

"Yet the circumstances that led to Zenji's demise suggest that this and other industrial unions were not destined, as a matter of cultural necessity, to fail in Japan. Industrial unions might well have survived had managers and white-collar workers headed for managerial positions not united during the 1950s to break up labour federations and replace them with pro-management, company unions." (p. 138 – 139).

The company union system is thus a cornerstone of what is in effect a core company – core worker alliance in the Japanese automobile industry (cf. Altmann 1995). The close ties between employers and employees in the large Japanese automobile companies is often uncritically interpreted as a result of superior human resource management, but this affiliation may also be related to the fact that core companies and core workers alike benefit from lower wages in peripheral supplier firms.

# REFERENCES

Altmann N (1995) "Japanese Work Policy: Opportunity, challenge or threat". Sandberg Å. (ed.), Enriching Production – perspectives on Volvos Uddevalla plant as an alternative to lean production, Avebury, Aldershot, pp 329 – 365.

Benders J (1995). "Leaving lean? Contemporary Developments in some Japanese Car Factories", Economic and Industrial Democracy, Vol 17 No 1.

Boyer R, Freyssenet M (1995). "The Emergence of New Industrial Models. Hypotheses and initial results", GERPISA, Second International Meeting, Paris.

Clark K B (1995). "Competing Through Manufacturing and the New Manufacturing Paradigm". Harvard Business School, Working paper 95-027.

Cusumano M (1985). "The Japanese Automobile Industry", Harvard University Press, Cambridge.

Engström T, Jonsson D, Medbo L (1996). "The Volvo Uddevalla Plant: Production Principles, Work Organzation, Human Resources and Performance Aspects – Some Results from a Decade's Efforts towards Reformation of Assembly Work". Department of Transportation and Logistics, Chalmers University of Technology, Gothenburg (report on Work Environment Fund projects, Nos. 93-0217 and 94-0516).

Engström, Jonsson, Johansson (1997). "Volvo Kalmar Survey", Department of Transportation and Logistics, Chalmers University of Technology, Gothenburg (primary materials).

Jonsson D (1995). "Lean Production in the Automobile Industry: Second Thoughts", Sandberg Å. (ed.), Enriching Production - perspectives on Volvos Uddevalla plant as an alternative to lean production, Avebury, Aldershot, 1995, pp 367 – 381.

Kenney M, Florida R (1993). "Beyond Mass Production. The Japanese System and its transfer to the US". Oxford University Press, New York, NY.

Lillrank P (1995). "Social preconditions for Lean Management and its Further Development". Sandberg Å (ed.). Enriching production". Avebury, Aldershot, pp 427 – 435.

Mishina K (1995). "Beyond Flexibility: Toyota's Robust Process-Flow Architecture". In "Vers une nouvelle organisation dans l'industrie automobile?", GERPISA, Third International Meeting, Paris.

Nomura M (1993) "The end of Toyotism - Recent trend of a Japanese automobile company", Department of Economics, Okay University, Yokohama.

Warnecke H-J, Huser M (1993). "Lean Production", Department for Industrial Manufacturing and Management, University of Stuttgart and Frauenhofer Institute for Manufacturing Engineering and Automation, Stuttgart.

Williams K, Haslam C, Williams J, Sukhdev J (1994). "Cars - Analysis, History, Cases". Berghahn Books Ltd, Oxford.

Womack J, Jones D, Roos D (1990). "The Machine that Changed the World", Rawson Associates, MacMillan International, New York.

# 038

Tom Keil
Institute of Strategy and International Business
Helsinki University of Technology
Otakaari 1M, U 512
02150 Espoo, Finland
Telephone:    +358-9-451 3081
Fax:          +358-9-451 3095
Email:        Tom.Keil@hut.fi

Tomi Laamanen
Institute of Strategy and International Business
Helsinki University of Technology
Otakaari 1M, Y 411
02150 Espoo, Finland
Telephone:    +358-9-451 3093
Fax:          +358-9-451 3095
Email:    Tomi.Laamanen@hut.fi

Erkko Autio
Institute of Strategy and International Business
Helsinki University of Technology
Otakaari 1M, U 517
02150 Espoo, Finland
Telephone:    +358-9-451 3087
Fax:          +358-9-451 3095
Email:        Erkko.Autio@hut.fi

# Processes of competence integration

Keywords: Competence integration; knowledge; absorptive capacity; company acquisition; new, technology-based companies

Category: A1, B1 or **H1**

Oral presentation only

# Introduction

Despite the recent criticism[1, 2], the complementary knowledge, competence, and resource-based views of strategy are well established [3, 4, 5, 6, 7, 8, 9, 10, 11]. The knowledge-based view of strategy is essentially based on the knowledge-based view of the firm [12, 13, 14, 15]. Complementing the knowledge-based view of the firm with the contractual view of the firm [16] adds issues such as the ownership of assets, opportunism, and the residual rights of control. This expanded knowledge-based view of the firm and the derived knowledge-based view of strategy are taken as a basic premise in this paper.

The adoption of the expanded knowledge-based view of the firm has a number of implications. First, as knowledge is company-specific and cumulative, the development of companies can be seen to be company-specific and path-dependent [17]. Due to the knowledge characteristics of companies, the scope of opportunities can be expected to limited. Companies can be expected to focus on opportunities that are within the scope of the general management dominant logic [18]. Companies can be expected to focus on opportunities that are within the scope of the dominant logic of the different subunits or departments of a company. Furthermore, companies can be expected to focus on opportunities that the companies are able to compile into viable business ventures after the opportunity identification in the different parts of an organization.

Second, according to the basic knowledge-based view of the firm, the companies disappear from the market when they face obsolescence of their knowledge-base [19]. The contractual view of the companies creates inertia in this respect. The companies still own their physical assets and have their contractually established positions which create the companies an option to renew their knowledge-bases. Rents can also be appropriated from an established positional advantage. Companies resist the obsolescence by attempting actively to renew their knowledge-bases. This can take place through internal development and external acquisition. Commonly both are needed.

Third, according to the complementary knowledge, resource, and competence-based views, the companies can be seen as collections of assets where the assets are seen to be the knowledge, resources, and competencies. According to the expanded knowledge-based view, the companies can be seen as collections of assets over which the owner of the company has *residual rights of control*. The owner of the company owns both the existing assets and the rights for the future assets derived from the existing assets. New assets can be developed from the existing internal assets or by combining internal and external assets into new assets [20, 21, 22].

These three issues, the scope of opportunities due to dominant logic and internalization capability, the knowledge-base renewal through internal development and external acquisition, and the ownership of the residual rights of control, would all seem to point towards the same direction: the importance of the knowledge, resource, and competence integration taking place in companies. Successful management of this internal integration process can be seen as a precondition for competence renewal. The technology, knowledge, resource, and competence integration capability is in essence the capability of a company to internalize external inputs and to compile them internally together with internal knowledge, resources, and competencies into new business ventures. The integration includes issues related to both internalization and governance.

For simplicity, the concept of competence integration is used in this paper instead of knowledge, technology, resource, and competence integration. The definition of competencies is adopted from Hendersson and Cockburn [23]. They define organizational competencies to include also tangible assets. According to this definition, also organizational knowledge and resources, both tangible and intangible, can be seen to be included within the concept of competencies.

## A framework for analysis

The present paper distinguishes between four different competence integration processes as depicted in figure 1. *Technological competence integration* is seen to take place when a firm integrates technologies held inside the firm with technologies held outside the firm. External technological competencies are internalized and integrated to existing technological competencies of the firm. Technological integration can also take place when the firm integrates different technologies all held inside the firm. *Technological competence internalization* is seen to take place when a firm acquires technological competencies and combines them to its existing non-technological competencies. The non-technological competencies can be market competencies, for example, the marketing and distribution competencies of the firm. The non-technological competencies can also include, for example, management competencies, administrative competencies, financing or fund raising competencies, et cetera.

Following a similar logic, *non-technological competence integration* is the integration of external non-technological competencies with other competencies of the firm that are of non-technological character. The fourth integration process is the *non-technological competence internalization* that takes place when a firm combines its technological competencies with non-technological competencies residing outside the firm.

| External competencies | | Internal competencies: Technological competencies | Internal competencies: Non-technological competencies |
|---|---|---|---|
| | Technological competencies | Technological competence integration | Technological competence internalization |
| | Non-technological competencies | Non-technological competence internalization | Non-technological competence integration |

*Figure 1 Integration processes in the firm*

It is beneficial to distinguish between technological and non-technological competencies and external and internal competencies. The existing literature on new product development focuses mainly on the internal integration of technological competencies into new technological competencies. The external inputs are assumed to be mainly information inputs from markets and scientific research. Recent research has increased the understanding of the role of more extensive external *technological* competence acquisition in the networked innovation process [24]. Technological competencies can be acquired, for example, through collaborative arrangements and company acquisitions. This paper strives to contribute to the existing research by expanding the focus further also to external non-technological competence acquisition. This brings up the interesting issue of non-technological and technological competence integration in creating successful new business ventures within an organization. The combination of these competencies into new business ventures requires certain degree of complementarity from the technological and non-technological competencies. Furthermore, this paper tries to build analogies between the integration of external competencies and the integration of internal competencies. The four processes of competence integration depicted in figure 1 are discussed in more detail in the following sections.

## Technological competence internalization and integration

Technological competence integration involving only technological competencies requires also internalization. The internalization stages are relatively similar both in connection with technological and non-technological competencies. In connection with the integration of technological competencies to technological competencies, the actual fusion can be seen to play a particularly significant role. The internalization of technological competencies has been studied in the context of technology transfer and in studies assessing the sources of innovativeness of a firm [25]. Especially in the technology transfer literature a multitude of factors has been identified affecting the transfer of technology from one company to another (See for instance [26]). The number of factors is so large that a detailed overview would exceed the scope of the current paper.

The capability of a firm to internalize outside technologies into its existing pool of technologies has been extensively discussed by Cohen and Levinthal under the concept of absorptive capacity [27, 28, 29]. Cohen and Levinthal find that the ability to internalize outside technologies is related to research and development activities carried out inside the firm. Related knowledge is found to be necessary to identify appropriate technologies to integrate, to assimilate, and to apply them. The internal research and development efforts have two functions within this process. On the one hand, the understanding of technology is supported by related internal efforts during the search, assimilation, and application of the technology. On the other hand, the internal research and development can create complementing technologies that are necessary to assimilate and exploit external technology [30]. Cohen and Levinthal identify several variables and processes supporting the absorptive capacity of the firm. First the relatedness of the knowledge has been found to affect the ease to internalize a technology. The less related a technology, the less related the knowledge the firm possesses to understand and assimilate the technology. The intensity of effort is the second variable correlating with the absorptive capacity. The more extensive the effort of a firm, the higher the probability that internalizing the technology succeeds.

A critical function in the internalization process is the interface with the environment. It relates the research of Cohen and Levinthal to the research on the technological gatekeeper function This concept was first introduced by Allen [31]. An important consideration is whether the interface function should be centralized or not. A decentralized function is expected to be most appropriate in situations in which the information flows are rather random and diverse. For example, in the case that a broad area of technologies is supposed to be scanned it might be more appropriate to expose several people for the task instead of only one. Contacts are usually informal and largely verbal. Also the diversity of the background of the organization's members is supportive for the absorptive capacity of the firm. Diversity facilitates the communication with external sources, as communication largely depends on shared knowledge [32].

The concept of absorptive capacity can be expanded. Every technology internalization process can be understood as a learning process taking place in the firm internalizing the technology. Building on concepts developed within the organizational learning and knowledge management literature [33, 34, 35, 36] technology internalization depends on two knowledge processes in the first place. Cohen and Levinthal stress within their concept of absorptive capacity that technology must be sufficiently understood to be able to integrate it. This understanding requires that the individuals involved in the knowledge integration possess sufficient related knowledge. The acceptance of the new knowledge is also crucial. Technological competencies have a strong social component. Thus technology coming from outside of the company is often not considered as valuable. To overcome this "Not-Invented-Here" syndrome an organizational culture [37] has to be created that allows to challenge existing technology and integrate outside knowledge and technology. To facilitate a culture positive to outside technologies is not a simple task for the organization as the cultural knowledge conflicting with the integration of outside technology is often tacit and cannot easily be altered or replaced.

After the external technological competencies are internalized within the firm, the next step is the integration with the internal technological competencies. After the internalization phase, the integration of external technologies resembles the technological competence integration taking place entirely within a firm. When combining external technological competencies to own non-technological competencies, the integration plays a different role. It resembles more adaptation than fusion.

It has been pointed out that the technology-base is becoming increasingly complex in a large number of industries [38]. This can be seen to increase the need for technology integration or *technology fusion* [39]. Particularly multi-technology firms [40] and firms concentrating on complex product systems [41] and system integration often have to manage the integration of a large number of diverse technologies. The integration of technology requires in the first place that appropriate technologies for integration be identified. It is necessary that knowledge about technologies held in an organization is available throughout the organization. Technology held in one part of the organization is not necessarily available in other parts of the organization. Especially in the case of multinational corporations are R&D activities, and thus the main source of internal technology development, increasingly geographically dispersed [42]. Mechanisms are needed that facilitate the transfer of meta-knowledge, i.e. knowledge about what is known elsewhere in the organization. Various authors discuss mechanisms in this context that are used to transfer knowledge within the multinational organization [43, 44]. The mechanisms used in this context include assignments of experts, boundary spanning roles, various forms of meetings, and different uses of information systems. In essence the discussion resembles much of the discussion on organizational memory [45, 46] and organizational learning.

Whereas the mere availability of the knowledge is a prerequisite in integrating technologies, it is not sufficient per se. Iansiti [47] points out, that the integration of technologies often requires significant adaptation of the technologies to be integrated. Apart from the adaptation of the technology to be integrated, also the process of technology development is affected by the integration of technologies. Iansiti and Clark [48] define based on these findings the concept of integration capability. The concept describes the companies capability to generate and capture detailed knowledge about the interaction between the technologies to be integrated and to use this knowledge in the product development process. The concept of integrative capability is thus close to the absorptive capacity as discussed by Cohen and Levinthal [49]. The processes overlap each other. Capability to integrate is related to the capability to internalize.

Also in connection with technology that has been developed internally, the problem of acceptance can occur. Especially within multinational corporations with dispersed research and development activities it is not self-evident that technology and knowledge developed in other parts of the organization is be accepted in other parts of the organization. Power relationships and reputation can be seen to play a significant role in this respect. They can lead to similar problems than in connection with the "Not-Invented-Here" syndrome.

The combination of external technological competencies to internal non-technological competencies involves integration to a lesser degree. Sometimes the technological competence integration is a prerequisite for the combination of the technological competencies to the existing non-technological competencies. For example, implementing a new externally acquired product into the distribution system of the acquired company may require also that the product is modified to fit to the product family of the acquiring company. The acquired technological competencies may need to be both integrated to the existing internal technological competencies and the existing internal non-technological competencies. Sometimes, it may suffice that the acquired external technological competencies are only combined to the internal non-technological competencies. For example, an acquired product may fit directly to the distribution system of the acquiring company. Adaptation or further development may not be needed.

## Non-technological competence internalization and integration

This paper has discussed mainly the internalization and integration of technological resources so far. The focus is widened here to cover also the acquisition of non-technological competencies. The acquisition of non-technological competencies can be considered an analogous situation to the acquisition of technological competencies. To profit from the technological innovation, Teece [50] argues that complementary assets are required. The commercialization of new technologies requires that actual technologies be combined with manufacturing, distribution, marketing, services, and other resources of the firm. Problems are caused if the new technologies do not fit with existing resources such as distribution systems. In case of competence destroying innovations [51] a firm may face the decision whether to combine the new technology with resources outside of the firm or to develop the necessary resources in-house. In an increasing number of industries the internal development of complementary resources is not feasible as the financial resources required are too high due to time compression diseconomies [52]. Sometimes it may also otherwise not be sensible to develop the needed complementary non-technological competencies internally. If a company is specialized on technological development, it is optimized for that purpose. Development of complementary competencies, for example, manufacturing or distribution systems, may be more efficiently taken care of by companies that have developed these other specialized competencies.

One of the largest problems in resource internalization is the need to identify the appropriate resources. The problem is twofold. On the one hand, the competencies of the firm are among the assets that cannot easily be identified in the course of normal business by another firm. Even if a firm is identified that possesses competencies in a complementary area, it is difficult to determine beforehand if these competencies can be integrated with the internal competencies. Also in this respect the firm has to build its absorptive capacity. Whereas Cohen and Levinthal [53] discuss only the integration of relatively close domains of knowledge, technological knowledge, for the internalization of non-technolocial competencies an understanding of two often very different domains of knowledge is required, both technological and non-technological knowledge.

Also the process of integrating or internalizing once identified competencies can pose a formidable challenge for the firm. Both the acquisition integration literature [54, 55] and the literature on the integration of marketing and research and development [56, 57, 58, 59] give valuable insights into the problems arising. Integrating, for example, marketing and research and development is generally accepted to be desirable for successful product development.[60] Problems have been caused, apart from unclear organizational responsibilities and physical barriers, also by personality differences and a lack of common culture. Analyzing the communication problems, one can identify the two knowledge dimensions already discussed above. On the one hand problems can result from a lack of related knowledge that is the prerequisite for a common understanding. On top of this cultural differences can result in a rejection of information coming from the other function. Integrative mechanisms are required. These include the relocation and physical facility design, personnel movement, informal information systems, organization structure, and formal integrative management processes.

Apart from the integration process, the use of external competencies poses the question of determining the appropriate mode of governance. Using outside competencies not only creates opportunities for competence leverage [61]. It also creates interdependence between the partners. This involves the risk that the partner appropriates the returns of the firm's competencies [62]. Especially in the case of arrangements that are geared towards the permanent use of an outside competencies, the careful selection of the type of relationship suitable to achieve the intended goals is of crucial importance. The modes of governance can be seen to range from contractual collaborative arrangements to different kinds of ownership arrangements.

To internalize or integrate non-technological competencies, a firm can utilize a wide variety of mechanisms ranging from alliances and joint ventures to the acquisition of companies. The key differences of these mechanisms are the control exerted [63] over the partner, on the one hand, and the organizational integration, on the other hand. The mechanism chosen often depends on the strategic intent of the firm using the outside resources. The use of outside resources can be intended as a permanent solution to focus operations. Firms can use different interorganizational arrangements also to learn from their partners. The development of the competencies can take place in-house at a later stage [64].

## Empirical evidence

Company acquisitions are a fruitful area of research when analyzing the technological and non-technological competence integration. For example, Lee discusses the mirroring and bridging of competencies as mechanisms of competence assimilation in connection with company acquisitions and more generally [65]. Company acquisitions represent situations where a complex bundle of external knowledge, competencies, and resources are injected into the acquiring organization. These include commonly both technological and non-technological knowledge, competencies, and resources.

The empirical evidence stems from a study of 111 new, technology-based company acquisitions carried out by one of the authors of the present paper [66]. In all cases analyzed either the acquiring or the acquired company was registered in Finland. These cases make it possible to analyze the technological and non-technological competence integration in detail. Due to space limitations only a few points can be discussed here.

The capability to carry out both technological and non-technological competence integration can clearly be seen to contribute to success in the new, technology-based company acquisitions. In new, technology-based company acquisitions, the technological competence integration, the combination and development of the acquired technological competencies, is often a prerequisite. The technological competencies developed by the small companies with commonly small budgets often need further development to result into successful distinctive competencies. The technological competence integration is not always sufficient. The combination to the non-technological competencies of the acquiring company is often also be needed. The highest potential for value-added in company acquisitions would seem to lie in leveraging the acquired or further developed competencies by replicating the competencies to many users. This can be done by combining the acquired technological competencies to the market-related non-technological competencies of the acquired company. Here the technological competence integration can be seen as competence building and the technological competence internalization as competence leveraging.

In new, technology-based company acquisition situations, the non-technological competence integration would seem to determine whether the acquisitions fail or succeed at all. The non-technological competence integration would seem to determine the timing of the success. Longer term success can be built by skillful technological competence integration. Even an initial failure would seem to transform into a success on a longer term if the technological competence integration is well taken care of. Failure in technological competence integration may make the success created through successful non-technological competence integration short-lived. The relationships between the non-technological and technological competence integration in new, technology-based company acquisitions is illustrated in figure 2. Due to the complex bundled nature of external competence acquisition, the company acquisitions include integration of different types of competencies. The integration of both technological and non-technological competencies can be seen to take place partly in parallel and partly sequentially. The competence integration processes can be seen to complement each other.

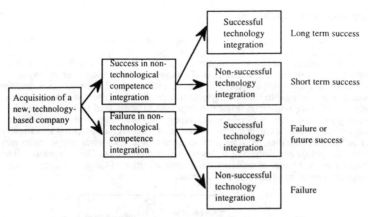

Figure 2    *Competence integration in new, technology-based company acquisitions*

In connection with 111 new, technology-based company acquisitions, the non-technological competence integration would seem to dominate the overall success, at least on a short term, as shown in figure 2. When studying the success of the company acquisitions involving different types of competencies integration, the technological competence integration gets eliminated from the regression equation in a backward elimination procedure. The backward elimination procedure eliminates the collinearity in the non-dependent variables. In the studied sample, the technological complementarity and distribution complementarity correlated strongly. As a result from an application of regression analysis with a large number explanatory variables and background elimination procedure, the resulting regression equation becomes

Compound success=    - 0.95    (Constant coefficient)
+0.66 * Industry_trend
+0.57 * Seller's_Proactive_Motive
+1.09 * Business_area_proximity
+0.99 * Distribution_complementarity
- 0.78 * Financing complementarity
where multiple R is 0.65 and $R^2$=0.42, and for all coefficients $p<0.05$

The compound success of the studied company acquisitions is measured as a compound measure of technological, market, strategic, and financial success. Based on the resulting regression equation, it would be tempting to link the business area proximity to the absorptive capacity. It would be tempting to conclude that the successful technological and non-technological competence integration are linked to the existence of a sufficient absorptive capacity as hypothesized in this paper.

The distribution complementarity is one measure of non-technological competence integration. The combination of the acquired technological competencies to a suitable distribution system would seem to effectively leverage the technological competencies of the acquired new, technology-based companies. The negative influence of the financing complementarity can be explained by the fact that the financing complementarity existed also in company acquisitions where there were no other complementarities present. The industry trend explained the success of the new, technology-based company acquisitions as expected. The existence of seller's proactive motives explained the success of the entrepreneurial new, technology-based company acquisitions as expected.

## Discussion and conclusions

The technological and non-technological competence integration processes can be used to illustrate the Penrosian growth cycle [67], figure 3. Companies acquire externally new, technological competencies integrating them to their own technological competencies. The existing non-technological competencies are used to complement the new, technological competencies. The new, technological competencies are, for example, implemented to the testing, manufacturing, or distribution systems. Sometimes the existing non-technological competencies may need to be broadened by acquiring externally non-technological competencies that better complement the new integrated technological competencies. As the non-technological competencies can often only be bought in bundles, the surplus of acquired non-technological competencies may necessitate further acquisition of technological competencies. The competence integration cycle can be seen as an extension or generalization of the growth cycle through management capacity as discussed by Penrose.

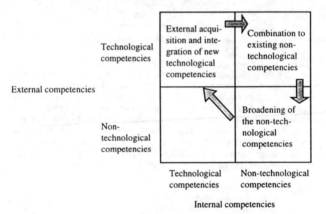

*Figure 3    The Penrosian growth circle through processes of competence integration*

The integration of non-technological and technological competencies on the different levels in an organization can be seen as basic elements of growth dynamics. An understanding of the growth dynamics requires an understanding of both internal and external factors affecting the growth. The technological and non-technological competence integration and internalization processes would seem to provide an inner view of competence integration. The different types of complementary competence combinations and competence fusion can be seen as results of different types of competence building and competence leverage. The different processes of competence integration can be seen to take place both in parallel and sequentially complementing each other. The processes of competence integration can be seen to interrelate.

The analysis in this paper would seem to imply that the different internalization and integration processes share common problems. In all the processes, the firm faces the problem that the competencies to be integrated might not fit. Aside from the capability of a firm to internalize or integrate the competencies, the attempt might be bound to fail. Understanding this fit requires an understanding of the competencies to be integrated. The need for such an understanding would seem to be supported by the empirical data. The understanding seems to be lacking in cases where external competencies are needed due to lack of any knowledge of the competencies. Even in cases where the competencies would be suitable for internalization or integration, cultural resistance may inhibit successful integration.

# References

1     Foss, N. J., Knowledge-based Approaches to the Theory of the Firm: Some Critical Comments,*Organization Science*, Vol. 7, No. 5, 1996, pp. 470-476.

2     Foss, N. J., More critical comments on knowledge-based theories of the firm,*Organization Science*, Vol. 7, No. 5, 1996, pp. 519-523.

3     Wernerfelt B., A Resource-based View of the Firm, *Strategic Management Journal*, Vol. 5, 1984, pp 171 - 180.

4     Peteraf, M. A., The Cornerstones of Competitive Advantage: A Resource-based View, *Strategic Management Journal*, Vol. 14, 1993, pp 179 - 191.

5     Mahoney, J. T., Pandian, J. R., The Resource-based View within the Conversation of Strategic Management, *Strategic Management Journal*, Vol. 13, 1992, pp 363 - 380.

6     Collis, D. J., Montgomery, C. A., Competing on Resources: Strategy in the 1990s, *Harvard Business Review*, July-August 1995, pp 118-128.

7     Rasche C., Wolfrum B., Ressourcenorientierte Unternehmensführung, *Die Betriebswirtschaft*, Vol. 54, No. 4, 1994, pp 501 - 517.

8     Bamberger, I., Wrona, T., Der Ressourcenansatz und seine Bedeutung für die Strategische Unternehmensführung, *Zeitschrift für betriebswirtschaftliche Forschung*, 48. Jg., Nr. 2, 1996, pp 130-153.

9     Rühli, E., Ressourcenmanagement, *Die Unternehmung*, 49. Jg., Nr. 2, 1995, pp 91-105.

10    Sanchez, R., Heene, A., Thomas, H. (Eds.), *Dynamics of Competence-Based Competition*, 1996, Oxford: Elsevier.

11    Hamel, G., Heene A. (Eds.), *Competence-Based Competition*, 1994, Chichester: Wiley.

12    Kogut, B., Zander, U., Knowledge of the firm, combinative capabilities, and the replication of technology. *Organization Science*, Vol. 3, 1992, pp 383-397.

13    Kogut, B., Zander, U., What firms do? Coordination, identity, and learning. *Organization Science*, Vol. 7 (5), 1996, pp 502-518.

14    Conner, K. 1991. A historical comparison of the resource-based theory and five schools of thought within industrial organization economics: Do we have a new theory of the firm? *Journal of Management*, Vol. 17, 121-154.

15    Conner, K., Prahalad, C. K., A resource-based theory of the firm: Knowledge versus opportunism. *Organization Science*, Vol. 7 (5), 1996, pp 477-501.

16    Williamsson, O.E., *The Economic Institutions of Capitalism*, 1985, New York: Free Press.

17    Nelson, R. R., Winter, S. G., *An Evolutionary Theory of Economic Change*, 1982, Cambridge, The Belknap Press of Harvard University Press.

18    Prahalad, C. K., Bettis, R. A., The Dominant Logic: a New Linkage Between Diversity and Performance, *Strategic Management Journal*, Vol. 7, pp. 485 - 501.

19    Lee, K., *Knowledge-Assimilation: Mirroring and Bridging Competencies*, COST A3 Final Conference on Management and Technology, Madrid, June 12-14, 1996.

20    Grossman, S., Hart, O., The Costs and Benefits of Ownership: A Theory of Vertical and Lateral Integration *Journal of Political Economy*, Vol. 4, 1986, pp. 691-719.

21    Hart, O., Incomplete Contracts and the Theory of the Firm, *Journal of Law, Economics, and Organization*,Vol. 4,No. 1, 1988, pp. 119-139.

22    Brynjolfsson, E., Information assets, technology, and organization, *Management Science*, Vol. 40, 1994, pp. 1645-1662.

23    Henderson R., Cockburn I., Measuring Competence? Exploring Firm Effects in Pharmaceutical Research, *Strategic Management Journal*, Vol. 15, 1994, pp. 63 - 84.

24    Rothwell, R., Towards the Fifth-generation Innovation Process, *International Marketing Review*, Vol. 11, No. 1, 1994, pp. 7 - 31.

25    Gemünden H. G., Heydebreck P., Herden R., Technological interweavement: a means of achieving innovation success, *R&D Management*, Vol. 22, No. 4, 1992, pp. 359 - 376.

26    Godkin L., Problems and practicalities of technology transfer: a survey of the literature, *International Journal of Technology Management*, Vol. 3, No. 5, 1988, pp. 587 - 603.

27    Cohen, W. M., Levinthal, D. A., Innovation and Learning: The two faces of R&D, *The Economic Journal*, Vol. 99, 1989 pp. 569 - 596.

28    Cohen, W. M., Levinthal, D. A., Absorptive Capacity: A New Perspective on Learning and Innovation, *Administrative Science Quarterly*, Vol. 35, 1990, pp. 128 - 152.

29    Cohen, W. M., Levinthal, D. A., Fortune Favors the Prepared Firm, *Management Science*, Vol. 40, No. 2, 1994, pp. 227-251.

30    Granstrand, O., Bohlin, E., Oskarsson, C., Sjöberg, N., External technology acquisition in large multi-technology corporations, *R&D Management*, Vol. 22, No. 2, 1992, pp. 111 - 133.

31    Allen, T. J., *Managing the Flow of Technology*, Cambridge, Massachusetts: The MIT Press, 1977, pp. 141-180.

32    Cohen W. M., Levinthal, D. A., Absorptive Capacity: A New Perspective on Learning and Organization, *Administrative Science Quarterly*, 35, 1990, pp 128 - 152.

33    Huber, G. P., Organizational Learning: The contributing processes and the literatures, *Organization Science*, Vol. 2, No. 1, 1991, pp. 88-115.

34    Kim, D. H., The Link between Individual and Organizational Learning, *Sloan Managment Review*, 1993, pp. 37-50.

35  DiBella, A. J., Nevis, E. C., Gould, J. M., Understanding Organizational Learning Capability, *Journal of Management Studies*, Vol. 33, No. 3, 1996, pp. 361-379.

36  von Krogh, G., Roos, J., *Organizational Epistmology*, 1995, New York: St. Martin's Press/Macmillan.

37  Schein, E. H., *Three Cultures of Management: The Key to Organizational Learning in the 21st Century*, Working Paper, 1996, MIT SLoan School of Management.

38  Patel, P., Pavitt, K., *Technological competencies in the world's largest firms: Characteristics, constraints and scope for managerial choice*, STEEP Discussion Paper No 13, May 1994, University of Sussex, SPRU.

39  Kodama, F., *Analyzing Japanese High Technologies: The Techno-Paradigm Shift*, 1991, London: Pinter.

40  Granstrand, O., Sjölander, S., Managing innovation in multi-technology corporations, *Research Policy*, Vol. 19, 1990, pp. 35-60.

41  Miller, R., Hobday, M., Leroux-Demers, T. & Olleros, X., Innovation in complex systems industries: The case of flight simulation, *Industrial and Corporate Change*,Vol. 4, 2, 1995, pp. 363-400.

42  Schmaul, B, *Organisation und Erfolg internationaler Forschungs- und Entwicklungseinheiten*, Wiesbaden: Deutscher Universitätsverlag, 1995.

43  Chiesa, V., Manzini, R., Managing knowledge transfer within multinational firms, *International Journal of Technology Management*, Vol. 12, No. 4, 1996, pp. 462-476.

44  Garud, R., Nayyar, P. R., Transformative Capacity: Continual Structuring by Intertemporal Technology Transfer, *Strategic Management Journal*, Vol. 15, 1994, pp. 365 - 385.

45  Walsh, J. P., Ungson, G. R., Organizational Memory, *Academy of Management Review*, Vol. 16, Nr. 1, 1991, pp. 57-91.

46  Huber, G. P., Organizational Learning: The contributing processes and the literatures, *Organization Science*, Vol. 2, No. 1, 1991, pp. 88 - 115.

47  Iansiti, M., Technology integration: Managing technological evolution in a complex environment, *Research Policy*, Vol. 24, 1995, pp. 521-542.

48  Iansiti, M., Clark, K. B., Integration and Dynamic Capability: Evidence from Product Development in Automobiles and Mainframe Computers, *Industrial and Corporate Change*, Vol. 3, No. 3, 1994, pp 557- 605.

49  Cohen, W. M., Levinthal, D. A., Absorptive Capacity: A New Perspective on Learning and Organization, *Administrative Science Quarterly*, 35, 1990, pp 128 - 152.

50  Teece, D.J., Profiting from technological innovation: Implications for integration, collaboration, licensing and public policy, *Research Policy*, Vol. 15, 1986, pp. 285-305.

51  Tushman, M. L., Anderson, P., Technological Discontinuities and Organizational Environments, *Administrative Science Quarterly*, Vol. 31, 1986, pp. 439-465.

52  Dierickx, I., Cool, K., Asset stock accumulation and sustainability of competitive advantage, *Management Science*, Vol. 35, 1989, pp. 1504-1510.

53  Cohen, W. M., Levinthal, D. A., Absorptive Capacity: A New Perspective on Learning and Organization, *Administrative Science Quarterly*, 35, 1990, pp 128 - 152.

54  Haspeslagh, P. C., Jemison, D. B. *Managing Acquisitions*, 1991, New York: Free Press.

55  Buono, A. F., Bowditch, J. L., *The Human Side of Mergers and Acquisitions*, 1989, San Francisco and London: Jossey-Bass.

56  Gupta, A. K., Raj, S. P., Wilemon, D., The R&D-Marketing Interface in High-Technology Firms, *Journal of Product Innovation Management*, Vol. 2, No. 1, 1986, pp. 12-24.

57  Moenaert, R. K., Souder, W. E., An Information Transfer Model for Integrating Marketing and R&D Personnel in New Product Development Projects, *Journal of Product Innovation Management*, Vol. 7, No. 2, 1990, pp. 91-107.

58  Moenaert, R. K., Souder, W. E., DeMeyer, A., Deschoolmeester, D., R&D-Marketing Integration Mechanisms, Communication Flows, and Innovation Success, *Journal of Product Innovation Management*, Vol. 11, No. 1, 1994, pp. 31-45.

59  Griffin, A., Hauser, J. R., Integrating R&D and Marketing: A Review and Analysis of the Literature, *Journal of Product Innovation Management*, Vol. 13, No. 3, 1996, pp. 191-215.

60  Griffin, A., Hauser, J. R., *The Marketing and R&D Interface*, Working Paper, MIT Sloan School of Management, 1991.

61  Doz, Y., Hamel, G., *The use of alliances in implementing technology strategy*, Working Paper, 1995, Fontainebleau, INSEAD.

62  Teece, D.J., Profiting from technological innovation: Implications for integration, collaboration, licensing and public policy, *Research Policy*, Vol. 15, 1986, pp. 285-305.

63  Granstrand, O., Bohlin, E., Oskarsson C., Sjöberg N., External technology acquisition in large multi-technology corporations, *R&D Management*, Vol. 22, No. 2, 1992, pp. 111-133.

64  Hamel, G., Doz, Y., Prahalad C. K., Collaborate With Your Competitors and Win, *Harvard Business Review*, 1989, pp. 133 - 139.

65  Lee, K., *Knowledge-Assimilation: Mirroring and Bridging Competencies*, COST A3 Final Conference on Management and Technology, Madrid, June 12-14, 1996.

66  Laamanen, T., *The Acquisition of Technological Competencies through the Acquisition of New, Technology-Based Companies*, Dissertation, 1997, Helsinki: Helsinki University of Technology.

67  Penrose, E., *The theory of the growth of the firm*, 1959 Oxford: Oxford University Press.

# 039

Papstel Jyri, Assoc. Professor
Tallinn Technical University
Ehitajate tee 5
Tallinn, EE-0026
Estonia
Phone: 372+2+620 3260   Fax: 372+2+620 2020   E-mail: jpapstel@edu.ttu.ee

Riives Jyri, Assoc. Professor
Tallinn Technical University
Ehitajate tee 5
Tallinn, EE-0026
Estonia
Phone: 372+2+620 3256  Fax: 372+2+620 2020

*Technology Education - Potential for Successful Existence of Small and Medium Enterprises in Estonia*

Key words: technology education, program evaluations, industrial challenge

Topical category: F

Oral presentation only

# Technology Education - Potential for Successful Existence of Small and Medium Enterprises in Estonia

*A good production engineer can put life into bad construction, but a bad one can kill a good construction (saying among engineers).*

## Background of the problem

Challenge of industry

Industry exists in the environment consisting of society, legal institutions, market, etc, and being influenced by these. Legal institutions( Ministry of Economy via the Government) should create by legislation an environment which would or wouldn't motivate the positive changes in industry. The press creates the public opinion on the industry. Ability and skills of industry in finding the market needs are supporting factors.

The same environment influences the educational institutions, yet the character is quite different. If public opinion is low there is no interest among young people to study technology. If the Ministry of Education is not able to evaluate trends in the economy and society, the technological education will be underfinanced. If the industry is on a low level it means there is no market for specialists and nobody wants to learn either. *So, one of the problems is to find ways to acknowledge the importance and position of technological education in the society.*

There exists a mutual influence of industry and educational institutions as well. Young specialists will go into industry with new ideas based on the development of engineering sciences. Industry returns the information about their needs. But often this link does not function or is very weak and as a result, a gap forms between industry and university. Breadth of the gap depends on the flexibility of the university as well as willingness.

In the early period of industrial engineering when the production technology was stable, for a long period the gap was quite small. The time passed and the technological development accelerated while universities' curriculum stayed quite academic. So, young engineer needed a period of acquisition in the company to learn real problems and the ways of resolving them. Big companies could allow such an "acquisition period" and as a rule it was compulsory. But the small and medium enterprises (S&M) were waiting for "the flying start". May be the problem is not so actual? Research showed that the role of S&M is quite big [1]. In the developed countries small enterprises make up 60-80 % of total number of enterprises. Most developed is small entrepreneurship in Japan (99.8% of companies and 88.4% of employees) followed by USA, Australia, Italy, Denmark and Switzerland. This tendency is explained by high flexibility of S&M.

S&M can't exist independently. They have to produce for someone, which means that they are linked to big companies and work as subcontractors. At the moment only a few big companies exist in Estonia and as a rule they try to produce the most themselves in order to load their own employees. The co-operation has not yet developed enough which can be explained by historical background too. So, a lot of our companies are working for Finnish, Swedish and other companies.

Hence the second conclusion - *our engineers have to be educated taking into account the experience and demands of industry in Estonia, as well as in the neighbouring countries.*

The stand and trends of Estonian industry. Following facts are taken from [2]. In Estonia exist 8,899 companies from which 320 are metalworking and machine-building companies. In table 1 a division of enterprises by their distance and a number of employees is introduced. There are altogether 20,000 employees in the companies but 65% of them are in the companies with number of employees over 100, from them about a half are in the companies with the number of employees over 500..

Table 1

**Division of engineering enterprises, the number of employees, and distance from capital**

| Distance of company from capital | The number of employees | | | |
|---|---|---|---|---|
| | up to 20 | 20-100 | 100-500 | over 500 |
| Tallinn | 54 | 56 | 14 | 4 |
| up to 50 km | 26 | 20 | 4 | - |
| 50-100 km | 18 | 9 | 3 | 1 |
| 100-200 km | 40 | 33 | 8 | 1 |
| over 200 km | 12 | 12 | 4 | 1 |
| Number of companies | 150 | 130 | 33 | 7 |
| Number of employees | 1,600 | 5,400 | 7,000 | 6,000 |

S&M forms about half of the whole, having turnover less than 3 mln. EEK which makes only 10% of the total turnover of the branch, however, about 25% of the employees are working there. At the same time, 12% of the companies with turnover over 10 mln. EEK are giving 66% of the total turnover.
In table 2 the main export articles are shown.
Half of the engineering companies export their products but companies with export volume over 3 mln. only 52 (16%) give 88% from the total amount. So, the export potential is quite large, as half of companies don't take part in the export. *One of the reasons is the lack of young eager engineers able to communicate in foreign language and being introduced to subjects related to market economy..*
The main export products are: heat exchangers, agricultural and forest machines, machine tools and parts, power equipment, etc. Subcontracting forms 55% of export volume. Main partners are from Finland 47%, and Sweden 5%. In total the export of engineering companies forms about 25% of the whole export. - to Finland (56%), Russia (11%), Sweden (9%), Germany, etc.
Speaking about the role of machine-building and metalworking, it holds the third place among industries (11.8%) (first is the food industry - 33.5%; the second, energetics - 12.7%). Sale of industrial production has increased in 8 month of 1996 compared with the same period of 1995, and is 17.7% in running prices.

Table 2
## Main article groups of export

| The article groups | 1933, % | 1994, % | 1995, % |
|---|---|---|---|
| Textile | 12,3 | 14 | 13,6 |
| Machines and equipment | 7,7 | 9,4 | 12,8 |
| Timber and wood products | 7,5 | 9,7 | 12,1 |
| Minerals | 7,6 | 7,7 | 8,2 |
| Chemistry products | 4,8 | 6,9 | 7,8 |
| Food | 10,7 | 12,5 | 7,7 |
| Metals | 10,7 | 8,2 | 7,2 |
| Transportation means | 10,5 | 7,7 | 7,0 |
| Equipment for cattle breading | 11,0 | 7,5 | 6,5 |
| Other | 5,1 | 5,5 | 5,8 |

### Investigation of the need in specialists

Since the re-establishment of Estonia's independence, rapid and considerable restructuring of Estonian industry and fundamental reorganisation of the Estonian higher technical educational system has taken place. Under Soviet compulsory and strictly fixed studying programmes a general type of engineers for machinery, covering the areas from machine design to manufacturing processes, were graduated from Tallinn Technical University. In 1991, a new type of study programmes, based on the worldspread subject-oriented study system with a substantial amount of optional courses was introduced in Tallinn Technical University. So, the way for the student to rule the specialisation area according to his own interests and capabilities was opened which leads to better competition ability on the labour market.

On the other hand the changes in Estonian industry need an urgent answer to the question: "What type of engineers does the Estonian industry really need?" So, the problem of "compatibility" of engineers' knowledge and industry's challenge becomes actual.

In 1995, under the grant of Estonian Innovation Foundation a research on the need for specialists - from skilled workers up to engineers with university education was undertaken. In the frames of this research not only the need for engineers but also the spectrum of expected fields of their knowledge was examined. In this article generalised results of the described investigation are discussed.

### Methodology of investigation

A questionnaire of 16 pages was used consisting of questions on needed specialists after 5 and 10 year periods, about the content of their knowledge, content of continuing education, and basic data of the company. These questions were on three levels: university-based engineer, technicians, and skilled workers.

Approximately 200 questionnaires were distributed and 50 received. No machine-building companies were not involved in this investigation, however, the machine engineering specialists are needed there as well. The data were inserted in Microsoft ACCESS and treated consequently.

## Investigation results in the field of manufacturing engineering

Although from the very start the main stress in the investigation was planned on university engineers we found it suitable to ask the same questions from technicians as well as skilled workers to have a complete picture. So, we got the answers on three levels: engineers, technicians and skilled workers.

*University based Engineers.* The largest request for engineers is in the field of cutting technology (Figure 1) because of its universality and mostly the expectations are rather for production managers with good engineering background than for the production planners. It can be explained by the trend towards small and medium enterprises where the need for engineers-generalists is more underlined. This opinion is supported by the answers on the structure of manufacturing engineers' knowledge as well. In fact, this is the information we have to take into account in our curriculum. There is a great need for welding specialists. On the one hand, this can be explained by the fact that up until now such kind of specialists were not prepared in Estonia, and on the other hand, that a lot of subcontracts in industry are connected with high quality welding operations.

The need for tooling engineers-designers of dies, moulds, and clamping devices is shown very clearly. These designers are technology-based and, therefore, their background has to be manufacturing engineering. Seemingly, it is a problem to be analysed more carefully, as the problem is universal but very specific in every particular company. At the university the specialist has to get the basic knowledge and skills in the field. Further experience they will get in companies. As companies are in a hurry to get high-level specialists it would be of good use to elaborate expert systems in this field in co-operation with industrial specialists. Until now tooling engineers have been of design inclination. Therefore, instrumental engineers with special technological preparation are needed. It is suitable to mention, that about 10% of manufacturing engineers need are engineers with technical highschool preparation. It seems to be rather lower than international experience shows. May be the technical high school curriculum would be revised.

*Need for technicians.* The structure of this need is about the same (Figure 2) as for the engineers' with some more need for welding specialists. It is quite logical to analyse the structure of activities of the companies. The need is rather great in the field of maintenance and repairing, as the equipment becomes more complex and production depends straight on qualified maintenance and reparation. It is the field we have to strengthen in technicums and technical high schools. In fact, the need is much greater as questionnaires were distributed in metalworking companies, while most companies in other industrial fields have complex equipment as well. So, the need for specialists in this field is much greater.

*The need for skilled workers.* The results are shown in Figure 3 .Analysing the results of questionnaires and the structure of specialisation of vocational schools we can say that such specialisation as milling workers, press tool workers, grinding workers are absent in these. Therefore, necessary conclusions by the officials have to be drawn.

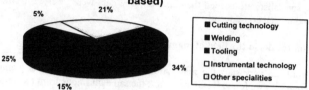

**Need for Manufacturing Specialists (University based)**

5%    21%

25%

15%    34%

- Cutting technology
- Welding
- Tooling
- Instrumental technology
- Other specialities

Figure. 1

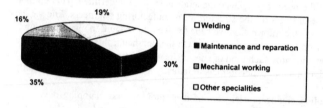

**Need for Technicians (Highschool based)**

16%    19%

35%    30%

- Welding
- Maintenance and reparation
- Mechanical working
- Other specialities

Figure 2

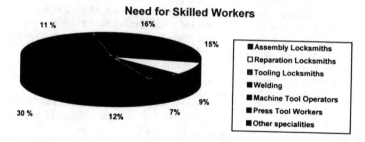

**Need for Skilled Workers**

11 %    16%

15%

30 %    12%    7%    9%

- Assembly Locksmiths
- Reparation Locksmiths
- Tooling Locksmiths
- Welding
- Machine Tool Operators
- Press Tool Workers
- Other specialities

Figure 3

Structure of curriculum

To meet industry's challenge best we have to know which knowledge in which field
industry is interested in. So, one of the questions was in this field. The tables with the
list of subjects in our curriculum was suggested and company had to evaluate
importance of the offered subject like in Table 3. There was one column more, not
important, but this is not introduced here. Of course, the results are quite approximate,
as the structure of industry is quite mixed, as some of them are extremely interested in

designers, the others in production managers, etc., but anyway we got information about practicality of our curriculum. The main results in summarised form are introduced in the Table 3.

Table 3

Which knowledge industry is interested in

| Field of knowledge | Knows basics %% | Can use %% | Can develop %% |
|---|---|---|---|
| Basic (mathematics, physics, heat engineering, hydraulics) | 20.5 | 54.0 | 13.8 |
| Design (methodology, calculations, tribology, control systems, tolerancing) | 23.0 | 36.0 | 40.0 |
| CAD/CAM | 20.0 | 45.0 | 20.0 |
| Production technique (cutting theory, production planning, machine-tools, productivity management, special technologies ) | 24.1 | 35.7 | 27.8 |
| Product development | 22.7 | 32.0 | 31.6 |
| Economics (marketing, business administration, organisation and management) | 25.4 | 39.5 | 20.5 |

The main conclusion we made from this questionnaire is that our curriculum is quite optimal from the point of view of the knowledge. But we have to reduce the number of subjects by merging them into groups of similar problems. Accent on the special problems will depend on the specialisation of students. Such a manner will spare the resources and enable in flexible way to react to the industry's need.

Teaching method One of the evergreen problems is the teaching method. There exists explicitly or implicitly two trends: knowledge driven and method driven methods.
Proclaimers of the first trend assure, that engineer has to be purchased with quite a lot of knowledge in order to manage with engineering tasks from the start of their career (some kind of "walking references").
The other thinks that knowing the methods of problem solution and the ways to find the necessary knowledge sources help them quite good.
As a matter of fact, the knowledge will be old or quite wrong during the period of 1-5 years. It depends on the field of activities, so, only the first method is not acceptable nowadays. To use references by resolving the elementary problems is not acceptable as well.
So, the method-driven knowledge acquisition will be most suitable for engineering education. The main problem will be the problem of knowledge acquisition. Therefore, the new curriculum based on above-mentioned principles is under the development.

# CONCLUSIONS

1. There exists a gap between industry and university and it depends on flexibility and ability to react to changes in society and industry.
2. The tendencies to small and medium enterprises are seen in development of industry, and as a result, more flexible engineers are needed.
3. The fields of engineers' specialisation based on related investigation are reached.
4. Knowledge groups, which interest industry are found.
5. In order to have the actual information about industry's needs, institutes of mechanical faculty are the members of Federation of Estonian Engineering Industries and their representatives take part in its monthly meetings.
6. The structure and principles of structuring of curriculum has to enable in shortest time to react to industrial challenge.
7. As market is mainly Scandinavia, challenge of this market has to be taken into account as well via contacts in northern technical universities and Tallinn Technical University or information available from Estonian companies being in close contacts with Scandinavian companies.

## References

1. Pavic, D.Hrzic *Die Flexibilität als ein Entwicklungsfaktor Kleiner Unternehmungen.* Proceedings of 6th International DAAAM Symposium, 26.-28. oct. 1995, p.267-268.
2. A. Hõbemägi Eesti Masina- ja Metallitööstus - traditsioonid-kvalifikatsioon-arengupotentsiaal, Tallinn. November 1996, 31 p.
3. Research Report of the Estonian Innovation Foundation Project 9it/95. On Need for the Specialists with Technical Education for Raising the Compatibility of Industry. Project Supervisor Assoc. Prof. Jyri Papstel, Tallinn Technical University, Institute of Machinery. Tallinn, 1995, 57 p.

# 041

# MUTUAL KNOWLEDGE CREATION IN INDUSTRIAL MARKETS - SYNERGY OF PERSPECTIVES

Author:
Helén Anderson
International Graduate School of
Management and industrial Engineering
Linköping Institute of Technology
Department of management and Economics
S-581 83 Linköping, Swedeb
Tel:  +46-13-28 25 17
Fax:  +46-13-28 18 73
Email: helan@eki.liu.se

Co-author:
Ms, Kristina Lee
Industrial Doctoral Student
Copenhagen Business School
Institute of Organization and Industrial Sociology
Blaagaardsgade 23B, 5
DK-2200 Copenhagen N
DENMARK
Phone: +45 3815 2815
Fax: +45 3815 2828

## ABSTRACT

In the forthcoming paper, we wish to combine the perspective of learning in communities of practice, legitimate peripheral participation (Lave & Wenger, 1991; Brown & Duguid, 1991) with that of industrial networks (e.g Axelsson & Easton, 1992; Håkansson & Snehota, 1995). The aim of this is to enhance our understanding of the technological knowledge creation processes taking place between industrial suppliers and customers.

By combining the above perspectives it is believed that both will be qualified further. Thus, the concepts of community of practice and legitimate peripheral learning will be extended and modified to a business context across organizational boundaries. On the other hand, the network perspective in industrial marketing is believed to be developed further with the focus of the technological knowledge creation processes taking place in those networks. The latter has only been dealt with to a limited extent (Håkansson 1987, 1989).

Specifically, we want to make two points. Firstly, the importance of regarding knowledge creation between suppliers and customers as two-way knowledge creation processes will be focused on. This is a departure from existing perspectives of learning, and through the analysis a preliminary conceptualization of knowledge-assimilation (Lee 1996) will be advanced.

Secondly, in cross-organizational knowledge creation processes different types of knowledge (Badaracco, 1991; Kogut & Zander, 1992) are mobilized and developed (Anderson & Andersson, 1996). This may imply that multiple organizing principles are needed in order to facilitate such processes, posing challanges to the participating organizations. We wish to investigate this issue further.

The above analyses seem to point to one key challange for suppliers and customers: How can an organization position itself as a worthy and attractive cooperating partner in terms of knowledge creation? We will provide some preliminary views on this issue. In doing this, we will also draw on our empirical work with a customer respectively a supplier in different industrial markets, as it seems like both sides of the interface face challange of cooperating with the supplier(s) respectively customer(s) each prefer.

For each of the conclusions we draw, means for empirical testing will be discusses and suggestions made.

# 042

# A FRAMEWORK FOR INNOVATION AND ITS AUDIT

H. K. Tang
MBA(Management of Technology) Programme Director
Nanyang Business School

K. T. Yeo
System and Engineering Management Division Head
School of Mechanical and Production Engineering

Nanyang Technological University
Nanyang Avenue, Singapore 639798
Republic of Singapore

## ABSTRACT

This paper gives a brief review on frameworks for innovation audit and then proceeds to propose a framework for describing and analysing innovation in products, processes and systems in organisations. The proposed framework is built upon existing theories from multiple disciplines related to innovation and consists of two components: an innovation funnel, and a systemic view of the innovation process and its variables. The former depicts idea nurturing through the enlargement of involvement in the organisation and the latter aims to satisfy the need to illustrate the many variables and the various ways that they can influence innovation. The variables considered include both soft ones such as motivation, culture and hard ones such as resources, processes. The framework can serve as the foundation on which an innovation audit can be constructed. The primary purpose of an innovation audit in an organisation is to identify areas that impede innovation and point to ways for improving innovation effectiveness and capabilities.

## KEYWORDS

Innovation, innovation audit, innovation process, innovation environment.

## INTRODUCTION

Innovation is a subject that has attracted attention from different disciplines which include personality and behavioural psychology, organisational theory and various fields of management studies. Most researchers on innovation tend to look at the subject from their own special perspectives and in so doing they provide in-depth knowledge in narrowly focused areas. However, researchers and managers of innovation also need a fuller understanding of and take a systemic view of the process of innovation, particularly for the purpose of conducting organisation-wide innovation audit. Therefore, it is worthwhile to develop an integrative and multidisciplinary framework.

Review of the literature shows that innovation audit is a rather recent term and is still infrequently referred to, even though innovation is sometimes referred to as the ultimate competence needed for competitive advantage. There is a great contrast when the popularity of innovation audit is compared with quality audit. Of course the latter's popularity is no doubt due to its longer history and it being a requirement for quality standard certification. The purpose of innovation audit is to gauge the effectiveness of an organisation in innovating, point out where problem areas lie and suggest possible ways for improvement. Besides effectiveness an innovation audit could also be used to take stock of an organisation's innovation capabilities which are indicated by, amongst others, its resources, knowledge and skills. What follows is a review of some of the available literature related to innovation audit.

To audit innovation of multi-business corporations, Burgelman (1996) suggests two separate but similar checklists. The first caters to the business unit level and the second the corporate level. The two checklists are variations on the same theme which consists of five elements: resource, technological environment, strategic management capacity, structure and culture, external monitoring. Taking a 'learn from the best' approach, McGourty et al. (1996) studied, through interviews and content analysis, fourteen best-of-breed, world-class, US-based companies and the behaviour of their R&D scientists and engineers. The major conclusion of their study is that an organisation's culture can be modified to encourage innovative behaviours through specific management practices. The identified innovative behaviours of individuals favourable to innovation are: inquisitiveness, advocating new ideas, collaboration, goal-directness. The management functions identified to have strong impact on innovation are: strategic direction, employee selection, rewards and recognition, support for idea generation, multi-functional teaming. Commissioned by the U.K. Department of Trade and Industry, a team of researchers from London Business School came up with a similar set of criteria for good management practices and a set of scorecards for an product innovation audit [Chiesa et al. (1996)]. In an audit the auditors will give scores to the items in the set of scorecards according to a scale of 1 to 4, corresponding to a series of typical practices that range from bad to best. The scorecards are meant for a quick first-level audit, the results from which will then lead to a more detailed audit in problematic areas.

The above three innovation audit frameworks look at innovation from top management's perspective and they need to be administered with or through the top management of the organisation to be audited. On the other hand, Amabile and Gryskiewicz (1989) use the Work Environment Inventory (WEI) to look at an organisation's environment for innovation through the eyes of the workers. The work environment is an intended or unintended end-product of the company's task environment, culture, value system, strategy, and organisation design. To the workers, the work environment is the one that they have to deal with everyday and know intimately. WEI is a multiple-choice instrument to be filled out by the respondents. It is designed to assess workers' view on the climate for creativity and innovation in their organisation. The questions in WEI are designed to measure the intensity of stimulants or obstacles that exist in the workplace. The stimulants to workers' creativity at work are: organisational and supervisory encouragement, work group support, sufficient resources, challenging work, and freedom. The obstacles are organisational impediments and work load pressure.

The four frameworks reviewed do provide collectively a comprehensive set of items to be checked in an innovation audit. However for more fundamental understanding, it would be advantageous to have a framework for innovation that delineates the essential variables and their inter-relations rather than just as checklists or ready-made instruments. To be holistic such a framework would also need to amalgamate the contributions from various disciplines. With better understanding of innovation, managers would be able to design their innovation audit according to their own scope and terms of reference. The rest of this paper proposes such a framework which comprises the following two components (1) the innovation funnel, and (2) a systemic view of innovation.

THE INNOVATION FUNNEL

The innovation process has been modelled by many as a sequential process that goes through separate stages. There are two kinds of stage models. The first treats innovation as a problem-solving process. The second treats innovation primarily as a new product development process, although the meaning of product is rather general and could include process and service. The stages identified in a classic example of the first kind is: preparation, incubation, illumination, and verification. Another example is: problem observed, problem formulated, available information surveyed, solution formulated, solution critically examined, new ideas formulated, and new ideas accepted and tested [Dacey (1989)]. Examples of the second kind are the stage-gate new product process and the development funnel model [Cooper (1993), Wheelwright & Clark (1995)].

The common feature of the problem-solving based process is their focus on the individual. They do not tackle the organisational or social aspects of innovation. New product development models, on the other hand, is implicitly organisation based. However, the emphasis here is on the process and its efficacy. Creativity of the individuals and its interaction with the organisational environment tend to be neglected. Moreover, they tend to emphasise too much on innovation as an elimination process. This is epitomised in the development funnel model: many ideas go into the large mouth of a funnel but only one emerges at the narrow end, after it passes through a series of screen. In between screens, the original ideas are processed and strengthened so as to avoid competitive elimination.

There is a simple alternative view of the innovation process as shown in Figure 1 which shows the progress of an innovation project through time and the scope of organisational involvement. An idea is conceived in an individual's mind which works on it for some time. At the end of this individual-stage, the idea generator either pursues it together with his or her colleagues or drops it. The team of colleagues examine, add their inputs and nurture the idea further. Colleagues who play the roles of gatekeeper and champion are particularly important at this stage [Allen (1977)]. By the end of this team-stage, the enhanced and enlarged idea may be given a project-charter to go ahead with full-scale development. Or it may be dropped because it does not have sufficient support from the team or management. Dropped ideas may fade away or persist and re-enter the process due to new insight or the availability of alternative channels for support. There are two famous innovations that exemplify this re-entry process, Post-It and Java. The former took the original idea generator many years to find a department in 3M to sponsor the development and the latter resurfaces as the ideal language for the Internet after it failed earlier to gain acceptance as an universal programming language for the control of home appliances. The important difference between the innovation funnel and the development funnel lies in the two different perspectives they give to prospective innovators in an organisation. The innovation funnel highlights idea nurturing, team support and organisational encouragement. The development funnel emphasises project discipline to reduce oversights and omissions. The two funnels are dual that complement each other, very much like photon and waves complementing each other in describing the propagation properties of light.

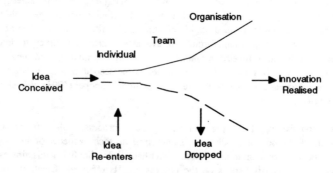

Figure 1: The innovation funnel which emphasises the nurture of ideas.

## A SYSTEMIC VIEW OF INNOVATION

The innovation funnel highlights the nurturing of idea at the individual, team, and organisation level as the fundamental process of innovation. This however does not happen in isolation. It is in fact intricately linked with the organisation's other functional processes, such as marketing and manufacturing, and subject to the influence of organisational variables. For an innovation project to succeed, the various functions and processes need to be integrated effectively [Wheelwright and Clark (1995)]. The contingency theory of organisation says that there is no one fit-all organisation design. Hence it stands to reason that there are some organisation designs that favour innovation more than others [Lawrence & Lorsch (1986), Galbraith (1977), Mintzberg (1989)]. Likewise, innovation in an organisation is also subject to the influence of the environment external to the organisation, especially societal culture and the national infrastructure and system that support innovation [Hofstede (1991), Shane (1993)]. At the individual and team level, behaviour and cognitive psychologists contribute to the understanding of innovation through their studies and theories on creativity, motivation and team behaviour [Guildford (1975), Koestler (1964), Amabile (1990), Belbin (1981), Payne (1990)].

In the proposed framework, the innovation variables are classified into four groups as shown in Table 1 and a systemic view of innovation involving these variables is shown in Figure 2.

Table 1: The four groups of innovation variables.

| Group | Variables |
|---|---|
| Environment | External: societal culture, national innovation system. Organisational: culture, mission, task, structure, reward, people, processes (besides the innovation process), resources. |
| Transformation Processes | Information capture, idea generation, project raising, project doing. |
| Process Output | Message, idea, project charter, project results. |
| Process Controller | Motivation, teamwork, integration, individual knowledge and skills (K&S), team K&S, organisational K&S. |

At the very front end of the process, even before idea generation, a potential innovator must receive information that is stimulating to the mind. The parabola in front of the information capture box signifies the analogy of information capture by an individual to an antenna that captures signals. The information can be captured as a conscious effort such as an exercise in technology monitoring and analysis [van Wyk

(1996)], or passively and serendipitously. It can come from a variety of sources, either within an organisation or external to it. Of particular interest to technologists are sources like journals, electronic media, experimentation, customers and suppliers [Allen (1977)]. What happens to the messages produced as a result of information capture depends on the knowledge, skills, particularly creative skills, and motivation of the individual. Koestler (1964) describes in details how a person, who faces a challenging task, may conceive novel ideas. This usually happens when a new message is bisociated with the person's existing knowledge. According to Amabile (1990) idea generation is strongly affected by a person's motivation, domain-related knowledge and creativity skills.

Formal or ad hoc teams that include idea generator, gatekeeper and champion are essential in pursuing and enriching a new idea so that it is transformed into a project charter that is recognised and supported by the organisation. This transformation is called project raising in the innovation framework. The culture, structure and task of an organisation have a great influence on teamwork and propensity in project raising [Galbraith (1982)]. Information capture, idea generation and project raising are the three transformation processes that form the front-end of innovation, which is typically characterised by much uncertainty and ambiguity. Thus the subsequent process of project doing is a process that reduces uncertainty and resolves ambiguity, as well as one of creation. It should be noted that, idea generation, project raising and project doing correspond to the three levels of involvement respectively: individual, team, and organisation which are described in the innovation funnel. Thus the innovation funnel and the systemic view of innovation are closely coupled.

During the process of project doing, the integration of knowledge and skills from different work functions and disciplines become important for innovation effectiveness [Wheelwright and Clark (1995)]. The sharing and integration of knowledge, both tacit and explicit, is also the basis for knowledge creation in an organisation [Nonaka and Takeuchi (1996)]. Furthermore, knowledge and skills in an organisation become its core competencies or capabilities only when they are integrated properly and uniquely [Hamel and Prahalad (1994)]. Thus project doing is also the primary process of knowledge creation and competence building for an innovating organisation.

Finally, an organisation's innovation effectiveness is a complex function of the variables listed in Table 1. To avoid cluttering Figure 2, only the direct relationships between some of the variables are indicated by arrows. There are many relationships, some of which represent feedback are not shown. For example, motivation exerts a strong influence on the inclination of an individual to generate and push ideas for innovation. Motivation depends on the challenge presented by the organisation's tasks, which in turn depend on its strategy. Furthermore, the strategy is influenced by experience of past innovation successes and failures. How other innovation variables affect the intermediate and final outputs of innovation are the continuing concern of managers and researchers of creativity and innovation.

# CONCLUSION

Innovation could be a significant source of competitive advantage for many organisations. Hence to better understand and monitor innovation within an organisation is one of top management's important tasks. In this paper, a framework is proposed that could assist in this task. The framework consists of two components: the innovation funnel and a systemic view of innovation. Managers or researchers of innovation could use this framework together with the theories and prior studies from multiple disciplines many of which are cited in this paper, to guide their work.

## REFERENCES

Allen J T (1977), *Managing the Flow of Technology*, Cambridge Mass.: MIT Press.
Amabile T M (1990), "Within you, without you: the social psychology of creativity, and beyond", Chapter 4 in Runco and Albert ed. *Theories of Creativity*, Newbury Park: Sage.
Amabile T M and Gryskiewicz N D (1989), "The creative environment scales: work environment inventory", *Creativity Research Journal*, Vol.2, 231-253.
Belbin R M (1981), *Management Teams: Why they succeed or fail*, London: Heinemann.
Burgelman R A (1996), *Strategic Management of Technology and Innovation*, 2nd ed., Chicago: Irwin.
Chiesa V, Coughlan P, and Voss C A (1996), "Development of a technical innovation audit", *Journal of Product Innovation Management*, 13:105-136.
Cooper R G (1993), *Winning at New Products*, 2nd. ed., Reading, Mass.: Addison-Wesley.
Dacey J S (1989), *Fundamentals of Creative Thinking*, Lexington, Mass.: Lexington Books.
Galbraith J R (1977), *Organization Design*, Reading Massachusetts: Addison-Wesley.
Galbraith J R (1982), "Designing the innovating organization", *Organizational Dynamics*, 11/3, 5-25.
Guildford J P (1975), "Creativity research: a quarter century of progress" from I A Taylor and J W Getzels ed., *Perspectives in Creativity*, New York: Aldine Publishing Company.
Hamel G, Prahalad C K (1994), *Competing for the Future*, Boston: Harvard Business School Press.
Hofstede G (1991), *Cultures and Organisations: Software of the Mind*, London: McGraw-Hill.
Koestler A (1964), *The Act of Creation*, London: Hutchinson.
Lawrence P R and Lorsch J W (1986), *Organization and Environment*, Boston: Harvard Business School Press.
McGourty J, Tarshis L A and Dominick P (1996), "Managing innovation: lessons from world class organizations", *International Journal of Technology Management*, Vol. 11, Nos. 3/4, pp. 354-368.
Mintzberg H (1989), *Mintzberg on Management*, New York: Free Press,.
Nonaka I and Takeuchi H, "A theory of knowledge creation", *International Journal of Technology Management*, Vol. 11, Nos. 7/8, pp. 833-845, 1996.
Payne R (1990), "The effectiveness of research teams: a review", Chapter 5 in West M A and Farr J L ed., *Innovation and Creativity at Work*, Chichester: Wiley.
Shane S (1993), Cultural influences on national rates of innovation, *Journal of Business Venturing*, Vol. 8, pp 59-73.
van Wyk R (1996), Technology analysis: a foundation for technological expertise, Chapter 5 in Gaynor G H *Handbook of Technology Management*, New York: McGraw-Hill.
Wheelwright S C, Clark K B (1995), *Leading Product Development*, New York: Free Press.

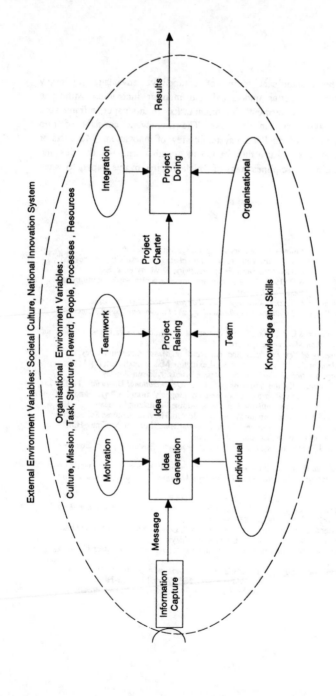

Figure 2: A systemic view of innovation in an organisation. The rectangular blocks represent transformation processes and the items in solid-line ovals are the process controllers which are programmable by the environmental variables. The dotted-line oval represents the porous boundary between the internal and external environment. To avoid cluttering the diagram, feedback and other paths are omitted.

# 046

# Management of Technology in New Zealand: A Cultural Development

R.A. (Bob) Mills and A.G. (Alan) Langdon,
University of Waikato, Hamilton, New Zealand

## ABSTRACT

This paper explores how the education sector, R&D organisations and companies in New Zealand have developed the management of technology during the past 25 years.

In 1953 New Zealand enjoyed the third highest standard of living in the world. Prosperity was built on exploitation of natural comparative advantage as a primary producer with direct access to the British market. Britain joined what is now the EU in 1973 which, coupled with the oil price shocks of 1974 and 1979, drove New Zealand to diversify and also invest in large energy based projects. These novel-technology-intense investments increased debt burden from NZ$4 billion to NZ$28 billion during that decade.

Radical New Zealand government action to deal effectively with the debt started in 1984 with stringent fiscal discipline. This was later followed by deregulation of the labour market which increased the flexibility of the workforce. A sharp contraction of import restrictions also invigorated the private sector and fully opened the door to a global marketplace. The result was ready adoption of technology.

The New Zealand tertiary education system responded to the need for education about the management of technology in the early 1970s at the University of Waikato. Primary and secondary education sectors, however, have been slow to change.

Local funding of R & D by the private sector is one third of the OECD average but growing, perhaps because New Zealand is a nation of smaller enterprises. Government funding is set to grow over the next 15 years and is focused in areas of "public good" applied science providing a pool of ideas in areas of strategic importance to the country.

The propensity for New Zealanders to avail themselves of new technology and their skill in making short production runs economic have both led to success and present business optimism. Triumphs are exemplified in the successful Team New Zealand challenge for yachting's Americas Cup, world class electric fencing systems and low volume, multi-model assembly line exports.

True to its heritage of isolation and survival, New Zealand has had to learn to manage technology, thereby improving its prospects and developing its culture.

## Management of Technology in New Zealand: A Cultural Development

R.A. (Bob) Mills and A.G. (Alan) Langdon,
University of Waikato, Hamilton, New Zealand

### Introduction

New Zealand is a group of islands in the Southern Pacific Ocean 2000 kilometres away from its nearest neighbour Australia. It is about the same size as the British Isles but has a population of only 3.6 million. A moderate climate and fertile soils have provided the basis for an economy built on low cost production of wool, meat, milk, fruit and forestry products. These are major contributors to the one third of GDP exported each year (Vandersyp, 1994). Today the GDP is NZ$74.7 billion, growing strongly for the last 3 years, presently at the real growth rate of 3.1%. Inflation stands at 2% per annum, the unemployment rate at 6.3% and the overseas debt a tolerable 84.7% of GDP (Statistics New Zealand, 1996).

A measure of the robustness of the New Zealand economy has been shown by the confidence of our trading partners and money markets during the transition from a traditional "First Past the Post" to a "Mixed Member Proportional" government election system used for the first time in October 1996.

However, the relative serenity of New Zealand's present circumstances belies the dramatic changes seen during the last 25 years. Changes sparked at the political level were solved by appropriate management of technology. Changes were driven by economic reforms, crystallised by legislation and accommodated by a society prepared to use its wits, wisdom and tolerance.

### Background

The prosperity of New Zealand has relied upon the entrepreneurial application of technology for the past 150 years. To be Britain's overseas farm, New Zealand was required to transfer product reliably and economically half way round the world. Transport technology was already moving from wind to combustion drives and in any case transit duration for textile wool, leather hides and ship spar timber were not major concerns.

The advent of refrigerated ships pioneered by Thomas Mort in the 1870s, however, provided a means for sheep meat carcasses, a by-product of the wool industry, to be exported and compete on the expanding British market (Critchell and Raymond, 1912). Mort, driven by a vision of a verdant Antipodes feeding a starving English homeland, was an early example of a technology champion. Beef and sheepmeat became important to the New Zealand economy so quickly that legislation regarding health and hygiene for meat export was enacted in 1900 by then Prime Minister Sir Joseph Ward.

The ability to grow grass and graze animals outside all year also allowed New Zealand farmers to diversify into dairying and export milk in the less perishable forms of butter and cheese. Co-operative ventures between dairy farmers to share the cost of further processing and benefit from the economies of scale was a necessity, whereas the animal disassembly industry which produced meat, was less constrained in its formative years. These legacies of tradition are maintained within the structures of these industries to this day and are still subject of much debate (Crocombe, 1991).

Efforts to improve conditions for workers by organised labour unions were seen to be at their most effective after the 1950s where meat plants and docksides were highly vulnerable to the effects of strikes. Yet these were halcyon days where more than 60% of New Zealand's production went to Britain with minimal domestic processing. By 1953 New Zealand enjoyed the third highest standard of living in the world. In March 1956 there were five people registered as unemployed! New Zealand was adrift in the South Pacific paradise with low production costs and a guaranteed market for its commodity products.

## New Paradigms for the 1970s

In 1973 Britain joined the Common Market, now known as the Economic Union (EU) and was required to phase out external suppliers. New Zealand was set to lose the major customer it had served for 100 years. Prospects looked bleak. Potential markets were either wealthy but protected or poor and volatile. Then followed the oil price rise shocks in 1974 and 1979 which focused international attention on Middle Eastern energy supplies. New Zealand infrastructural transport fuel sources were seen to be particularly vulnerable (Bollard, 1987). These problems were long term but demanded urgent action.

We now briefly examine the responses from politicians, the education sector, R&D laboratories and private companies with respect to the role of technology.

## The Political Response

The signals warning of the risk of heavy dependency of trade with Britain had been read well by politicians. Britain's share of New Zealand exports dropped each decade from 1960 to 1990 from 53% to 36%, 14% and 8.5% respectively (Statistics New Zealand, 1993). Trade posts and temporary financial incentives helped increase exports to Australia and Japan by four and five-fold respectively and establish trade from virtually zero to 9% of total export sales to South-East Asia in the same period. However, the new customers did not want the old products. It was seen as the responsibility of R&D organisations and companies to find appropriate technologies and sometimes create new ones to provide desirable products to meet the needs of new customers.

Less successful was the political move, started in 1975 by then Prime Minister Rob Muldoon, to create energy self-sufficiency by state-funding new technology "think big" projects. A novel "gas to gasoline" plant fed from newly discovered natural gas deposits around the west coast of the North Island was a feature of the programme. It met with moderate technical success and helped create temporary employment for skilled tradesmen who assembled the overseas developed and manufactured technology. It also provided a full size pilot plant for a major oil company. However, during the subsequent decade national debt rose from NZ$4 billion to NZ$28 billion as a direct result of raising funds for "think big" ventures.

## Education's Answer

Response to the change in New Zealand's trading patterns and the flow-on effects of the oil crisis was dealt with only as an "interesting topic" in social studies by the primary and secondary education sectors. However, languages and management were subjects seen as having new relevancy to New Zealanders. Furthermore, awareness of the intrinsic value of the environment and the promotion of sustainability had its roots in the 1970s and was stimulated by the prospect that nuclear power was seen as an economic solution to energy self-sufficiency and sustainability. Although researchers at the Department of Scientific and Industrial Research in Wellington had already devised earthquake resistant nuclear reactor mounting systems, politicians soon correctly sensed that New Zealanders would not find this energy option acceptable!

At tertiary institutions, like Massey University and the newly established University of Waikato, some pure science disciplines became conscious that interdepartmental awareness and links with industry, long a feature of engineering education, was required to provide communication between those who understood what was possible and those that knew how assemble and operate what was profitable. The "co-operative education" undergraduate degree BSc (Technology) was created in the early 1970s by Professor Liley of the Physics Department at Waikato. It's purpose was to turn out science graduates with work experience who were directly and immediately useful to an industry that could benefit from the application of new ideas. By the late 1970s both Chemistry and Biology Departments had joined the programme (Langdon, 1990a).

## Research & Development Reaction
Until the mid-1970s government had strongly supported research in the pastoral industries to increase efficiency of conversion from grass to wool, meat and milk. New Zealand's largest agricultural research campus at Ruakura in Hamilton, for example, had gained its international reputation through research into animal and plant genetics, nutrition and disease. The emphasis changed dramatically to encourage work on new and improved products and processes reaching across and beyond the farm gate. New programmes were started on deer farming, kiwifruit production and automated milk harvesting. Economists, engineers and business people worked directly alongside agricultural scientists, perhaps for the first time, and were confronted by the values and expectations of other players involved in the innovation process. Some interesting and worthwhile technologies did, however, emerge from research centres during the late 1970s and early 1980s.

Mechanisation of lamb slaughter and dressing chains was undertaken at Ruakura by the Meat Industry Research Institute of New Zealand (MIRINZ) (Authier, 1992). Each manual operation was examined and replaced by hygienic and rugged machinery where it could be shown to be cost effective. Traditional manual chains operating at 9.5 carcasses per minute required 49 butchers and 32 labourers whereas by introducing 10 technically simple machines and by inverting the carcass for machine convenience, only 27 butchers and 25 labourers were needed. Contrast this worker replacement approach with the Australian Fututech project at Kilcoy which focused on completely automating cattle slaughter and dressing (Doonan, 1993). In this case, the animal was to be processed through 80 fully automated workstations not designed for manual intervention. The efficiency and reliability of each workstation was consequently required to be extremely close to 100% for essentially continuous and economic chain operation, a feat not achieved in spite of considerable cost and dedicated effort over 16 years.

Two other meat technologies of great commercial significance were the development of electrical stimulation of carcasses to stop quickly frozen meat from getting tough and the use of electrical stunning of the animal's brain without affecting heart function to allow humane Halal slaughter (Chrystall, 1976 and Gilbert, 1993). This latter technology simultaneously satisfied animal rights groups and Muslim customers.

A final more radical example of the response of the research community at Ruakura was the leaf fractionation project which ran from 1974 through to 1985 to explore new ways to use grassland (Vaughan, 1984). Green leafy pasture was harvested, pulped and mechanically squeezed to express a high-protein pigmented juice. The juice was separated into two fractions. One fraction contained green protein and natural pigments and could be used for poultry feed and egg yolk colouring. The other fraction was a molasses type syrup suitable for a ruminant feed supplement. The fibre residue was refined into a feedstock for a fermentation process which produced ethanol for transport fuels. The process is technically viable but expensive, however, some preliminary fractionation stages are in use today.

Direct diesel fuel substitution from tallow and ethanol from sugar beet was investigated by researchers at Massey and Lincoln agricultural universities while at Auckland and Canterbury engineering universities attention was given to battery powered vehicles.

## How Companies Responded

Primary processing companies also started to pay attention to "adding value and variety" to their exports by fractionation. Milk fractionation into products beyond commodities like butter, cheese, powders and casein became popular. For companies like the New Zealand Dairy Group whey fermentation and distillation into alcohol became a successful new export product. The technology effectively creates relatively high value from a bulk by-product.

Manufacturing industries in New Zealand gained new respect as a potential export earner from a surge in further processing of primary products. However, manufacturing was not a large business in New Zealand because of transport costs. For example, because the Tasman Sea between New Zealand and Australia has the reputation for being the "most expensive stretch of water in the world", bulky manufactured items like farm machinery and household electrical appliances had only been produced for local consumption.

The availability of the microprocessor occurred in the early 1970s and provided a new technology base for some New Zealand companies who were looking to respond to government encouragement to export. Let us briefly introduce three examples, the publicly listed Fisher & Paykel (F&P) and the private family companies of The Gallagher Group and PEC (TRADENZ, 1995).

F&P in Auckland assembled consumer appliances under license principally from companies in the US and Japan. Japanese radio and television equipment were early users of solid state electronics whereas controls on the laundry and kitchen appliances were not as modern. F&P began to design their own electronic controls and used them extensively, not just on final products but also on the production line equipment used to assemble them. The small domestic market required that appliance assembly needed to be done on a one by one, order by order basis. For the F&P Refrigerator Division any one of 1400 different models could need to be assembled side by side on the production line. The ability to customise production to this degree was a growing international need so the automated low volume assembly line to achieve this led to a new export business for F&P in its own right.

F&P also produced a completely new product for a market new to F&P in the early 1970s. The medical gas humidifier, brainchild of Auckland Hospital staff, helped to make patients more comfortable during operations. It had taken 14 years of development. The product only became practically realisable with the availability of low cost electronic controls. Its export started to reverse the inbound flow of new technology for F&P.

The Gallagher Group had built their local reputation on providing grassland farming equipment since the 1940s. The orange coloured grass harvesting equipment was a common sight in the early 1970s but the uncertain future of the pastoral industry was biting into sales. Another product, however, unshortable electric powered fencing, was ripe for development. The original idea had come from, Doug Phillips, a scientist at Ruakura and was promoted as a means to simplify stock grazing management by temporarily sub-dividing fields into smaller blocks. Problems like short circuits caused by long wet grass, power control monitoring and reliability were all able to be solved with the availability of microprocessor controls which were built into energiser units. A large network of Gallagher product distributors was built up throughout the world by John Gallagher, the founders son, leading to the rapid growth of exports.

The third company capitalising on electronic control technology was PEC located in the small rural town of Marton, in the southern part of the North Island. The mechanical engineering company found itself providing and servicing petrol pumps as its main business at the end of the 1960s. In a visionary move John Williams, the son of the founder, decided that microprocessors provided the opportunity for flexible control and management of the streetside fuel pumping operation. In response to the fuel crises he decided that existing fuel distribution systems would require greater monitoring and accuracy. He reasoned that the rising value of petrol should be able to support the purchase of more sophisticated management products. PEC produced the first solid state electronic coin operated pump in 1969, self-service pumps in 1972 and microprocessor controlled forecourt petrol pumps in 1977.

## The Government Reforms Launched in 1984
New Zealand has had a history of major reform by first term socialist governments as witnessed in 1891 and 1935 (James, 1986). By 1984 it was evident that tinkering with policies in the then current political system was failing to control wages, prices, markets, trade and investment succeeding only in creating even greater debt and considerable concern for the future by the nation at large. However, few could foresee the radical nature of the changes handed down by the new Labour government of 1984, heralded as it was by the pressure of an inherited currency crisis which resulted in an immediate 20% reduction in exchange rate. The reformists took the view that New Zealand had come of age, had a sound infrastructure in place and could see no reason for government to be directly involved in commercially viable services.

The major internal policy changes that unfolded targeted:
- the return to fiscal balance (not seen since the early 1970s and incidentally finally achieved in 1994),
- reduction of public expenditure and reassessment of government spending priorities,
- deregulation of state owned monopolies, like electricity generation
- tax base increase by the introduction of Goods and Services Tax (now at 12.5%) and corresponding reduction of personal income tax,
- financial liberalisation, notably the abolition of interest rate controls,
- monetary reform, specifically statutory requirement for the Reserve Bank to maintain inflation in the range 0 - 2%,
- and finally the removal of exchange rate controls.

External policy changes revolved around promoting trade liberalisation, notably Closer Economic Relations with Australia (CER) and the General Agreement on Tariff and Trade (GATT).

The impact of all these changes during the late 1980s created as much anxiety to New Zealanders as the events that had set them in place in the 1970s. Firms were either responding to the new environment or failing. Redundancy had not been common and had often been the only way to offload inadequate staff. Now those faced with job loss consoled themselves by looking beyond their own grief to recognise the larger transformation at hand for individual companies and the nation. Firms needed first to survive and then reshape. Redundancy was more often the result of companies not adopting effective technology rather than realisation of labour union fears of new technology displacing worthwhile jobs.

It took a return to conservative National government in 1990 to bring a final plank to the platform of change started in 1984. The Employment Contracts Act of 1991 provided for individual contracts of employment without the obligation of labour union representation. This provided the flexibility many companies believed necessary to make the most of deregulation. The first MMP coalition government policies announced in December 1996 have promised a review of social service funding now that fiscal matters are perceived to be under control.

Let us again visit the education, R&D and company examples introduced earlier to follow through the second wave of political changes resulting from the most recent government reforms.

## Progress in Education
Along with all other government sectors, expenditure in primary and secondary education was constrained and operational governance transferred away from central bureaucracy to, in this case, locally elected School Boards of Trustees. The major change in curriculum development has been the recognition of technology as one of the seven areas of essential learning in the National Education Framework (Ministry of Education, 1993). The proposal is not to teach technology in isolation but rather recognise its stage of development and influence within in each traditional subject area as it is encountered. Technology will be set in broad and overlapping contexts including; personal, home, school, recreational, community, environmental, energy, business and industry (Jones, 1995). It is evident that resources outside the school will be called upon to contribute to the learning experience helping to foster respect for the multi-disciplinary approach required of technology managers of the future. A non-prescriptive approach to implementation has slowed its formal introduction which is now set for 1998.

Post-graduate teaching in technology management was introduced to science courses in 1987 (Langdon, 1990b). Contributions by industry speakers contacted through the co-operative education programme have always been a significant feature. Today there are four courses for MSc (Tech) students including the Management of Innovation Projects and Technology Forecasting. A separate and comprehensive modular executive education programme for a Masters degree in Technology Management (MTM) was launched in 1994 (Kirk, 1995). Fifteen topics are each covered during intense one week long interactive modules and are popular with mid-career technical and management professionals who recognise that in this new era they must take personal responsibility for regular technology education upgrades. The value of acquiring internal company knowledge and know-how has been lowered by the formalisation of quality systems and the prospect of unexpected career changes. Corporate interest in the Technology Management programmes is growing and is becoming the preferred qualification above the traditional MBA by several of the largest New Zealand companies.

At the tertiary level second year undergraduate courses in technology management were introduced at Waikato in 1991 and third year courses in 1993.

## Changes in the R&D Community
Government has drawn back from its original total liability for public good research by creating originally 10 Crown Research Institutes (CRI's) as limited liability companies in 1991. Government money goes instead to directly fund research programmes on topics of national importance for which CRI's bid and if successful become contractually bound to deliver. An allocation of an additional 10% of government bids won by the CRI's is also provided for discretionary use of CRI's to otherwise fund unsuccessful researchers or explore new topics for future potential. As a result there is a temptation to bid low risk scientific and developmental experiments rather than not meet contractual obligations. While all parties are sensitive to this counterproductive tendency the better management of innovative projects has been a subject of concern and interest to the authors (Mills, 1996).

Traditional primary production oriented R&D continues to decline in favour of projects dealing with processing, differentiation and quality of presentation to the customer. Moves by the private sector to shoulder greater responsibility for R&D, however, are becoming evident. However, while companies increased funding for R&D from 0.29% of GDP to

0.35% between 1993 and 1994, and during the same period government share moved from 0.57% of GDP to 0.56%, these levels are still only one third of OECD reference levels for companies and three-quarters of the levels for governments (Ministry of Science and Technology, 1996a). In its strategy document outlining R&D funding proposals upto the year 2010 the New Zealand government proposes to gradually increase its contribution to 0.8% of GDP (Ministry of Science and Technology, 1996b). There seems no reason to suggest that a trend toward greater private contribution to R&D will not continue even though New Zealand is a nation of small companies.

Returning to our specific cases in the meat industry R&D we note some dramatic changes. The drive for further on-shore processing of lamb saw effort going into the development of machines that automatically removed whole meat tissues from the loin, shoulder and leg areas. By 1993 over 60% of exported lamb loin was processed by machine. However, progress on mechanisation of the lamb slaughter chain had reduced significantly. Government assistance to maintain farm incomes were withdrawn in 1987. True market signals were felt for the first time by beef and sheep farmers which led to a steady reduction in the national sheep flock from 70 million in 1987 to 48 million today. Meat companies were short of animals to process and so stock prices soared. This in turn reduced meat plant spending on automated equipment and its subsequent further development. The position was further aggravated by greater productivity from a more willing and flexible workforce, no doubt as a result of widespread unemployment (11.6%) in the late 1980s and the effects of the Employment Contracts Act. Meat plant technology and its development has effectively been managed by allowing true market signals to be received and responded to by meat companies.

Meat quality issues remain dominant although now further on-shore processing has resulted in a priority for the development of packaging and storage technology.

**The Growing Confidence of Companies**
For the New Zealand Dairy Group the management of technological innovation has become a key issue. Opportunities and freedom to diversify into new product development in the past 12 years have been seized, limited only by the debatable constraints of a co-operative industry structure and centralised marketing. The sources of new products and processes derive from a dynamic mixture of customer needs and requests, technology development and availability and business risk and opportunity. Management of the innovation process has been a company priority for the past 2 years. Mechanisms are in place for technological innovation management through the channels already provided by obligatory quality systems. Emphasis is placed on meeting criteria at each stage of a development project to allow an informed decision to be made about whether to proceed. Time only will tell if the quirks of human nature under the inspiration of a new concept and the pressure to deliver a result will feed the quality system with useful input data.

F&P have flourished. Rather than spend money to transfer bulky product across the Tasman Sea to Australia, F&P now export their technology in know-how form to their own production plant in Queensland.

During the mid-1980s F&P engineers developed a motor directly cast into the plastic agitator of a domestic clothes washing machine to eliminate expensive and vulnerable gearboxes. The product paved the way for international recognition and product sales. The breakthrough also focused attention on the innovation process itself. For all three electronics companies discussed earlier in this paper a tool considered key to managing technology was to first manage staff. This can often best be done by opening up opportunities for staff to participate in new projects. F&P have done this by mixing the physical location of functions associated with the creation or implementation of new technology within large open plan offices, close to the primary production floor. However, formal management of the innovation process is shunned. The portfolio of innovation projects is also informal, being recognised as the collection of opportunities at any given time considered by senior managers to be worth exploring.

The Gallagher Group have also flourished by paying attention to customers, lead users and employing BSc (Tech) graduates from the University of Waikato! Lateral thinking suggested that electric fences developed to keep pastoral animals enclosed can be equally effective in keeping the human animal excluded. Gallaghers are now therefore involved in security systems. Electric fence wires strung across pastoral farms can also be seen as farm information highways. This leads to the prospect of supplying data from around the farm and collecting and analysing data at the farmhouse to help farmers make cost effective management decisions. Each product development project at Gallaghers is reviewed every month and allocated resources by management for the following month. It has proved to be an effective way to balance income-bearing and profit-consuming activities.

PEC have moved on to the production of a comprehensive forecourt retail outlet management system and diversified into an equally profitable security access card business. This small company is adamant about the need to formalise and spread the responsibility for the innovation process for fear that good ideas from its employees are inadequately researched or bad ones consume profits.

Recent studies on technology strategy in the New Zealand industry have shown that exporting firms with an offensive competitive strategies focus on doing a lot more product and process development (Johnson, 1991 and Frater, 1995). However, while there has been a recent move toward the formal recognition of technology management, firms did not exhibit a strong link between their competitive and technology strategies.

### A Summary New Zealand Case: Yachting's Americas Cup
New Zealand made its first bid to win yachting's most prestigious prize, the Americas Cup, in 1986/87. America had always held the Cup, for 132 years in fact, until it was wrested from them in 1983 by Australia, who claimed its winged keel technology provided winning edge performance. New Zealand's bid started sluggishly with a Belguim born Australian, Marcel Fachler, finally putting up a $50,000 establishment stake in 1984. Money was raised in earnest from a wide range of sponsors by merchant banker Michael Fay. He capitalised on New Zealanders love of sport and intense rivalry with neighbour Australia to woo the public into supporting what became a national obsession.

Controversy has always surrounded the Americas Cup with many a battle fought in the Clubroom regarding the interpretation of rules. The New Zealand challenges maintained that tradition. In the first challenge, New Zealand used fibreglass hull technology rather than the usual aluminium alloys. A consistent feature of the New Zealand challenge has been pre-match optimisation by match racing identical boats. The US challenger regained the Cup from Australia, this time the US claiming low friction hull paint was the advantage. The second New Zealand attempt in 1988 was subject of more jury room battles than waterborne ones. In this case the ability of New Zealand boat builders to construct a very large composite monohull was utilised. However, a twin hulled defender was raised from the US camp and easily won the race on the water and eventually won the battle in the courts after over 3 years of litigation. Michael Fay's third attempt in 1992 again demonstrated that New Zealand was in the top four of the competition.

Success came at last in May, 1995 and again featured New Zealand pre-match tuning using twin boats. The Americas Cup was won by New Zealand by the largest margin in 100 years using composite material construction for the hull, spars and sails, an optimised design and sophisticated boat performance analysis. However, the crowning key to success was hailed by leader Peter Blake as total teamwork, a team focused on people and attitude. This attitude was exemplified by the way in which the 66 team members, female and male, were listed in the official programme in strict alphabetical order and without rank or duty (Becht, 1995).

## Some Lessons for the Management of Technology from Recent New Zealand Experience

Our observations and experience of the management of technology in New Zealand suggest that:

1. Technological innovation today is a necessarily democratic process which crosses traditional boundaries and borders.
2. Membership of the community of nations is best served when each country manages technology in an appropriate, constructive and sustainable manner.
3. Trade provides for the sharing of resources but brings with it the challenge and responsibility of contributing to the world market place with desirable and useful goods and services.
4. The market is the arbiter of useful technology but may not be benign.
5. If technology is the mechanism through which goods and services are presented to customers, then people are the essential agents that make the process happen.
6. Politicians determine environments, educators prepare minds, researchers and customers create potential, companies assemble transactions but leaders are essential to drive the overall process.
7. The management of technology, at an international level, is a self-controlling process.

## Acknowledgements
The authors would like to express their appreciation for contributions from Christopher Nixon, of the New Zealand Institute of Economic Research, Peter Hobman and Dean Stockwell of the New Zealand Dairy Group, Henry van der Heijden of Fisher & Paykel, Neil Richardson and John Walley of the Gallagher Group, John Williams and Kevin Low PEC of Marton and many researchers from New Zealand universities, CRI's and MIRINZ.

## References
Authier, J. F., (1992). Mechanical Dressing and Beef boning/processing. Proc. Twenty-seventh Meat Industry Research Conference, Hamilton, New Zealand. pp. 327-338.

Becht, R., (1995). Black Magic:Team New Zealand's Victorious Challenge. Hodder Moa Beckett, Auckland.

Bollard, A. E. and Buckle, R., (1987). Economic Liberalisation in New Zealand. Port Nicholson Press, Auckland.

Chrystall, B. B. and Hagyard, C. J., (1976). Electrical Stimulation and Lamb Tenderness. NZ J. Agric. Res. 19, 7.

Critchell, J. T. and Raymond, J., (1912). A History of the Frozen Meat Trade. Constable, London.

Crocombe, G. T., Enright, M. J. and Porter, M. E. (1991). Upgrading New Zealand's Competitive Advantage. Oxford University Press, Auckland.

Doonan, R., (1993). Fututech, Proc. Meat'93: The Australian Meat Industry Research Conference, Surfers Paradise, 11-13 October.

Frater, P., Stuart, G., Rose, D and Andrews, G., (1995) The New Zealand Innovation Environment. A BERL Report, May, Wellington. 196 pp.

Gilbert, K. V., (1993). Electrical Stunning and Slaughter in New Zealand. MIRINZ Technical Report No. 908, 29 pp.

James, C., (1986). The Quiet Revolution: Turbulance and Transition in Contemporary New Zealand. Port Nicholson Press, Auckland.

Johnston, R., (1991). Technology Strategy in New Zealand Industry. Ministry of Science and Technology, Wellington.

Jones, A., (1995). Technology Education in the New Zealand Curriculum: from policy to curriculum. SAME papers, University of Waikato, Hamilton.

Kirk, C. M. and Mills, R. A., (1995). Innovation & Technology Management for Engineers. Proc. IPENZ Annual Conference, 10-14 February 1995, Palmerston North. Vol. 1, p 68-71.

Langdon, A. G. and Kirk, C. M., (1990a). Bridge Building at Waikato: Co-operative Education in Chemistry. Chemistry in New Zealand, Vol. 54, p. 125.

Langdon, A. G. and Kirk, C. M., (1990b). MSc. (Technology): Co-operative Education at the Graduate Level. Chemistry in New Zealand, Vol. 54, p. 128.

Mills, R. A., Dale, J., Kirk, C. M. and Langdon, A. G. (1996) Upfront with Uncertainty - A Planned Approach for Managing Innovation Project Duration. Proc. Project Management Institute New Zealand Chapter, Auckland Conference, 14 - 15 November, pp. 43 - 58.

Ministry of Education, (1993). The New Zealand Curriculum Framework, Learning Media, Wellington.

Ministry of Science and Technology, (1996a). New Zealand Research and Development Statistics 1993/1994. Wellington.

Ministry of Science and Technology, (1996b). R, S&T:2010. Wellington.

Statistics New Zealand, 1996. Key Statistics, December.

Statistics New Zealand in Ministry of Foreign Affairs and Trade, (1993). A Multi-track Approach, New Zealand Trade Policy: Implementation and Directions, Wellington. p 107.

TRADENZ, (1995). Innovation Case Studies. Proc. Innovation Seminar, Hotel du Vin, Pokeno, March.

Vandersyp, C., ed., (1994). Summary of Short-term Prospects. Quarterly Predictions, September. New Zealand Institute of Economic Research, Wellington.

Vaughan, S. R., McDonald, R. M., Donnelly, P. E., Mills, R. A. & Hendy, N. A., (1984) The biomass refinery as a route to fuel alcohol from green crops. Proceedings of the 6th International Symposium on Alcohol Fuels Technology 3:3-46-3-47.

# 047

# SUPPLY MANAGEMENT FOR EFFICIENT INTEGRATED PRODUCT DEVELOPMENT: A PILOTSTUDY

Author:
Pia Eneström
Integrated product development
Department of Machine Design, KTH
S-100 44 Stockholm
Tel:        +46 8 790 91 42
Fax:        +46 8 723 17 30
E-mail:     pia@damek.kth.se

Margareta Norell
Integrated product development
Department of Machine Design, KTH
S-100 44 Stockholm
E-mail:     maggan@damek.kth.se

## ABSTRACT

To become and remain a competitive purchaser in industry today many aspects have to be considered. Of major importance is to involve suppliers early in the product development process. Integrated product development is a concept where activites are performed more in parallel than sequentially. This imply that many people are engaged in the product development and the development time will be reduced.

The purpose is to create an efficient product development process and make the supplier a part of it. Some of the goals to achieve are shorter lead time, increased quality in delivered products, more deliveries "Just In Time" and reduced prices. Possible ways of achieving these goals are through integrated product development in early phases and integrated planning between supplier and purchaser. Other ways are through improved co-operation, understanding, communication and information.

This paper will describe a pilot study within the aluminium industry as a supplier of aluminium profiles. The relation between aluminium profile companies and their customers are somewhat special since the customer in many cases is the owner of the press tool. Another typical thing is the "profile thinking" when designing in aluminium.

Some questions at issue in this study are: How is co-operation between supplier and purchaser carried out in product development? What roles and responsibilities do the involved people have? What are the key factors for good co-operation? How are good relations implemented between supplier and purchaser?

The research method that is used is empirical, such as open ended interviews, to obtain an understanding of the co operation model of today. The researchers perform deep interviews with people both in the aluminium industry and their customers. People to be interviewed are at the design department in both parties and at the sales and purchase departments. Results and experiences from this study will be discussed in the full paper.

# 048

# Computer Aided Manufacturing:
## The Missing Link between New Technological Developments and the Production Process

Lars U. Kreul
Department of Chemical Engineering, University of Dortmund, 44227 Dortmund, Germany

Andrzej Górak
Department of Process Engineering, University of Essen, 45141 Essen, Germany

## 1. Introduction

Biggest changes in growth arise due to technological innovation resulting into new patterns of production or even a generation of completely new products. The lure of devising a breakthrough gives a temporary monopoly to innovators and therefore large financial returns. Accordingly, new growth theory favors a world market with permanent fluctuation between monopoly and equilibrium. The importance of temporary monopolies for industrialized countries is striking: They will be able to defend their wages high above the world average only if they manage to jump from non-equilibrium to non-equilibrium, depending on two important dynamic ingredients: the velocity of new technological developments and even more the velocity of their transformation into actual production. Knowledge, as well as capital, is increasingly mobile, while the period of time remaining to actually exploit innovation is becoming more and more important. Simultaneously, it is more and more decreasing. The ability to organize the manufacturing process itself as fast and as efficient as possible will determine the success of a company. The only promising way to achieve this goal is the use of innovative technology itself, namely the so-called Computer Aided Manufacturing (CAM) or Computer Aided Engineering (CAE). as it is referred to for technology intensive production as in the presented example. In this paper, different parts and methodologies of CAM/CAE are investigated and evaluated. Examples are presented from the fields of chemical, pharmaceutical and environmental engineering. Computer aided investigation of production processes is necessary to evaluate in advance risks and chances of new productions, but as well to determine quickly optimal manufacturing structures and conditions. Once the chance to launch a new product on the market is given in terms of technological knowledge and promising economic expectations, it will be the factor *time* which decides about the profit, the cost-price correlation, and the final success of launching [EID89], see Figure 1.

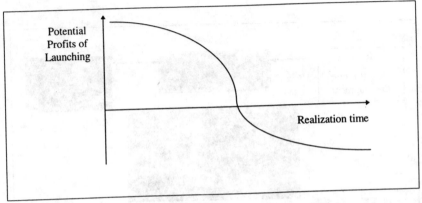

**Figure 1: Time as key factor for success of launching**

## 2. Structuring of Production Process Development

The beginning of a new production line is generally marked by a new idea, a new product development, it is completed with the realization of the actual production, see Figure 2. A very important, cost and time intensive step in the organization of the manufacturing process is planing period. In this phase the general structure of the new production process must be specified, the sequence of necessary apparatuses, their functions and connections, etc. At first, the development of the new production process has to be structured clearly due to the d the definition of planing areas, e.g. Process Design, Unit Design and Unit Control, as well as considerations dealing with scheduling and logistic. Secondly, possible interactions of these sections have to be regarded and the parts have to be integrated again in order to come to an overall optimum for the entire process. Accordingly, we try to show possible ways to investigate the separated units and to connect them again in order to create one network with constant feedback between the different parts. General conditions for the creation of such a network are given only by the fact, that the size of the problem must be limited and the possibility must be given to structure the problem in question properly, as it becomes necessary to splitting up the problem in different models and subsystems. In chemical engineering, a process consists of a number of different units, presenting specific different apparatuses or groups of them. They have different function in the treatment of the process components like performing chemical reactions, heating or cooling, separation of mixtures for purification, etc. Each of these units can be constructed and run differently. In addition, they are connected in very complex ways. It can be understood easily, that pure reasoning and experience therefore is insufficient and slow because the human mind is restricted in its ability to predict results of changes of parameters within a highly complex system with completely interdependent variables.

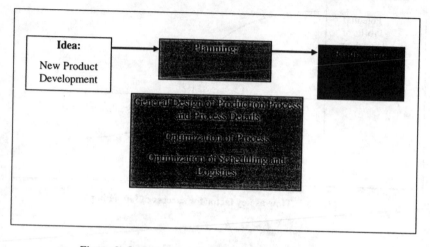

Figure 2: Organization of a new manufacturing process

In this regard, these problems are actually very meaningful examples for problems in society, environment, industrial decision making etc., that have reached nowadays quite similar levels of complexity. All single units can be analyzed using computer simulation if it is possible to build up the physico-chemical processes in mathematical terms. Then, the optimization of these parts of the process becomes possible by an extensive use of sophisticated numerical mathematics. Besides, the sequence of these units can be varied. A different combination of apparatuses may result in a major increase in process efficiency and the optimum of the single units will be changed. This leads to a completely interactive research operation consisting of Process Design, Unit Design, Unit Control and finally Scheduling and Logistics, see Figure 3. Consequently, on the one hand, single parts of the system have to be investigated accurately, on the other hand, the complete system that is built from these parts must be considered, the functions of the parts within this system, and their mutual interaction. These equally important directions of planning of manufacturing can only be combined using a systems or integrated approach. In this systematic circle, the basic subsystems for the production processes in chemical engineering are represented. Process Design (PD) deals with the structure of the complete process, which unit operations should be used at all, which sequence, internal recycles, etc. In Unit Design (UD) specific features of single units are determined in order to enable the apparatus to achieve the aims predicted in PD. This section therefore needs high data input, as e.g. specific physical properties, reaction kinetics, mass transfer resistance, etc.

Unit Control (CU) deals with the operation and control strategy of the units and tries to predict their behavior not only under standard but as well emergency and unexpected situations. Scheduling and Logistic considerations finally try to optimize the operation sequence of the complete production considering its connections with the outside world.

1. Process Design (PD)
2. Unit Design (UD)
3. Unit Control (UC)
4. Scheduling and Logistic (SL)

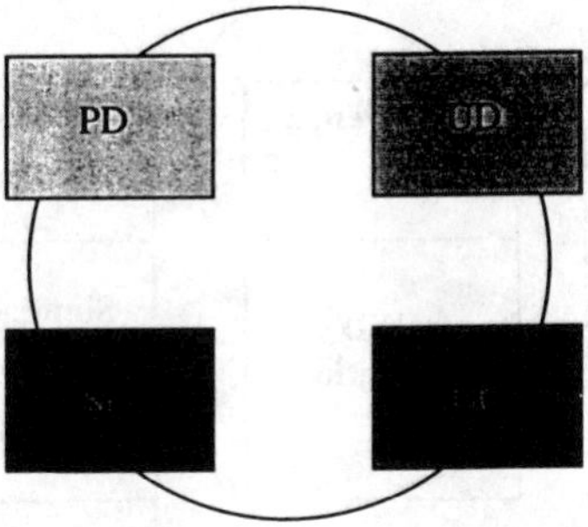

**Figure 3: Systems Approach**

It is evident that the quest for the overall optimum of the manufacturing process results into a highly iterative procedure, where the cycle must be followed over again and again. Accordingly, the information flow between its different parts is crucial. It is this systematic and iterative procedure that can be supported by modern computer technology. Computer Aided Engineering (CAE) is a concept which contains these steps in subsystems, which are linked together in order to make the entire realization process faster and more efficient. Figure 4 shows how the different parts of CAE can be connected to support the process and unit design, unit control and scheduling. Computer Aided Design (CAD) is becoming more and more intelligent, being already far more than a simple drawing device. It can be used above all to interact with expert systems and programs containing mathematical rules for feasibility analysis. In the control section, Computer Aided Control and Quality Control system, CAC and CAQ can be used, e.g. on the grounds of neuronal networks. Scheduling and Logistics finally are based on modeling supported optimization, using different mathematical solution tools.

## 3. Single Methodologies

While modeling a certain process one will always be faced with a trade off between accuracy and simplicity, see. Figure 5. The overall costs are determined by the summation of costs produced through high accurate models, due to cost intensive model development itself, need for physical properties, detailed information from the process, etc., and the error costs of inaccuracies and risk related costs.

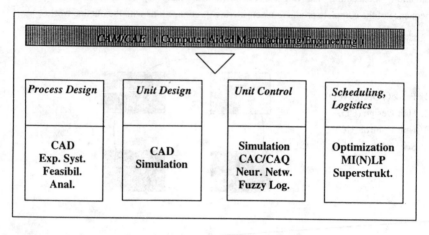

| *Process Design* | *Unit Design* | *Unit Control* | *Scheduling, Logistics* |
|---|---|---|---|
| CAD Exp. Syst. Feasibil. Anal. | CAD Simulation | Simulation CAC/CAQ Neur. Netw. Fuzzy Log. | Optimization MI(N)LP Superstrukt. |

**Figure 4: Interacting between different software tools for design and planning production processes**

It therefore is always necessary to subdivide the entire system into different part as discussed above and to find the most suited model description for each of these parts separately. The following section explains in detail how the parts of the structure work and which tools should be applied.

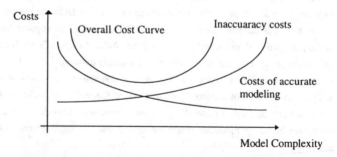

**Figure 5: Optimal Model Complexity**

**Expert Systems.** The best known tools to solve process design problems of high complexity and a large number of possible combinations are so-called Expert Systems, which are formed by complex rules and databases. On the contrary to Neural Networks (see below) information cannot be changed automatically but is implemented as knowledge of experts in logical proceedings. The quality of the systems depends to a very high degree on the quality of the considered expertise, and the range of application is limited to processes they are specially adapted for. Inside of this range they are able to select between various possibilities and are not limited to follow one specific pre-defined way. Therefore, they are ideal design, where not only 'if-then' solutions, but complex combinatorial analysis is required. To create an Expert System the experience of professionals has to be documented and to be translated into formal computer language, including the risk that even important information or experience does not find it's way into the databases. Furthermore, there is a risk that the user of the system loses interest because of always repeating questions. Therefore, the system has to be developed carefully together with the users, engineers, technicians and management in order to ensure its acceptance.

**Simulation: Differential-Algebraic Equation Systems.** Continuously, smoothly changing processes which can be formulated as Initial or Boundary Value Problems are commonly described by Differential-Algebraic Equation Systems (DAE-Systems). The systems can be implemented into programs or modeling platforms and solved using suited numerical routines. If a DAE-description is possible, the process can be simulated quite accurately, if all physical properties and model parameters are available. Computer simulation and simulation based optimization becomes possible. The design of specific unit operations, including the optimization of geometries, operation conditions, etc., are usually based on this approach.

**Neural Networks.** Highly non-linear process can be handled using Neural Networks. The results can be used to predict adequate actions of the control devices and operation policies for the units. Neural Networks represent a tool, where new information can be learned and 'experience' acquired. This is realized by a complex interconnection between the different parts of the Neural Network with the possibility to store new data. The use of Neural Networks therefore is of great advantage, if learning is required. In principle, the learning process which the network can undergo constitutes a simple comparison between two different states. The phases of Neural Network utilization usually consist of *training, testing* and *validation* [REI80].

**Fuzzy Logic.** Fuzzy Logic is commonly used to control processes. It does not need an exact input signal to react appropriately, but a signal which is more or less *similar* to the one which is expected, because the system is based on a relational matrix, so that results of the Fuzzy Logic corresponds to pre-defined linguistic expressions. A model using fuzzy logic can report its results in three different ways: at first, the output may have the form of a fuzzy set, it could be in pre-defined linguistic expressions or finally, after the so called 'defuzzification process', the results can be presented in exact numbers [REU93].

**Combinations.** Fuzzy systems can be used in fields of non linear dynamic processes where differential equations are difficult to use. To analyze or to synthesize a *new* process, the combination of Fuzzy Logic and Expert Systems seems to be promising to overcome the problem, that existing rule languages are not expressive enough to capture the heuristic knowledge needed to control complex processes. A so called *Expert Fuzzy System* (EFS) allows more complex hierarchies of rules, and the formulation of meta-rules that are used to decide which low-level rules are to be applied. A combination of Fuzzy Systems with Neural Networks on the other hand, means that the amount of data and saved information will increase if the Neural Network saves its new obtained information. New information about a process is certainly positive, but due to the properties of Neural Networks the clear structure and the transparency of the database decreases, because the Neural Network is not able to save new information in the database according to human understanding [REU96]. A way out of this dilemma is the use of different databases which have to be connected, so that the relational matrix and the data of the Expert Systems retain their original structure in the first one, while the Neural Network saves new unstructured information inside of database in the second.

**Superstructures and Mixed Integer (Non-) linear Programming.** A Superstructure combines all models in one network, where the structural and operational alternatives of the process are integrated in a complex scheme, e.g. reactors in series, parallel, series-parallel, arrangements with side streams and recycles, bypasses, different feeding strategies, etc. An optimization based on such a general representation enables the simultaneous consideration of all macro- and micro alternatives and is capable of revealing new, non-conventional process configurations [MAR96]. Due to the complexity of such a system the structural optimization needs Mixed Integer Nonlinear Programming (MINLP), which represents a *mixed integer optimization method*. As industrial problems involve many reactants and paths, the simultaneous study and exploitation of all design alternatives at once is normally not possible. Therefore, binary (decision) variables (e.g. 0/1, false/true, on/off) are used to denote the existence or nonexistence of process units and streams. These binary variables can be considered as switches which can activate or disactivate some parts of the process model [BAU96]. Parameter changes can be introduced with connected probabilities. Using MINLP it will be possible to consider complex configurations of all parts included. Nevertheless, it is of course advisable to look for a clear, easy and understandable structure in order to assure the simplicity of the model and to enable for the convergence of the mixed integer optimization [BAU96].

## 4. Integration in the Environment of the Complete System

From the organizational point of view the sequence of the different steps which have to be considered during the planning of a new production plant is always similar. To return to the question of how the variety of models and methods for different parts can be linked together in order to create one large network, and how a constant feedback between these different units can be assured, the following framework is proposed, see Figure 6. All single parts are embedded into an integrated structure. Its shell activates the *User Interface*, has constant feedback with large *Databases* with 'fixed' information, as e.g. expert rules and mathematical models, and 'flexible' parts for Neural Networks, etc. It must be underlined, that this *Shell* can also be used for other applications, which are not directly linked to chemical process engineering, for the logistic, organizational and designing parts do not differ in it's logical order from that of other industrial applications.

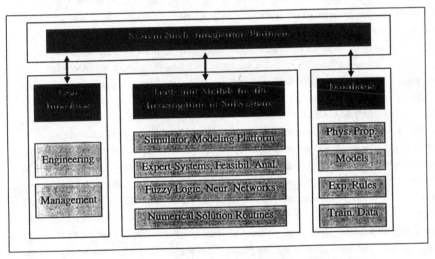

Figure 6: Proposed integration of the mathematical tools for *CAE*

## 5. Application Example of Integrated Approach

Many processes in chemical process industries consist of two major steps, namely transformation by chemical reactions and separation. In the reaction step the desired chemical products are formulated, but reactions are almost never complete and sufficiently selective, so that unreacted feed stocks, side-products, intermediates, etc. are still present in the reaction mixture, and must be removed from the commercial product and recycled back to the reactor. The separation step is most often carried out using a combination of distillation columns. Complicated processes are broken down into simple steps, combinations of chemical and physical transformations within one unit, so-called Reactive Distillation Processes (RD) have been avoided because of the resulting problems regarding their control and operation. However, modern computer technology enables for the deliberate combination of both phenomena, which has shown to be very efficient for specific purposes. The reactor is placed inside the separation unit, so that reaction products are formed and removed simultaneously. Raw materials and by-products are automatically recycled inside the column. As a result, high conversion rates and selectivity can often be achieved. In addition, since the costs of separation are very high (approx. 50% or more of the complete production costs), the combination in RD may be very promising in terms of capital investment and energy consumption.

### An Integrated Design, Synthesis, and Optimization Approach for Efficient Chemical Process Configuration Combining Reaction and Distillation

If a new production should be realized, RD can now often be considered as valuable process alternative. It has to be investigated however in detail, if it is the most effective solution. So far, the design has been based on expensive and very time consuming sequences of laboratory and pilot plant experiments. On the contrary, using CAM/CAE, it is possible to reduce these highly restricting factors, costs and time. In a European consortium of large chemical process industries in collaboration with several universities, including the university of Dortmund in a leading position, an Integrated Design, Synthesis, and Optimization Approach for Efficient Chemical Process Configuration Combining Reaction and Distillation is realized at the moment on the basis of CAM/CAE. In the frame of this project, a synthesis tool is in development, which allows for the rapid evaluation of the feasibility of RD for new products and processes, and if RD is a valuable production alternative. In addition, a design tool is built to evaluate the best complete production cycle, as well as a predictive tool finally using the results of the to former steps and completing them by detailed simulation of the units, enabling the analysis and optimization of its operation policy. The three different parts are fully compatible and connected with each other in a way explained above. They interact with a large databases containing all necessary informations about physical properties, about best suited catalysts, packings, etc. The application of the integrated tool will give the using companies a strategic advantage in terms of highly reduced realization time of new productions.

## 6. Conclusion

The ability to organize the manufacturing process as fast and as efficient as possible will determine the success of a company. The presented report gives an overview about different computer-aided techniques used in the field of Chemical Engineering, which can also be applied in other fields of production and planning, namely the so-called Computer Aided Manufacturing (CAM) or Computer Aided Engineering (CAE). The use of CAM/CAE decreases the realization time significantly, while increasing the overall efficiency of the production process. It therefore can be regarded as the missing link between new technological developments and their concretization in terms of manufacturing. Additionally, the considered methodologies allow for their generalizations towards other fields of industrial application, as e.g. in aeronautics, microelectronics etc.

# Reference

[TIM96]    Timothy F. McKenna: *Computer Aided Process Design: Short- Cut design for polymer production.* Computers chem Engng. Vol. 20. p 237-242. 1996.

[ACE96]    J. Acevedo and E. N. Pistikopoulos : *Computational studies of stochastic optimization algorithms for process synthesis under uncertainty.* Computers chem Engng. Vol. 20. p1-6. 1996.

[MAR96]    E. Marcoulaki and A. Kokossis : *Stochastic optimisation of complex reaction systems.* Computers chem Engng. Vol. 20. p 231-S236. 1996

[BAU96]    M. H. Bauer and J. Stichlmair : *Superstructures for the mixed integer optimization of non-ideal and azeotropic distillation processes.* Computers chem Engng. Vol. 20. p 25 - 30. 1996.

[CIT96]    K. Damert and L. Teichert: *Anwendungsorientierte Prozeßmodellierung und -simulation bei der Entwicklung eines Suspensions-Polymerisations-verfahrens.* Chemie Ingenieur Technik, p 1086. 1996

[SZR96]    I. Skrjanc and O. Hecker: *Fuzzy predictive control based on relational matrix models.* Computers chem Engng. Vol. 20. p 931-936. 1996

[TUR96]    P. Turner, G. Montague and J. Morris : *Dynamic neural networks in non-linear predictive control (an industrial application).* Computers chem Engng. Vol. 20. p 937-942. 1996.

[REI80]    L. E. Reichl. *A modern course in statistical physics.* University of Texas press. 1980.

[REU93]    B. Reusch. *Fuzzy Logic.* Springer. 1993.

[FAN89]    G. Fandel. *Produktions- und Kostentheorie.* Springer. 1989.

[EID89]    B. Eidenmüller. *Die Produktion als Wettbewerbsfaktor.* TÜV Rheinland. 1989.

[JEH89]    E. Jehle. *Durch Wertanalyse optimierte Logistikprozesse.* TÜV Rheinland. 1989.

[Zel96]    M. Zeller, *Modellgestützte Reihenfolgenplanung*; Colloquium on Logistics of Production, Dortmund. 1996.

[BUT93]    D. Butz, *Interpretation of a neural network for control with topologically ordered visible units in the light of fuzzy logic.* Springer. 1993.

[CON91]    Confection 2000, *Le planning de fabrication informatisée: Prévoir et organiser une production harmonieuse.* Confection 2000. Vol. 121. p 49- 51. 1991

# 050

# SUCCESS WITH INTEGRATED ENVIRONMENTAL INFORMATION SYSTEMS

Author:
Andreas Schlatter
Dipl. Ing. ETH, lic. oec. HSG
Research Group "Eco-Performance"
Institute of Industrial Engineering and Management
Swiss Federal Institute of Technology, Zurich (ETH)
Zuerichbergstr. 18
CH- 8028 Zuerich, Switzerland


Co-authors:
Michael Frei
Dipl. Ing. ETH, Switzerland

Johannes Rueegg-Stuerm PD Dr. oec. HSG Research Group "Organizational
Change" Institute of Management University of St. Gallen Dufourstr. 48
CH- 9000 St. Gallen, Switzerland

Rainer Zuest Prof. Dr. Research Group "Eco-Performance" Institute of
Industrial Engineering and Management Swiss Federal Institute of
Technology, Zurich (ETH)

## ABSTRACT

The environmental dimension is becoming more and more important in
the economic world. Many organizations are seeking ways to understand
and improve their environmental performance, ie improvement of the
environmental aspects of the organization's activities, products and
services. To provide the management with reliable and verifiable
information economically on an ongoing basis an environmental
information system is required.

In a two-year research project involving our institute and four different
companies, environmental information systems have been investigated,
developed and are being introduced.
The initial results of this ongoing project will be presented:
a) Experiences in development and application of environmental
information systems in different enterprises
b) Concept of environmental information systems for preparing user
oriented, (and not data oriented!) environmental information, based on the
requirements of the environmental management system.
c) Concepts of necessary procedures for creating organizational change and

learning processes in environmental aspects.

Objectives of the project:
a) Investigation of environmental aspects and their diversity in industrial field studies (Electrical and Electronical Industry, Sanitary Industry, Trading). Development of environmental information systems in cooperation with the organizations investigated.
b) Analysis and application of the requirements of international standards for environmental management (ISO 14000), e.g. Environmental Performance Evaluation (ISO 14031) and Life Cycle Assessment (ISO 14040ff). Application of Enterprise Modelling (ISO/TC 184) to requirements of environmental management.
c) Study of the organizational change process while investigating information requirements, e.g. change of the environmental conciousness of empoyees and change of the awareness on environmental aspects within the companies.


Keywords:
Environmental Information Systems, Environmental Management Systems, Environmental Performance, ISO 14000, Enterprise Modelling, Environmental learning, Organizational Change, ActivityBased Information


Oral presentation

# Success with environmental information

Setting up an environmental information system: A learning process

Schlatter A., Dipl. Ing. ETH, lic. oec. HSG
Frei M., Dipl. Ing. ETH
Rüegg-Stürm J., Dr. oec. HSG
Züst R., Prof. Dr., Dipl. Ing. ETH

**Summary**

A fundamental realization of our research has been that the provision of purely scientific-technical data as undertaken up to now is not enough in a company's environmental conservation program. In addition to improving user-oriented information design it is crucial to investigate how this data generates concrete alterations in behavior and thereby a process of change in the enterprise.

In the first section of this contribution the current deficit in the provision and design of environmental information is illustrated. In the second the knowledge and criteria significant for environmental information system design is presented with reference to the areas 'management and staff', 'products and services' and 'processes and infrastructures'. Subsequently, transposition procedures for the application of environmental information are presented. The criteria which are important for starting and maintaining the process of change are illustrated in particular.

## 1. Point of departure

The problem involved in the environmental information elaborated up to now in companies lies less with the methods used than with basic questions of understanding of processes; communication; and contentual information design. Are environmental information systems the solution to this problem? The thoughts presented below are based upon empirical examinations and knowledge stemming from projects in large Swiss companies.

### 1.1 Data flood or environmental information?

Growing worries concerning the maintainance of our natural environment have stimulated the attention of companies to their own environmental impact. Companies must establish what impact they are causing, minimize it and if possible avoid it. For this, a fact-oriented decision-making basis is, firstly, required; secondly, the knowledge and understanding for using it must be built up in the company. Today companies are increasingly battling with a data flood and a simultaneous shortage of information. More and more, companies are asking themselves the question: are environmental information systems the solution to this problem?

Environmental information systems aid the provision of data for the ecological management of a company. In literature and practice any deployment of informatics in the processing of environmentally-relevant data is termed an "environmental information system". A consistent and generally-accepted definition of the term is, however, still lacking (Eschenbach and Neumann 1994). We define an environmental information system as that part of the company information system which draws/ascertains the necessary raw, environmentally-relevant data primarily from existing company information and measuring systems, processes it in a user-oriented manner and correspondingly communicates the requirements implicated (fig. 1).

The following differentiation is to be made: the level of *data application and interpretation* requires something from the enviromental information system. The *infrastructures*, including all informatic means, provide the necessary support. In between lies the level of the *environmental information system*, the actual systematic processing of the information (see Schlatter 1996, Wollnik 1988). Via receiver-specific, user-friendly processing and representation the persuasive impact of data may be increased. Particularly in the company environment, the effort involved in interpretation by individual receivers may be minimized by this means.

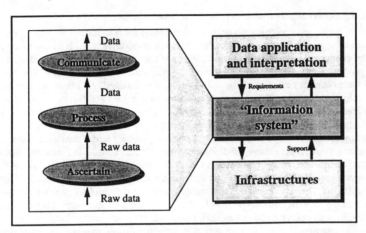

**Fig. 1:** Definition of an environmental information system
We define an environmental information system as that part of the company information system which draws/ascertains the necessary raw, environmentally-relevant data primarily from existing company information and measuring systems, processes it in a user-oriented manner and correspondingly communicates the requirements implicated (Schlatter 1996).

By "data" is meant all inflowing, still unprocessed items of information. It may involve symbols, numbers, pictures or information in text form. Data is independent of who receives it and requires interpretation. Only its interpretation by the respective receiver lends it an informative character. The interpretation of data by the receiver takes place inseparable from the receiver's knowledge and contextual experience (see Rüegg-Stürm and Gomez 1994). Thus data must be interpreted by the respective receiver. Only in the context of the respective receiver, and via the latter's processing and interpretation of data, does information result. (see Giger 1992).

The exchange of data among the players in the company requires a basis of understanding. This means that a minimal common basic understanding regarding the data to be exchanged must be present between the data sender and the data receiver. Only if the data receiver possesses the necessary pre-knowledge and a certain amount of expertise is he in the position to interpret the data received. Thus it cannot always be assumed that the receiver can interpret and use the data sent to him.

This examination of data and information against a background of radical constructionism (von Foerster 1995, Schmidt 1987) has far-reaching consequences for the provision of environmentally-relevant data and its application. In the context of the building-up of an environmental management system in a company this means that it cannot be taken for granted that a head of a company department understands the data made available to him right away and that he can influence environmental performance in his sector on its basis. The required thematic understanding, expertise and experience must be developed in the context of an internal negotiation and communication process.

In the following it is therefore illustrated that, for an environmental management system to be effective, it is not enough to concentrate only upon the provision of data in the areas of products, processes and infrastructures. It is primarily important to examine the side of the data receiver, ie. data interpretation; and the building up of knowledge and understanding concerning the potential influence of the individual players in the company with regard to environmental impact. In addition, the social and organizational contexts, and those of the individual players, must not be neglected. The issue at hand is to examine whether the data currently available in the company, and its application, suffice for the demands being made on a modern environmental information system.

## 1.2 Do the data currently available in practice suffice?

The economic, social and ecological contexts build the basis for activities in environmental protection. The aim of an environmental management system in companies is, with an eye to the requirements of the economic and social framework, to shape and continually improve products and the connected processes and infrastructures in a more environmentally-correct manner. This means that an internal improvement process must be introduced and maintained. Additionally, interest groups need to be informed regarding the company's environmental impact and the measures being taken. The difficulties in the designing of an environmental program for the improvement of environmental performance lie in the data basis available; its application; and in its use.

In the company there are various information systems and locations where data administration takes place. These are mostly application- or department-specific and contain the data required for the corresponding application. Among this data is also to be found a large body of data useful for environmental investigations. This can mean that certain data are redundant in a company. Depending upon local definition, system delineation and understanding of the problem by those holding it, inconsistencies in the data may be the result. A further problem is that an environmental management system, as a company-comprehensive function, also needs company-comprehensive data. Because of a lack of data transparency in the company it is often impossible to determine what data is already available. Another problem lies in insufficient availability of pointers to the exactness, origins, reliability and limits of data. Via combination and evaluation of the data available in a company, initial knowledge can be gathered and measures developed with relatively little effort. It is easy to see, however, that this is not enough for the systematic and ongoing improvement of environmental performance in the long term.

The issue is thus to remove the largest deficits, ie. the causes of major environmental impact, with minimal expenditure of effort and resources. The prioritizing of measures to be taken may take place with the help of a portfolio in which environmental effects are compared with the efforts/expenditure necessary to get rid of them. The prerequisite for such prioritizing is the provision of corresponding data material, as a basis for decision-making. On the other hand, for the provision of meaningful data it is necessary to know what the data needs to cover. The deficits in environmental protection and/or the significant environmental aspects must therefore be known in order that data be collected. The problem of the chicken or the egg thus arises, and must be addressed.

In summary, it is apparent that a substantial body of useful environmental data is already available. The deficit in this data lies in the lack of goal- and receiver-orientation in its gathering and processing. In the use of data too little significance is attached to the context and initial knowledge of the receiver, and to the form in which data communication takes place.

## 1.3 Existing concepts of information provision

Approaches to the provision of environmental data up to now, such as ecological accounting (Müller-Wenk 1972), eco-balances (Goedkoop et al. 1995, Ahbe 1995, Hofstetter and Braunschweig 1994, Steen and Ryding 1992) or eco-controlling (Schaltegger and Sturm 1995, Hallay and Pfriem 1992) have in common the depiction of an ideal end-state with fully-available data. The complete provision of this data means a large amount of effort if it does not take place via an integrated information system. This is also the reason why the application of these concepts has been hesitant, particularly in smaller and more middle-sized enterprises. Data provision in these concepts is carried out primarily for a group of experts. Too little attention is paid to the application-oriented processing, communication and use of the data.

An important contribution to the reduction of this deficit has been made in the series of standards ISO 14001ff. Here an organizational framework, and thereby a systematic procedure for the setting up of the environmental management system in organizations, has been proposed. Norm ISO 14001, 'Environmental Management System', sets companies two important requirements. Firstly, the company must determine the *significant environmental aspects* involved in its products, activities and services. In addition, a deeper knowledge of the enterprise is required. Secondly, the company must take measures for the *ongoing improvement of environmentally-oriented performance* (see Züst 1996b). In order to answer the questions regarding significant environmental aspects and the possibilities for ongoing improvement, the corresponding data are indispensible. ISO 14001 does not explicitly require an environmental information system or specifically demonstrable amounts of knowledge. It requires, however, the provision of data as a decision-making base for management and for the carrying out of the corresponding management tasks (see ISO 14001, 4.5.3 and A.5.3).

The existing and applied concepts partially demonstrate good and practicible approaches. But they leave open a networked, integrated and dynamic means of investigation. In particular, all of these approaches neglect the question of the data receiver, the latter's context and his possibilities for using the data provided.

## 1.4 Summarizing modes of looking at the information deficit

The emphasis of ecological activities up to now has lain primarily on a post-event-oriented mode of looking at the situation. The visible and thereby recognizable environmental problems are the enviromental effects of waste, emissions, and the use of materials and energy. The concepts of eco-balances and eco-controlling are oriented towards this approach. In the future, however, anticipatory, pre-event modes will be increasingly required, as well as the taking into account of how information is used.

In the following are described the connections between problem recognition in society; the generation of environmental problems by decisions; and the emergence of environmental effects and their impact on nature (fig. 2).

- It is to be investigated who takes the important decisions which affect the scope of future environmental impact. Here we are also talking about the 'determination' of environmental impact. Data which allows him to recognize effects in good time is to be made available to the decision-maker. The decision-maker also needs, for example, guidelines for examining the ecological dimension in his decisions, or life cycle modelling to render the ecological effects visible.
- Until now mainly physical and chemical factors were understood under the term environmental information. Correspondingly, today input/output analyses and products, processes and operative location are examined with a post-event emphasis. Here we are talking about the 'yields' of environmental impact.
- The natural sciences viewpoint is concentrated simultaneously on effects upon nature. The 'effect' of the respective change is the emphasis here.
- Public discussion of these results aids problem recognition and the building of consciousness in society as well as informing it (see Beck 1986, Luhmann 1986). The 'recognition' of the problem in society takes effect on the company via staff awareness, market mechanisms and political and social demands.

Modes of viewing the problem up to now have limited themselves to the materially-rational level. The focus lies on technological improvements, which involve high levels of investment. Because of this it is usually forgotten in the company that ecological impact is determined by the actions of people as individuals and as exponents of the entire company. Much too rarely is the question asked as to who it is who determines ecological impact. Also important is the design of data as regards content and user orientation. For effective data provision it is thus not enough to rely only on data concerning physical processes.

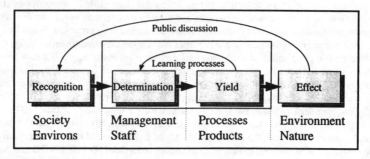

**Fig. 2:** Connecting environmental effects with their causes
Ascertainable environmental effects are determined within the framework of decisions. Social and company-internal values permeate thinking, decision-making and action.

A second, much more fundamental problem must be taken into account in addition to that of efficient and economical company data compilation and processing. This is the problem of what the distribution of data in a company actually generates in terms of *behavioral change*, behavioral change expressed in altered communication and decision-making habits. It is exactly this that every type of company information system (financial and ecological) should aim to reach: that the capacity for company self-steering grows, and that people begin to behave correspondingly differently, more *appropriately*. Consequently, increased attention must be given to the *structural framework*, the local *organization of work* and the *habits* and *organizational routines* prevalent in these (Rüegg-Stürm 1996).

## 2. Prerequisites for new information concepts and procedures for putting them into practice

The setting up of an environmental management system in the company demands a general process of company change, with regard to company behavior. This means that both the individual staff member and the organization as a whole must learn to integrate and economically shape environmentally-correct action in their daily work. A basic point is that the up-to-now purely scientific-technical view of data provision and analysis must be regarded in combination with that of individual and organizational learning and organizational change, in order to achieve a more comprehensive understanding of connections and informational requirements. The consequences of this for data provision and for the elaboration of an environmental information system are represented in the following. In the first section elements for new environmental information concepts are illustrated. In the second follow pointers for the putting into practice of environmental information provision.

### 2.1 Elements for new information concepts

As mentioned, the attempt was made in the past to alter existing environmental effects via process optimization. These measures led mostly to improvement of energy and materials efficiency and to the reduction of emissions in production. The measures soon reached their limits, however, as the developers of the products **determine** most environmental effects on the basis of general rules, empirical values and habit, while the effects **show up** in other phases of the product life cycle. The largest proportion of environmental impact thus has its origins in management, ie. in company culture, company policy and in the values expressed in leadership and management style and in communication. Individual players act and decide on the basis of this value system and the general management model in the company (see Baitsch et al. 1996).

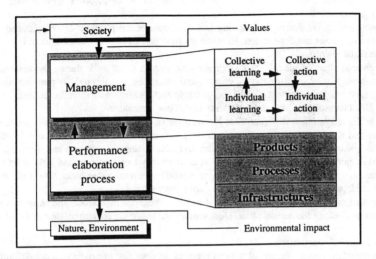

**Fig. 3:** **Learning processes in environmental management**
The up-to-now purely scientific-technical view of data provision and analysis must be regarded in combination with that of individual and organizational learning and organizational change, in order to achieve a more comprehensive understanding of connections and informational requirements.

The checking and ongoing improvement of a company's environmental performance relate to four interdependent areas. These are those of *products and services* generated by the company. They require *processes*, based among other things upon corresponding *infrastructure* such as grounds, building, lighting, heating or machinery. The *management and staff*, as a fourth, higher area determine the environmental impact of products, processes and infrastructure. Correspondingly, codes and information concerning all four areas are required for the environmental management system (fig. 3).

**Management and staff**
With their decisions and the measures they take, the management and staff determine the environmental impact of products, processes and infrastructures. In order to recognize the effects of their actions and to improve them the players in a company need information and codes concerning the corresponding areas. In the draft standard (ISO 14031.5; Caduff 1997) the three following classes of code are proposed:

- Environmental Management Indicators (EMI), which describe management success at putting into practice
- Environmental Performance Indicators (EPI), which provide information concerning the improvement of the environmental performance of process, product and infrastructures
- Environmental Condition Indicators (ECI), which describe the environmental requirements and their improvement.

**Products and services**
Products and services should not just be looked at within the context of the company generating them. Responsibility for products stretches over all phases in product life, from development over production, use and disposal. Environmental effects should be continually improved over all these phases (see ISO 14040-43):

- *Planning and development*: In planning and development the products to be produced and the required processes are determined. Here the greatest part of environmental impact is also determined (Züst 1996b).
- *Manufacture*: Part of the 'planned' environmental impact takes place during the manufacturing phase through the use of materials, energy, and resources, and through by-products and emissions. Environmental impact is only recognizable and measurable within the company in question. This fact must not limit improvements to this one area alone.
- *Use*: In the usage phase differentiation between active and passive products, as described by De Winter and Kals (1994), is important. In *active products*, as for example cars, around 80% of energy use takes place during use and only around 20% during manufacture and disposal. Speerli (1995) demonstrates in his investigation that an electricity meter uses around 70% of its total energy consumption in the use phase. In passive products, on the other hand, no significant additional environmental effects are generated during the use phase.
- *Disposal*: Disposal involves expert reintroduction of products, byproducts and emissions into the production cycle or the natural cycle. Disassembly and recycling are current themes (Züst 1996a).

**Processes and infrastructures**
The viewing of processes and infrastructures requires, as does that of products, a pre-definition and delimitation of individual process steps or infrastructure functions. The definition and delimitation must not consist of the isolated views of experts, but must be determined together with those involved according to the development of the understanding of the problem. For structuring as well as for later condensing of data the creation of an illustration aiding the ecological view is necessary. Here the delimitation and the scope of the ecological view are to be represented in a transparent manner and justified. With such an illustration/figure the influences and links between effects may be demonstrated. In this connection four aspects are of particular significance, and justify the interest in ecological representations (see Kremer and Schwarzer 1994):

- Figures create transparency regarding the elements, relationships and effects within the organization illustrated.
- Figures may be used for clarification of organization functioning as well as for delimitation of the area under investigation.
- Figures simplify communication.
- Figures may be used for the representation and analysis of various (organizational and technical) approaches.

On the basis of such illustrations it becomes possible to find a consistent delimitation for environmental investigations which is also understood within the company. Precise determining of system limits is, finally, an aid to the provision of reliable environmental data (see ISO 14031).

Thus the entry into the environmental problematic does not begin at zero. Even if, when planning begins, the significant environmental aspects are still unknown and no concrete environmental data is available, there exist in the company a great body of experiential knowledge among its staff and a more or less concrete general data basis to be activated. This is the lead-in to a step-by-step building up of a consistent and reliable data basis with attention to the prerequisites and concepts described above and the corresponding specialist, experiential and interactive knowledge (Rüegg-Stürm and Gomez 1994).

## 2.2 Putting-into-practice procedures for the use of environmental information

Concepts are elaborated themes. Every concept is based upon differentiation, which someone must undertake. Whoever does so gains a different, new understanding of the corresponding theme. This understanding is not so easily transmissable. Every text and thereby every concept is *in need of interpretation*. Interpretation depends upon context, and upon previous relevant background knowledge. If this is lacking or insufficient the most wonderful concepts will appear to the resultingly ignorant addressee not as stimuli but as meaningless text (see Luhmann 1986).

Pragmatic information only emerges if a point comprises both confirmation and newness (von Weizsäcker 1986). In the area of environmental information systems a large body of background knowledge cannot be taken for granted. Environmental information systems represent a great unknown. For this reason the corresponding concepts depend largely on newness, and not on confirmation, to prove themselves; in other words there is a great danger that no one will understand what such systems are about at all.

Here the focus shifts from the contents and the concept of an environmental information system to the *process of elaboration* of the system desired. Here the course is set. For it is precisely the collective elaboration of an environmental information system which offers the chance to build up the required background knowledge via a common reconnaissance of in-house company reality. Later on this provides the prerequisite that data -- processed oh-so-beautifully and in a user-oriented manner ... -- be understood, used as information and thereby be effective as regards behavior.

In other words the failure of an environmental information system is preprogrammed if the development of its concept is left to a handful of experts whose interest thereby is in the rapid scaling of the ivory tower. So that ecological communication potential be built up and a deeply-reaching environmental consciousness be able to grow, it is decisive, especially at the outset of a new environmentally-strategic redirectioning, to involve at least the key players and promoters in a collective learning process. Here the new system concepts are developed and the corresponding structural changes planned. If open conflicts and controversial disagreements result, all the better. These are nothing other than an indication that something is actually happening. In addition, it is important in every process of change to confront conflicts and points of friction as early as possible. Otherwise these will later begin to unfold a diffuse life of their own, and make life difficult for all involved.

In the process of change itself it is up to those involved -- as a sort of pioneer effort -- to test out and train in those habits and routines which should later permeate everyday work activities. There is a great difference in whether this will take place merely cognitively, or whether it will be transposed upon structures and collective working habits and really *applied* personally. It is exactly the latter which should be attempted in the process of change.

To generate a corresponding process of change regarding environmental consciousness and behavior, it is -- as empirical studies (Buschor 1996, Rüegg 1996) indicate -- recommended to concentrate on the following four 'pre-tasks':

- *Substantial disturbances and points of inaccessibility* in the company must be brought to the fore and indicated as being in need of attention. Where and how do people experience deficits in the area of ecologically-correct behavior? Where and how may these be articulated? Where and how will the people in the company be approached in a general manner with regard to this theme?
- For the theme of change 'environment' a *viable basis of legitimacy* must be built up which differentiates the reasons upon which the necessity for change rests. Which reasons indicate that the deficits diagnosed should be promptly and sustainably dealt with?
- *Possibilities for the realization of ideas for change* must become a *common point of experience*. With regard to which challenges is rapid, symbolic experience gained? With what symbols can it be convincingly demonstrated that change in the direction of environmentally-aware performance is achievable?

- A theme must be (politically) *positioned*, ie. in some way the framework of influences must be worked on through structural and personal change such that increasingly powers fostering change will have an influence on events. How can attention and energy be directed sufficiently towards the handling of the theme?

Due to this theme underlined by the process of change, the point of departure and the current problem may be selected variously. For example, the environmentally-relevant management goal-setting process, environmentally-correct product design or the optimizing of energy and material flows in production may be thematized. Here the emphasis is less on theme selection than on the stimulus and the thematizing of the environmental problematic. If change has already begun, the following functions should be anchored in structural and personal company rules:

- *Maintenance of the change context* via ongoing further development of the *basis for legitimacy*, through adaptation of the *structural framework* and through *personal* decisions
  This function should be dealt with primarily by a steering committee or by top management, as also proposed in ISO 14001 "Environmental Management Systems".
- Use of internal (and certainly also external) *expertise* for the analysis and new development of areas of competence
  This function may be carried out by making sure that internal experts consistently come to the fore in environmental working groups (as far as the latter exist and are identified). Here the corresponding compositions might change, so that the largest number of staff members as possible may have the opportunity of bringing their own experience and views to the process of change and, vice versa, to undergo a socialization process regarding new habits and routines.
- *Integration* of analysed and newly developed areas of competence
  As soon as a process of change is tackled on a part-time basis by various parties, it is necessary that a core team integrate the elaborated fragments of knowledge and be available as a contact point.
- *Moderation/supervision* (self-observing of habits)
  Finally, one must reflect continuously upon one's own behavioral habits and in the process of change train in those which are more suited to the future organization of work.

## 3. Prospects

The basis for environmentally-correct behavior and learning in the company lies in fact-oriented environmental data. This must be so arranged that it stands in close contact with the activities of the information receiver and allows the latter to recognize the effects of his actions and to adapt his behavior accordingly. Next to individual learning, the problem lies primarily in the change in the basic value structure. Only when it is possible, via a combination of the collective buildup of understanding and a redesigning of company processes, to break through behavioral, perceptual and interpretive habits, may real and sustainable development steps in the direction of the environmentally-correct economy be expected. Only then may environmentally-correct thinking and action go without saying.

# 4. Literature

Ahbe S. (1995): Ökologische Bewertung als Instrument bei der Produkt- und Prozessplanung. Diss Nr. 11214, ETH-Zürich.

Baitsch C., Knoepfel P., Eberle A. (1996): Prinzipien und Instrumente organisationalen Lernens. Dargestellt an einem Fall aus der öffentlichen Verwaltung. Organisationsentwicklung, No. 3, p 4 - 21.

Beck U. (1986): Risikogesellschaft. Suhrkamp, Frankfurt.

Buschor F. (1996): Baustellen einer Unternehmung. Das Problem unternehmerischen Wandels jenseits von Restrukturierungen - Resultate einer empirischen Untersuchung. Haupt, Bern.

Caduff G. (1997): Instrumente zur Beschreibung und Beurteilung umweltbezogener Leistungen (ISO 14031, ISO 14040-43).GWA, No.1, Schweizerischer Verein des Gas- und Wasserfaches, Zürich.

Caduff G., Züst R. (1996): Increasing Environmental Performance via integrated Enterprise Modelling. 3rd International Seminar on Life Cycle Engineering. io-Verlag, Zürich.

De Winter A., Kals J.A.G. (1994): A methodic approach to the environmental effects of manufacturing. In: RECY '94, 2nd International Seminar on Life Cycle Engineering, Erlangen, Germany. Verlag Bamberg, Miesbach.

Eschenbach, Neumann (Hrsg.) (1995): Betriebliche Umwelt-Informationssysteme. Ist Umweltschutz auf Knopfdruck möglich? Manz-Verlag, Wien.

Giger P. (1992): Globale Datenmodelle als Mittel des Datenressourcenmnagements. Diss., Universität Zürich.

Goedkoop M. et al. (1995): The Eco-Indicator 95. NOH Report, No. 9523, Holland.

Hallay H., Pfriem R. (1992): Öko-Controlling. Umweltschutz in mittelständischen Unternehmen. Ein Informationssystem für die Zukunft von Natur und Unternehmen. Campus, Frankfurt.

Hofstetter P., Braunschweig A. (1994): Bewertungsmethoden in Ökobilanzen - ein Überblick. GAIA 3, Nr. 4, S. 227 - 236.

ISO/TC 207/SC 1 (1996): International Standard ISO 14001, Environmental Management System - Specification with guidance for use.

ISO/TC 207/SC 4 (1996): Working Draft ISO/WD 14031.5 Document N187, Environmental Performance Evaluation.

ISO/TC 207/SC 5 (1996): Draft International Standard ISO/DIS 14040, Life Cycle Assessment - Principles and Framework.

Krcmar H., Schwarzer B. (1994): Prozessorientierte Unternehmensmodellierung - Gründe, Anforderungen an Werkzeuge und Folgen für die Organisation. In: Scheer A.-W. (Hrsg.): Prozessorientierte Unternehmensmodellierung. Schriftenreihe zur Unternehmensführung, Band 53. Gabler, Wiesbaden, S. 13 - 14.

Luhmann N. (1986): Ökologische Kommunikation. Westdeutscher Verlag, Opladen.

Müller-Wenk R. (1978): Die ökologische Buchhaltung. - Ein Informations- und Steuerungsinstrument für umweltkonforme Unternehmenspolitik. Campus, Frankfurt.

Rüegg-Stürm J. (1996): Die Erfindung von Organisation - vom Mythos der Machbarkeit in Unternehmenstransformationen: eine theoretische und empirische Erkundung. Unveröffentlichte Habilitationsschrift, Universität St. Gallen HSG.

Rüegg-Stürm J., Gomez P. (1994): From Reality to Vision - From Vision to Reality. An Essay on Vision as Medium for Fundamental Knowledge Transfer. International Business Review, Vol. 3, No. 4, pp. 369 - 394.

Schaltergger S. Sturm A. (1995): Öko-Effizienz durch Öko-Controlling. Schäffer-Poeschel, Stuttgart; vdf, Zürich.

Schlatter A. (1996): Erfolgskriterien bei der Erstellung eines Umwelt-Informationssystems. Symposium "Umweltgerechtes Handeln", 4. - 7. September, Bern.

Schmidt S. (Hrsg.) (1987): Der Diskurs des Radikalen Konstruktivismus. Suhrkamp, Frankfurt.

Speerli, F. (1995) Unternehmens-Umwelt-Management-System. ETH-Diss. Nr. 11'065, Zürich.

Steen B., Ryding S.-O. (1992): The EPS Enviro-Accounting Method. Swedish Environmental Research Institute, Federation of Swedish Industries, Göteborg.

von Foerster H. (1995): Einführung in den Konstruktivismus. Karl Friedrich von Siemens Stiftung. Piper, München.

von Weizsäcker E. (1986): Erstmaligkeit und Bestätigung als Komponenten der pragmatischen Information. In: ders. (Hrsg.): Offene Systeme I: Beiträge zur Zeitstruktur von Information, Entropie und Evolution. 2. überarb. Aufl., Klett-Cotta, Stuttgart, S. 82 - 113.

Wollnik M. (1988): Ein Referenzmodell des Informations-Managements. Information Management, Nr. 3, S. 34 - 43.

Züst R. (1996a): Sustainable Products and Processes. 3rd International Seminar on Life Cycle Engineering. io-Verlag, Zürich.

Züst R. (1996b): Ökologie als unternehmerische Chance. Bulletin - Magazin der ETH, No. 263, Zürich.

# 051

## DESIGN FOR DISASSEMBLY AND ECO-FORECAST - A TOOL FOR INTERACTION BETWEEN MANAGEMENT AND DESIGN

Author:
Conrad Luttropp
KTH ; Machine Design, Stockholm, Sweden
Brinellvägen 68
S-10044 Stockholm, Sweden
Tel:        +46-8-790 74 97
Fax:        +46-8-10 61 64
Email: conrad@isk.kth.se

ABSTRACT

Recycling decisions can not be made by the designer himself. Management and design together with several others have to find out what is economically and technically possible to recycle.

Design for Disassembly, one of several challenges in Design for Recycling, is thought of as design efforts in order to make disassembling and separation easier. One way of early adapting for disassembly is the authors concept of "sorting borders, separating surfaces and resting loadcases" [Luttropp_1,5,6].

It is difficult to make the right recycling decisions during early design phases. It is easier to make a review of a complete design and thereafter redesign in order to adapt the product for recycling. However, this means that many important decisions of global importance for the product have already been taken and can not be changed. When adapting the product for recycling, only decisions of minor importance can be changed.

The ECO-forecast is meant to be a procedure in the end of the concept-design-phase before the actual drawing work starts. At this point management and design together can project the recycling history of the product.

What can be recycled, what can be reused and what is suitable for energy recovery. What will be disassembled by the consumer, scrapper etc. The forthcoming paper will describe this ECO-forecast-process.

REFERENCES
[1] Luttropp, C. Design for disassembly-The resting Loadcase, Poster paper ICED, Praha, 1995
[2] Tjalve, E. Systematisk udformning av industriprodukter, Akademisk förlag, Copenhagen, 1989
[3] Hubka, V. and Eder, W. E. Engineering Design, Heurista, Zürich, 1992

[4]VDI 2243 Konstruieren recyclinggerechter technischer Produkte, VDI-Verlag, Düsseldorf, 1990

[5] Luttropp, C. Design for Disassembly-The approach of sorting borders and separating surfaces, ECOperformance 1996, Zürich, Switzerland.

[6] Luttropp, C. Design for Disassembly - Good separating surfaces a key to sorting borders NORD Design '96 Helsinki, Finland

# 052

# DISTURBANCES IN THE BOUNDARY OF PRODUCT DEVELOPMENT AND PRODUCTION RAMP-UP - A CASE STUDY

Author:
A. Simola,
Helsinki University of Technology
Laboratory of IndustrialPsychology
Otakaari 4 A FIN - 02150 Espoo, FINLAND
Tel:        +358-0-451 2856
Fax:        +358-0-451 2107
Email:      Anni.Simola@hut.fi

Co-author:
M. Hakonen, N. Hakonen, K. Hulkko, T. Rantamäki & M.Vartiainen

## ABSTRACT

An important factor contributing to the success of the product development process is the speed and the flexibility of the process. Lowering the time spent for introducing new products means the management of several different functions (e.g. product design and production) simultaneously to the same direction. The aim of this case study is to analyse disturbances between a specific new product development project and it,s production ramp-up. The results of the study will be utilized in the next product development project.

This case study is part of a research project at the Helsinki University of Technology, Laboratory of Industrial Psychology. The project aims at enhancement of the product development process by improving team work, process management and reward systems. In this case study, the part analysed is the ramp-up phase of the R&D process. The objects of the analysis will be both the border between the product development process and the production process and the disturbances inside and between the cross functional teams.

The process will be analysed retrospectively by examining a project that has already been realized. First, the process of a new product ramp up will be modelled by the existing documents and interviews of the key persons of the project. Second, the events and disturbances during the process will be reconstructed by interviewing all the key participants of the process. The result of the study will be a reconstruction of the process. A shared understanding of the lessons learned with an emphasis to create a modell of a successfull ramp-up phase will be formed. The results will be transformed to the next product development project.

Key words: Technology Management, Product Development Integration, Cross-functional teams

# 053

*The Sixth international conference on management of technology*
*Göteborg, June 25-28, 1997*

# Choice of technology in developing countries:
# The case of flexible automation in Turkey

Erol Taymaz
Department of Economics
Middle East Technical University
Ankara 06531, Turkey
Tel: +90 312 210 2068
Fax: +90 312 210 1244
e-mail: etaymaz@rorqual.cc.metu.edu.tr

Yavuz Yaşar
Department of Economics
University of Utah
308 BUC, SLC, UT 84112, USA
Tel: +1 801 581 7481
Fax: +1 801 585 5644
e-mail: YASAR@econ.sbs.utah.edu

Ayla Yılmaz
Department of Economics
University of Pittsburgh
Pittsburgh PA 15260, USA
e-mail: ayyst+@pitt.edu

Key words: Flexible automation, choice of technology, development, flexibility, CNC machine tools, diffusion of new technology

Topical category: H.2

The paper seems to be suitable for oral presentation. Poster presentation is also possible.

# Choice of technology in developing countries: The case of flexible automation in Turkey

## Abstract

The development of new flexible automation technologies (CNC machine tools, CAD, CAM, FMS, etc.) are considered as essential for gaining international competitiveness in engineering industries. Many researchers claim that computer-based automation technology is the key to enhance flexibilty of production processes, which is now the main competitive factor for firms facing a turbulent economic environment characterized by economic fluctuations, consumers' desire for differentiated products, and rapid pace of technological change. The need for flexibility explains the rapid diffusion of flexible automation technologies in the developed countries.

Although there are a number of studies on the use of these technologies in the developed countries, there is almost no econometric study analyzing the determinants of the diffusion of flexible automation in the developing countries. We claim in this paper that the factors behind the diffusion of flexible automation technologies are quite different among developed and developing countries. Developing country firms adopting these technologies emphasize the importance of flexible automation technology for precision production. Flexible production technology is used to produce high quality and/or complex products in relatively low batch sizes.

In this paper, we use the logit and survival analyses to study the choice of technology in engineering firms in Turkey. We investigate the factors that determine the choice of investment in flexible automation technologies. The results support our hypothesis that product characteristics and the existence of complementary technologies are very important in adopting flexible automation technology. Macroeconomic factors are also important for the timing of investment.

# Choice of technology in developing countries:
# The case of flexible automation in Turkey

## 1. Introduction

This study is undertaken as a part of a wider project that attempts to provide a comprehensive examination of flexible automation technologies in Turkey within the framework of a technological systems approach. The objective of the paper is to examine the diffusion of Computer Numerically Controlled (CNC) machine tools in the Turkish engineering industries[1] since the late 1980s.

The second section of the paper is devoted to a brief discussion of CNC machine tools with an emphasis on their diffusion in both developed and developing countries. The third section reviews theoretical and empirical studies of diffusion of a new technology. The fourth section presents diffusion models used in this study and discusses estimation results of various models for Turkey. Basic results of the paper are summarized in the final section.

## 2. CNC Machine Tools

The first numerically controlled (NC) machine tool was developed in the 1950s. However, the technology could not diffuse widely due to high cost and unreliability of the numerical control unit. With the introduction of microcomputers following minicomputers as the basis of numerical control unit, diffusion of NC gained momentum during the late 1970s. Early diffusion of NC machine tools took place in developed countries. The user firms were mainly large firms demanding high performance machines often with custom designed features (Edquist and Jacobbson, 1988).

As it is well known in the diffusion literature the technology and supply conditions change over the diffusion path. In the mid-1970s some of the Japanese producers introduced low performance, smaller and cheaper NC machine tools designed for medium and small firms, which resulted in wider diffusion of the technology while Japan capturing the largest share of the world market (Jacobbson, 1986).

The major characteristics of the new technology embodied in CNC machine tools can be stated as follows. Thanks to microcomputers' capacity to handle and process a large amount of information, a greater extent of flexibility, which is defined as the capacity to switch rapidly to the production of a new type of product, is obtained. Moreover, higher product quality and greater precision are achieved. In addition, a significant reduction in the skill level of the operator is obtained as compared to conventional machine tool operators, even though the nature of skills changes as well.

The diffusion of CNC machine tools in developing countries began in the 1980s and concentrated mainly in a few newly industrialized countries (Alcorta, 1995). Comparative diffusion studies found out that relatively slow diffusion of the technology in most of the developing countries mainly caused by macroeconomic instabilities which has profound effects on the cost of imported machines. The lag between developed and developing countries in the adoption of the technology is accounted partly by the fact that it is designed to meet the needs of producers in the former countries. The advent of relatively cheaper and smaller CNC that are more suitable to the production patterns of the small and medium sized firms in developing countries resulted in a wider diffusion.

---

[1] Engineering industries are classified as ISIC 38.

There are many studies that attempt to explain possible effects of new technologies. It is argued that flexible automation technologies will result in a de-scaling in production and will increase competitiveness of developing countries which had difficulty in realizing economies of scale in production due to their smaller internal markets ( Acs, Audretsch and Carlsson, 1990; Kaplinsky, 1990; Piore and Sabel, 1984). On the other hand some researchers argued that empirical evidence proves the opposite. New technologies will lead to scaling up of production (Alcorta, 1994). However, there is a consensus over the argument that the developing countries should adopt the new flexible automation technologies not to fall behind the technological level of the developed countries.

## 3. Theoretical and Empirical Studies on Diffusion
The early theoretical studies on technology diffusion are based on the epidemic approach. It is argued that late adoption is caused by lack of information about the new technology. As individuals and firms have contacts the knowledge of the technology transmits and diffusion spreads like an epidemic at a growing rate in the early phase of the diffusion process (a refined example of this approach is proposed by Mansfield 1968).

Karshenans and Stoneman (1993) claim that the majority of empirical diffusion studies are still based on epidemic theory, although there are significant advances in the diffusion theory. Recent theoretical developments put increasing emphasis on the explicit treatment of a firm's decision to adopt while neglecting epidemic effects.

Karshenans and Stoneman (1993) argue that diffusion theory proposes three major effects that determine profitability of new technology and its adoption: rank, stock, and order effects. Rank effects state that potential adopters will have different characteristics (firm size etc), and are expected to have different rate of returns on investments in the new technology. As a result, the date of adoption of each firm will be different (early examples of this type of models are proposed by David [1969] and Davies [1979], and a recent model by Ireland and Stoneman [1986]). Stock effects claim that the benefit of marginal adaptor declines as the number of actual adopters increases since production cost will decline as the new technology is employed by more firms. Order effects state that profitability depends on the position of an adopter in the order of adaption.

They concluded that rank and epidemic effects are proved to be decisive in the diffusion of CNC machine tools in the UK. Stoneman and Kwan (1994) argue that diffusion of a particular technology should not be studied in isolation from other technologies and their empirical study of the diffusion of CNC machine tools shows that degree of complementarity influences the rate of diffusion and the date of adoption. Similarly Columbo and Moscani (1995) examines the diffusion of different types flexible automation technologies together.

Our approach to technology diffusion is in line with recent advances in the diffusion theory. We consider it as an explicit decision of a firm to adopt. Unlike the previous empirical studies, our modelling attempts to provide a more comprehensive account of factors behind this particular decision.

A profit maximizing firm will adopt a new technology if it is more profitable as compared to the alternative of non-adoption. It is misleading to take the objective of profit maximization in the narrowest sense. We argue that firms value their long term survival and profits more than current profits. Adoption can take place at the expense of current or short term profits, if it is expected to increase long term profits or enable the firm to survive in the face of an intense competition. Therefore, studies of technology diffusion should pay more attention to the medium or long term firm strategies and expectations.

Keeping in mind the wider conception of profitability we present a brief discussion of factors that are expected to affect the decision to adopt.

*Firm Characteristics:* It is theoretically and empirically well established that certain firm characteristics may increase profitability of adoption. The most commonly used one is the firm size which is generally proxied by total number of employees. Firm age is an other example of this type of variables.

*Sector Characteristics:* Firms operating in a particular sector may find it more profitable to adopt due to the special characteristics of that sector. For example, a firm in a rapidly growing industry is more likely to adopt the new technology compared to a firm in a declining industry even if both firms are similar in all other respects.

*Firms' Aims and Expectations:* We mainly refer to long term expectations regarding the state of the technology, changes in demand structure (for example towards better quality products), nature of competition, conditions of the labor market etc.

*Technological Complementarities:* It can be argued that a firm is more likely to adopt a new technology if it is familiar with a technology in the similar vein. Again if there are complementarities between technologies this will affect decision to adopt.

*Risks:* Diffusion may be prevented if the technology is conceived to be risky. It can be argued that there are some factors that increase or eliminate the risks associated. For example if a firm have access to a supporting network of relations including producers, other firms, public institutions including universities etc., the risk of adoption will be lower since the firm would be better informed about the technology and can receive support to solve problems encountered during the early phase of adoption.

*Expected Cost of Acquisition:* Developing countries like Turkey usually import CNC machine tools. The domestic price of those machines are to a large extent determined by real exchange rate which is much more volatile than the foreign price. Thus, the cost of acquisition of imported technology become more dependent on movements in exchange rate rather than the change in price itself.

*Availability of Finance:* A firm that find it profitable to adopt a new technology at the going rate of borrowing may not adopt it if it has no access to the credit market. The lack of access to external funds may be due to credit rationing resulting from high default rates caused by very high interest rates and macroeconomic instabilities.

## 4. The Model

Turkey is a middle income developing country. Since the 1930s an import substituting industrialization strategy had been persuaded. In 1980, following a major foreign debt crises a stabilization and structural adjustment program supported by the IMF and the World Bank began to be applied. The import substitution strategy was replaced by export oriented policies accompanied by trade and financial liberalization.

Although the program was successful in increasing exports and achieving higher growth rates in some years, it could not succeeded in restoring macroeconomic stability with low inflation (see Table 1). The diffusion rate of CNC machine tools increased sharply in the 1990s. The share of CNC machine tools in total machine tool investment (in units) jumped from 8% in 1990 to 20% in 1995 as a result of investment in the engineering industries in this time period.

## The sample

Our sample is composed of 95 firms operating in the engineering industries and are located in nine different provinces. The choice of firms is not completely random. A balance between users and non-users, large and small firms is tried to be achieved to justify our claim of representative power of the sample. Data are collected by a detailed questionnaire and by personal interviews with the executive and production managers of the firms. (For the number of firms, see Table 2).

## Models
We use three different diffusion models: adoption decision model, investment model, and adoption timing model. In the first model, the determinants of the adoption of CNC machine tools are tested in a logistic model in which the dependent variable is a categorical variable which takes the value 1 if the firm adopted CNC machine tools before 1996, 0 otherwise. In the second model, the determinants of investment in CNC machine tools in the period 1990-95 are analyzed in a logistic model in which the dependent variable is a categorical variable which takes the value 1 if the firm acquired a CNC machine tool in the last five years, 0 otherwise. In the third model, we analyze the timing of adoption by estimating a hazard function. In this model, the time of adoption of CNC machine tools is the dependent variable. The dependent variable is, of course, censored for non-users.

## Explanatory variables
The following variables are used as explanatory variables in our models (see Table 3 for descriptive statistics).

*Firm characteristics*
LMACHINE    Logarithm of the number of machine tools in a firm,
LSIZE       Logarithm of number of total employees,
ENGSH       Share of engineers in total employment.
PTYPE       A dummy representing product type. PTYPE = 0 if the firm produces
            parts and components, and 1 if the firm produces a final product.

Three variables are proposed to stand for firm characteristics. We first intended to use LSIZE as a proxy for the firm size. However, labor saving nature of the technology concerned creates a bias. To avoid from this LMACHINE is also used as a proxy for the firm size as well. ENGSH serves as an indicator of technological capabilities of the firm. Each of these variables are expected to take a positive sign. By employing PTYPE we attempt to find out whether part production induces adoption of CNC machine tools.

*Sector characteristics*
GROWTH  Nominal percentage growth rate of the sectoral output in 1985-1992,
MDOMES  Sectoral share of imports in domestic supply,

We use GROWTH as a proxy for future demand in a particular sector. If growth rate is high we expect that firms are more likely to undertake costly investments in machine tools. MDOMES indicates whether the sector is an import competing one. If it is higher we expect that import competition may force the firms in that sector to adopt new technologies.

*Firms' aims and expectations*
Firms are asked to state their aims while investing in CNC (for users) conventional

machine tools (for non-users). The following variables were computed to measure the factors behind investment decisions.

ACAPA      Aim is to increase capacity and speed of production,
AENERGY    Aim is to lower energy cost,
AQUALITY   Aim is to be able to produce more complex products, increase precision and achieve flexibility in production,
ATECH      Aim is to acquire the recent technology,
AWAGE      Aim is to lower total wage bill.

These variables take a value of zero if the firm's objective is not to do so. If it is stated that any one of them is the objective of the firm in undertaking investment in machine tools, then the degree of fulfilment of the objective is asked. Full realization is assigned the value of 3, partial realization 2, and nil 1. ACAPA takes the value of 6 at most indicating full realization of joint objectives of increasing capacity and production speed. AQUALITY takes value of 9 at most if three of the joint objectives (complexity, precision, flexibility) are fully realized. The rest of the aim-variables are expected to be assigned at most the value of 3 in case of full realization of the concerned objective. ACAPA and AENERGY can take either sign. We expect all other variables to take positive sign because it is suggested that CNC machine tools substitute for labor and increase the accuracy, precision, and flexibility of manufacturing processes.

*Technological complementarities*
DAUT    A dummy variable for automatic machine tools (DAUT = 1 if the firm uses automatic machine tools, 0 otherwise)
DCAD    A dummy variable for computer aided design (CAD)
DCMM    A dummy variable for coordinate and optic measuring machines (CMM)
DEDM    A dummy variable for electro-discharge machines (EDM)

These variables are proposed to search for the effect of complementarities or substitution opportunities between technologies on the decision to adopt. DAUT can take either sign. It is claimed that mass production technologies are followed by flexible automation technologies. If the correlation turns out to be positive this claim will be supported. DCAD is expected to have a positive sign if it is complementary technology. DCMM is expected to have a positive sign for the same reason. DEDM is a machine that is mainly used in die and mold-making. It is expected to take a negative sign because this type of production may not require the use of CNC machine tools.

*Risks*
We designed some variables to be used as a proxy for reliance on supporting networks. We observe that only very few big firms has such networks. Therefore these variables are excluded completely.

*Cost of acquisition*
PRICE    Trade weighted real effective exchange rate of Turkish Lira,
PRICED   The rate of change in real exchange rate $(PRICE_t - PRICE_{t-1})/PRICE_{t-1}$.

We could not obtain reliable price series for machine tools that are used by firms included in our sample. To find out the effect of changes in the cost of acquisition we use trade weighed real exchange rates. Almost all CNC machine tools used in Turkey were imported tools whereas, as a recent study by the State Institute of Statistics shows, around 50% of non-CNC tools were imported. Therefore, the PRICE variable can be used as a proxy for the relative price of CNC machine tools. The higher the value of the PRICE variable, the lower the relative price of CNC machine tools.

The PRICED variable is used as a proxy for the expectation of appreciation. Firms will delay their CNC investment if they expect a (further) decline in the price of these machines.

*Availability of finance*
FINOWN  The source of investment finance. FINOWN=1 if the firm financed machine tool investment by its own resources, 0 by external funds (borrowing).

The coefficient of this variable is expected to have a negative sign because investment decisions are constrained by the lack of resources.

**Estimation results**
*Decision model*
The decision model (Table 4) attempts to find out the factors that account for the firm's decision to adopt CNC machine tools. Since the ENGSH and PTYPE variables have the least significant coefficients, they are excluded from the second estimation of the model.

The estimation results confirm our expectations. AQUALITY, AWAGE, DCAD, GROWTH and LSIZE proved to be significant with positive coefficients. If firms intent to improve quality of their products and to increase flexibility they invest in CNC machine tools. Similarly, an objective of lowering wage bill increase the tendency to adopt CNC machine tools. However, it is contradictory to argue that firms substitute capital for labor in a low wage country like Turkey. The significance of the AWAGE variable needs another explanation. Although wages are very low and rate of unemployment is high in Turkey, it is difficult to find skilled workers. Moreover, the labor turnover rate is very high. Firms may want to decrease their dependency on skilled workers by investing in labor and skill saving technology.

As the firm size and the growth rate of the sector goes up, the likelihood of adoption increases. The significance of the coefficient of the DCAD variable indicates the importance of complementarity between CAD and CNC technologies.

On the other hand ACAPA, DEDM, FINOWN, LMACHINE and MDOMES have significantly negative coefficients. If the objective is to increase capacity conventional machine tools are preferred. EDM is not a complementary technology and takes a negative sign as expected.

The negative coefficient for the FINOWN variable indicates that the lack of access to external financial resources may prevent a wider diffusion. LMACHINE is used as an index of the firm size. Its sign turn out to be negative as oppose to what is expected. The negative sin for the LMACHINE variable may confirm the observation made by interviewees. It is usually claimed that a CNC machine tools can replace 3-5 conventional tools so that CNC user firms employ fewer machine tools.

The negative coefficient for the MDOMES variable shows that import competition is negatively correlated with the acquisition of new technology. Domestic firms in the import competing sectors may not choose to invest in new, expensive technology partly because they consider those sectors too risky to compete on the basis of product quality and product changes. In stead they may choose to supply cheaper and low quality versions of the imported commodities for the low end of the market.

## Investment decision model

The model's objective is to find out whether there is a change in the determination of firm decision to adopt CNC machine tools before and after 1990 (Table 5).

The DAUT, DCAD, DCMM, and DEDM variables of the decision model are replaced by the DAUTOLD, DCADOLD, DCMMOLD and DEDMOLD variables. The later group of variables show whether corresponding technologies were adopted before 1990. A new dummy variable DCNCOLD denoting whether CNC adopted before 1990 is also added. DCNCOLD takes the value 1 if the firm adopted CNC machine tools before 1990, 0 otherwise.

The estimation results are almost the same with the first model. The new variable DCNCOLD is significant and takes a negative coefficient indicating that if a firm bought CNC machine tools before 1990 they do not invest in CNC tools after 1990. This may show that they already made the investment they needed in CNCs, therefore not making further investments. Alternatively, it may indicate that the first adopters are not choosing to invest in CNC because they are dissatisfied with the ones they already installed. This seems an unlikely reason since non of the early adopters report significant dissatisfaction.

## Timing model

The model tries find out what determines the timing of actual purchase of the first CNC machine tool (Table 6). Only three of the variables are significant. The positive coefficient of the AQUALITY variable indicates that if the objective of the firm is to improve product quality it will adopt sooner. The positive sign of the PRICE variable proves that firms will buy when exchange rate is appreciated. The negative coefficient of the PRICED states that if real appreciation of the currency is anticipated investment will be delayed until the machine gets cheaper enough. Overall the model indicates the importance of exchange rate fluctuations in an unstable economy in the determination of technology diffusion.

## 6. Conclusions

Our first conclusion is that theoretical and empirical studies should pay more attention to the explicit analysis of firm's objectives and expectations in the examination of decision to adopt. Our study makes it clear that firm characteristics, expectations and objectives exert strong influence on the diffusion of a new technology. Sectoral characteristics are also important. Finally macroeconomic instability and imperfections in the financial markets may erect obstacles on the way of a wider diffusion of a new technology.

## REFERENCES

Acs, Z. S., D. B. Audretsch and B. Carlsson (1990), "Flexibility, Plant Size and Industrial Restructuring" in Z. S. Acs and D. B. Audretsch (eds.) *The Economics of Small Firms*, Kluwer Academic Publishers.

Alcorta, L. (1994), "The Impact of New Technologies on Scale in Manufacturing Industries: Issues and Evidence", *World Development*, 22(5), 755-769.

Alcorta, L. (1995), "The Impact of Industrial Automation on Industrial Organizations: Implications for Developing Country Competitiveness", Paper presented in *Global*

Forum on Industry: Perspectives for 2000 and Beyond, Organized by UNIDO.

Colombo, M. and R. Mosconi (1995), "Complementary and Cumulative Learning Effects in the Early diffusion of Multiple Technologies", *Journal of Industrial Economics*, XLIII(1), 13-48.

David, P. A. (1969), *A Contribution to the Theory of Diffusion*, Stanford Center for Research in Economic Growth, Memorandum, No:71, Stanford University.

Davies, S. (1979), *The Diffusion of Process Innovation*, Cambridge University Press, Cambridge.

Edquist, C. and S. Jacobbson (1988), *Flexible Automation: The Global Diffusion of New Technology in the Engineering Industry*, Basic Blackwell, Oxford.

Jacobbson, S. (1986), *Electronics and Industrial Policy: The Case of Computer Controlled Lathes*, Allen and Adwin, London.

Ireland, N. and P.L. Stoneman (1986), "Technological Diffusion, Expectations and Welfare", *Oxford Economic Papers*, 38, 283-304.

Kaplinsky, R. (1990) *The Economics of Small: Appropriate Technology in a Changing World*, Intermediate Technology Publication, London.

Karshenans, M. and P. L. Stoneman (1993), "Rank, Stock, Order and Epidemic Effects in the Diffusion of New Process Technologies: An Empirical Model", *Rand Journal of Economics*, 22(4), 503-528.

Mansfield, E. (1968), *Industrial Research and Technological Innovation: An Economic Analysis*, Norton, New York.

Piore, M. J. and C. F. Sabel (1984), *The Second Industrial Divide: Possibility for Prosperity*, Basic Books Inc., Publishers, New York.

Stoneman, P. and M-J Kwan (1994), "The Diffusion of Multiple Process Technologies", *Economic Journal*, 104 (March), 420-431.

**Table 1.**  Turkish economy in 1989-1995

| Year | Inflation rate (%) | Real exchange rate (80=100) | Engineering imports value (mil $) | Engineering imports share (%) | Engineering exports value (mil $) | Engineering exports share ($) | CNC share in machine tool invest. (%) |
|------|------|------|------|------|------|------|------|
| 1989 | 63  | 82.3 | 4308  | 27   | 795  | 7    | 8  |
| 1990 | 60  | 86.5 | 7563  | 34   | 1148 | 9    | 8  |
| 1991 | 66  | 79.4 | 7921  | 38   | 1313 | 10   | 10 |
| 1992 | 70  | 80.1 | 8520  | 37   | 1697 | 12   | 12 |
| 1993 | 66  | 79.0 | 11193 | 38   | 1688 | 11   | 14 |
| 1994 | 106 | 69.3 | n.a.  | n.a. | n.a. | n.a. | 14 |
| 1995 | 86  | 70.0 | n.a.  | n.a. | n.a. | n.a. | 20 |

*Sources:* State Institute of Statistics
n.a. "not available"

**Table 2.** Sample size by CNC users/non-users and plant size

| Plant size | Number of plants | | |
|---|---|---|---|
| (# employees) | User | Non-user | Total |
| 1-24 | 27 | 20 | 47 |
| 25-49 | 11 | 8 | 19 |
| >50 | 17 | 8 | 25 |
| Total | 55 | 36 | 91 |

**Table 3.** Descriptive statistics

| Variable | Mean | Std Dev | Min | Max | n |
|---|---|---|---|---|---|
| ACAPA | 3.86 | 2.27 | 0 | 6 | 95 |
| AENER | 0.99 | 1.20 | 0 | 3 | 94 |
| AQUALITY | 4.68 | 3.23 | 0 | 9 | 95 |
| ATECH | 1.54 | 1.30 | 0 | 3 | 95 |
| AWAGE | 1.55 | 1.28 | 0 | 3 | 94 |
| CNCSH | 0.13 | 0.23 | 0 | 1 | 95 |
| DAUT | 0.52 | 0.50 | 0 | 1 | 94 |
| DCAD | 0.44 | 0.50 | 0 | 1 | 95 |
| DCMM | 0.14 | 0.35 | 0 | 1 | 95 |
| DCNC | 0.60 | 0.49 | 0 | 1 | 95 |
| DEDM | 0.13 | 0.33 | 0 | 1 | 95 |
| ENGSH | 0.12 | 0.13 | 0 | 1 | 89 |
| FINOWN | 0.83 | 0.38 | 0 | 1 | 81 |
| GROWTH | 3815.66 | 1542.5 | 1814 | 6864 | 95 |
| LMACHINE | 2.78 | 0.69 | 0.69 | 5.15 | 94 |
| LSIZE | 3.33 | 0.90 | 1.61 | 5.75 | 93 |
| MDOMES | 29.33 | 23.32 | 6.97 | 107.64 | 95 |
| PRICE | 74.83 | 5.81 | 69.3 | 89.91 | 94 |
| PRICED | -0.01 | 0.04 | -0.13 | 0.05 | 95 |
| PTYPE | 1.58 | 0.50 | 1 | 2 | 95 |

**Table 4.** Estimation results for the decision model
Dependent variable: DCNC

| | Coeff | Wald | Coeff | Wald |
|---|---|---|---|---|
| ACAPA | -1.490 ** | 5.620 | -1.560 ** | 6.506 |
| AENER | 0.915 | 2.066 | 0.859 | 2.296 |
| AQUALITY | 1.805 ** | 6.371 | 1.924 ** | 6.746 |
| ATECH | -1.328 | 1.803 | -1.309 | 1.760 |
| AWAGE | 1.297 * | 3.181 | 1.182 * | 3.055 |
| DAUT | -0.183 | 0.027 | -0.304 | 0.079 |
| DCAD | 2.987 ** | 3.983 | 2.827 ** | 4.017 |
| DCMM | -0.285 | 0.030 | -0.355 | 0.049 |
| DEDM | -3.544 * | 3.083 | -3.963 * | 3.737 |
| ENGSH | 0.029 | 0.001 | | |
| FINOWN | -6.152 * | 3.329 | -6.255 * | 3.796 |
| GROWTH | 0.001 * | 2.800 | 0.001 * | 3.672 |
| LMACHINE | -1.015 | 0.798 | -2.012 ** | 4.683 |
| LSIZE | 0.718 | 0.774 | 1.265 * | 2.779 |
| MDOMES | -0.057 ** | 4.221 | -0.065 ** | 5.351 |
| PTYPE | -0.317 | 0.067 | | |
| Constant | 2.098 | 0.257 | 3.251 | 0.757 |
| n | 75 | | 78 | |
| $\chi^2_{(d.f.)}$ | 61.4 (16) | | 60.5 (14) | |
| % correct | 93.3 | | 91.0 | |

*Note:* ** (*) means statistically significant at the 5% (10%) level.

**Table 5.** Estimation results for the investment decision model
Dependent variable: DCNC1990

| | Coeff | Wald | Coeff | Wald |
|---|---|---|---|---|
| ACAPA | -1.285 ** | 4.359 | -0.828 ** | 5.277 |
| AENER | 1.292 ** | 4.066 | 0.582 | 1.772 |
| AQUALITY | 2.055 ** | 4.716 | 0.798 ** | 4.179 |
| ATECH | -2.721 * | 3.149 | -0.478 | 0.417 |
| AWAGE | 2.120 ** | 5.333 | 1.307 ** | 5.412 |
| DAUTOLD | 2.097 | 2.191 | 0.713 | 0.506 |
| DCADOLD | 3.400 * | 3.089 | 2.189 * | 3.280 |
| DCMMCOLD | -4.375 * | 2.870 | -2.356 | 1.873 |
| DCNCOLD | -7.363 ** | 4.267 | -2.726 ** | 3.961 |
| DEDMOLD | -16.106 | 0.128 | -3.456 * | 3.133 |
| ENGSH | 2.250 | 0.433 | | |
| FINOWN | -5.588 * | 3.705 | -2.568 * | 3.139 |
| GROWTH | 0.001 * | 3.024 | 0.001 * | 3.575 |
| LMACHINE | -4.383 ** | 6.488 | -2.274 ** | 7.708 |
| LSIZE | 0.024 | 0.001 | | |
| MDOMES | -0.068 * | 3.505 | -0.044 * | 3.662 |
| PTYPE | -2.085 | 1.585 | | |
| Constant | 13.573 * | 3.373 | 5.359 * | 3.230 |
| n | 75 | | 80 | |
| $\chi^2_{(d.f.)}$ | 66.7 (17) | | 54.1 (14) | |
| % correct | 93.3 | | 83.8 | |

*Note:* ** (*) means statistically significant at the 5% (10%) level.

**Table 6.** Estimation results for the timing model
Dependent variable: The time of adoption

|  | Coeff | Wald | Coeff | Wald |
|---|---|---|---|---|
| ACAPA | -0.170 | 1.167 | -0.157 | 1.778 |
| AENER | -0.075 | 0.241 | | |
| AQUALITY | 0.195 * | 2.843 | 0.180** | 5.955 |
| ATECH | -0.078 | 0.091 | | |
| AWAGE | 0.134 | 0.405 | | |
| DAUT | 0.344 | 0.935 | 0.246 | 0.584 |
| DCAD | 0.349 | 0.729 | 0.37 | 0.962 |
| DCMM | -0.332 | 0.431 | -0.231 | 0.290 |
| DEDM | -0.714 | 1.462 | -0.719 | 1.919 |
| ENGSH | 1.138 | 0.738 | | |
| LMACHINE | -0.363 | 1.340 | -0.178 | 0.474 |
| LSIZE | 0.079 | 0.145 | | |
| PRICE | 0.784** | 24.863 | 0.519** | 34.373 |
| PRICED | -37.544 ** | 16.941 | -26.071 ** | 17.869 |
| $\chi^2_{(d.f.)}$ | 108.5 (14) | | 106.6 (9) | |
| n user | 52 | | 56 | |
| n non-user | 35 | | 37 | |

*Note:* ** (*) means statistically significant at the 5% (10%) level.

# 054

# CRITICAL DIMENSIONS FOR THE MANAGEMENT OF TECHNOLOGY IN "SME" OF TRADITIONAL SECTORS

Author:
Isak Kruglianskas
Faculty of Economics, Business Administration and Accountancy
University of Sao Paulo
Av. Prof. Luciano Gualberto, 908 - Cidade Universit·ria
05508-900 - Sao Paulo, SP
Brazil
Tel:      +55-11-210-4640
Fax:      +55-11-816-8044
e-mail:   ikruglia@usp.br

Co-author
Roberto Sbragia
Faculty of Economics, Business Administration and Accountancy
University of Sao Paulo
Av. Prof. Luciano Gualberto, 908 - Cidade Universit·ria
05508-900 - Sao Paulo, SP
Brazil
Tel:      +55-11-210-4640
Fax:      +55-11-816-8044
e-mail:   rsbragia@usp.br

ABSTRACT

Since the beginning of the 90s, when there was a big change of the government policy toward the international commerce trade, the Brazilian enterprises are being subjected to an increasing exposure to the global market place. This movement has been a challenging one to all companies, small and big, from traditional or emergent sectors. They are being pressed to conceive and implement new approaches for managing their business. In particular small and medium enterprises (SMEs) of traditional sectors that are suppliers of big companies that compete in the global market are suffering big threats because their clients are pressing very hard in order to select suppliers that are very competitive and reliable. These big companies are not hesitating in changing supplier or buying from abroad if they feel that their competitiveness is being, or can be, threatened by any supplier that is not enough: innovative, fast, reliable and competitive.

In order to contribute for facing this new situation the researchers conducted a big project with the objective of identifying and understanding the technological barriers of the SMEs of traditional sectors in order to foster their technological capacity. This project involved twenty sectors and more than 1300 enterprises.

The paper presents the results of a survey involving a sample of 89 SMEs, belonging to eight different traditional sectors composed of enterprises that participated in the referred research project. The objective of this study was to get a better understanding of the management of technology in this type of companies and to detect weaknesses in this process.

It was found that it is possible to devise many improvements for the actual practices of the management of technological innovation in SMEs of traditional sectors. The data suggest that the organizational and managerial aspects are those that have the greatest potential for improvement. In particular it was possible to detect that those interactions that involve the external system of Science and Technology - S&T and the organizations located abroad are practically not considered in the management of technological innovation of the SMEs studied. It could also be seen that the differences of the practices related to the process of management of the technological innovation among the enterprises of the different studied sectors are not significant.

Key words:
- Management of Technology
- Small and Medium Enterprises
- Management of Innovation
- Organization for Technological Innovation
- Technological Innovation and Competitiveness
- Competitiveness and Globalization

Oral Presentation

# 055

# EXPERIENCES WITH TEACHING A WEB-BASED COURSE

Ed Rodgers, Department of Computer Science, University of West Florida
Pensacola, FL 32514 (904) 474-2542 erodgers@uwf.edu

## ABSTRACT

Since the fall semester of 1995 almost 1,000 students have completed the Web-based course, "Exploring the Internet", at the University of West Florida. The course, developed by faculty and graduate students from the Department of Computer Science, has proved to be popular not only with UWF students, but also non-student members of the Pensacola, Florida community and beyond. This paper describes the nature of the course, critiques from students who have been enrolled, and recommendations for teaching such courses. Although the course is designed to teach students about the Internet and the Web, the lessons learned in teaching the course and the critiques by the students are relevent to teaching any Web-based course.

# 056

# XPEDITE - THE ORGAN INFORMATION SYSTEM (OIS): APPLYING INFORMATION TECHNOLOGY MANAGEMENT CAPABILITIES TO SUPPORT ORGAN PROCUREMENT AND TRANSPLANTATION

Jon W. Beard, Ph.D.
University of Tulsa

David H. Klein, M.E.A.
United Network for Organ Sharing (UNOS)

Myron Kauffman, M.D.
UNOS

Otis P. Daily, M.D.
UNOS

## Abstract

*Xpedite*, a computer-based system built around Lotus *Notes*®, facsimile, and alphanumeric pagers, was developed to enhance cadaveric (i.e., non-living) organ procurement and placement. Organ transplantation is unique among lifesaving medical procedures in that it requires not only the skill of the physicians, but also one or more organs from an individual who has been declared legally dead. These organs must be recovered, preserved, and transported, often over great distance, in a short amount of time for a successful transplant to occur. This process requires careful matching of available organs with viable donors and the immediate scheduling of surgery by skilled transplant teams. *Xpedite* was developed to streamline data collection and transmission on available organs, shortening the time from organ availability (i.e., donor death) to transplant thus reducing organ wastage.

*Xpedite* faced common difficulties and obstacles of a new technology-based approach, including resistance to change and limited resources. Similarities between organ procurement/transplantation and sales force automation were used to guide *Xpedite* design. A Rapid Application Development (RAD) methodology was used to develop and pilot-test a prototype in the field. This approach contributed to the evolution of thinking and system design. Resource constraints required off-the-shelf solutions where possible, with customized interfaces where required.

Several important outcomes have been realized. Collecting data and translating it into electronic form facilitated the critical communication and coordination between donor site and transplant center. The integration of the OIS with the United Network for Organ Sharing (UNOS) computer Match system was vital to organ procurement coordinators. To be successful *Xpedite* was designed to be platform (i.e., Mac-based, Unix-based, PC-based, etc. systems) transparent.

Currently, *Xpedite* is being used at ten Organ Procurement Organizations (OPO) nationwide. By the end of 1997 it is anticipated that *Xpedite* will be installed in 30 of the 67 OPO's in the United States. Future directions for system development include extending the system nation-wide (USA) to facilitate and support organ procurement and transplantation, continuing the evolution toward an electronic data interchange system that will collect and disseminate scientific data on transplant recipients, and, through Lotus *Notes*®, to support communication and collaboration among transplant professionals.

# XPEDITE - THE ORGAN INFORMATION SYSTEM (OIS): APPLYING INFORMATION TECHNOLOGY MANAGEMENT CAPABILITIES TO SUPPORT ORGAN PROCUREMENT AND TRANSPLANTATION

*The real crisis in transplantation today is the critical shortage of organs available for transplant. For all patients awaiting a life-saving heart, lung, liver, kidney, or pancreas, 10 will die – today and every day – because an organ was not available. Increasing the supply of donated organs should be national policy.*

James, M. Burdick, M.D.
Transplant Surgeon, Johns Hopkins Medical Center
President, UNOS Board of Directors

## INTRODUCTION

Among lifesaving medical procedures, organ transplantation from a cadaveric (i.e., non-living) donor is unique. Like most medical procedures, organ transplantation relies upon the skills of the recipient's physician and surgeon. In addition, it requires the "donation" of one or more organs from a person who has been declared legally dead (i.e., in the United States, officially brain dead)[1] for transplantation in one or more recipients.

Organ viability for transplantation is measured in hours (UNOS Handout, 1996). Therefore, careful and timely coordination is required to match donor organs with recipients[2], communicate essential medical information between donor and recipient hospitals, and recover, preserve, and transport organs, often over great distance, before the transplant can take place. A breakdown in any element of this process can lead to the wastage of desperately needed organs and perhaps the death of a potential transplant recipient before a transplant can occur.

*Xpedite*, the Organ Information System (OIS), is a client-server technology environment developed to facilitate and streamline the organ procurement, placement, and transplantation process. It is an integrated system built around Lotus *Notes*®[3], SkyTel pagers, and facsimile (OIS, 1995; Rapid transplants, 1995). While it can't eliminate the organ shortage, *Xpedite* can assist in better managing the procurement and placement of available organs while reducing organ wastage. This manuscript begins with a brief overview of the organ procurement, placement, and transplantation process. Next, the process of analysis, design, and implementation for *Xpedite* is presented. Finally, the current status of *Xpedite* is addressed.

## OVERVIEW OF ORGAN PROCUREMENT AND PLACEMENT

### UNOS

UNOS, the United Network for Organ Sharing, coordinates the allocation of organs from cadaveric donors throughout the United States (UNOS, 1994). It is a private, nonprofit corporation, formed in 1986 following the passage of *The National Organ Transplant Act (NOTA). P.L. 98-507*. UNOS operates the national Organ Procurement and Transplantation Network (OPTN) under contract with the U.S. Department of Health and Human Services. As administrator of the OPTN, UNOS maintains a computerized waiting list of all people awaiting a cadaveric organ transplant in the U.S. and develops national guidelines for organ allocation. Under a separate contract, UNOS also maintains the Scientific Registry of Transplant Recipients. This registry consists of data on all U.S. transplants and tracking information on all transplant recipients as long as they survive with a functioning transplanted organ. All transplant centers, organ procurement organizations, and histocompatibility[4] laboratories involved in transplantation are members of UNOS. As of November 14, 1996, there were 443 members[5] (UNOS, 1997).

UNOS, therefore, has two fundamental missions: to assist in the procurement and placement of organs for transplantation, and to maintain a database of transplant recipients to support research directed at improving organ allocation criteria and national policy and to improve the transplant process (Beard, 1996).

### Transplant Waiting List

With the passage of NOTA in 1984, the improvement in transplant procedures and immunosuppressive[6] therapies, and the centralization and coordination of organ matching through UNOS, the number of transplants in the United States has grown dramatically in recent years. The number of cadaveric organ transplants has risen from 12,786 in 1988, to 19,145 in 1995 (the last year for which complete data is available) (UNOS, 1997). However, during this same time frame the OPTN waiting list has grown from 16,026 in 1988 to 50,384 (as of January 15, 1997)[7]. Some speculate that another 50,000 to 100,000 people in the U.S. may need an organ transplant, but are never placed on the UNOS waiting list for a variety of medical and financial reasons.

### Organ Procurement and Match for Transplantation

All potential recipients for an organ transplant are placed on the OPTN transplantation waiting list (i.e., a database) maintained by UNOS. This waiting list is accessible 24-hours a day. The criteria for being placed on the list were established through an advisory process of participating physicians, surgeons, medical organizations, and public comment. When a recipient's name is added to the waiting list, their medical profile is entered and stored in the UNOS database. Instead of being added to an already ranked list, the recipient is added to a "pool" of patient names. The "pool" approach was used because of changing availability of recipients due to fluctuations in health and varying match characteristics due to differences in histocompatibility between donors and potential recipients; i.e., not all organs are suitable for all candidate recipients (Klein, et al., 1994).

When an organ donor becomes available, the facility with the donor accesses the UNOS computer with donor information; the UNOS *Match* program generates a ranked list of patients based on the donor information[8]. Rankings are determined by both medical and scientific criteria (i.e., UNOS policies and pre-established priorities), such as tissue match, blood type, age, body size, length of time on the waiting list, immune status, and medical urgency (for heart, liver, and intestinal organs). The criteria are under constant assessment and scrutiny for modification through analysis and evaluation of the Scientific Registry of Transplant Recipients to better allocate the scarce resource (i.e., organs) for transplantation[9].

Historically, an organ procurement coordinator at the donor hospital makes a series of individual phone calls to several transplant centers, then faxes detailed donor information to the transplant teams. Potential recipients within the local area have first priority; if no suitable matches are found, the search is broadened to a larger regional focus, and then nationwide, if necessary. Offers are made in sequence according to a priority ranking of potential recipients; the coordinator often has to repeat the process several times for a given organ if one or more centers decline the offer. Since each center may take up to one hour to respond to an offer, several hours may pass before an organ is placed. Offers are also made individually for each organ available (e.g., kidneys, liver, pancreas, intestine, heart and/or lungs), adding to the time consumed by this process. During this time, the (officially "brain dead") donor's vital functions are being sustained artificially to preserve organ viability; this may last from a few hours to a few days. Should artificial respiration and circulation end prematurely, the opportunity to recover any organ is lost. The intended transplant recipient may die if another donor is not found in time.

The top person on the ranked list often will not receive the transplant. The individual must be available, healthy enough to undergo major surgery, and willing to be immediately transplanted. A laboratory test is also often given to ensure compatibility between the recipient and the organ to be transplanted. Once the patient is selected, surgery is scheduled and the transplant takes place within hours.

## Organ Shortage

Unfortunately, there are not enough organs available for those awaiting a transplant. It is obvious that increasing the donor pool remains the single best method for eliminating the organ shortage. And, extensive efforts have been made to increase the number of donors. Yet, on average, ten people from the waiting list die per day because an organ is not available. The number of donors has not grown significantly since 1988 (when UNOS began tracking organ transplants). There are a variety of reasons for the limited supply, including improvements in medical treatment for traffic-accident, knife-wound, and gun-shot victims; the increase in transmittable disease (e.g., AIDS, hepatitis, etc.) among the general, and especially the younger, population; medical personnel neglecting to seek permission for procuring organs from the recently-deceased's family; and a reluctance to donate organs for personal and/or religious reasons. Given this limited supply, it is desirable that every available organ from the existing donor pool be effectively "utilized."

Utilization is defined as maximizing the number of organs available per donor and minimizing discard rates. Multiple organ donation (i.e., procuring two or more organs from the same donor) has been steadily increasing over the years, with 81 percent of donors in 1993 involving multiple organs. Unfortunately, discard rates have also been increasing. Removing multiple organs increases the time between death, placement of the available organs, and their removal and transplantation. The need for a larger donor pool has led to the use of organs from individuals from a broader range of ages, especially older donors. Organs from older donors are typically more difficult to place, leading to prolonged ischemia[10]. All of these delays may result in delayed graft function for kidneys and primary non-function for hearts, livers, and lungs when transplanted, or to cadaveric organ discards (i.e., the organ are not used). Therefore, a reduction in time to place and transplant a donor's organs can lead to a reduction in organ wastage.

## XPEDITE

### Conceptual Perspective

From 1991 to 1995, UNOS studied ways to streamline transplant data collection and data transmission using on-line computer technology. While several areas in the process were identified for enhancement and development, the most critical domain was that of organ placement: accessing a list of potential organ recipients for a given donor's organs, contacting the transplant centers where the patients are located, and conveying donor information to those centers to speed the decision process (Klein, et al, 1994). For example, in 1993, placement time averaged 3.4 hours (range 0.5 to 37 hours) for the organs processed through the UNOS system (UNOS Handout, 1996). This realization led to the creation of *Xpedite*.

In 1994, UNOS began development of a computerized organ information system, later named *Xpedite*, to collect, process, and disseminate essential donor information. The development was driven by three approaches or conceptual perspectives. First, a guiding framework was realized that the support of organ procurement and placement heavily resembled sales force automation. The second parameter was that the outcome was to be a client-server environment providing the procurement and transplant centers autonomy in transferring, manipulating, and using the available information with centralized database support by UNOS. Finally, given the limited resources, the need for a high-quality software environment, and the speed required for development, a Rapid Application Development (RAD) methodology was used.

**Sales Force Automation.** The concept for *Xpedite* was based on the existing paradigm of sales force automation. In sales force automation, the sales force is often outfitted with laptop computers, hand-held PCs, and even pen-based computers (O'Brien, 1996). This is to not only improve the individual productivity of the sales people, but to significantly enhance the capture, recording, and analysis of relevant sales data for use by corporate marketing and other organizational decision makers. In turn, the marketing area can then better support the sales people. Ultimately, this increased and improved coordination among sales and marketing can yield improvements in organizational productivity and responsiveness.

For organ procurement and placement, the goal is quick and accurate capture of relevant data, transmission of that data to the appropriate decision makers, more rapid decision making, and coordination of communication among the various constituencies. There were enough potential parallels between the two notions to warrant investigation of the idea to support organ procurement and placement.

**Client-Server Environment.** Client/server computing is the model for enterprise-wide computing for the 21$^{st}$ Century (O'Brien, 1996). It is an information architecture consisting of an integration of computer hardware, software, and people, where computing power and information are distributed across an interconnected network of computers. The client, i.e., the user workstation, is able to perform most of the information processing tasks locally. These tasks include data entry and update, database inquiry, transaction processing, report generation, and other interface and decision support activities. Network servers manage network operations and overhead, collaboration and communication within and among workgroups, and the sharing of application programs and data throughout the network. Client/server computing is directed at allowing the large, centralized server computers to concentrate on those tasks for which they are best suited, such as network communications, high-volume transactions, network security and control, and database management and maintenance. Client machine and user activities can, therefore, be more responsive to and focused on their own application effectiveness and efficiency. For organ procurement and placement, this type of independent, yet integrated network of computers is the appropriate framework for design.

**Rapid Application Development (RAD).** Rapid Application Development is a software application development methodology first elaborated by Martin (1991). The goal of this methodology is to "use people and automation to achieve higher quality applications than those built with traditional lifecycle" approaches (p. vii). RAD has as its goal high quality, lower cost, and more rapid system development than more typical approaches. This is accomplished by using CASE-based toolset(s), rapidly evolving prototypes, and having significant user involvement. In a competitive business environment, speed (to manufacture a product, fill an order, provide an answer, construct an application, etc.) is increasingly important as organizations look for ways to outperform the competition. For organ transplantation, speed is of the essence in placing organs to avoid organ wastage and to possibly save a life through a successful organ transplant. Developing a more functional information technology-based system to support organ placement needed to be accomplished in a short time frame.

## Preliminary System Design and Trial(s)

At the start of the project, the development team decided that a prototype would be built using Rapid Application Development (RAD) methodologies to get quick feedback on the viability of the concept. Because of the nature of the task, many ideas had to be demonstrated and tested along the way. For example, during the prototype phase, donor information captured and sent to UNOS was used to actually place organs. The original idea was to build a pen-based application using wireless communications to collect donor information in the field. The data would be collected via laptop, sent back to UNOS, and distributed to the transplant centers.

Six pilot sites from across the nation were selected for this trial. During the initial trial, coordinators at six organ procurement organizations (OPOs) affiliated with the donor hospitals used portable computers to enter pertinent donor data electronically using a common format. This process eliminated the use of handwritten donor sharing forms. The results determined that legibility was greatly improved, the forms generated were more complete, and the time required to enter donor data was comparable to the written method. This verified that placement could be enhanced through this technology.

The preliminary study also revealed several important facts that changed the direction of the effort. First, electronic data collection was important, but communication between the donor site and the transplant center was vital. Both fax and electronic document capability were necessary. And, paging was sometimes required. While it was originally felt that wireless communication was an important consideration and goal, many donors come from remote areas where wireless communication is difficult or impossible; therefore, the wireless approach was dropped from the agenda. Second, organ procurement coordinators wanted the system to integrate with the UNOS computer *Match* system. This would enhance the placement process by providing greater autonomy to the placement coordinators. Third, it had to work across various technology platforms, such as UNIX, Macintosh, and IBM-compatible personal computers, to preserve existing technology investment among the various procurement and transplant centers. Fourth, instead of the anticipated pen-based approach, users actually preferred the keyboard for data entry. Finally, two additional constraints had to be met. The system needed to be developed quickly and cheaply.

To meet these requirements, UNOS needed technologies that could satisfy the infrastructural aspects of linking devices and people along with a rich applications environment. The desire was to use off-the-shelf ideas and solutions where possible. Custom programming was limited to the interfaces. Based on this trial, a subsequent project to integrate all phases of organ procurement and placement was initiated. The original name for the project was already copyrighted, so *Xpedite* was chosen.

The prototype for *Xpedite* was developed in Visual Basic using the RAD methodology. It had an elegant user interface, but demonstrated very poor communication capabilities. Since improved and more rapid communication was one of the primary justifications for *Xpedite*, another approach was used. Lotus *Notes*, with capabilities such as data replication, faxing, paging, e-mail, on-line collaboration, and possible Internet connections, was selected as the software environment for supporting the system. *Notes* could meet both planned and potential future communication needs. In addition, *Notes* was compatible with multiple platforms.

**Final Design, Configuration, and Implementation**

*Xpedite* is fully operational at UNOS headquarters and a number of organ procurement sites across the country. It has exceeded the goals defined at the start of the project. It takes advantage of the *Notes* platform to replicate donor information from the field to UNOS and improves communication among the various participants. Although the goal was to use as much off-the-shelf software as possible, in the end much of the system had to be customized to meet performance and quality criteria for organ placement. In addition, only IBM-compatible interfaces have been implemented.

With the revised design, the organ procurement coordinators collect donor data using portable computers (pen optional), replicate this information back to the UNOS *Notes* server, where it interfaces with the computer *Match* system, and transmits the results of the match back to the coordinators. The coordinators can contact the often geographically dispersed transplant centers via the SkyTel paging system to let them know that a particular organ is available and where their patient is on the list (for example, it could say "a kidney is available for patient x" and that "patient x is ranked second on the match run"). The transplant center dials into the

UNOS *Notes* server to replicate all information on the donor or uses Phone *Notes* to request a fax of the donor information through a fax gateway. This process can occur simultaneously at multiple transplant centers for all organs being placed. Without this technology, simultaneous transmission of data on various organs would be impossible.

In addition, much of the same on-line donor information can be entered directly into the Scientific Registry of Transplant Recipients database, reducing the amount of time and effort previously required for manual data entry. Productivity is enhanced for UNOS staff and organ procurement coordinators in the field. In many cases, more usable organs may be recovered from a given donor due to timely and more widespread transmission of organ offers. The result is a more efficient management of the organ placement process, improved organ utilization, and decreased donor hospital time and costs.

## Obstacles to Change

This project faced and endured many obstacles common to an innovative idea. Initially it was necessary to convince the users (i.e., UNOS and the medical/transplant profession) that this concept of an integrated, client-server-based information system, which only existed on paper, was a worthwhile endeavor given limited resources. The first step is always the toughest, because it requires an act of faith. In developing *Xpedite*, it took almost a year before funds were available to construct a prototype.

Following the success of the prototype, and the lessons learned from it, the decision to produce a production version required a more intense round of justification that ultimately resulted in approval from the UNOS Board of Directors. Because this was a new idea, it was necessary to continually build understanding and support for this effort.

*Xpedite* has gone through a typical adoption cycle, with supporters and detractors. Most agreed that better communications among the procurement coordinators and the transplant centers would benefit the organ placement and transplantation process. Early adopters of the system greatly appreciated the system. Others, some of whom may be described as technology-averse Luddites, did not want information technology intervention or support. Some physicians were vocal supporters; others were not. For example, as *Xpedite* is more fully implemented, the one-hour window for a transplant center to respond to a coordinator about an available organ could be radically reduced. This potential change in policy would remove some of the control from the physicians, threatening their autonomy.

Finally, technologically *Xpedite* stretched the limits of software, hardware, and communications. It required real-time communication and interaction among independent organizations that are geographically dispersed. Collaboration and close teamwork between the interface developers, Lotus Corporation, SkyTel, the transplant community, and UNOS staff was essential to the development process. It took the coordination of all concerned to make this project work on time and within the limited budget. In the end, the most difficult challenge was overcoming the fear of change and failure among the users. However, the resulting system is a significant achievement in collaborative technology and a landmark enhancement in the efficiency and productivity of the medical professionals saving lives through organ transplantation.

## System Benefits

Several benefits have occurred with the introduction and use of *Xpedite*. The obvious benefit is the reduction in time required to place available organs for transplantation[11]. This more rapid placement has significantly reduced the number of viable organs that go unused. In addition to saving human life, there are other significant benefits (medical/technical, financial, and humane) that have occurred in conjunction with *Xpedite*'s installation and propagation.

The job of the organ procurement coordinator requires intense, focused effort to rapidly and successfully place organs from an available donor. *Xpedite* simplifies the job of the organ procurement coordinator by automating much of the placement process in a client/server environment. While data must still be entered into the system, laptop computers can simplify and support this process. *Xpedite* then transfers the donor data to UNOS, where it is then automatically disseminated to the appropriate transplant centers. The coordinator does not have to worry with the details related to distributing the donor data. This allows the procurement coordinators to concentrate on donor management. The result is higher productivity and a reduction in stress.

Organ transplantation is still a relatively young domain of medical practice. The entire domain — from organ procurement and placement, to donor-recipient matching, to patient maintenance following transplantation — requires constant observation and assessment. The donor information that has been electronically captured and transmitted can be placed in the Scientific Registry on Transplant Recipients; data collected through *Xpedite* produces a research-rich database that did not previously exist. This database can be used by medical researchers for study and inquiry on the donor placement process and may ultimately improve national policy on organ allocation.

Once an individual is pronounced dead they are assessed as to whether they may be viable organ donors. If determined to be a candidate for organ donation, permission is sought from the immediate family to acquire the organ(s)[12]. Prior to organ recovery, donors are maintained (i.e., circulation and respiration are artificially supported) in expensive critical care facilities. The donor must be kept "alive" while the organs available for transplant are matched with potential recipients. Once all organs have been matched to a recipient (within certain time constraints), the organ(s) may be removed for transport to the transplant facility. These costs affect everyone through higher insurance rates and increased Medicare/Medicaid costs. *Xpedite* reduces the time donors spend in these expensive facilities, translating into lower medical costs.

Finally, donor families, who have altruistically consented to donate their loved one's organ(s), often must wait hours until organs are placed and recovered before the body can be released for funeral arrangements. *Xpedite* speeds the placement process, which spares the family a lengthy and anxious wait.

## FUTURE DIRECTIONS AND CONCLUSIONS

*Xpedite* is the first system of its type within the organ transplantation field. Before its development, organ sharing and placement had remained essentially the same for the more than ten years since the passage of the *National Organ Transplantation Act*. Over that period the number of transplants has more than doubled with the number of interacting organizations numbering over 400. The complexity of placing organs in this dynamic, life-and-death environment was contributing to the increase in organ wastage. *Xpedite* was developed to address some of the coordination and communication problems.

Future extensions and plans for the *Xpedite* Organ Information System are to link the entire transplant community electronically using Lotus *Notes* as the basis for communications. This would include the transmission of organ donor-specific information, as well as real-time communication among organ procurement coordinators and medical personnel. A part of this growth and evolution is to develop an electronic data interchange system that will collect and exchange scientific data on transplant recipients. The ultimate objective is to provide transplant surgeons, physicians, and researchers with an easy method for collecting and sharing scientific data from the Scientific Registry on Transplant Recipients. Communication between all transplant professionals could be enhanced through this system. E-mail could facilitate timely professional contact and discussion where little now exists. Transplant professionals could share ideas and collaborate with ease through discussion databases. Interaction of this type might improve coordination in better procuring, placing, and monitoring transplantation and transplant recipients worldwide. *Notes* even has the ability to link to the Internet, perhaps an emerging goal for UNOS and the organ transplant community. Finally, this system could easily be extended to link transplant programs globally. It may even serve as a model for other health care groups in developing systems for managing and disseminating critical information

However, uncertainty on the ultimate status of *Xpedite* exists. Since its introduction and initial installation in a number organ procurement organizations and hospitals, several of *Xpedite*'s developers and strongest advocates have moved on to other responsibilities in UNOS or have left the organization. As with any innovation that alters the status quo, there is some resistance to and indifference toward *Xpedite*. It is not clear at this date what the ultimate outcome for *Xpedite* will be or whether it will ever be fully implemented.

*Xpedite* was developed using the RAD methodology to facilitate rapid, low-cost development of a high-quality system. It is a client/server environment designed to resemble the operations and functionality of sales force automation. *Xpedite* leverages human capability through the use of information technology. *Xpedite* allows the organ procurement coordinator to concentrate on donor management, which requires extensive human interaction (among donor family members and medical personnel), while the system handles communications and dissemination of donor information.

## REFERENCES

Beard, J. W. 1996. To Be or Not to Be: The Application of Management of Technology to Organ Procurement and Transplantation. Working Paper.

Klein, D. H., Daily, O. P. Boyd, K, Stockdreher, D. D., & Kauffman, H. M. 1994. *"Xpedite"*-ing Organ Placement - A Status Report. Tele-Lecture.

Martin, J. 1991. *Rapid application development.* New York: Macmillan.

O'Brien, J. A. 1996. *Management information systems: Managing information technology in the networked enterprise, 3rd Edition.* Chicago, IL: Irwin.

OIS. 1995. OIS - Organ Information System. Submission Application for The *Computerworld* Smithsonian Awards.

"Rapid Transplants." 1995. *CIO*, November 15, 22.

UNOS, 1997. UNOS Membership Data. Available at Internet address: http://www.ew3.att.net/unos or http:204.127.237.11/ .

UNOS Handout, 1996. Packet of information distributed by UNOS.

UNOS, 1994. 1994 Annual report of the U.S. Scientific Registry of Transplant Recipients and the Organ Procurement and Transplantation Network, Transplant Data: 1988-1993. Contract Numbers 240-93-0051 and 240-93-0052. Richmond, VA: UNOS and the U.S. Department of Health and Human Resources.

# ENDNOTES

[1] This manuscript makes no assumptions about and does not comment on definitions of death or procedures of organ procurement and transplantation for any country other than the United States.

[2] Because up to eight organs, i.e., heart, liver, pancreas, intestines, two kidneys, and two lungs, may be donated, the process can be arduous.

[3] Lotus Notes is a registered trademark of Lotus Corporation, a subsidiary of IBM Corporation.

[4] **Histocompatibility** is a state or condition in which the absence of immunological interference permits the grafting of tissue or the transfusion of blood (*American Heritage Dictionary, Second College Edition*, 1982).

[5] These include 281 transplant centers, 4 consortium members, 54 independent organ procurement organizations (OPOs), 55 independent tissue typing laboratories, 12 voluntary health organizations, 8 general public members, and 29 medical/scientific organizations.

[6] **Immunosuppressive** therapies are combinations of drugs, including steroids, to suppress a natural immune response of an organism to antigens produced by a foreign body; i.e., prevent the body from "rejecting" a transplanted organ by immune system attack. This attack will damage and subsequently destroy the transplanted organ.

[7] UNOS policies allow individuals awaiting an organ transplant to be listed with more than one transplant center (i.e., multiple listing) and for more than one organ (i.e., heart, lung, kidney, etc.). Thus, the number of registrations may be greater than the actual number of patients.

[8] Each donor will generate a different ranked list due to differences among individuals.

[9] A new policy for liver allocation was unanimously approved by the UNOS Board of Directors to be effective January 20, 1997. Hearings were held on December 10, 1996, by the Department of Health and Human Services, concerning the new allocation criteria.

[10] Ischemia is a prolonged period without a blood supply. Too long a period of ischemia will result in a reduction in organ viability.

[11] All improvement data is essentially anecdotal. Without an experimental and control group for comparison, it is impossible to state with certainty that *Xpedite* is any "better" than the previous approach. However, the general consensus is very positive and the anecdotal evidence supports a positive assessment.

[12] Although the law supports acquiring organs from an individual who has a signed donor card without any additional consent, the general practice is to also seek permission from surviving family members. The physicians and medical facilities are legally protected, but the additional permission is considered more compassionate to the family, avoids misunderstandings, and reduces the likelihood of "frivolous" lawsuits.

# 059

## ENGINEERING DESIGN VS. CUSTOMER SATISFACTION, PROGRESS AND TRENDS (THE EAST-EUROPEAN EXPERIENCE)

Ivar Märtson and Mart Tamre
Chair of Engineering Design
Tallinn Technical University

## Introduction

Estonia was incorporated into former USSR during last half-century and had to manage and operate inside the closed structure of the totalitarian formation. Science and technology developed fast all over the world during the time and a systematic education of design engineers started also in Estonia in sixties according general technical education scheme.

Preparation of design engineers satisfied the situation until Estonian economical contacts were limited with USSR and East-European countries. Design engineers were able to develop products well conformed and competitive in East-European market.

Shortages at design engineers' education and experiences (not only in Estonia but also in East-Europe) appeared after collapse of the USSR and restoring independence of Estonia when rapid growth of contacts started with industrially developed countries. The education seems not adequate for creating competitive products at market economy situation. An essential change in design methodology has taken place starting 60-70s up to now all over the world and design engineers from East-Europe and particularly from former USSR have been excluded from the experience due to lack of free communication.

An analysis is presented in the paper to find answers to questions why the backlog have arisen, what is the matter of the backlog and what to change at education of design engineers and at their actual work, what are the key points for ability to understand the development of product design methodology taking place all around the world and to follow the process. The approach bases on the general progress of the process of design methodology.

## 1. Evolution of engineering design

The evolution process of engineering design [1] is rational to divide into four stages. The first stage began obviously when human started to make instruments for himself wittingly and intently (Fig.1). The stage may be defined as **Primeval Design**. A product was made according usage and continuous improvement of a natural model supposedly at that time.

A subject analysis of the design process needs to consider personal categories bounded with a product. The categories are: **Sponsor S, Designer D, Manufacturer M** and **Consumer C**.

The involved categories were commonly integrated and represented at one person at primeval design process. The period lasted until coming into usage first design tools. Such kind of tools is considered as primitive drawings (on

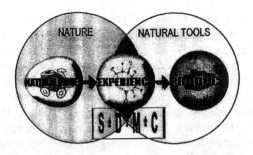

**Fig.1.** Principal scheme of Primeval Design process.

rock or first papyrus drawings). The period of primeval design could be terminated with the stage of taking into wide usage of papyrus at about 3000 BC.

The next period is pointed as **Antique Design** characterized with starting usage of graphical images as aids for design process. The process spread quickly dominating at XII - XV century. A principal scheme of the characteristic design process is given on Fig.2.

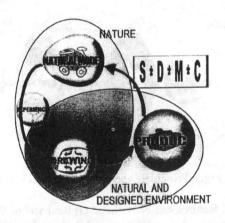

**Fig.2.** Principal scheme of Antique Design process.

The process characterized with spreading usage of a graphical image of a natural model joints to practical experiences of the natural model usage as an aid for natural model improvement. Personal categories of the design process were still represented at one person or at tightly bounded personal group.

New products were made quite few during the first two periods. Despite the fact the products were thoroughly finalized and perfect satisfying almost ideally needs and expectations of the community. The period of antique design ended with starting industrial revolution at XVIII century. Important inventions of the XVIII century (spinner and steam engine) and growing manufacture production together with spreading usage of railway and electricity made it possible to appear **industrial production in large quantities** at XIX century.

The industrial production meant separation of consumer and manufacturer from the one hand and the production required professional designing from the other hand. A **design engineer profession** formed. The personal categories of the design process separated completely as result of the process.

The designing process as profession required aids to simplify and support figurative or 3D thinking. Therefore descriptive geometry concept formulated by Gaspard Monge firstly in his monograph on 1799 advanced fast. A certain graphical and design language grew up on the base of descriptive geometry called **Engineering Graphics** (drafting technology, engineering drawing). Engineering graphics uses several different implements. The first one was mainly paper and pencil method. Different instrumental or mechanical drawing aids were used later reaching to computer aided drafting and CAD today. The design language and his various implements have had a significant influence on design process the matter not discussed in the paper.

The design period started at XVIII - XIX century and methodology developed at that time is called **Classical Design** (Fig.3).

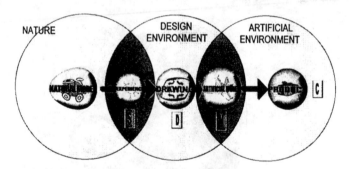

**Fig.3.** Principal scheme of Classical Design process.

Two essential features can be outlined on the basis of the above characterizing difference between classical design and design of previous periods. The design categories were completely separated at first and graphical modeling obtained significant importance.

Engineering graphics, professional designer who had got rid of other tasks and automated manufacturing enabled to accelerate substantially product making process. Every new product was more complicated and perfect satisfying more completely the certain needs of each single consumer. A split between single consumer and community satisfaction started to appear as effect of the products mentioned on second half of this century. The satisfaction with single products does not expand to more complicated product systems that mean to whole artificial environment surrounding individuals more and more. The artificial environment consisting of human made products conflicts frequently with natural environment and the fact causes well-known civilization disasters as waste, noise, urbanizing, traffic problems and other environment problems

## 2. INABILITES OF CLASSICAL DESIGN

A conclusion that methods of classical design are not more suitable for creating products matching needs and potentiality of nature and existing artificial environment can be made on the base of the above. Methods of classical design need to be improved. The reason of the inability and ways of avoiding this can be discussed on the base of design development process (Fig.4).

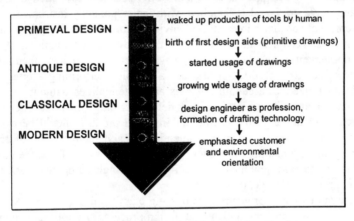

Fig.4. Historical progress of Engineering Design.

At first it is taken into consideration that products made in primeval and antique design period met well consumer needs and were ideally harmonized with nature and mutually. Personal categories of design isolated mutually at the period of classical design. The subject matter of the process was breaking the link between designer and consumer. Designer should stand proxy for consumer needs as self-evident conclusion. The problem rises from the difference of product experience of designer and consumer. A product is mutually interrelated set of single parts for designer. A product is *vice versa* an integer fulfilling a certain function having a certain quality and needs for consumer. Further more the product has some relation with nature and environment. Thereby consumer is not generally interested in component consistence of a product and how the components are mounted together. An interest of a consumer focused on separate parts of a product realizes oneself by investigating whole product concentrating on relations of product properties or functions and separate parts. Summarizing can be said that the consumer approach to product has **deductive character** directed from integer to single, from whole to component and from complicated to simple.

Designers opposite have used inductive approach commonly. They seek and find components and corresponding ways for jointing to guarantee a certain function or giving a certain quality to a set of components. A problem arises as the deductive activity is some way uncommon for individual and most of human activities have inductive character. Study, training and self development start from simple elements and are directed to more complicated complex abilities and activities, for example. Research is concentrated into fact and single phenomenon accumulating and a generalization follows. Manufacturing of a good or production is clearly inductive activity in which single parts are manufactured and mounted into the whole later. Consequently can be pointed that today's designer has to be trained in **deductive approach** at design process and have to be also supplied with corresponding instruments to be able represent consumer interests and environment needs and requirements at design process. Technical interpretation of the above means cognition of the need of supplementing of classical design with methods and instruments enabling to describe the product made as a whole performing certain functions, characterized with certain qualities and potentialities without considering any components. This kind of model describing only functions, qualities, requirements and potentialities of intended product should be agreed at first with needs of consumer and potentialities and requirements of environment. Sequentially making the model concrete step by step follows the process above leading to exact graphical description of the single components and connections of a product at the end.

Second essential problem at comparing classical design with modern design is the role of graphical modeling at design process. The noticeable increase of the importance of modeling comparing with design processes of earlier periods have caused some fetishing of drawing or computer screen image. The tendency expresses oneself in widely spread opinion that compilation of drawings or images exhausts design process matter. It is difficult to understand from the point of view above that design by drawing does not satisfy modern design and compiling of a scale drawing can brake efficiency of process of making new product. The matter of this question lies in principal description of a product as a set of components even working with computer graphical modeling. The fact excludes usage of deductive approach. Therefore drafting technology as a design language can be used only at last stages of product making process when problems are concentrated on determining of composition of components and parameters of the parts. The process is a secondary phase from the point of general product development.

## 3. PROGRESS OF DESIGN AND SITUATION IN EAST-EUROPEAN COUNTRIES

Our experience bases mainly on work of former Soviet Union design engineers. The adequate description of design progress and situation requires a preceding analysis of designer activity depending on his tasks, activity subjects and surrounding of the activity. Two types of design engineers can be distinguished on the base of character of the product worked out at conditions of planned economy.

The first group of products constitute **products with identified consumers**. Arrangements, stamps, conductors, test devices, special measuring instruments, specific automation aids or unique scientific apparatuses, etc. used in a certain firm for example. The design engineer of this kind of products could be called designer of products with identified consumer (**DIC**). The products mentioned were designed and made by enterprises himself at planned economy. This means that design engineer and consumer worked in the same surrounding and could be in close contact.

The second group constitute industrial products, consumers' goods, home machines, universal scientific equipment, universal test and measuring devices and automation aids, etc. These are products with very wide group of consumers. A well-succeeded product of this group inheres rise of demand and widening of circle of consumers. The process means that the product will be used by consumers not intended to use it at the stage of product creation. The consumers are anonymous at first stage. Therefore the products of this kind **are products with anonymous consumer**. The design engineer involved with making products named is designer of products with anonymous consumer (**DAC**).

The distinction of two types of design engineers DIC and DAC allow to characterize more closely the design situation in East-Europe.

The work made by DIC was very needful at conditions of planned economy and design engineer as a profession represented especially by DIC was widely spread. University syllabuses were oriented into DIC preparation. In essence DIC works at conditions similar to antique design. He worked closely collaborating with a consumer. The consumer solved all general problems of the product so that DIC' relation into the product could be inductive and he could start directly to design separate parts of the product coming to the complete product at the end. The classical drafting technology was on the right place in this case and any needs for general methods did not rise.

The problem was completely different in the case of DAC where designer had to put himself into the role of consumer. He had to see future product by consumer way and cognized immediately inability of classical design. However the dissatisfaction of DAC with methods of classical design increased noticeably later in East-Europe compared with developed industrial countries. There were two reasons of the process.

At first. Design engineers were trained, tought and they worked inside very narrow and closed specialties. Qualification of the design engineer was often determined by special kind of products, cinema equipment designer, photo apparatuses' designer, designer of length measuring devices, etc. General solution of the product was quite strictly fixed by limits of the specialty. The common requirement for designers to work obligatorily according to design methods enforced by standards explains very limited freedom of designer to produce completely original and general solutions. The designer's activity was directed to some improvements of a certain predetermined application that mainly led to inductive approach to problem.

At second. Lot of attention was given to analysis of existing designs in East-Europe. Finding of an appropriate prototype was considered very essential at product creation. It was easy to find a prototype satisfying well needs of a customer because of technical backwardness of East-Europe. Replacement of a technical assignment with a working model and concrete improvement task was general accepted way [2]. The whole process of making a new product was an improvement of chosen prototype according to technical possibilities of the enterprise in this case. The last one is evidently inductive activity. Therefore shortages of classical design have cognized only starting seventies in East-Europe. The usage of aids and alternatives to prevent the shortages can be discussed on the base of so called **normative method of design**.

## 4. NORMATIVE METHOD OF DESIGN

Standards were strictly obligatory in former Soviet Union. Ignoring the requisitions of a standard was even formally infringement of the law. It was tendency to regulate different activities by norms. Number of standards was very high, they were very detailed and strict and also quite well compiled.

Design process was naturally very detail normed. This kind of set of activity method ruled by state standards (GOST) was called **Normative Method of Design** NMD and will be more closely discussed below. NMD was created in late sixties when a whole system of standards (approximately 150 standards) was completed. The system was called **Unified System for Design Documentation** (USDD). Standards of this system were marked by sign GOST 2.xxx-xx [3]. Considerable amount of the standards was also transmuted into the standards of CMEA (Council of Mutual Economic Aid) marked as ST SEV xxx-xx. The process led to spreading of NMD over East-Europe and even to some part of Middle-Europe. Different stages of design fixed in USDD standards (GOST 2.103-68) are introduced on Fig.5. First three stages given on Fig.5 are different drawing sets for design and remained ones' drawings for manufacture. USDD deals with composing of drawings and corresponding requirements as become evident from Fig.5.

Standard for general principles GOST 2.001-70 determined USDD as whole set of standards establishing rules for design documents for compilation of main drawings, drawing them up and usage. Accordingly could be noted that NMD established by USDD deals design process as compilation of drawings. USDD norms were followed 20 years in Estonia and therefore it is understandable why not only students but also lot of engineers is convinced that creation of a product means compilation of drawings. The conviction is one of essential restrictions for understanding today's process of product creation and for dissemination and development of it in Estonia and also in whole East-Europe.

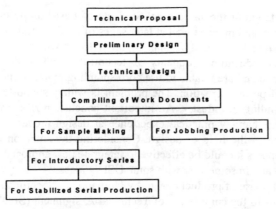

**Fig.5.** Stages of Design by USDD standards.

The ideology described were tried to break in former Soviet Union only in late seventies. The process expressed oneself in outlining and introducing new set of standards called **System of Product Development and Launching it into Manufacture** (SPDLM) [4]. Standards of the system were marked GOST 15.xxx-xx. A particular attention was concentrated into the earlier stages of product creation in the set of standards. The subject matter of technical assignment and rules for compiling needful for making new products were thoroughly normed. A concept of avant project was introduced enabling creation of alternative and rivaling variants. Following standards were introduced: Procedure of Patent Research (GOST 15.011-82), Procedure of Scientific Research and Development (GOST 15.101-80), Supervision for Mastering and Manufacture of Products (GOST 15.304-80), Launching of Licensed Production (GOST 15.311-82), Production withdrawal from Manufacturing (GOST 15.801.80), etc. emphasizing idea of substantiality of wide process of product creation compared with compilation of drawings. A conclusion arises from the set of standards that a product is influenced substantially by earlier phases in which design problems in a more abstract and solution neutral form instead of usage of drafting technology must be formulated. The SPDLM system of standards and corresponding approach was introduced in engineering design courses at Tallinn Technical University right away. In spite of the fact even these principles could not spread among industrial engineers because most of the standards were canceled already at the beginning of "Perestroika" and design process was guided back to more formal and ruled situation.

## 5. POTENTIALITIES AT DESIGN ENGINEERS PREPARATION ON THE BASE OF EXISTING MENTALITY

Standards of USDD deal and describe very well possibilities, methods and aids of drafting technology. They are in good accordance with ISO standards but more detailed at the same time. Students of East-Europe master well drafting technology and manage well at later sages of product design as result. This kind of overemphasized and formal attention to drawings is one shortcoming at engineers' education. Students of technical faculties do not recognize the importance and are unable to use corresponding practical methods of the earlier stages of product creation. The problem is widely supported by the prevailing understanding in industry. An important conclusion rises from the situation to emphasize namely practical experience at design process earlier stages at the education in the field of design. Considering the situation and background of our engineers it could be effective to integrate new approach with widely spread SPDLM and in some way with some USDD ideas.

The first phase of product design by Ullman [5] - Specification Development is analogous to the completing of Technical Assignment (SPDLM GOST 15.001-73). The objective of both cases is to create a general model of a product. Main difference is that the Technical Assignment had to be conformed formally and could not be modified during further design process. Specification *vice versa* is a dynamic formulation improved until launching the product and even during the whole life cycle. It is relatively simple to learn methods and ways of developing and improving a general model of a product considering consumer needs and requirements and requirements of environment as brainstorming, synectics, interviewing users, questionnaires, value analysis, boundary searching, interaction matrix, ranking and weighting, quality function deployment, decision matrix, etc. on the base of literature. More hard is to adopt practice of not including strict drawings into output specification determining concrete solutions. A more abstract solution-neutral presentations or formulations should be used instead of limiting oneself with only one certain solution at early stages of design. Product model immoderate concretization should also be avoided at second phase of product design if possible. Restricting oneself cuts off lot of possible solutions potentially comprising an optimal or ideal one. USDD includes parts that are effectively used at conceptual design or specification development phases although the set of standards enfolds rules for drawings. Namely USDD includes group of standards (GOST 2.7xx-xx) [6] dealing schemes and diagrams. Standard GOST 2.701-84 - Diagrams. Kinds and Types giving very complete classification and well defined rules for composing and using schemes and diagrams. Regulations of usage of this kind of documents are not discussed so thoroughly in any other international even national standards. A method for composing a general model of a product was developed in 7th group of standards of USDD (more than fifty standards) enabling to compile a product model as a set of requirements, functions and provisions (structural scheme, functional scheme, divisional scheme, principal scheme). Specifying and concretizing the schemes is possible to reach to quite detailed product model that may be presented in graphical form (kinematics, optics, hydro, electric and other schemes for example). Oriented investigating of the system supports well study of subject of product design at earlier phases.

## 6. CONCLUSION

The DAC qualification scheme should be set as an objective at design engineers basic and continuing education in East-European countries to assure understanding of today's development process of methods used at product design, to support being inside the process and to assist the process development if possible. A rational moment can be found at former approach of design. We consider that the following activities and changes should be intake into the syllabus of design engineer:

1. students have to be introduced and trained at differences of goals and practical actions of DIC and DAC to be able to switch operatively;
2. training of students have to be focused on giving practical experience at distinguishing advantages of inductive and deductive approach emphasizing deductive approach;
3. the methodology of deductive approach should be more closely investigated on the base of literature and practical experience of advanced countries;
4. introduction and learning parts of USDD that enable to compose product general models (GOST 2.7xx-xx) needful at early stages of product creation in detail;
5. clarifying and clearing principal difference between SPDLM' Technical Assignment and output specification used at product design today;
6. clearing and introduction essential reasons of usability of NMD only latest phases of product design and braking efficiency of activity at earlier phases.

## REFERENCES

1. J.Käosaar. Historical Development of Design. Paper for the 23$^{rd}$ Symp. of the International Committee for the History of Technology. 7-11.08.1996, Budapest.
2. P.I. Orlov, Fundamentals of Design. Moscow: Mashinostroyenije, 1988 (in Russian).
3. Standards of Unified system for design documentation. General principles. GOST 2.001-70 - GOST 2.121-73 (in Russian).
4. Standards of the System of Product Development and Launching it into manufacture. GOST 15.001-73 - GOST 15.311-82 (in Russian).
5. David G. Ullman, The Mechanical Design Process. McGraw-Hill, 1992.
6. Standards of Unified System for Design Documentation. Diagrams. GOST 2.701-84 - GOST 2.797-81 (in Russian).

# 061

## AN INSIGHT INTO THE DETERMINANTS OF
## THE PRIVATE R&D INVESTMENT RESPONSE TO R&D SUBSIDIES[#]

VAN POTTELSBERGHE DE LA POTTERIE Bruno

and

PANITCH Arkadi


*Correspondance to:*
Bruno VAN POTTELSBERGHE DE LA POTTERIE
    Université Libre de Bruxelles
    Unité d'Economie Spatiale et de la Technologie  CP-140
    Avenue F.D. Roosevelt 50, B-1050 Brussels, Belgium
    tel : ++ 32 2   650 46 01, fax : ++ 32 2   650 38 25, E-mail : bvpot@ulb.ac.be


Arkadi PANITCH
    Université Libre de Bruxelles
    Inter-university Institute for High Energies  CP-230,
    Boulevard du Triomphe 1, B-1050 Brussels, Belgium
    tel : ++ 32 2   629 32 06, fax : ++ 32 2   629 38 16, E-mail : panitch@hep.iihe.ac.be

## ABSTRACT

The objective of this paper is to assess whether government R&D subsidies stimulate private R&D investments in the G7 countries, both at the aggregated manufacturing level and for 22 disaggregated industries. The estimated impact of government R&D on private R&D is slightly sensitive to modifications of the empirical model. However, the heterogeneity across industries of the response profiles of private R&D to subsidies may partly be explained by the law of decreasing returns to R&D subsidies and by the stability of the R&D subsidization policy. The more subsidy-intensive an industry is, the more the impact of government R&D is likely to be weak or negative. The less volatile a subzidization policy is, the more it is likely to stir up private R&D.

**Key words:** R&D subsidies, Private R&D, stimulation.

**Topic:** C (National Technology Policies)

**Category:** 2 (Empirical)

**Paper suitable for oral presentation only**

---

[#] The authors would like to thank Professor Henri Capron, Michele Cincera, and Marcelo Fernandes for usefull suggestions and remarks on this paper.

# An Insight into the Determinants of the Private R&D Investment Response to R&D subsidies

## Introduction

The main objective of this paper is to assess whether or not government R&D subsidies have stimulated private R&D investments over the period 1973-1990 in the USA, Canada, Germany, France, Italy, Japan, and the UK, both at the aggregated level and for 22 disaggregated manufacturing industries. It is conjectured that the impact of government R&D on private R&D may substantially vary across industries. The second objectif is therefore to apprehend some of the potential factors which may explain the estimated response profiles of private R&D investors to subsidies. The two factors put forward are the R&D subsidization rate and the stability of R&D subsidization policies. The existing empirical literature on the effectiveness of R&D subsidies is surveyed in the next section. Section 3 presents the empirical model which gives particular attention to the determinants of private R&D expenditures. The dataset is described in the fourth section. The fifth section is devoted to the interpretation of the empirical results. Finally, the conclusions including some suggestions related to the design of public investment policies are drawn in the last section.

## The Efficiency of Government R&D: Evidences and Ambiguities

A first category of studies considers a production function in traditional log additive form. In this function the total R&D input is disaggregated into its two main components: private R&D ($RP$) and government R&D ($RG$). While in other countries such exploration has been quite unheard-of, the conclusions brought through the few US applications at the industrial level stay quite controversial. Private R&D is associated to a substantial and significant effect on the growth of productivity which is greater than the impact of total R&D, whereas public R&D appears to have a much weaker, if not insignificant, effect (see the survey by Capron (1992)). What may be seen as controversial is that the sole procedure which allows for a positive and significant estimated impact of government-financed R&D on productivity is to withdraw some sectors - generally R&D subsidies intensive - from the dataset (see Leonard (1971) and Reiss (1990)).

This failure to find significant direct productivity effects of R&D subsidies has led some analysts to hypothesize and investigate an indirect path of stimulus to productivity, via an inducement to perform private R&D. According to Levy (1990), a firm could consider government R&D as a public good which can be employed without private cost. He argues that if government R&D can be employed by the private sector at zero cost, then, in equilibrium, its marginal product must be equal to zero. Therefore the non significant impact of RG on output growth can not be taken as a validation for the (in)efficiency of R&D subsidies. The question which arises is to understand the influence of R&D subsidies upon the marginal physical product of private R&D. Assume, for instance, that the amount of private R&D investments is an upward sloping function of its marginal physical product. Hence, since the marginal physical product of private R&D is likely to increase with R&D subsidies, an increase of the latter should foster private R&D expenditures. Most of the investigations which implicitly test this « supply » assumption are presented in Table 1. Only a small share uses manufacturing sectors in the empirical analysis, preferring micro and, to a lesser extent, macro-economic approaches. Out of the seven analyses at the micro level, 3 support the supply assumption, 3 reject it, and one is inconclusive. Concerning the three US meso-economic studies the results are also mitigated. Nadiri (1980) estimates that private R&D and R&D subsidies are complementary while for Levin and Reiss (1984) the two variables are substitute. Lichtenberg (1984) fails to obtain any significant relationship. The three macro-economic estimates support the supply hypothesis for the USA, Japan, Germany, Sweden and France, but reject it for the UK and the Netherlands and are inconclusive for Italy and Switzerland. Although these studies are mostly related to the US economy, such comparison may be hazardous. Quoting Capron (1992, p. 100), *«...a large part of discrepancies between the coefficients estimated may be explained by data and regression characteristics»*. More particularly, columns 4 to 7 in Table 1 indicate that the empirical models differ markedly across studies. One could wonder whether this divergence among the econometric results is consequencial to the models' diversity or not. In this respect, four issues disserve to be discussed.

**Table 1. Estimated Private R&D Elasticity (or Marginal Impact) of Public R&D.**

| Author | Country - years - (1) | Sample | $RP_{t-1}$ | $Q_t$ | t | other | β |
|---|---|---|---|---|---|---|---|
| Nadiri (1980) | US 1969-75 T.S.C.S. | 10 industries | + | + | | + | 0.01* |
| | | 5 durable | | | | | -0.04* |
| | | 5 non durable | | | | | 0.02* |
| Carmichael (1981) | U.S. 1976-77 C.S. | 46 transport firms | + | | | | -0.08* |
| Levin-Reiss (1984) (4) | US 1967, 72, 77 C.S. | 20 industries | | | | + | 0.12* |
| Levy-Terleckyj (1983) | US 1949-81 T.S. | Private Business | + | | | + | 0.21* |
| Lichtenberg (1984) | US - 1963-79 T.S.C.S. | 12 industries | | | + | | 0.01 |
| Lichtenberg (1984) | US - 1972 - C.S. | 991 firms | | | + | | 0.10* |
| | US - 1977 | | | | | | -0.22* |
| | US - 1972 to 77 | | | | | | -0.17* |
| | US - 1967 to 77 | | | | | | -0.26* |
| Switzer (1984) | US - 1977 C.S. | 125 firms | + | + | | + | 0.08 |
| Lichtenberg (1987) | US - 1956-83 T.S. | Macro | + | + | | | 0.33* |
| | | | | | | $Q_g$ | 0.11 |
| | US - 1979-84 T.S.C.S. | 187 firms | | | | | 0.13* |
| | | | | | | $Q_g$ | -0.00 |
| Holemans - Sleuwagen (1988) | Belgium 1980-84 C.S. | 59 firms | + | | | + | 0.30* |
| Levy (1990) (3) | Macro 1963-84 T.S.C.S. | USA | + | | | | 0.30* |
| | | UK | | | | | -0.73* |
| | | Italy | | | | | 0.05 |
| | | Japan | | | | | 0.16* |
| | | Germany | | | | | 0.23* |
| | | Sweden | | | | | 0.41* |
| | | Netherl. | | | | | -0.13* |
| | | France | | | | | 0.33* |
| | | Switzerl. | | | | | 0.02 |
| Leyden & Link (1991) | US - 1987 C.S. | 137 laboratories | + | | | | 1.99* |
| Fölster & Trofimov (1996) (4) | Sweden 1982-90 T.S.C.S. | 249 groups | + | + | + | + | 0.20* |

(1) T.S. = time series; C.S. = cross section; T.S.C.S. = panel data. (2) RP = private R&D, Q = total sales; Qg = sales to government; t = time dummies. (3) The estimates reported for Levy (1990) are taken from Capron (1992). (4) The parameters have to be interpreted as a negative relationship between RP and RG because the dependent variable is RT. * Significant at a 10% probability threshold.

*First*, most studies estimate the mean effect of *RG* on *RP*, restricting the parameter to be invariant across manufacturing industries or firms. There is, however, empirical evidence that the relation between government and private R&D may be different from one industry to the other. When the dataset of Nadiri (1980) is subdivided into two groups, the estimated private R&D elasticity of government R&D becomes negative and significant for the 5 nondurable industries. It is therefore conceivable that R&D subsidies may either stimulate or replace private R&D investments, depending on industry-specific features. Another reason which may explain why R&D subsidies can have a negative impact on private R&D investment has been raised by Aghion-Dewatripont-Rey (1996). They develop a theoretical model of entrepreneurial behavior as regards to the adoption rate of new technologies. One of their findings is that R&D subsidization policies may either foster or hinder the rate of technology adoption, depending on the 'conservative' or 'profit maximizing' management feature of the firms. The theoretical results suggest that R&D subsidies are likely to incite technology adoptions if the firms are characterized by a 'profit maximizing' behaviour. On the other hand, government R&D is likely to substitute for private R&D among 'conservative' firms. The *second* issue is related to the dynamic perspective of the model to be estimated. Only three out of the eleven studies of Table 1 adopt a partial adjustment mechanism for R&D investments. On *a priori* grounds, the inclusion of lagged R&D may be seen as an important determinant of present R&D investments. Mansfield (1964, p. 32) notices that « *First it takes time to hire people and build laboratories. Second, there are often substantial costs in expanding too rapidly because it is difficult to assimilate large percentage increases in R&D staff. ...Third, the firm may be uncertain as to how long expenditures of (desired) R&D levels can be maintained. It does not want to begin projects that will soon have to be interrupted.* ». It is therefore essential to test whether an adjustment process is at work and whether the inclusion of the lagged endogenous variable among the explanatory variables affects the estimated impact of R&D subsidies on private R&D.

The *third* point concerns the influence of technological competition, inside a given industrial sector, on the R&D investors' behaviour. In Table 1, Fölster and Trofimov (1996) is the only study which attempts to comprehend the role of R&D rivalry. Their main finding is that total R&D efforts of several competing firms in Sweden tend to decline when they receive subsidies. If only one firm benefits from subsidies, its R&D activities increase but the total R&D by all competing firms is likely to decline. Thus, it is not surprising to evaluate an eviction effect at the sectoral level. The potential presence of such negative impact of government R&D on private R&D at the aggregate (sectoral) level amplifies the requisite for empirical studies at the sectoral level. If the focus is put on international rivalry, the idea would be that domestic R&D teams can react in diverse way when they are challenged by foreign competitors. A *fourth* issue is the one introduced by Lichtenberg (1987) who provides empirical evidence, through both macro and micro US data, that most of the models which estimate regressions of private R&D expenditures on federal R&D funding and other variables give an overstatement of the federal R&D coefficient. This misspecification could be a direct implication of the failure to distinguish government sales from other sales. The econometric analysis supports the view that "*a large part of what had been interpreted as the effect of federal R&D funding on privately funded R&D expenditure is in fact attributable to variation in the government's share of output*" [p. 103]. However, these results should be taken cautiously since they mean that government purchases and government R&D are correlated. Hence, both variables could reflect the degree of government interventionism, rising again the question of whether or not such interventionism has a stimulating impact on private R&D. In a nutshell, the empirical evidence suggests that the two sources of funds for R&D may be either complementary or substitute. To the public authorities' views, a correct answer to this debate is crucial. In what follows, we attempt to provide a better understanding of the relationship between government and private R&D.

**Empirical implementation**

In order to gauge empirically the link between private and government R&D, we follow the traditional approach which consists in estimating the impact of R&D subsidies and other determinants on the private decision to invest in R&D activities. The model is constructed in the light of the four issues discussed in the previous section. Total sales, $Q$, seem to be one of the main determinants of private R&D; an increase in output means that more funds may be injected in research activities. Next, we allow for a dynamic specification because R&D activities are obviously a continuous process. Therefore, the amount invested in year $t$ should depend, at least partly, on the amount spent the previous year. R&D projects last several years, the inclusion of $RP(t-1)$ seems to be a parsimonious way to identify the feedback effect of past on current spending. International technological competition may also be a key factor in the decision-making process concerning domestic R&D activities. It is proxied by the sum of total R&D investments $(RT)$ performed by the competitors divided by domestic total R&D. A negative sign associated with $RTOTH$ would mean that R&D activities lie down as the challenge from abroad increases, illustrating a submissive reaction adopted by domestic industries. A positive sign would mean a rise in the technological efforts to cope with the threats from abroad. Such a reaction is said to be aggressive. $RTOTH$ is lagged one year in order to avoid simultaneity biases with $RP(t)$. For each manufacturing industries ($j = 1,...22$), the empirical model has the following form:

$$rp_{it} = \beta_1\, rp_{it-1} + \beta_2\, q_{it} + \beta_{3i}\, rtoth_{it-1} + \beta_{4i}\, rg_{it} + c_i + \varepsilon_{it} \qquad (1)$$

The subscript $i$ represents the countries ($i=1,...,7$) and $t = 1,..., 17$ indexes the years 1974 to 1990. The lower case letters $rp$, $q$, $rtoth$, and $rg$, are the natural logarithm of private R&D, total sales, technological competition, and R&D subsidies. $\varepsilon$ is the error term. The parameters $\beta_1,.., \beta_4$ are the private R&D elasticities of the four corresponding exogenous variables. Previous private R&D investments and total sales should positively influence $RP$. R&D subsidies and international competition may have either a positive or a negative impact on $RP$. This model can be considered as a generalized version of the private R&D models in Table 1. Unfortunately, it is practically impossible to get valid estimates of the parameters $\beta$ for each sector in each country because the degree of freedom is not so high. In order to obtain an adequate number of degrees of freedom it is more convenient to rely on datasets that combine both time series and cross-sections and to impose some restrictions on the parameters across countries or industries. Consequently, the observations for each industry are piled up over the 7 countries, forming a panel dataset of 119 observations. There is most probably an international heterogenity, temporally persistant, generated by country-specific features (such as economic power, culture, S&T systems) which may act upon the investors decision. As far as such features are stable over time, they are seized by country fixed effects.

How restrictive are the cross-countries equality contraints on the parameters? Concerning the parameters associated to the lagged dependent variable and to total sales it is highly probable that they have similar positive values across countries. However, the sign of the parameters associated to $RTOTH$ and to $RG$ is a priori not predictable. It is therefore compulsory to release the parameters $\beta_3$ and $\beta_4$ across countries, as in equation (1). The conventional econometric technique in the framework of a panel dataset is to compute the within transformation by cross section unit to eliminate the fixed effects. However, in a dynamic context, this procedure would yield inconsistent estimates because of the presence of the lagged endogenous variable among the right-hand side variables. Indeed, Nickell (1981) shows that the within transformation introduces, by construction, a correlation between the lagged endogenous variable and the error term. In order to suppress the fixed effects we use the transformation of all variables into orthogonal deviation suggested by Arellano and Bover (1995) which consists in computing the deviations of each data point from its future mean. The estimation procedure, which corrects for autocorrelation, cross-country heteroscedasticity, and cross-sectional correlation, follows four steps: (i) Compute the fitted value of $rp_t$ on the exogeneous variables in time $t$ and $t-1$; (ii) Run instrumental variables (IV) estimates of the model, using the fitted value of $rp_t$ as instrument for the lagged dependent variable. (iii) With the IV error terms, estimate the autocorrelation $\rho_i$ for each country and operate the Cochrane-Orcutt transformation of the variables. If the autocorrelation coefficient is not significantly different from zero at a 10% probability threshold, set $\rho_i = 0$. Run OLS on the transformed variables. (iv) Compute the variance-covariance matrix of the new residuals and run FGLS estimates on the transformed variables of point (iii).

## The data

A balanced panel is composed by seven countries (USA, Japan, Canada, France, Germany, Italy, and the United Kingdom) for each industry. For some industries, data were available for only five or six countries. The sectoral breakdown is composed by 22 industries at 3 or 4 ISIC-digits and one aggregated manufacturing sector. The data are drawn out from the OECD databases. All the variables are expressed in constant 1980 US$. $Q$ is the output indicator proxied by total sales which are deflated by sectoral production price indices. Complete series of total R&D investments $(RT)$ are provided in the ANBERD OECD database. The disaggregation of total R&D investments in four sources of funds is available in the OECD STI database, which is not complete with respect to the time dimension. The sources of funds are: private, government, funds from abroad, and other national funds. Private and government R&D are by far the most important components of $RT$. Then come the funds from abroad and other national sources. The former are generally of no great importance as compared to private and government R&D, while the latter are negligible. Data availability is not homogenous across the four sources of funds. There are much more data on private R&D investments than on government R&D, and data on the two other sources of funds are scarcer than data on government R&D. The computation of complete time series for private R&D and government R&D relies on one broad hypothesis: total R&D investments are essentially composed by private investments and government subsidies. This assumption permits to estimate R&D subsidization rates from private and total R&D investment data as follows: $(RG / RT) = 1 - (RP / RT)$. Therefore, the number of available data on subsidization rate is maximized. Then, missing data are interpolated from the available subsidization ratios. The interpolation procedure works by fitting polynomial curves between the available specified points. Our data did not suggest using any particular order of interpolation. Visual testing of different order interpolations over different sectors and countries suggested us to use the quadratic (2-order) interpolation, which allows for abrupt (unsmooth) behaviour of government subsidization policies and relies on more information than the simple linear interpolation. The time series of RP and RG are calculated from the RT investment series.

## Empirical results

Table 2 presents the econometric results for the aggregated manufacturing sector. The first column shows the regression results of a restricted version of equation (1), whithout dynamism and the technological competition variable. This restricted version has been used in the bulk of the empirical analyses presented in Table 1. The coefficient associated to total sales is positive, as expected, and is significant. This confirms the idea that increases in sales have a positive effect on private R&D investments. Concerning the impact of government R&D on private R&D, the estimated parameter is positive and significant in the USA, Canada, Germany, Italy, and Japan, which is conform to the hypothesis of complementarity between the two variables. This hypothesis can not be supported for France where the coefficient supports the view that government R&D is a substitute for private R&D. For the UK the parameter is positive but insignificantly different from zero. The confrontation of these first estimates for the aggregated US industry with the figures presented in Table 1 shows that our results are compatible with their reciprocates provided by Lichtenberg (1987), Levy (1990) and Levy and Terleckyj (1983). The three studies, which used an identical empirical model (i.e. with output and government R&D as right-hand side variables), highlight a significant stimulating effect in the USA at the macroeconomic level. However, the results provided by Levy (1990) are different for three countries. His impact's evaluations are positive for France, negative for the UK and non significant for Italy. Our estimates are negative for France, non significant for the UK, and positive for Italy. These divergent results may partly be explained by differences in the econometric model, in the studied periods, or in the data sources.

Table 2. Estimates of the private R&D equation for the aggregated manufacturing sector.

| | [1] | [2] | [3] | [4] | [5] | [6] |
|---|---|---|---|---|---|---|
| RP (t-1) | | .874 * (.035) | .897 * (.033) | .871 * (.035) | .714 * (.056) | .753 * (.057) |
| Q (t) | .365 * (.072) | | .319 * (.038) | | .470 * (.041) | .481 * (.050) |
| Q (t-1) | | | | .096 * (.040) | | -.066 (.054) |
| RTOTH (t-1) USA | | | | | .332 (.231) | .322 (.234) |
| RTOTH (t-1) Canada | | | | | -.637 * (.217) | -.596 * (.220) |
| RTOTH (t-1) Germany | | | | | .556 * (.159) | .534 * (.157) |
| RTOTH (t-1) France | | | | | .258 (.161) | .213 (.162) |
| RTOTH (t-1) Italy | | | | | .223 (.349) | .286 (.362) |
| RTOTH (t-1) Japan | | | | | -.226 (.179) | -.194 (.179) |
| RTOTH (t-1) UK | | | | | .099 (.151) | .061 (.144) |
| RG (t) USA | .895 * (.055) | .106 * (.040) | .030 (.049) | .085 * (.041) | .235 * (.079) | .191 * (.081) |
| RG (t) Canada | .166 * (.048) | -.023 (.034) | -.087 * (.029) | -.038 (.034) | -.139 * (.045) | -.139 * (.045) |
| RG (t) Germany | .792 * (.193) | .087 (.073) | .008 (.079) | .048 (.068) | .063 (.100) | .085 (.098) |
| RG (t) France | -.192 * (.043) | -.112 * (.026) | -.081 * (.028) | -.097 * (.027) | -.109 * (.027) | -.108 * (.028) |
| RG (t) Italy | .061 * (.029) | -.017 (.029) | -.048 * (.026) | -.024 (.026) | -.017 (.031) | -.012 (.032) |
| RG (t) Japan | .450 * (.043) | .073 * (.025) | -.003 (.025) | .043 (.027) | .026 (.039) | .026 (.039) |
| RG (t) UK | .039 (.140) | .300 * (.059) | .302 * (.070) | .293 * (.057) | .172 * (.097) | .201 * (.093) |
| TSS | 3.433 | 3.116 | 3.116 | 3.116 | 3.274 | 3.227 |
| RSS | 1.499 | .410 | .302 | .439 | .161 | .154 |

All variables are transformed in orthogonal deviation. Panel data estimates, including country-specific fixed effects; cfr the econometric methodology in main text, IV correction method for autocorrelation and FGLS estimates to correct heteroscedasticity and contemporaneous correlation between countries. * the estimated parameter is significantly different from zero at a 10% probability threshold.

The results presented in columns (2) to (5) investigate to what extent some modifications of the empirical model may change the estimated relationship between private and government R&D. In column (2) the lagged endogenous variable replaces total sales among the right-hand side variables. The new variable has the expected positive sign and is highly significant, lending some support for the assumed partial adjustment mechanism for R&D. Past R&D investments play an important role in the decision process underlying new investments in private R&D. The inclusion of this adjustment process in the model modifies the significance of the parameters associated to government R&D. The point estimates for Canada, Germany, and Italy are not more significant while for the UK it is now significant. Taking into account simultaneously an adjustment process and total sales does not change significantly the coefficients associated to these two variables but modifies further the estimated impact of government R&D. As compared with column (1), column (3) shows that the inclusion of an adjustment process may alter the sign of the estimated impact of R&D subsidies. This is the case for the Italian and the Canadian industries which are now characterized by a significant negative sign. The parameters for the USA and Germany are not more significant. In column (4) the output lagged one year replaces $Q(t)$. The weaker parameter associated to this variable clearly shows that the private decision to invest in R&D is influenced more by contemporaneous sales than by the past performance of firms. This result is consistent with the general view that technical change responds to economic stimuli. The technological competition variable, differentiated across countries, is added to the empirical model in column (5). The impact of this variable is mainly insignificant. However, it is positive and significant for Germany and negative for Canada. That is, the behaviour of private R&D investors is characterized by an aggressive reaction in Germany and a submissive behaviour in Canada. In comparison with the results presented in column (3), the presence of this new variable in the model also affects the estimated private R&D elasticities of government R&D for some countries. The positive sign of the estimated parameter for the USA retrieve its significance while for Italy the negative parameter is not significantly different from zero. Taking into account simultaneously present and one year lagged output, as in column (6), does not bring any change in the estimated parameters and the parameter associated to lagged sales is insignificant.

We now turn to the examination of the econometric results, for each of the 22 desaggregated industries. The estimated model is equivalent to the model presented in the fifth column of Table 2, with the lagged endogenous variable, total sales, international technological competition, and government R&D as explanatory variables. Other specifications have been estimated, without adjustment process or with output lagged one year. These changes in the specification affected mainly the significance rather than the signs of the estimated impact of R&D subsidies on private R&D. Table 3 summarizes the number of positive, insignificant, or negative estimated private R&D elasticities of government R&D according to the countries and to four sub-aggregated groups of industries. The sub-aggregation reflects the quartile distribution of the mean R&D intensity of each industry across the seven countries from 1973 to 1990. For instance, among the six high-tech industries in the USA, the estimated effect is positive for three industries, insignificant for two, and negative for one. Three comments may sum up these figures. *First*, Table 3 clearly validates our conjecture that the studies which estimate an average impact, either at the aggregated level or across industries, eclipse heterogeneous behaviours from one industry to the other. The relation between R&D subsidies and private R&D is far from being uniform accross countries and/or industries. This shows that although average impacts are informative about macro-economic policies, they should not be generalized to all industries. The insignificant impact of the Japanese government R&D at the aggregated level may be explained by the fact that, at the disaggregated level, the impact is insignificant for half of the industries. Similarly, the negative impact estimated at the aggregated level for France is conform to the majority of negative coefficients estimated for the French industries. Concerning Germany the estimated parameters at the disaggregated level, which are positive and significant for 55% of the 22 manufacturing industries, do not corroborate the insignificant estimates at the aggregated industrial level. For this country an aggregation bias may seemingly lead to the misjudgment of the R&D subsidization policy's efficiency measured at the aggregated industry level.

**Table 3. Number of positive-insignificant-negative estimates of private R&D elasticities of R&D subsidies**

| | High-tech. | Medium-high | Medium-low | Low-tech. | Total | Total (%) |
|---|---|---|---|---|---|---|
| USA | 3-3-0 | 1-3-1 | 2-2-0 | 2-2-2 | 8-10-3 | 38-48-14 |
| Canada | 0-3-2 | 0-3-1 | 2-1-1 | 0-3-2 | 2-10-6 | 11-56-33 |
| Germany | 2-3-1 | 2-3-0 | 5-0-0 | 3-2-1 | 12-8-2 | 55-36-9 |
| France | 1-0-4 | 1-3-1 | 0-1-3 | 0-4-2 | 2-8-10 | 10-40-50 |
| Italy | 0-3-3 | 1-2-1 | 1-2-2 | 2-0-2 | 4-7-8 | 21-37-42 |
| Japan | 0-4-1 | 2-2-0 | 3-2-1 | 2-3-1 | 7-10-3 | 35-50-15 |
| UK | 3-2-1 | 2-1-1 | 4-0-1 | 2-3-1 | 11-6-4 | 52-29-19 |
| TOTAL (%) | 26-54-21 | 35-52-13 | 47-31-22 | 28-49-23 | 33-47-20 | |

*Second*, focusing on the last column of Table 3, a classification of the seven countries into three sub-groups emerges. The UK and Germany are the two countries in which R&D subsidies stimulate private R&D in more than half of the 22 manufacturing industries. For these countries the effect of R&D subsidies is negative for only 10 to 20% of the industries. Then comes the group constituted by the USA and Japan, in which the impact of government R&D is insignificant for about half of the industries and positive in more than 35%. The last group, composed by Canada, Italy, and France, is characterized by a relatively high percentage (30 to 50%) of negative parameters. In the three countries, the number of non significant coefficients is also fairly high (37 to 55%), leaving very few industries (10 to 20%) with a positive impact of R&D subsidies on private R&D. *Third*, different reaction patterns also appear across the four sub-groups of industries, independently of the country of origin. In the medium-tech-high and medium-tech-low industries, R&D subsidies have a stimulating impact in 35 to 47% of the industries, which is above the average of 33% for all industries in all countries. It is worth noting that such generalization is subject to variation across countries. On average, however, one may infer that R&D subsidies are more likely to be efficient in stimulating private R&D when they are directed towards medium-tech industries.

Table 4 aims at further investigating the factors which may influence the response schemes of private R&D investments to R&D subsidies. For each country, it presents correlation coefficients across the 22 industries between the estimated private R&D elasticities of government R&D and either the average R&D subsidization rates or one indicator of R&D subsidization instability. The indicator of instability for each industry is the steady deviation of the R&D subsidization ratio's annual growth rates over the period 1973-90. Table 2 clearly indicates that the estimated impact of government R&D may vary with the empirical specification. In order to test whether these correlations are stable with respect to the specification used, three different models have been estimated. The first one includes only total sales and government R&D in the set of explanatory variables. The second one adds a dynamic structure in the model by incorporating the one year lagged private R&D. The third one corresponds to our prefered specification, which includes the *RTOTH* variable. The correlations across the 22 industries between the private R&D elasticities of R&D subsidies and the average subsidization rates are negative and mainly significant in all countries but the UK and the USA, independently of the specification. In the former countries, it seems that the more an industry is subsidized, the more the impact of R&D subsidies on private R&D is likely to be weak or negative. This tends to support the view that R&D subsidies may be exposed to the law of decreasing returns. For the UK and, to a lesser extent, the USA, the correlation coefficients are positive which means that, in these countries, the more an industry is subsidized, the more R&D subsidies are efficient in stimulating private R&D. The last three columns provide the correlation coefficients between the estimated parameters obtained from the three specifications and the indicator of R&D subsidization instability. The negative and significant correlation coefficients for the USA, Canada, Italy, and the UK give a first indication that the more an industry's R&D subsidization rate is unstable, the less R&D subsidies in this industry are likely to be efficient in promoting private R&D investments. In Germany, Japan, and France the correlation coefficients are positive but not significant, which prevents any policy implications for these countries. The last row presents the correlation coefficients across all industries and all countries. The negative and significant coefficients confirm the idea that, on average, the more an industry is subsidized, the less likely R&D subsidies stimulate private R&D investment. Further, the more a R&D subsidization rate is volatile, the weaker the efficiency of R&D subsidies.

**Table 4. Correlation between the reaction parameters and industry characteristics**

| correlation with : | obs. | RG/RT | | | Steady deviation of $\Delta$(RG / RT) | | |
|---|---|---|---|---|---|---|---|
| | | (1) | (3) | (5) | (1) | (3) | (5) |
| USA | 21 | .440 * | .189 | .126 | -.531 * | -.490 * | -.373 * |
| Canada | 18 | .137 | -.148 | -.437 * | -.506 * | -.485 * | -.335 * |
| Germany | 22 | -.647 * | -.348 * | -.246 | .172 | .043 | .028 |
| France | 20 | -.832 * | -.813 * | -.751 * | .296 | .285 | .245 |
| Italy | 19 | -.258 | -.357 * | -.381 * | -.326 * | -.343 * | -.298 * |
| Japan | 20 | -.690 * | -.560 * | -.847 * | .021 | .032 | .193 |
| UK | 21 | .066 | .399 * | .553 * | -.380 * | -.596 * | -.573 * |
| Total | 141 | -.243 * | -.119 * | -.134 * | -.132 * | -.259 * | -.194 * |

Correlation coefficients between the estimated private R&D elasticities of government R&D and industry specific characteristics across the 22 manufacturing industries. RG/RT is the average R&D subsidization rate, $\Delta$ is the growth rate operator. These indicators are computed over the period 1973-90. (1) specification which includes Q(t) and RG(t) as explanatory variables. (3) The specification includes RP(t-1), Q(t), and RG(t). (5) The specification includes RP(t-1), Q(t), RTOTH(t-1), and RG(t). * the correlation coefficient is significantly different from zero at a 10% probability threshold.

## Summary and Conclusions

The empirical analysis leads to the following methodological and policy implications. *First*, the estimated impact of government R&D on private R&D is sensitive to slight modifications of the empirical model. The discrepancies among the existing estimates are likely to be the consequence of contrasting empirical specifications. More specifically, the inclusion of an adjustment process may modify both the sign and the significance of the parameters of interest. *Second*, at the aggregated industrial level, government R&D has a crowding out effect on private R&D investments in Canada and France, while in the USA and the UK R&D subsidies stimulate private R&D expenditures. No significant relationship is estimated for Italy, Japan, and Germany. However, estimates at the aggregated level should not lead to conclusions generalized for all industries. Estimates across the 22 disaggregated industries confirm this statement. Further, it seems that an aggregation bias may seemingly lead to a misjudgment of the R&D subsidization policy's efficiency measured at the aggregated industry level. This is the case for Germany, where the stimulating impact in more than half of the 22 manufacturing industries does not corroborate the insignificant estimates at the aggregated industrial level. *Third*, the seven countries may be classified into three sub-groups as regard to the relative efficiency of R&D subsidies across the 22 manufacturing industries. The UK and Germany apparently implemented the more efficient R&D subsidization policies which seem to stimulate private R&D in more than half of the industries. Canada, France and Italy are characterized by a weaker effectiveness of R&D subsidies. Japan and the USA stand in an intermediate position, with a majority of non-significant impact of R&D subsidies, but the share of complementary relationships is at least twice larger than the share of substitutive relationships. *Fourth*, the heterogeneity across industries of the estimated response profiles of private R&D investors to subsidies may partly be explained by the law of decreasing returns to R&D subsidies and by the stability of the R&D subsidization policy. The more subsidy-intensive an industry is, the more the impact of government R&D is likely to be weak or negative. Further, the industries which have benefited from unstable subsidization rates are more likely to have substituted government R&D for private R&D. That is, the less volatile a subzidization policy is, the more it is likely to stir up private R&D investments.

## REFERENCES

ARELLANO M. AND BOVER O., (1995), "Another look at the instrumental variable estimation of the error-components models", Journal of Econometrics, 68, pp.29-51.

CAPRON H., (1992), "Economic Quantitative methods for the evaluation of the impact of R&D programmes - A state-of-the-art", Commission of European Communities, Brussels, 241 p.

CARMICHAEL J., (1981), "The Effects of Mission-Oriented Public R&D Spending on Private Industry", Journal of Finance, 36(3), pp. 617-27.

FÖLSTER S., TROFIMOV G., (1996) "Do subsidies to R&D actually stimulate R&D investment?", Mimeo, The Industrial Institute of Economic and Social Research.

HOLEMANS B., SLEUWAEGEN L., (1988), «Innovation Expenditures and the Role of Government in Belgium», Research Policy, Vol. 17, p. 375-379.

LEONARD W., (1971), "Research and Development in industrial growth", Journal of Political Economy, Vol. 79, N°2, pp. 232-256.

LEVIN R. AND REISS P., (1984), "Test of a Schumpeterian model of R&D and market structure ", in Z.Griliches (ed.) "R&D, Patents and Productivity", Chicago, University of Chicago Press, pp.175-208.

LEVY D., (1990), "Estimating the impact of government R&D", Economic Letters, Vol. 32, N°2, pp. 169-173.

LEVY D. AND TERLECKYJ N., (1983), "Effects of government R&D investment and productivity : a macroeconomic analysis", Bell Journal of Economics, Vol. 14, N°4, pp. 551-561.

LEYDEN D.P., LINK A.N., (1987) "Why Are Governmental R&D and Private R&D Complements?", in Applied Economics, vol. 23, n°10, pp.1673-81.

LICHTENBERG F.R., (1984), "The Relationship Between Federal Contract R&D and Company R&D", The American Economic Review, Vol.74, N°2, pp. 73-8.

LICHTENBERG F.R., (1987), "The effect of government funding on private industrial research and development : A re-assessment ", Journal of Industrial Economics, Vol. 36, N°1, pp. 97-104.

NADIRI I., (1980), "Contributions and determinants of Research and development expenditures in the US manufacturing industries", in Von Furstenberg G. (ed.), "Capital, Efficiency and Growth", Ballinger Publishing Company, Cambridge, pp. 361-392.

NICKELL S., (1981), "Biases in dynamic models with fixed effects", Econometrica, Vol. 49, pp. 1417-26.

REISS P., (1990), "Detecting multiple outliers with an application to R&D productivity ", Journal of Econometrics, Vol. 43, N°2, pp. 293-315.

SCHANKERMAN M., (1981), "The effects of double counting and expensing on the measured returns to R&D", Review of Economics and Statistics, Vol. 63, N°3, pp. 454-458.

SWITZER L., (1984), "The Determinants of Industrial R&D : A Funds Flow Simultaneous Equation Approach", The Review of Economics and Statistics, Vol.66, N°1, pp.163-6.

TERLECKYJ N., (1974), "Effects of R&D on the productivity growth of industries : and exploratory study", National Planning Association, Washington.

TERLECKYJ N. (1980), "Direct and indirect effects of industrial research and development on the productivity growth of industries", in J.Kendrick and Vaccara (eds), "New developments in productivity measurement and analysis", University of Chicago Press, Chicago, pp.359-385.

# 062

# Uncertainty and Indeterminacy in Emerging Markets

(Paper intended for an oral presentation at IAMOT's 1997 Conference, Göteborg, Sweden)

Key words: uncertainty, indeterminacy, hyperselection, emerging markets

F. Xavier Olleros

Associate Professor of Innovation and Technology Management

Université du Québec

Case postale 6192, succursale Centre-ville

Montréal (Québec) Canada

H3C 4R2

Tel. (514) 842-1912

Fax: (514) 987-3343

olleros.xavier@uqam.ca

# UNCERTAINTY AND INDETERMINACY IN EMERGING MARKETS
## F. Xavier Olleros

## Introduction

The conventional model of industrial competition is strictly linear and meritocratic. According to this model, the market's acceptance of a new technology depends simply upon that particular technology's merits, relative to those of competing technologies. Once those merits are identified and contrasted with the needs of potential users, the twin forces of supply and demand will lead to a distribution of market shares roughly proportional to the ranking of merits. Whether the market ends up monopolized by one technology or shared by several alternatives, the outcome is presumed to be optimal under the circumstances. The market's screening of winners and losers is thus seen as a process of "natural selection" which, as such, transcends the small accidents of history and, at least in principle, is fairly predictable.

Despite its simplistic assumptions, this model has proven to be enormously influential, both as a pedagogical artifact and as a research template. Indeed, modifying it minimally to make room for the incumbency advantages of well-established technologies and for any instance of serious mismanagement by any of the firms advocating the various technical options, we are left with a close representation of a real competitive setting, namely, the competition often taking place between *compatible* variations of the same technological regime in a *mature* market. Thus, the current contest between, say, Toyota, Ford, Honda, Chevrolet and Nissan in the North American mid-sized automobile market is a good example of the sort of competition faithfully captured by the conventional model.

This model, however, is totally inadequate when it comes to describing and explaining a type of market contest which is increasingly observed today, that is, the contest often taking place between several *incompatible* technologies vying for the same *emerging* market. As Brian Arthur and other economists have shown, in this kind of context, markets tend to become very unstable and hyperselective, as several mechanisms – notably, scale economies, learning effects, reputation effects and network externalities – combine to turn superior market share into a decisive, self-reinforcing and irreversible source of competitive advantage. Driven by this self-reinforcing dynamic, the market will tend to discriminate sharply between winners and losers, often on the basis of minimal, perhaps almost random, differences among the various offers. The meritocratic paradigm is thus turned on its head: dominant technologies are not chosen by the market because they are superior; rather, they are *made superior* by the fact that they have been chosen. And often they are chosen simply because they arrived in the market first, or because the reputation and/or deep pockets of their sponsors carried the day in the race to market dominance that ensued. The typical result of this sort of situation is altogether foreseeable: very aggressive battles for market share, with very high stakes and very slanted and unpredictable outcomes.

In the present article I do not intend to survey in any detail this, by now, well-trodden terrain (for recent attempts at doing so, see Olleros, 1995 and Arthur, 1996). Instead, I would like to dwell on the implications that market instability and hyperselection have for the management of risk in innovative ventures.

The literature on the management of risk in innovation seems solely concerned with one source of risk, namely, uncertainty. The main purpose of this paper is to show that in emerging markets, besides *uncertainty* (that is, ignorance in the face of a future outcome that one *cannot* influence), there is *indeterminacy* (that is, ignorance in the face of a future outcome that one *can* influence). As we shall see, the latter is generally much harder to manage than the former. A second purpose of the paper is to highlight the fragility of most emerging markets and the fact that, in those markets, prior to the risk of losing the race to market dominance, there is another risk which the literature on hyperselection has so far neglected, namely, that of letting a still embryonic market sink into a low-growth trap from which it may never come out.

In terms of possible implications, our analysis will underline the drawbacks and limitations of the conventional model of risk management in a world in which more and more firms try to profit from the hyperselective dynamics of the market in order to impose, by dint of massive preemptive investments, the technical options which favor them the most, and this not only to the detriment of their direct rivals, but often of their own clients as well.

## Meritocratic Markets and "Natural Selection"

*Whether a given technology is a winner or a loser is immaterial: if the former, it doesn't need a subsidy; if the latter, it doesn't deserve one* (The Globe and Mail, 1993).

This phrase captures well the basic thinking that dominates economic discourse in most Western countries today: the "natural selection" of technologies and firms by an efficient market (Alchian, 1950; Friedman, 1953; Demsetz, 1973; Bork, 1993). Derived from a simplistic brand of economic Darwinism, this model spouses a strictly meritocratic view of the market - sooner or later, the market rewards every technology or firm in proportion to its merits. Consequently, it would be myopic and inefficient to want to interfere with the market selection process.

Clearly, in a strictly meritocratic market, competitive dynamics would be strongly deterministic, weakly historical and relatively easy to foresee (David, 1985; Arthur, 1990). Superior technologies being destined to succeed, the innovation contest would have the simple structure of a "treasure hunt" (Olleros, 1991). A treasure hunt, however, without end or respite, for no technology - regardless of its success - would be protected from obsolescence, once a superior alternative emerged. For all practical purposes, the game of new technology commercialization would be played strictly and constantly at the patent office. Beyond the obtaining of a suitable patent, success or failure would be fairly inevitable. In particular, only gross mismanagement, or terribly bad luck could possibly hinder the commercial success of a superior new technology.

The meritocratic model has a simple elegance and an optimistic bent. Is it a faithful reflection of commercial reality? Rarely, we must say. This model does make some room for uncertainty, but almost none for indivisibilities and other inertial forces. Above all, it completely ignores the self-reinforcing mechanisms that drive the emergence of new technologies, and thus neglects a crucial source of indeterminacy in market dynamics. The meritocratic model depicts a world of decreasing returns and unique, inevitable equilibria. Many mature markets approximate that deterministic archetype. Emerging markets, on the other hand, are subject to increasing-return dynamics/processes which open them to a multiplicity of possible equilibria (Arthur, 1990; Krugman, 1991 and 1994). In the real world, it can often be said of a specific new technology that it is destined to fail, but rarely can it be said of a specific new technology that it is destined to succeed.[1]

## Hyperselective Markets and Strategic Selection

*A technology is not chosen because it is the most effective; rather, it becomes the most effective because it has been chosen* (Foray, 1989, p.16).

This lapidary phrase by Dominique Foray shows to what extent the conventional economic logic must be revised, as a result of Brian Arthur's work on the competitive dynamics of emerging markets (Arthur, 1984, 1989, 1990, 1993 and 1996). Arthur and others (David, 1985; Foray, 1989, 1991; Cowan, 1991) have shown that, all along the stages of market emergence and growth, the diffusion of a new technology is subject to self-reinforcing mechanisms. Technology-specific scale economies, learning effects, reputation effects and/or network externalities are tightly connected to the technology's diffusion rate by positive feedback loops which render the diffusion process self-reinforcing. Consequently, regardless of a new technology's relative merit and potential, its diffusion will always be subject to a sort of *snowball effect*. Arriving at a critical diffusion threshold (the hill's summit, so to speak) is increasingly difficult (we must push a heavy ball up the slope, with the force of gravity working against us), but beyond that threshold, the diffusion process will become increasingly easy. If one, or several, of the self-reinforcing mechanisms affecting a new technology's diffusion is very strong, this snowball effect will itself be very pronounced (the hill will be very steep on all sides). Two successive risks will result: firstly, the risk of failing to trigger the emergence of the market, and later, the risk of being displaced from a hyperselective market in full growth.

### a) The risk of an aborted market emergence

As I just indicated, there are two sides to a snowball effect. Generally, we have a tendency to emphasize the happy side: the accelerating growth of demand, once the critical diffusion threshold has been reached. Unfortunately, in order to get there, we must first "climb the slope, as we carry an increasingly heavy burden". In other words, in order to reach the crucial threshold, *we must be ready to subsidize the emerging technology in a sustained manner*. It won't suffice to invest heavily in production capacity and in marketing. It will also be necessary to maintain an aggressive policy with regard to innovation and pricing, for besides being expensive, a radically new technology also tends to be little reliable and difficult to use. Moreover, if the new technology also happens to highly systemic, two additional problems must be dealt with. First, the slow initial diffusion of the core technology will hinder the emergence of a suitable infrastructure of complementary technologies *and viceversa* (e.g., why buy an automobile if there are no suitable roads, *and* why build highways when so few people yet have

---

[1] The specificity of the technology is important for our argument. Sooner or later, the automobile and the computer were destined to succeed. The same cannot be said, however, of the gasoline powered engine or of the MS-DOS operating system. Needless to say, it is at this level of specific choices that the game is really played and that fortunes are made and lost.

automobiles?). A vicious circle could easily develop and lead to a deadlock, as every concerned party awaits "a signal from the market" indicating that the impasse is finally about to be resolved. Secondly, to the extend that the new technological system is subject to strong network externalities, the compatibility between the various components of the system - be they hardware, software or tacit knowledge and skills - becomes primordial. Alas, as a new technology emerges, several incompatible versions often compete for the same market. This multiplicity of incompatible alternatives in a contest that can only accommodate a big winner - a dominant standard - can also contribute to the impasse. Faced with the risk of choosing one of the losing options, many of the prospective users of the new technology will instead decide to postpone their purchase. The logic is impeccable: why buy today if in a few months, aside from being more powerful, more reliable, more user-friendly and less expensive, the new technology is likely to have become standardized, thus eliminating our risk of choosing a losing option?[2]

In the context of our discussion, it is important to underline the crucial role played by collective perceptions and expectations in the emergence of new markets. In effect, as described in more detail elsewhere (Miller and Olleros, 1993), the emergence of a new market is essentially a socially constructed, indeterminate process. Even if a technology's long-term future proves to be golden, its emergence is *always* precarious and fragile. It will be particularly so if all the major players involved in the emergence process (entrepreneurs, venture capitalists, regulators,..) happen to espouse a strictly meritocratic view of innovation. In this case, they may all misinterpret the negative signals they could be getting from a market still embryonic: instead of understanding that they need to do more, do better and, perhaps, do together, they might conclude that, despite their dreams and their best efforts, the market is simply not there, at least ·ot as yet. Of course, an aborted market emergence will only serve to corroborate their worst fears.

#### b) The risk of losing the sprint to market dominance

*In a growing market, a business cannot stand still: it must grow in order to survive. Owing to increasing returns(...) success breeds further success and failure begets more failure* (Kaldor, 1981, p.596)

We have just described how a strong *snowball effect* can seriously hinder, or at least delay, a new market's take-off. This would be bad enough for the firms committed to the development of the new market, but it might not be the end of their troubles. The very same set of self-reinforcing feedback loops that can deadlock the emergence of a promising new market, will also tend to render that same market very unstable and hyperselective, once the take-off does arrive. As a consequence, even if in terms of inherent merit and long-term potential the differences between the various technical options vying for the new market were unknown or negligible, the market could still force the emergence of one or two dominant standards and the marginalization of all the other alternatives. If so, the contest at hand would no longer be a simple "treasure hunt" where *intelligence* (in the largest sense of the word) and *chance* are likely to be decisive. Instead, the innovation contest would have turned into a "sprint" to market

---

[2] In an industrial market, where many prospective buyers are competing against each other, this argument for postponing the purchase of a new technology becomes self-reinforcing. The more firms accept it, the more it will appeal to their rivals, and the more difficult the market takeoff will become.

dominance, where *speed* and *boldness* in the establishment of a suitable production and marketing network would be primordial. Thus, in a strongly hyperselective market, a theoretically suboptimal technology, if it is developed and commercialized by an aggressive and well reputed firm, could well obtain a dominant, durable and very profitable market position against rival technologies which, while being more promising, have been managed with meager means or in a more timid fashion.

### Theoretical and Strategic Implications of Hyperselection

#### a) Beyond uncertainty

> *Divide uncertainty into two kinds: chance and choice. How the dice will roll is a very different question from what another player may do if he has a strategic choice (Mcdonald, 1975, p.xxiii).*

In emerging markets, as in many parlor games, strategic interaction is rooted in more than just the simple interdependence of rewards. The very choices of our opponents - indeed, even their bluffs and signals - will influence our own choices and viceversa. Moreover, competition in emerging markets is not a simple zero-sum game. Rivals must cooperate in building up the market and insuring its timely takeoff, lest there be no market to compete for (Brandenburger and Nalebuff, 1995). This makes the business game a lot more intricate and challenging than, say, playing *Battleship*, let alone *Roulette*. It takes us into a realm which is not simply uncertain, but rather indeterminate.

Even though we generally speak loosely about uncertain events, environments or processes, uncertainty is strictly an epistemological attribute or state. It inheres in the observer, rather than in the action observed. It is simply another word for ignorance and, as such, it has a simple solution: information. More and better information allows us to move from a state of greater or lesser uncertainty to one of certainty. Indeterminacy, on the other hand, is an ontological attribute or state. Environments, events and processes cannot, in themselves, be uncertain but they can be indeterminate, that is, open to several different outcomes (*multiple equilibria*, in the economist's jargon), depending upon how history unfolds. Their results, in other words, may be strictly contingent and unpredictable. Needless to say, indeterminacy is the very stuff of life: it is deep within us and all around us (Waldrop, 1992). As we hope to have shown in the foregoing, it also is the stuff of business competition, particularly in emerging markets[3].

Even in a purely meritocratic market there will always be, of course, considerable elements of indeterminacy. Human errors and the irreversibility of major commitments will certainly conspire in that direction. But, in as much as we can expect a certain proportionality between technical merits and market rewards, the latter are traceable to the former and the market selection process is strongly deterministic. Barring major mistakes or disasters, the initial conditions of the selection process ( the merits of the various technical options and the resource

---

[3] Mystified by uncertainty, however, most business theoreticians have neglected indeterminacy altogether or, as John Mcdonald does in the above quotation, have mistaken it for just another type of uncertainty. Still others (cf. Belland and Bhardwaj, 1996) use the terms *uncertainty* and *indeterminacy* indistinctively.

endowments of the competing firms) contain the seeds of the final result. History then becomes the unfolding of the inevitable and, as such, eminently predictable.[4] There is nothing predictable about most emerging markets. Since early commercial success tends to be a strongly self-reinforcing process, industry emergence is not simply indeterminate at the margin. Rather, it tends to be a highly unstable, wide open process, with a bias for extreme outcomes: either sustained success or abject failure.

### b) Strategic indeterminacy in embryonic markets

In business, as in any other competitive context, it is vital to grasp well the nature and rules of the contest at hand. In particular, it is important to be able to tell whether we face an uncertain or an indeterminate scenario. The strategic implications of the one and the other could not be more different. Generally speaking, an uncertain scenario puts a premium on superior information and cautious flexibility, whereas an indeterminate scenario puts a premium on bold moves and deep pockets.

There are two "golden rules" to managing uncertainty in innovation projects. The first one says: *try to eliminate - or at least reduce - uncertainty by gathering as much pertinent information about the target market as you can.* The second rule adds: *while you go about in gathering information and until you manage to bring uncertainty - and therefore risk[5] - down to a reasonable level, be cautious, don't focus your commitments prematurely, stay flexible, hedge your bets.* These rules are undoubtedly the ones to follow at a very early stage in any innovation project. They are also likely to be adequate for the commercialization of new *meritocratic products*: simple, self-contained, easy to appraise, easy to use products with a strong patent protection (think of the proverbial improved mousetrap or, for that matter, the improved pharmaceutical drug). But such rules - and the incremental mindset which they embody - are bound to be useless and even dangerous when it comes to the commercialization of a highly complex, systemic and radically new technology. The stronger the self-reinforcing mechanisms affecting the success of such a technology, the more barren and counterproductive this cautious approach will prove to be.

Proponents of this approach to innovation seem to assume that, in trying to successfully commercialize a new technology, all they face is an information problem. Often, they furthermore assume that the information needed is already out in the market, though perhaps hidden from the view of ordinary mortals. They are generally wrong on both counts. Difficult, expensive and time consuming as understanding the basic characteristics of a new market can be, the toughest problems concerning the development and commercialization of a new technology often lie elsewhere. Given the self-reinforcing mechanisms inhibiting its emergence, a new market will rarely materialize by a smooth and gentle process. Rather, it will have to be persuaded, prodded and force-fed into life. Indeed, as hinted in our discussion of the risk of an aborted emergence, the basic challenges facing the advocates of a new market typically are that

---

[4] In this kind of scenario we may still lack the information necessary to correctly predict the market outcome, but it is important to emphasize that such an incapacity would only reflect our ignorance of the selection process, rather than its inherent unpredictability.

[5] We here use the term *risk* not in the economist's sense - i.e., weak, measurable uncertainty - but rather in the risk analyst's sense - i.e., the probability of project failure, multiplied by the investment sunk in the project.

of maintaining a *committed vision* in the face of often disappointing commercial results and that of insuring a minimum of *inter-firm coordination* to allow the market a chance to take off.

Clearly, the capacity to see beyond the obvious and to push ahead in spite of a market's sometimes repeated rejections, is crucial for anyone trying to commercialize a complex, highly systemic and radically new technology. In addition to taking the technology to a level of performance where it stands a chance of succeeding, the innovators will generally have to carry out a very aggressive marketing campaign - plenty of information, user training and free trials; generous guarantees; a reassuring after-sales service and very low prices. Without that, the immense majority of potential users, no matter how intrigued by the new technology, may decide that they have nothing to lose and much to gain from postponing their purchases. Furthermore, without a minimum of rapid market success, some complementary technologies which would be crucially needed for a solid market takeoff - whether they be ancillary hardware and software or general infrastructure - may never materialize, thus further sealing the fate of the fledgling technology.

Needless to say, triggering the takeoff of such a market will generally require more than just a visionary entrepreneur with considerable financial support. A shared vision and a coherent effort involving many different firms - and perhaps also government bodies - will often be necessary. Without this kind of collective commitment, the market can easily sink into a low-standardization, low- infrastructure, low-diffusion trap and stay there. In sum, a smooth and timely industry emergence is not the natural and almost inevitable result of a new technology's innate vigor and fertility, but rather the indeterminate, contingent achievement of a set of closely interdependent economic agents who, against heavy odds, succeed in "getting their act together".[6]

### c) Strategic indeterminacy in growing markets

One could perhaps get away with a prudent, wait-and-see attitude in an embryonic market populated by bold rivals bent on laying the industry's groundwork without our help[7]. But once the sluggish stage is over and the market gears up to a takeoff, a cautious approach to market development surely is the way to lose.

Hyperselective mechanisms discriminate sharply between winners and losers in two different ways. Firstly, by raising the ante for those firms wanting to participate in the market contest. And secondly, by polarizing market outcomes, so that what could have been a standard, low-risk competition for market space becomes a vigorous battle for dominance and survival. Clearly, to the extent that the market's takeoff is bound to be hyperselective and to the extent that our rivals know this and are determined to compete for market dominance, our choices are stark: either to engage them in a high-stake contest with very few winners, or to quit the market as soon and as gracefully as possible.

---

[6] For an interesting contrast of two contemporaneous and fairly comparable technologies, one of which scored a great success while the other never made it to the market, consider the introduction of the French Minitel and the Canadian Telidon systems of videotex, back in the 1980s. From a technical point of view, Telidon was superior to Minitel. Why did Minitel succeed where Telidon failed? Essentially, because the French stormed the market with a stubborn boldness that their Canadian counterparts never dared to approach (Olleros, Favard and Williams, 1997).

[7] Even at such an early stage, however, an overcautious approach could cost us dearly, were our rivals to succeed in developing highly effective and strongly proprietary technologies, thereby foreclosing our later entry into the fray.

## Conclusion: In Praise of Boldness?

*The best way to predict the future, technologists say, is to create it yourself*
(Ramo, 1997, p.44)

We shall never know how many worthy technologies have been robbed of their place in the market by the misguided efforts of their advocates and promoters. In this paper we have emphasized the fact that it doesn't take big blunders to spoil the commercial prospects of a new technology, whether still embryonic or already spreading through the market. In particular, we have argued that in both an embryonic market that, despite its potential, refuses to take off and in a rapidly hyperselective market (perhaps the very same market, at a later stage), a cautious, halfhearted commercialization effort can severely curtail the survival chances of a promising new technology.

Does this mean that a company which has developed a worthy new technology should, as a matter of principle, barge ahead with it and - alone or with others - try to make it a winner by dint of massive preemptive investments? It would be nice if the emerging-market game were that simple. But consider what could go wrong with a "big bully" approach to competition in emerging markets.

First of all, there is the risk of misreading the nature of the contest at hand. What might look to us like a highly indeterminate contest which we can influence in our favor, might prove to be instead a strongly meritocratic one where choosing *the* right technology matters most. Hyperselective forces, after all, can only allow a suboptimal technology to survive and thrive when alternative options are only slightly superior, or else grossly mismanaged. What if one of our rivals' technical choice happens to be far more powerful than we had surmised, or if our own technology only shows some important weakness well after its commercial launch but before it has had a chance to earn us a decent return, let alone become solidly entrenched?[8]

Furthermore, even if the stage is clearly set for a race to market dominance - that is, for a contest between comparable technologies where, due to strong hyperselective mechanisms, the big prize will surely go to the boldest and best managed effort - such a contest entails some daunting risks of its own. A firm trying to decide whether or not to boldly venture into a growing but hyperselective market would, in this case, have little to fear from superior technologies in rival hands, but much to fear from misjudging the identity, resourcefulness or determination of any of its future rivals. "Who are likely to be our rivals in this market? Might they be too strong

---

[8] There are countless examples of firms that decided to plunge ahead with the commercialization of a new technology only to find out later that they had bet on a product that could not be saved from its shortcomings. The fiascoes of the germanium-based transistor (Olleros, 1986) and the light-emitting-diode electronic watch (Business Week, 1980) are particularly good illustrations of this problem.

and aggressive for us? Indeed, might they be too aggressive and stubborn for *anyone* to make money in this market?"[9] These are the basic imponderables that must be addressed.

Notice that we have used the word *imponderables* advisedly. Unlike a situation of strict uncertainty, where further research may yield information capable of reducing our ignorance, a scenario of strategic indeterminacy, such as the one here described, is inherently unpredictable. After all, our rivals' plans cannot yet be crystallized and definitive, since they are bound to be a function of our own intentions and moves. More generally, no research could possibly unearth precise information about an indeterminate process before the process runs its course.

Moreover, there may be cases where the indeterminacy and unpredictability affect not only the moves of the various players but also the very nature of the contest at hand. Indeed, if there is a moderately superior technical option *and* moderate self-reinforcing mechanisms at work, whether the contest shall turn out to be a meritocratic hunt for the best technology or an aggressive race to market dominance will depend strictly on how the various players choose to conduct themselves as the market emerges. In such a case, in fact, we can expect one of two things to happen. If *all the contenders* believe that the contest at hand is essentially meritocratic and, consequently, they all choose to be prudent and to withhold any major commitment until the superior new technology has been identified, then the contest will remain a pure search and the superior technology will indeed end up dominating the market. But if *one contender* (one would suffice) believes that the contest is likely to turn into a hyperselective race to market dominance and, consequently, chooses to bet heavily on the commercialization of one of the suboptimal options, the contest might in fact become a race to market dominance and the aggressive player might indeed succeed in imposing its technical choice upon the market.

As can be seen from the foregoing, there are no easy recipes for managing risk in a hyperselective environment. There is, however, a rule of thumb which has a fairly universal applicability in emerging markets, namely, "don't try to play the lone ranger, team up, share your treasure, open yourself generously to partnerships and alliances". In recent years, in fact, the practical understanding of hyperselective dynamics has gone hand in hand with an ever-growing recourse to strategic alliances, and this for good reasons. If timidity has robbed many technologies of a fair chance to succeed, so has shortsighted greed. In a revised version of this paper, I shall give more prominence to the need to combine a penchant for coalition building with raw boldness in order to stand a chance of succeeding in most emerging markets.

---

[9] Hyperselective markets - particularly if their entry barriers are low and their self-reinforcing mechanisms are weak - can easily turn into *hypercompetitive markets*, where no one quite achieves dominance, no one gives up the fight easily and no one makes a decent return on investment.

408

# REFERENCES

Alchian, Armen A., 1950, «Uncertainty, Evolution and Economic Theory», Journal of Political Economy, vol. 58, June, pp. 211-222.

Arthur, W. Brian, 1996, «Increasing Returns and the New World of Business», Harvard Business Review, July-August, pp. 100-109.

Arthur, W. Brian, 1993, «Pandora's Marketplace», New Scientist, Supplement, February 6, pp. 6-8.

Arthur, W. Brian, 1990, «Positive Feedbacks in the Economy», Scientific American, February, pp. 92-99.

Arthur, W. Brian, 1989, «Competing Technologies, Increasing Returns and Lock-In by Historical Events», The Economic Journal, vol. 99, mars, pp. 116-131.

Arthur, W. Brian, 1984, «Competing Technologies and Economic Prediction», Options, April, pp. 10-13.

Belland, Roger and Vinay Bhardwaj, «Uncertain Economists: Futurity in Strategic Decisions», Canadian Business Economics, Spring 1996, pp. 18-32.

Bork, Robert H., 1993, The Antitrust Paradox, New York : Free Press.

Brandenburger, Adam and Barry Nalebuff, 1995, «The Right Game: Use Game Theory to Shape Strategy», Harvard Business Review, July-August, pp. 57-71.

Business Week, «Japanese Heat on the Watch Industry», May 5, 1980, pp. 92-96.

Cowan, Robin, 1991, «Technological Variety and Competition : Issues of Diffusion and Intervention», in OECD, Technology and Productivity, Paris, pp. 509-521.

David, Paul, 1985, «Clio and the Economics of QWERTY», American Economic Review, vol. 75, May, pp. 332-337.

Demsetz, Harold, 1973, «Industry Structure, Market Rivalry and Public Policy», Journal of Law and Economics, vol. 16, pp. 1-10.

Foray, Dominique, 1989, «Les modèles de compétition technologique : une revue de littérature», Revue d'économie industrielle, vol. 48, pp. 16-34.

Foray, Dominique, 1991, «Dynamique économique et nouvelles exigences de l'investigation historique», Revue économique, vol. 42, no 2, pp. 301-311.

Friedman, Milton, 1953, «The Methodology of Positive Economics», in Essays in Positive Economics, Chicago: University of Chicago Press.

Kaldor, Nicholas, 1981, «The Role of Increasing Returns, Technical Progress and Cumulative Causation in the Theory of International Trade and Economic Growth», Économie Appliquée, vol. 4, pp. 593-617.

Krugman, Paul, 1994, «Complex Landscapes in Economic Geography», American Economic Review, vol. 84, n. 2, May, pp. 412-416.

Krugman, Paul, 1991, «History versus Expectations», Quarterly Journal of Economics, May, pp. 651-667.

Mcdonald, John, 1975, The Game of Business, Garden City, New York: Doubleday.

Miller, Roger and F. Xavier Olleros, 1993, «Efficient Oligopoly : the Case of Flight Simulation», Advances in Competitiveness Research, vol. 1, n. 1, pp. 119-142.

Olleros, F. Xavier, 1995, «Battles for Market Share in Hyperselective Markets», in Jagdish Sheth, ed. Research in Marketing, Vol. 12, Greenwich, Conn.: JAI Press, pp. 181-218.

Olleros, F. Xavier, 1991, «The Innovation Process : Manageable or Unmanageable ? A Survey of the Literature», Chaire Hydro-Québec en gestion de la technologie (UQAM), October.

Olleros, F. Xavier, 1986, «Emerging Industries and the Burnout of Pioneers», Journal of Product Innovation Management, vol. 3, no 1, mars, pp. 5-18.

Olleros, F. Xavier, Laurent Favard and David Williams, 1997, «The Prehistory of the Internet in Canada», in process.

Ramo, Joshua C., 1997, Welcome to the Wired World», Time, February 3, pp.42-51.

The Globe and Mail, «Voodoo, All Over Again», editorial, March 7,1993.

Waldrop, Mitchel, 1992, Complexity: The Emerging Science at the Edge of Science and Chaos, New York: Simon and Shuster/Viking.

# 063

## TECHNOLOGY-RELATED DEGREE PROGRAM INITIATIVES
## AT MARSHALL UNIVERSITY

James W. Hooper, Anthony B. Szwilski, Richard D. Begley
Marshall University
Huntington, WV 25755 USA

**ABSTRACT**

Marshall University is a state-supported university located in Huntington, West Virginia, USA. It serves a region in which many technology-based companies and agencies operate. Marshall has extensive interaction with business, industry, and government leaders in the region, resulting in the identification of four recurring technology-oriented thrusts, with accompanying educational needs. The thrusts identified are environmental management, manufacturing systems, information technology, and biotechnology.

Regional leaders have participated with faculty and university administrators in planning degree programs to meet the educational needs. Within the past year Marshall University has received approval from the University System Board of Trustees to offer three new technology-related degree programs that respond to the identified needs. They are an M.S. degree in Technology Management, a B.S. degree in Integrated Science and Technology, and a B.S. degree in Environmental Science. This paper provides an overview of the new degree programs and their status, as well as the planning process and the beneficial working relationship between Marshall and regional technology-oriented organizations.

# 066

"Dancing with Giants"

- Collaboration for Technological Change in the 21st Century

Richard K. Smith, CPROST

Akihiro Takanashi, HITACHI

Mohi U. Ahmed, SFU

## Abstract

*Technological innovation is now widely acknowledged as a key element in firm success, but in the competitive global marketplace of the late twentieth century, the circumstances for technological innovation have changed. In this paper we consider the combined impact of two trends that have changed the character of innovative activities. We note a shift from introspective and proprietary solutions to externally focused, "open" collaborations, frequently with firms of much different size and culture. This paper uses the metaphor of "dancing" to highlight insights into technological collaboration between dissimilar-sized partners. These insights are based on case studies involving Canadian and Japanese firms and their partners. The paper concludes with examples of measures organizations can take to prepare themselves for collaboration. We call this preparation "dance lessons."*

## 1. INTRODUCTION

As we head toward the 21st century, collaboration for technological change has emerged as an important issue in the field of technology management [1-5]. The initiation, formulation, and diffusion of advanced technology depends on complex interactions between individuals and groups of people in science-based and research organizations, firms acting as vendors, customers, partners and competitors, and the changing demands of governments and individuals as customers and regulators. These "systems of innovation" [5, 6] represent a web of connections between firms, educational institutions, government programs and policies, and sources of capital. When these connections are formalized in order to develop new products and technologies and access new capabilities these linkages are defined as technological collaboration, according to Dodgson [3].

The importance of collaboration has grown as managers look for the skills to support a growing number of strategic alliances, partnerships, cooperative agreements, mergers and acquisitions, strategic networks, and joint ventures. In the next section we argue that technological collaboration is particularly important for building and maintaining core-competencies that enhance the global competitiveness and the environmental, social and cultural sustainability of firms. We suggest that there is a special the role for smaller firms in this process but that collaboration between large and small entities carries with it considerable difficulties. This paper uses the metaphor of "dancing" to focus our insights into technological collaboration between dissimilar-sized partners. These insights are based on case studies involving Canadian and Japanese firms and their partners. The paper concludes with examples of measures organizations can take to prepare themselves for collaboration. We call this preparation "dance lessons."

## 2. GLOBALIZATION AND SUSTAINABILITY: DRIVERS OF TECHNOLOGICAL COLLABORATION

In this section we look at the impact of global competition and environmental sustainability as drivers of technological collaboration. We also point out that these two drivers carry with them paradoxical demands on large multinational firms and that this paradox may in part account for the growth in collaboration with smaller enterprises.

### Globalization and competition

One of the most important drivers of technological collaboration is the global economy. In her 1989 book "When Giants Learn to Dance," Rosabeth Moss Kanter noted that:

"the global economy in which American businesses now operate is like a corporate olympics -- a series of games played all over the world with international as well as domestic competitors. The Olympic contests determine not just which business team wins but which nation wins overall. The metaphor reminds us that the competition is governed by rules...a team's members may compete as individuals in some contests but compete as a team in others. Collaboration thus plays a role[7]."

In a more recent book, Kanter emphasizes that "success in the global economy derives not just from meeting high standards for competition in world contests, but also from strong relationships -- networks that link to global market and networks that build collective local strength. In the future, firms that flourish will be 'best partners' to their customers, suppliers, employees, and allies in joint ventures [8]."

Several other sources point to the role of globalization as a factor in the growth of collaboration. John Hagedoorn's research indicates that in the late 1980s strategic technology partnering became common in a large number of sectors of industry and fields of technology, where its growth led to tighter networks of cooperation [9] . As pointed out by Bleeke and Ernst, of McKinsey & Co., many leading companies use these alliances as a part of a wider competitive strategy [1]. Collaboration allows a firm to draw on resources it otherwise could not deploy without diluting its attention to core businesses and technologies. This enables a firm to participate in markets and develop technology around the world and yet retain mastery of core competencies.

Hitachi is a good example of the breadth and scope of technological collaboration in multinational firms today. Hitachi is a large Japanese firm with a diverse set of products ranging from consumer electronics to heavy equipment. The company has considerable experience with the process of technological collaboration, particularly in South-east Asia. Singapore is one of the countries in which they have been most active. Hitachi classifies its technological collaboration with Singapore into four types: A) Support and promotion of present Japanese business; B) Responding to Asian needs through innovation; C) Development of environment friendly activities; and D) Common, basic technologies. Hitachi is currently making considerable efforts to localize their manufacturing systems through technology transfer and joint technology development activities to increase productivity and competitiveness. They also collaborate with local experts to enhance knowledge about local and regional markets; undertake local research and development for environment-friendly activities with long-term prospects; making efforts

413

in technology transfer, development, and research of common and basic technologies to local subsidiaries and other partner firms.

*Sustainability and core competencies*

Since the 1992 Earth Summit in Rio de Janeiro, Brazil, sustainable development has become a common theme for activities in industry, government and academia all over the globe. Sustainable development is defined in different ways by different sectors, but a common goal is to "retain development in harmony with local and international ecological, economical and social imperatives". In the A/E/C (architecture/engineering/construction) industry, for example, more than 700 industry, government, and academic leaders from worldwide gathered in Washington, D.C. in February 1996 to develop an international collaborative research agenda for sustainable development [10].

Many would argue that sustainable development is impossible to achieve without continuous innovation [11]. One part of the solution is the use of "clean technologies" that fundamentally alter current pollution and resource consumption patterns [12]. To achieve truly sustainable development, firms must link their efforts to remain competitive and survive in a technically complex global economic situation with the environmental, social and cultural implications of these actions.

To keep development in harmony with local and international ecological, economical and social imperatives, firms must acquire an extremely diverse set of skills. In fact, it seems unlikely a single firm could develop and deploy those skills and technologies effectively. This focus on diversity and breadth of skills runs counter to current thinking on managing "core competencies." [13]

*Two trends and a paradox*

It would appear that the growing importance of collaboration may be in part due to these two trends of globalization and environmental sustainability. First, global competition, and rapid advances in basic science has caused firms to focus on their *depth* by building and maintaining core-competencies [14]. Second, the demand for greater environmental, social, and cultural sustainability, issues that require multidisciplinary and multistakeholder responses, has caused firms to look for unprecedented *breadth* of capabilities [15, 16].

The confluence of these two trends brings with it a potential paradox for firms. Pressures for both innovative (building on core competencies) and integrated (with a broad scope) solutions means pressure in two directions. We suggest here that firms look at collaboration for technological innovation and in particular collaboration with smaller firms, as a solution to this paradox [17]. Kodama has suggested that if it is necessary to tap into the core competencies of a variety of firms across many industries in different countries, this can be done by forming global partnerships [18]. To effectively manage core competencies and still achieve sustainability, firms may need to collaborate. As we note above, this may be a viable solution when faced with both competitive and sustainability challenges.

But how should firms prepare for collaboration, how should they select the right partner, how can they build trust, negotiate, manage risk, and share the benefits? In other words, how can firms collaborate for core competence and sustainability, and at the same time manage the communication in order to make the collaboration itself sustainable? These topics remain largely unexplored in the literature. The problems are particularly acute, we will argue, when the one of the partners is much smaller than the other.

*Collaboration with small firms*

Technological innovation has not just taken on a global flavor. Recent research on the role of small firms in the innovation process suggests that collaboration among dissimilar size firms brings numerous advantages to both parties. An OECD study on technology and competitiveness of small-to-medium sized enterprises shows several variables that seem best able to explain the competitiveness of SMEs, including the ability to obtain and use appropriate scientific and technological information, tangible investment in appropriate technologies and flexibility [19].

Complementary assets in technology or marketing, while attractive in principle, may be difficult to access if collaboration skills are not well developed. Smaller firms frequently cannot afford the overhead costs of collaboration, such as extensive travel, working in other languages . Large firms, which may have highly developed skills for managing peer-to-peer relationships and have technologies that a small firm might be able to use, can be at a loss when managing collaboration with a small or medium sized firm. Even though in the long-run such collaboration may contribute in building core competence and sustainability for dissimilar sized firms, cultural and capability differences may stand in the way. In this paper the major focus is on collaboration between dissimilar sized firms.

The next section provides summaries of two case studies of technological collaboration between organizations of different sizes in which a central feature of the collaboration was to gain access to skills which would enhance competitive advantage in a globally competitive world or create a more sustainable product or process.

## 3. TECHNOLOGICAL COLLABORATION: CASE STUDIES

In this part, two case summaries are provided. Both are focused on technological collaboration between dissimilar size firms. We suggest that the outcome in each of these cases indicates the need for skills training in collaboration (or, "dance lessons"). Although firms see the potential value in technological collaboration, the operationalization of the process needs to be optimized.

*Case 1: MPR & Samsung - Technological Collaboration for Global Competitiveness*

MPR Teltech (MPR) was a contract research and development company owned by BC Telecom, a regional telecommunications services company in British Columbia, Canada. MPR has recently been sold. At the time of this case MPR specialized in five main lines of business relating to telecommunication equipment and services. As an R&D company for a telephone company, MPR did not have a direct outlet for its innovations in equipment. It had very limited manufacturing and marketing capability and therefore actively sought licencing arrangements for its technologies.

As a result of a trip to Asia by one of the vice-presidents of the company in 1988, MPR engaged in a series of technological collaborations with east Asian, south-east Asian and south Asian companies over a period of eight years. The case reported below took place after several of these collaborations had already occurred, including two previous collaborations with Korean companies and organizations.

A Korean company, Goldstar, and the Korea Enhanced Telecommunications Research Institute (ETRI), contracted with MPR to supply technology for satellite ground station and the design of satellite receiver equipment. Although Goldstar is a large, technically advanced company, they did not have the necessary expertise to rapidly develop and deploy satellite technologies, which the Korean government planned to implement for "direct to home" (DTH) broadcasts of television. In particular, Goldstar intended to manufacture the satellite receiving equipment for the DTH service.

The collaboration was complicated by the usual factors including language and cultural differences, but these were, for the most part, overcome during the course of the contract. One factor suggests the impact of the small size of the Canadian firm. MPR, as a much smaller firm than Goldstar, had some difficulties explaining that key resources, in this case digital compression experts familiar with the MPEG-2 standard, were not available because of conflicting schedules within the organization.

The project, which began in 1994, was completed in 1996 on time and on budget. MPR built the broadcast centres, the satellite transmitting station, the broadcast network management billing system and "demonstration" receiving stations for system testing. The satellite receivers were designed to fit in with Goldstar's existing tooling, manufacturing methods and component preferences. MPR retained North American rights to manufacture the equipment and Goldstar purchased the Korean and international rights. The company was able to get a new product to market quickly without compromising its core competencies in manufacturing and marketing.

The technological collaboration was facilitated by an MPR staff member who had gone to university in Korea and was familiar with the culture and the business process. The company also benefited from previous experience with Korean companies in general and ETRI in particular. One lesson from the earlier experiences led MPR to construct the relationship to ensure than there were fewer players involved. A previous contract, which involved training for a consortium of high technology firms in Korea, suffered from multiple reporting paths and the inevitable confusion that produced. Along with the previous experience in Korea came an awareness of each other's needs and capabilities and therefore a faster startup phase for the contract. MPR also received permission to select who would be involved from the Korean side. This allowed the company to pick people with the appropriate skills and background. Finally, the project involved considerable new technology and as a result was more interesting to the engineers at MPR, who enjoyed the challenge.

*Case 2: Technological Collaboration and Environmental Sustainability*

Shimizu Corporation, a large Japanese construction firm, is active in the development of sustainable technologies. Shimizu's R&D policy emphasizes that they will identify areas where the company can make a contribution to the preservation and renewal of the global environment. Toward this goal, Shimizu has implemented a "green design" policy, and prioritized four factors for the overall activities of the firm: ecology, technology, energy and recycling. In this case technological collaboration for a new product contributed to Shimizu's access to the Canadian infrastructure market.

Shimizu developed an advanced material for concrete reinforcement that is light-weight, free from rust and corrosion and has a higher tensile strength than steel. New Fibre Composite Material for Reinforcing Concrete, or NEFMAC, can be used to increase the durability of concrete structures by protecting them from corrosion by salt and damage by chemicals. NEFMAC has been used in dam slope reinforcements (Japan), shotcrete reinforcement for tunnels (Japan), and reinforcements for parapet walls on highways (Canada).

Large quantities of salt are used on Canadian highways every year because of heavy snowfall and cold temperatures. As a result, steel reinforced concrete associated with roadways is subjected to corrosion and subsequent disposal and replacement, a serious environmental problem both in terms of inputs and waste. To cope with this problem, a Canadian manufacturer, Autocon, collaborated with Shimizu to experiment with the durability of NEFMAC in Canada. The National Research Council of Canada (NRC) supported the collaboration through its support for industrial research program.

Although the research was initiated in order to increase capabilities in the area of environmental sustainability, both partners achieved business objectives as well. The Canadian partner, Autocon, benefited from collaboration by increasing its competitiveness through innovative technology. Shimizu gained some access to the local market. As is sometimes the case, however, the collaboration may not have been optimal for both parties. In the case of Shimizu, their local market access is limited to a royalty agreement with Autocon. Local subsidiaries of Shimizu, who might have been involved, did not benefit directly from the arrangement. This pattern of "going over the heads" of local branch operations also occurred when the R&D group engaged in collaborative research with a research institution in Singapore, leaving local subsidiaries out of the picture until late in the game.

## 4. "DANCE LESSONS": PREPARATION FOR THE 21ST CENTURY

Many commentators have suggested that the basis of management is "common sense" [20]. When the management problem covers more than one organization, and those organizations are of different sizes or have different core competencies, there is good reason to believe that they have different cultures and in such circumstances common sense is not necessarily "common" [21]. Based on our experience, it appears that when dissimilar organizations work together they need more concrete skills to guide their actions.

We suggest that specific collaboration skills, which can be taught, are necessary in this delicate and sensitive aspect of management. In order to better explain the role and importance of these collaboration skills, we suggest a metaphor from another activity which requires sensitivity and delicacy: dancing. The process of learning to dance is our metaphor for learning to collaborate for technological innovation. The organized, deliberate process of acquiring these skills is what we call "dance lessons." The metaphor is intended as a heuristic, a better way to understand the steps that an individual or an organizations learns to be a better collaborator. Below we use the metaphor as a way to consider why and when training in technological collaboration is appropriate.

*Why dance lessons?*

Why would a firm seek to increase its skills in technological collaboration? One reason might be so that firms can put more "fun" in their collaborative activities, which we consider in more detail in the conclusion. Other possible reasons include learning how to lead, how to follow, how to communicate, how to select the right partner (customer, supplier), how to build trust, how to manage risk and avoid danger, how to negotiate with a partner from a different culture, how to communicate effectively and efficiently, how to share risk and benefits, how to collaborate for sustainability, how to make collaboration sustainable, and how to collaborate on the global stage. A common thread in these reasons is the focus on having the skills needed to make choices before entering a collaboration.

*When are dance lessons appropriate?*

When should firms take "Dance Lessons"? Firms may consider dance lessons at any time. Instead of initiating training just before starting to collaborate or negotiate on an issue, we suggest a firm consider taking lessons as early as possible. While there is merit in postponing training in cross-cultural communication until one is about to travel on the assumption that this 'just in time' training will be fresher and more relevant, training for technological collaboration is presumably about more than "doing things right" in an existing or established plan. Instead, training for technological collaboration should include significant attention to the selection of partners and projects, or "doing the right things." In this sense it is closer to management of innovation than the management of operations.

5. CONCLUSION

Our review of the reasons why firms engage in technological collaboration suggested an interesting metaphor for the training that must inevitably support this activity. The use of "dance lessons" as a metaphor revealed several reasons for technological collaboration, including the importance of choosing partners. From a "dance lessons" perspective it is hard not to think of the Shimizu situation as one of a prospective dancer (collaborator) looking far and wide for partners and ignoring the next-door neighbour.

Here we would like to point to an example of training for technological collaboration work and suggest an unexpected connection between the metaphor of dancing and real-life benefits to training in technological collaboration.

*One approach*

There is an initiative currently underway which seeks to foster more and better technological collaboration.. Sponsors include the Human Resources Development Working Group of the Business Management Network of the organization for Asia-Pacific Economic Cooperation (APEC), the Max Bell Foundation, the Asia Pacific Foundation, and Simon Fraser University. This group sponsored an international workshop on "Cross-cultural Management of Technical Collaboration" in August of 1996. The goal of the workshop, which included representatives from several APEC nations, was to design training modules to be used in executive education. The participants all prepared case studies which are being used in the design of courses on technological collaboration. Each participant, by contributing a case study, gained the rights to use all of the material in a course in their own country. It is further hoped that the cases and course materials will be continuously improved and the results shared among all participating countries. This project in executive education for managing technological collaboration in a cross-cultural environment illustrates one way that the mechanisms for technological collaboration might be enhanced in the future.

*Unexpected connections*

Somewhat unexpectedly, it has highlighted an aspect of management that is fundamental to exceptional performance: fun. In the MPR case, the potential "fun" from the collaboration (here the prospect of developing hot new technology), can be a significant motivator for participants. There is a small but growing literature on the role of humour and fun in the workplace [22-24]. Although not without its critics (see, for example [25]), the beneficial role of fun in management training seems to be gaining credibility. One of the reasons for this is that in a learning environment, humor has the ability to break down barriers and increase learner involvement and information retention.

Given the very great cultural and core competence divides that may separate innovation teams engaged in collaboration, this ability to surmount resistance to change will be an important aspect of any training program. For this reason, we suggest, there may be more than metaphorical importance to the use of the "dance lessons" concept when deploying skills training for technological collaboration. It may be that "having fun," just as in dancing, becomes the mechanism for inspired and not merely acceptable performance.

In this paper, we have proposed "dance lessons" with a difference: skills training to enable organizations to collaborate for innovation, to "do the right thing" with firms of any size and in any part of the globe. In order to build and maintain core-competencies, enhance economic, social and environmental sustainability and prepare for the competitive global market place of the 21st century, we urge firms to learn how to *dance* with their collaborators and their customers on the world stage. Our focus has been on collaboration among dissimilar sized firms but the metaphor could certainly be used more broadly. Technological collaboration could also be among similar sized firms, as well as governmental, and academic organizations of any size and any part of the world.

REFERENCES:

[1]     J. Bleeke, D. Ernst, and McKinsey, "Collaborating to Compete, Using strategic alliances and acquisitions in the global marketplace," . New York: John Wiley & Sons. Inc., 1993.

[2]     R. Coombs, A. Richards, P. P. Saviotti, and V. Walsh, "Technological Collaboration: The Dynamics of Cooperation in Industrial Innovation," . Cheltenham, UK: Edward Elgar, 1996.

[3]     M. Dodgson, *Technological Collaboration in Industry-Strategy, Policy and Internationalization in innovation*, First Edition ed: Routledge, 1993.

[4]     McKinsey & Co. Inc., *Collaborating to Compete - Using Strategic Alliances and Acquisitions in the Global Marketplace*: John Wiley & Sons, Inc., 1993.

[5]     J. Niosi, "Strategic technological collaboration in Canadian industry," in *Technological Collaboration: The Dynamics of Cooperation in Industrial Innovation*, R. Coombs, A. Richards, P. P. Saviotti, and V. Walsh, Eds. Cheltenham, UK: Edward Elgar, 1996, pp. 98-118.

[6]     G. Dosi, C. Freeman, R. Nelson, G. Silverberg, and L. Soete, "Technical Change and Economic Theory," . London: Pinter Publishers, 1988.

[7]     R. M. Kanter, *When Giants Learn to Dance*. New York: Simon and Schuster, 1989.

[8]     R. M. Kanter, *World Class*. New York: Touchtone, 1995.

[9]     J. Hagedoorn, "Strategic technology partnering during the 1980s:trends, networks and corporate patterns in non-core technologies," *Research Policy*, vol. 24, pp. 207-231, 1995.

[10]    CERF, "Creating the 21st Century through Innovation," Civil Engineering Research Foundation, Washington, D.C., U.S.A., Summary findings of an international research symposium held in Washington, D.C., Feb 4-8, 1996. CERF Report #96-5016.E, 1996 1996.

[11]    United Nations, *The Global Partnership for Environment and Development: A Guide to Agenda 21 Post Rio Edition*. New York: United Nations, 1993.

[12]    OECD, *Technologies for Cleaner Production and Products - Towards Technological Transformation for Sustainable Development*: OECD, 1995.

[13]    G. Hamel and C. K. Prahalad, *Competing for the future*. Boston: Harvard Business School Press, 1994.

[14]    C. K. Prahalad and G. Hamel, "The core competence of the corporation," *Harvard Business Review*, pp. 79-91, 1990.

[15]    R. Y. Qassim, "Environmental management in industry: historical evolution and future perspectives," *International Journal of Technology Management*, vol. 9, pp. 129-131, 1994.

[16]    B. T. Oakley, "Total quality product design - How to integrate environmental criteria into the production realization process," *Total Quality Environmental Management*, vol. 2, pp. 309-321, 1993.

[17]   M. P. Joshi and A. C. Inkpen, "Cooperation in a competitive world: A framework of global strategic alliances," *Competitive Intelligence Review*, vol. 7, pp. 46-55, 1996.

[18]   F. Kodama, *Emerging Patterns of Innovation, Sources of Japan's Technological Edge*. Boston: Harvard Business School Press, 1995.

[19]   OECD, *Small and Medium-sized Enterprises: Technology and Competitiveness*. Paris: OECD, 1993.

[20]   J. Z. Nitecki, "In Search of Sense in Common Sense Management," *Journal of Business Ethics*, vol. 6, pp. 639-647, 1987.

[21]   C. Geertz, "Common sense as a cultural system," *The Antioch Review*, vol. 33, pp. 5-26, 1975.

[22]   P. Brotherton, "Managing to Have Fun: How Fun at Work Can Motivate Your Employees, Inspire Your Coworkers and Boost Your Bottom Line," *HRMagazine*, vol. 41, pp. 118-119, 1996.

[23]   C. A. Jaffe, "Management by Fun," *Nation's Business*, vol. 78, pp. 58-60, 1990.

[24]   R. Holden, "Enjoyment in employment: How to utilize the power of laughter, humour and a winning smile at work," *Employee Counselling Today*, vol. 5, pp. 17-20, 1993.

[25]   S. B. Rodrigues and D. L. Collinson, ""Having fun"?: Humour as resistance in Brazil," *Organization Studies*, vol. 16, pp. 739-768, 1995.

067

# Four-leaf Clover Holistics in Management of Technology

Jan-Crister Persson , Swedish Institute of Production Engineering
Research, Argongatan 30, 431 53 Göteborg, Sweden
Phone: +46 31 706 61 00

Johan Stahre, Dept. of Production Engineering,
Chalmers Univ. of Technology, 412 96 Göteborg, Sweden
Phone: +46 31 772 12 88

### Abstract

Successful industrial enterprises must be able to quickly adapt to fast-changing conditions set by the market or by competitors. The speed and efficiency of the company's change-process determines the outcome, and eventually the company's market profitability. This paper describes a holistic approach where the *four-leaf clover of excellence* clearly visualizes how maximized improvement achieved by a change, or set of changes, is the result of the change vector of four aspects. The vectors are improvement: 1) by competence, 2) by investment in hardware, 3) by organizational control structure, and 4) through the informal rules and routines perceived by the individuals in the company. The resulting addition of, preferably coherent, company resources provides a strategic instrument for company managers.

## 1. Introduction

The opportunities and risks for today's industrial enterprises are evident. More customer-driven and environmentally driven products and services will be in the marketplace of the future. Enterprises must adapt to changing market conditions to maintain profitability. Strategic choices are essential, and operations must be seen as a joint set of processes across whatever organizational, physical, or national boundaries that may exist. All profitable companies must have at least one sustainable and unique selling proposition, or market characteristic in a monopoly situation.

On the back of the coin are of course the extensive efforts required to change fast enough to cope with competition and to be able to grab future markets before the competitors. Overall company goals for customer satisfaction, time-to-market, precision of delivery, cost effectiveness, and environmental "position" must be clearly communicated, decided and followed-up. This may be expressed in a starker manufacturing language:

- to be better,
- to be faster, and
- to be less expensive.

Having clear strategies and goals is essential for total quality results. Many companies are designing boundary-less process management. Operational decision-mechanisms supported by research should encompass all important activities and areas such as product concept, product system and subsystems, production processes, logistics, team-formation, and soft and hardware investments. Decision-making should be extended to operative personnel on the shop-floor and sales organization. Within each area substrategies, principles, and routines govern daily and weekly operations and have to be linked to effective change management and operational results. Such holistic views of company operations should provide the speed and decision accuracy needed for future competitiveness.

## 2. Background

Numerous efforts to achieve the above goals and requirements are continuously being implemented at companies throughout the world. Successful examples taken from Swedish industry are ABB (project T50) [Berger, 1994], Volvo [Ahlinder, 1996], and Tetra Pak Converting [Högström, 1995].

Among a manifold of academic and industrial efforts, research focusing on holistic company views may be exemplified by several multinational projects within the framework of a global initiative called *Intelligent Manufacturing Systems* (IMS). Applicable IMS projects in operation are: *Globeman 21, Next Generation Manufacturing Systems, Holonic Manufacturing Systems, GNOSIS*, and *Metamorphic Material Handling Systems (MMHS)*.

Other holistically oriented research approaches tend to focus either on manufacturing system or on product development. In the area of product development three broad avenues of interest can be identified:

- *Design theory* is a topic representing various schools of design methodology. An advanced holistic approach to design theory is Axiomatic Design, introduced and developed by Suh [1990]. Recent developments of Suh's theories in the direction of concurrent engineering have been made by Vallhagen [1996]

- *Product modeling* has attracted the attention of standardization efforts as well as research and development. A broad survey of results as well as practical implementations and standardization efforts was presented by Krause et al [1993].

- *Concurrent engineering*, or simultaneous engineering provides the dynamics of product development and also provides the means to bridge the gap between designers and the shop-floor. Insights into development trends in concurrent engineering are given by Carter and Baker [1992].

The development of manufacturing systems is represented by an extremely broad set of approaches; the above mentioned IMS projects represent just a fraction. Standardization efforts have been aimed primarily towards standardization of manufacturing system components, including software and information technology. Examples are MAP and MMS. European efforts in the manufacturing system area have been promoted and financed by e.g. the ESPRIT and BRITE/EURAM research programmes while US efforts have been promoted by e.g. NSF and NIST. Similar efforts have been made in Japan and the Pacific rim countries.

Manufacturing system concepts containing more or less autonomous sub-systems for manufacturing are emerging. Relevant examples are *bionic, fractal, holonic,* and *agile* manufacturing. These concepts focus on the organization and integration of complex systems and provide the opportunity to handle large systems as well as low-level subsystems within a unified reference framework.

Within a holistic view of manufacturing the need to describe and integrate humans (be it operators, maintenance personnel, designers, or other company resources) increases, resulting in a greater interest in human competence and organization. On shop-floor level, for example, the balance between the operators' joint capability and the technical complexity of the manufacturing system is of vital importance for the productivity and reliability of the system. This has been described by Johansson [1996] and Stahre [1995a], who have developed a methodology to analyze unbalanced situations in such systems.

Previous efforts by the European Community to provide holistic and future-oriented strategies focused on human competence may be exemplified by the Human-centred CIM [Rosenbrock, 1989] and Anthropocentric Production Systems [Newsletter, 1990; Wobbe and Charles, 1994; Brödner, 1994]. An international round-table discussion regarding the potential of holistic company views and the integrative aspects of *People, Organization, and Technology in Advanced Manufacturing* was held in 1994, resulting in a prioritized list of needed future research efforts [Karwowski *et al.*, 1994]. Specifically, this discussion focused on the importance of the human contribution to company competitiveness, and what could be done to further support the competence of people in future organizations. A review of this research area was made by Stahre [1995b].

## 3. The four-leaf clover of excellence

Judging from the broad range of practiced and suggested alternatives for future management of technology it is obvious that a clear picture yet has to emerge. However, the notion of a holistic operational model of the company as well as the importance of autonomy and decentralized decision-making is common to several views. In order to achieve future competitiveness one more crucial success factor has to be introduced: added holistic mind-set(s). The thesis is that real, maximized improvement achieved by a change or set of changes is the result of the change vectors of four aspects. We consider the four-leaf clover model to be relevant in research, engineering, manufacturing, sales, and services.

An important aspect of this is that many of the above mentioned research approaches often restrict themselves to analyzing and describing present and/or future situations within a company or manufacturing system. An added value of mind-sets for change processes is that they will assist the practitioner in the planning and performing of the actual change from the present to the future.

Figure 1. Four-leaf clover of excellence.

The aspects are visualized in figure 1 and can be defined as improvement: by competence, by investment in hardware, by organizational control structure, and through the informal rules and routines perceived by the individuals in the company.

By improving each aspect in the direction of fulfilling the overall goals of the company the resulting effect may be "calculated" as a vector addition of the four components. Consequently, each "vector", when developed in the opposite direction of the company goal, or if not developed at all, will decrease the total effectiveness of the concerned decision, project, change or of the company as a whole.

$$+ E_{Improvement, competence}$$
$$+ E_{Improvement, investments}$$
$$+ E_{Improvement, org. structure}$$
$$\underline{+ E_{Improvement, informalities \& routines}}$$

Total effectiveness = $\quad E_{tot}$

Very often executive as well as industrial management of enterprises overestimates or believes that it is enough to change only one or two of the vectors. The three most common errors made are:

a)  Changing formal organizational structures without changing people's behavior or the corresponding operational processes. See figure 2.

Figure 2. One-leaf solution.

b)  Making more or less huge hardware and/or software investments - money which could be used in other profitable projects - without preparing people. This includes management in some cases taking IT (Information Technology) solutions to be the only one. Usually the change of a tool or a method has limited value or effect. See figure 3.

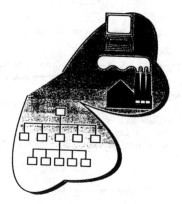

Figure 3. Two-leaf solution.

The four leaves of the clover must genuinely go together to get maximum possible results from a change-process. If it is impossible to manage and change all four leaves simultaneously in one leap, select two or three in a first step, and plan carefully the follow-up with the rest of the leaves. Each leaf, or mechanism, is a component in a coupled system. The mechanisms can be treated independently, but that will give unsatisfactory results.

## 3.1 Overall company goals

The goals of the enterprise or research should be set clear to give direction to strategic as well as operational changes. When the goals are connected to the four-leaf clover, not only direction but also speed and efficiency are achieved.

The four-leaf clover of excellence and its change vectors should be used as a strategic or tactic instrument, to implement overall company goals. We suggest a number of goals, that should be included in all companies and at all company levels in order to target changes, projects, and such.

1    **Quality:** Customer complaints are most important inputs. Aim for defect rates of ppm (parts per million) or ppb (parts per billion). Support the improvement of quality with certification according to ISO 9000 and 14000, and self-assessment according to USK, EFQM, or Malcolm Baldrige.

2    **Deliveries:** Precision timing to customer. Shorter and shorter lead-times in product development as well as manufacturing.

3    **Economy:** Halve the cost as a first step. Then halve it again.

4    If above three main goals are not enough for your ambitious organization, we suggest that you add, for example, targets related to:

- technology level in product or service

- uniqueness of a product or service

- environmental, lifecycle characteristics

- real development and empowering of your own work force.

One example of targeting technical research and development is given in table 1. This example is presently a "pilot" in a big company.

Table 1. Examples of targets for research and development projects.

## Electronic Company Progress Control Table (pilot)

| Items | Person in Charge | Target | Degree of importance | Dev. Stage | Schedule | Alternative Method |
|-------|------------------|--------|----------------------|------------|----------|--------------------|
| 1. Laser welding | Dept A, Nils Nilsson | Speed Freedom UP | Want | Prototype Dev | B ⎯⎯ A ▽ | Spot welding |
| 2. New material | Dept C, Anna Andersson | Weight -30% Cost -20% | Want | Prototype Dev | B ⎯⎯ A ▽ | Aluminium |
| 3. High-speed cutting | Dept X, Leonard Smith-Ljungqvist | Cutting speed + 20% | Want | Basic research | C ⎯⎯ B ▽ | |
| 4. Solder abolition | Dept Z, Petra Persson | Reliability + 50% Cost -30% | Must | Prototype Dev | B A ▽ A | |

We suggest that company goals should be extensive and ambitious, but one has to add, that they must at the same time be ethical and mutually elaborated within the enterprise. The conclusive process is delicate. Normally the organization's real push for change is weak [Barnevik (ABB), 1996], which has be to counterbalanced by leadership.

Some successful applications of strong and consistent goalsetting are: ABB's T50 [Berger, 1994], Volvo Car Corp "KLE" [Ahlinder, 1996] among others. The main strategic goals of the company must, of course, govern the direction of the enterprise, its people, organization, and investments. The four-leaf clover shows how you must change with a holistic view of the situation, for maximum return on the changes.

When setting the goals we would like to stress that *strategic gap analysis* should be applied. Japanese companies working worldwide now have entered the "Period of Creativity", focusing on improved business results through concept development of technology, product, systems, and business. Within this context, targets and systems to measure customer quality, cost, and delivery precision are applied rigorously according to "Japanese Manufacturing Strategy to Compete with the Tigers" by Professor Hajime Yamashina, Kyoto University [Yamashina, 1996].

We observe that in decentralized organizations, with especially knowledge- or competence-based activities, possible fragmentation will occur within the company. Virtual or decentralized organizations mean that power is within the group, "holon", or distributed system. Identification with the company and its customers is weaker. This means that fewer people know the strategic whole, unless information technology is used to at least disseminate information. Dissemination of competence and identification or identity is more difficult.

## 4.    Conclusion

It has been stated in this paper that maximized improvement achieved by a change or set of changes is the result of the change vector of four aspects, i.e. improvement: 1) by competence, 2) by investment in hardware, 3) by organizational control structure, and 4) through the informal rules and routines perceived by the individuals in the company.

Literature supports such a holistic view of a manufacturing company. Even though the four vectors of the four-leaf clover do not represent all influenceable factors in a company, the four-leaf clover of excellence provides a practical model for a holistically oriented improvement of company assets. By applying the mind-set visualized by the clover, improvements and changes in various parts of the company may be directed towards a common vision.

The four-leaf clover can be used as a strategic decision aid when streamlining processes within a company or businesses at large in order to reach customer-driven targets. Decisions concerning in- or outsourcing, location of development or manufacturing centers can be governed by assessments using the holistic four-leaf clover and its resulting vector.

As a strategic rule of thumb, we believe that you should "sell out" if you can be strong in only one or two leaves, but go on if you have three strong leaves. If your activity or process actually has successful activity in all four leaves, then you have excellence, you have *the four-leaf clover of excellence*.

## 5.    References

Ahlinder, J. *et al.*, "Ett underlag för erfarenhetsutbyte" Volvo/Ergoma, 1996.

Barnevik, P., (ABB) "Presentation, at VI's 100 Year Symposium", Stockholm, the 15 of November, 1996.

Brödner, P., "Design of work and technology", in: Design and development of personnel in advanced manufacturing, Salvendy, G., Karwowski, W., (Eds.) , John Wiley & Sons, New York, 1994.

Carter, D. E. and Baker, B.S., "Concurrent Engineering — The Product Development Environment for the 1990s", Addison-Wesley Publishing Company, Inc. New York, 1992.

Gustafsson, B., Nonås, K., "The welding workplace 2000 Project - integrated technology and organizational development", The Swedish Institute of Production Engineering Research and Lindholmen Development, IIW-Conference, XII-1416-95, Stockholm, 1995.

Högström, A., "Vinna tillit", Industrilitteratur, 1995.

Johansson, A., "An Initial Methodology for Operator Support Tool Development in Advanced Manufacturing Systems". licentiate thesis, Dept. of Production Engineering, Chalmers University of Technology, 1996.

Karwowski, W., Salvendy, G., Badham, R., Brödner, P., Clegg, C., Hwang, S.L., Iwasawa, J., Kidd, P.T., Kobayashi, N., R., K. *et al.*, "Integrating People, Organization, and Technology in Advanced Manufacturing: a position paper based on the joint view of Industrial managers, Engineers, Consultants, and Researchers.", *Int. Journal of Human Factors in Manufacturing* 4, 1994.

Krause, F.-L., Kimura F., Kjellberg, T. Lu, S.C.-Y., van der Wolf, Alting, L., ElMaraghy, H.A., Eversheim, W., Iwata, K., Suh, N.P., Tipnis, V.A., Weck, M., "Product Modelling", Annals of the CIRP, Vol 42:2, 1993.

Newsletter, A.T.S.A.S., "Newsletter No 1", MONITOR/FAST programme, 1990.

Rosenbrock, H.H., (Ed.), "Designing Human-centred Technology — A Cross-disciplinary Project in Computer-aided Manufacturing", Springer-Verlag, 1989.

Stahre, J., "Evaluating Human/Machine Interaction Problems in Advanced Manufacturing", Computer Integrated Manufacturing Systems, Butterworth—Heinemann, ISSN 0951-5240, Vol 8:2 1995a.

Stahre, J., "Towards Human Supervisory Control in Advanced Manufacturing", doctoral thesis, Dept. of Production Engineering, Chalmers University of Technology, 1995b.

Suh, N.P., "The Principles of Design", Oxford University Press, New york, 1990.

Vallhagen, J. "An Axiomatic Approach to Integrated Product Process Development", 1996.

Wobbe, W., and Charles, T., "Human roles in advanced manufacturing technology", in: Organization and management of advanced manufacturing Karwowski, W., Salvendy, G., (Eds.) , John Wiley & Sons, New York, 1994.

Yamashina, H., "Japanese Manufacturing Strategy to Compete with the Tigers", Tvärkontakt Conference, Gothenburg, Sweden, Nov 1996.

# 068

# Strategic technological choice in mobile telecommunications

Fredrik Gessler, Dept. of Industrial Economics and Management, KTH.

## Abstract

This paper discusses the concept of strategic technological choice in mobile telecommunications. In the area of telecommunications, technological development has a strong historical dependency. It can be described as path dependent in the sense that technological choices made in the past influence the avenues of development possible today. This can lead to lock-in effects.

Three examples from the mobile telecommunications industry are presented. Firstly, the data services in the GSM standard are discussed as an example of technological lock-in. Secondly, the debate between TDMA and CDMA systems is discussed from the perspective of CDMA breaking the reign of TDMA. Thirdly, and finally, the shift in focus from systems development to mass production of terminals for mobile networks is discussed as an example of a strategic development that the industry is undergoing today.

The conclusion that is drawn from the study is that the strategic nature of a technological choice is defined by its implications. To view these, the time period must be lengthened and the context in which the choices are made must be taken into consideration.

## Contents

# 1. Introduction

A topic that has been discussed thoroughly by economists over the last few years is that of strategic technological choices, that in effect determine the direction of firms over long periods of time. In this paper this concept, often described as path dependency, will be discussed from the perspective of the mobile telecommunications industry.

My proposition is that several examples can be found, where path dependency has led to lock-in effects, influencing the development of services, etc. offered to the end-users. This will be shown in the case of data communication in GSM. However, there are also cases of players stepping out of their fore-ordained path, attempting to change structures within the industry and doing so with considerable success. The case of CDMA vs. TDMA gives us an interesting illustration of a firm, Qualcomm, trying to break into the mobile telecommunications industry.

Finally, I will argue that the major choice that faces firms in the mobile telecommunications industry today, is that of what core businesses they should actually have. By this I mean whether they should be systems developers or mass producers of telecommunications equipment, or both. These questions have their basis in technology, but also demand an understanding of telecommunications regulations, the industry structure and existing and potential competition.

## Strategic technological choice

The initial hypothesis of this paper was that technological development in telecommunications has a strong historical dependency, i.e. it is path dependent. This path dependency can be made visible by studying technological lock-in, which in turn was assumed to be an effect of strategic technological choices in various stages of a development effort.

All technological choices made within firms are not strategic ones, however. In their day-to-day work researchers and product and systems developers make a number of choices, without perceiving them to be of a strategic nature. This is of course partly a problem of perspectives, the researchers cannot overview all the effects of their decisions, but there are also other aspects. Whether or not a certain choice should be considered strategic is defined by the nature of it's implications. This in turn means that individual choices seldom, or never, can be described as strategic since the implications are a result of many different choices, made over a long period of time.

The very nature of strategic choice makes it difficult to study. Discerning the historical choices that have led to strategic effects today is fraught with the peril of different explanations dependent on the chosen perspective. Trying to find the strategic choices being made here and now is yet more difficult since the choices made today are set in a different context than the implications, that become apparent tomorrow. We thus have to interpret both the effects that technological choices may give, and the evolution of the environment in which these effects will appear.

## Consequences of strategic choices

The concept of strategic choice within a firm is closely related to the idea of a path-dependent economy, i.e. where the strategic choices that a firm makes determines along what path it will develop. Path dependency in turn leads to two concepts that are covered by several economists[1] namely lock-in and increasing returns. I will elaborate on the way Brian Arthur (1994) discusses increasing returns in a recent book of collected essays.

In identifying the existence of increasing returns, Arthur opposes a major portion of conventional economics, which as he notes "... is built largely on the assumption of diminishing returns on the margin ..." (Arthur, 1994:111). The school of thought to which Arthur belongs, on the contrary, believes that many, especially developing, markets have increasing marginal returns (at least during a certain degree of penetration). His most well-known example is the competition between the two standards for Video Cassette Recorders, VCRs: VHS and Betamax.

The reasoning is fairly straight-forward. The more people that have VHS, the more it becomes attractive for the potential new customer who is considering buying a VCR. The reasons being, simply, that he or she will be able to borrow films from friends, that film-rental agencies will appear, etc. The potential benefits for the customer on the margin will thus always be increasing, thereby also increasing the returns for the supplying firms. According to the theory of path dependency, one of the two standards will eventually prevail. Once the difference in the number of followers becomes large enough, the negative impact of choosing the less fortunate standard will be so great that there will simply be no market for it. As we all know, in the VCR example VHS emerged as the winning standard.

The discussion here, on the emergence of winners in the struggle between standards for VCRs, illustrates a way that consequences of strategic technological choice can be described. The concepts of path dependency, positive feed-back loops, increasing returns and lock-in can be carried over to the area of telecommunications, which is the focus of this paper.

## The telecommunications industry

In order to give a background to the discussions in the paper, a brief outline is here given of the structure of the telecommunications industry. It should be noted that this industry has undergone large changes due to the global efforts to deregulate telecommunications operations. This has shifted the power balance, away from former national PTTs having monopolies on their respective markets, to the supplier side which is dominated by a few transnational firms.

## Systems and equipment

Today technological development in telecommunications is dictated mainly by the large systems suppliers. This reflected in the organisation of work with technical standards. A decade ago, standards for the European market were developed by CEPT[2], an organisation in which only the national PTTs were allowed membership, not private industry in any shape or form. Today CEPT has become ETSI[3], an organisation in which all players in the telecommunications industry are welcome to participate in and influence standardisation efforts.[4]

The market for telecommunications systems is dominated by a few large companies, of which Motorola, Ericsson and Nokia seem to be the most successful ones this far. Among the suppliers, there has been a trend of mergers and acquisitions, over the years decreasing the number of active firms and increasing their size. Today there are but a handful of firms that can be considered to cover a major part of the systems concerned. The entrance difficulties are apparent when the necessary R&D resources to be an effective competitor are considered.

There also exist a number of small niche producers, typically developing and manufacturing subsystems or components. A Swedish example is Allgon, who produce antennas and batteries for both radio base stations and mobile telephones. A more uncommon niche firm is Qualcomm, essentially an engineering firm that has developed a complete mobile telephony system, IS-95, but who don't have manufacturing capabilities of their own choosing instead to license their patented solutions to other firms.

## Operators

Practically from the birth of telephony as we know it today (i.e. transmission of sound by electricity), at the end of the nineteenth century[5], and for more than a hundred years the national PTTs enjoyed untroubled monopoly positions[6]. The apparent lack of competition in many ways was positive, because the PTTs from different countries could co-operate in development efforts without fearing to share vital technology. The national operators therefore became the dominant force in the industry, dictating the terms under which supplier firms developed new systems and technologies. The operators themselves became technologically competent buyers of telecommunications systems.

Looking to the Swedish market today, we note that there are several suppliers of telecommunications services to both corporate and private customers[7]. This marked change has had a major impact on our former PTT, Telia, who has been forced to change pricing tariffs, personnel structure, etc. It is also quite obvious that the services, and the pricing of these, offered by the new actors on the market is largely dependent on services and prices offered by Telia. For example, Tele2, a firm in the well-known Kinnevik corporation, has offered international traffic for private and corporate customers for a few years now.

The new operators are seldom entirely new firms. Most of the firms present on the Swedish market have foreign ownership. The NetCom Systems group of the Kinnevik corporation is the largest operator, apart from Telia, with predominantly Swedish interests, but even they are partly-owned by a British firm, Cable & Wireless. So, the surge of new-comers on the Swedish markets should rather be described as a geographical expansion of a number of international telecomm operators.[8]

# 2. Providing services - not transmission

The market development in telecommunications has led to a weakened technological competence among operator firms. At the same time the telecommunications systems are becoming increasingly complex, with an ever increasing amount of customers receiving an ever increasing amount of services[9]. This has led to what could be described as a shift in power in the production chain for telecommunications equipment. Influence over technological development has moved from the operators to the suppliers.

The niche focus that can be seen among many new operators has also led to tangible consequences. The term operator is no longer a homogenous concept. Three kinds of providers in the telecommunications services product chain have emerged; transmission providers, service providers and content providers. The hypothesis is that customers are willing to pay only so much for simple transmission, what they in fact spend their money on is services. The operators' objectives, therefore, become to provide services of value for the customers, rather than to transmit a large amount of traffic in the most efficient way.

The transition from providing transmission to providing services is not an easy one. Social factors enter into the equation when operators shift their focus from the transmission networks, i.e. the technology, to the services they must provide in order to be a competitive alternative for the consumers. However, a very important technological aspect is also the lock-in effects that existing technological solutions can lead to. One example of this is the case of data transmission provided by the GSM standard for mobile telecommunications.

## Data services in the original GSM standard

The original specifications for the GSM standard for digital mobile telecommunications were developed during the first half of the eighties. The general preconception in those days was that a mobile telephony system would be used mainly for conventional telephony, i.e. speech between two parties. There already existed solutions for mobile package data systems, for example the Swedish Mobitex system, but they had not been a commercial success. At the time it therefore made sense not to allow for large data transfer capabilities in GSM, focus should be on creating a system with good qualities for speech.

GSM has had the capabilities of an ordinary fixed telephone system as its main role model when it comes to service development. By this I mean that the system has been designed mainly as a system for speech transmission, and only secondly as a system for data transmission. GSM is basically able to handle the same protocols for fax and data that an ordinary telephone system can use with modem technology. It is also transparent towards ISDN networks. The main difference is the transmission rate. Due to the design of the air interface in GSM, it is theoretically limited to 12 kbit/s (in practice there are no applications using more than 9,6 kbit/s). This is a transmission rate that is acceptable for fax services, but compared to computer communication using modems or ISDN access, it is pitifully slow.[10]

Apart from the point to point transmission described above, GSM also allows asynchronous data packages to be sent to and from the terminals. This is called SMS, Short Message Service, and has been designed for messages with a maximum length of 160 characters[11]. The messages are sent in the form of packages without any direct connection between the originator of the message and the receiver. They can be received during conversations and thus operate outside the normal transmission of speech between the terminal and the base station. In the original specifications there was no method for transmitting packaged data in greater quantities.[12]

## New demands from operators and end-users

When the GSM systems started to come into operation throughout Europe, it soon became apparent that the tide had turned. The demand for data services increased as computer communication became more widespread. The solutions for data communication in GSM is simply not efficient for computer communication, e.g. file transfer or world wide web applications.

Research and development efforts put into developing new methods of data transmission have so far been slow to establish effective solutions. The standard itself has been a major constraint in these efforts, since the new solutions have to function in concert with all existing aspects of the standard. Although data services are essential for the operators to offer their clients, they cannot be allowed to create havoc in other parts of the system.

Two approaches have been chosen for the development of data services in GSM. The first one, HSCSD[13], is based on the use of several speech channels operating in parallel, thereby enabling a terminal to send and receive data at a higher rate. This is fairly straight forward since GSM is a TDMA[14] system and

435

sequential time-slots on the same carrier frequency thus can be used. The second approach, GPRS[15] instead entails asynchronous package transmission on separate channels, a more radical development of GSM. The fundamental technological problem of high speed data transmission still remains: It steals bandwidth from the speech services.

In either of the two outlined solutions for higher data rates in GSM, the design of the existing standard must be taken into consideration. There are many millions of subscribers all over the world who use GSM telephones. This means that all developments of the standard must be backward compatible in order to not render any existing equipment useless. Despite increasing demands of, for example, wireless access to the Internet we experience a technological lock-in due to the original design of the GSM standard.

# 3. CDMA - creating a new ball game

Although the number of operators on the deregulated telecommunications markets of tomorrow seems to increase steadily, quite the opposite can be said about the equipment manufacturers. Here the number of players has decreased over the last decade and there are substantial entrance barriers for new firms. There has really only been one example of a new firm attempting to become a systems developer: Qualcomm. What makes them especially interesting when discussing strategic technological choice is that they represent a new technological approach to air interface[16] of the mobile telephony systems.

While all existing systems for mobile telecommunications use narrow band solutions for the air interface Qualcomm has opted for the broadband CDMA[17] approach. By doing this they hope to create a new arena of competition where their solution offers substantially better value for the customer than existing ones.

## Access technologies

The established standards for digital mobile telecommunications all use different variants of TDMA-techniques to modulate the carrier frequency over which calls are broadcast. This technology allows several channels to exist in different time slots on the same frequency. In general, TDMA comes in two varieties: broadband and narrowband. Broadband TDMA means that one wide frequency band is used and is divided into a large number of time slots. Narrowband TDMA instead uses relatively few time slots, but has a number of parallel frequencies in use at the same time.

For example, in GSM there are eight time slots per frequency. This means that frames of 8 time slots, each 0,577 ms long, are repeated approximately 220 times per second. In a time slot within one of these frames, a burst of data bits are sent, that contain a portion of the ongoing call. The frequencies, in turn, have a spacing of 200 khz.[18]

The inefficiencies of a narrowband TDMA system are due to mainly two things: the spacing needed between two frequencies and the spacing needed between two time slots in a frame. Frequency spacing is necessary to avoid interference between channels, and time slot spacing (guard-time) is needed because the it is impossible to exactly synchronise transmitters and receivers so that no overlap occurs between two different slots.[19]

An alternate access technology is CDMA, traditionally used in military applications[20]. Here the call is translated to a data stream, which is then coded to a signal stream using a unique code for each individual call. The signalling rate of the coded data stream is normally very high. This is due to the need for individual codes that do not interfere with each other, i.e. they must be orthogonal. In practice this means that a CDMA system demands rather wide frequencies (i.e. a broad frequency band), and that synchronisation between transmitter and receiver is of vital importance. It also turns out to be difficult to find perfectly orthogonal code sequences, wherefore sequences that are close to being orthogonal are used. Unfortunately the risk of interference thereby increases.[21]

The potential benefits of CDMA are higher capacity and dynamic allocation of bandwidth. Since a wide frequency spectrum is used, no spacing between carriers is necessary, which means a theoretically more efficient usage of the air ways. In practice however, this is a contested fact.

## Technological benefits of CDMA - a contested position

There are a number of CDMA systems around the world that are on the verge of going into full-scale operation. The standards based on CDMA technology were also exceptionally successful in the distribution of PCS licenses on the US market, where approximately half of the PCS market[22] will be served by IS-95[23] CDMA systems. The American firm Qualcomm strongly argues for the technological superiority of the new IS-95 standard in comparison with GSM and D-AMPS. Their case is that the new access technologies used will more than double the capacity of the system, which can be shown through theoretical calculations. Ericsson counters this argument by pointing out that the complex system structure of IS-95 both gives an expensive system and an inefficient call processing[24]. They also maintain that a large portion of the capacity increase is due to new speech-coding techniques that demand less bandwidth, but at the same time impair speech quality. Also it has nothing to do with the choice of access technique.

Whether Ericsson's or Qualcomm's arguments are right is very difficult to establish. It seems to be a matter of choosing which experts in the field to listen to, and I will not enter into this debate. One interesting aspect worth noting however, is that Qualcomm obviously is trying very hard to establish itself in a new area. They are attempting to define a new, successful standard which, in their mind, is technologically superior to existing digital cellular solutions, instead of attempting to enter the GSM/D-AMPS scene. By doing this they hope to create a "new ball game", free from competition.

## Why challenge an established standard?

It still remains to be seen if IS-95 will become a success story and if it can measure up to all the expectations put on it. Even if it does turn out to be technologically superior to GSM and others, the superiority will probably not be profound. The system may offer higher capacity, but will essentially have the same type of functionality as GSM[25]. Why would potential customers want to go for an unproved solution that is marginally better than the established ones, is the question posed by Ericsson. The answer to this question may lie elsewhere than in technology. Political and other factors may well be enough to tip the scales in the favour of IS-95.

The IS-95 example is especially interesting because it can be described in terms of a firm trying to break an existing technological lock-in. They way Qualcomm has done this is not by developing a standard in competition with existing TDMA based standards, but by launching a system that they claim to be beyond competition from existing solutions. To speak metaphorically, they have rejected the TDMA ball game and have invited all the spectators to the new and better CDMA field.

Looking at the situation in this way sheds new light on Qualcomm's actions, and their claims regarding the IS-95. They have been criticised by, especially, Ericsson for their reluctance to make a fair comparison[26] between GSM and IS-95. The point is however, that Qualcomm has little or no interest in competing with the TDMA paradigm. Rather, they want CDMA systems to be viewed as the next generation of mobile communications, offering a new level of service.

Qualcomm has skilfully played upon US telecommunications manufacturers' fear of Ericsson's globally dominant role in mobile telephony. They have thus been able to establish co-operative efforts with both Lucent Technologies and Motorola, who in turn hope to get the upper hand on Ericsson. What we see is how a firm has used non-technological factors to break a technological lock-in.

# 4. Systems suppliers or mass producers?

I would argue that several firms involved in telecommunications today face the choice of going into the production of terminals full-scale, or remaining predominantly systems suppliers. This is especially obvious when it comes to the Swedish telecomm firm Ericsson. I will elaborate on the strategic nature of being a systems supplier, a mass producer of terminals, or both.

# Current industry structure

Traditionally the networks or systems have been in focus for equipment suppliers in mobile telecommunications, since they involved the major investments. It has also always been natural to technologically describe telecommunications in a systemic fashion. One indication of this was the fact that the PTTs normally owned the terminals that subscribers to their networks were allowed to use[27]. The terminals were considered to be part of the system.

When the first high-capacity automatic mobile telecommunications systems were introduced, this changed. The subscribers were allowed to buy their own mobile phones, and in time phones for a certain standard were supplied by several different firms[28]. From a technological point of view this is reasonable, because the air interface is the easiest to specify. Partly because it is so near the periphery of the access network and partly because signalling has to be kept to a minimum in order to save frequency spectrum.

Swedish Ericsson has its roots partly in the development and production of switches, etc. for fixed networks and partly in the development and production of radio base stations.[29] Both these areas involve complex systems, where products demand large efforts in research and development to be realised, and are then produced in relatively small volumes, i.e. tens and hundreds of thousands on a global market. Ericsson's success in mobile telecommunications is often attributed to their merging of these two fundamental areas.

As late as 1993[30] the terminals were not considered by Ericsson to be a strategic part of mobile telecommunications systems. With market forecasts of 20-30 million handsets being sold each year during the rest of this century[31], this attitude has changed. a reflection of this is Ericsson´s reorganisation per January first of this year[32]. Three business areas have been established, of which Telephones & Terminals is one. This marks a redefinition of what Ericsson considers to be its core business.

# The mass production era

The great difference between being a systems supplier and being a supplier of terminals lies in production volumes. For each base station in a mobile telecommunications system, the number of subscribers can be counted in hundreds. Therefore, mass production is what its all about when it comes to terminals.

In the case of Ericsson, the transition from focusing mainly on the network to focusing equally as much on the terminals connected to the network, has not been easy. The difficulties have mainly been in the area of production management, it has simply been difficult to manufacture the phones in a cost effective way[33]. This is probably the reason behind putting a production expert as manager for the business area Telephones & Terminals.

The question that is of interest here is of course, how come Ericsson has had a change of heart? Why are they now focusing on the production of terminals? What consequences will this have for Ericsson?

## Future competitiveness and competitors

Today a small number of established firms are present in the mobile telecommunications industry. They have been present over a long period of time, and have consolidated their positions through mergers and acquisitions. Since mobile telecommunications is originally a research intensive industry, it has been difficult for new firms to develop products that compete successfully with those of the dominant players. A fundamental knowledge of the technological systems involved has been necessary to develop equipment.

The situation has, however, changed. Mobile telecommunications has become a mature technology, where different systems solutions have become thoroughly standardised in open and transparent standards. This development started in the development of the Nordic NMT system and is yet more apparent in GSM. The most well described part of the mobile telecommunications system is the air interface, between the terminal and the radio base station. This means that from a technological point of view, the terminals represent the subsystem where products from different manufacturers are most exchangeable. This is a well-known fact that can be seen in all digital standards that are in operation.

Looking to the market side, we note that the terminals have become a commodity. They are no longer sold only in specialists stores, but have appeared at household appliances retailers and even in supermarkets[34]. At the same time, the marketing value of the mobile phones has become more and more apparent, even to traditional systems suppliers. This has been amplified by the bad-will suffered when mobile telephony systems have been implemented without having a supply of sufficient amounts of terminals. One well-known example of this is the launch of the Japanese PDC system.

Choosing the Japanese system as an example was not done arbitrarily. The Japanese consumer electronics manufacturers are expected to start selling mobile phones in a large scale[35]. Considering the great experience of these companies in consumer electronics they ought to pose a very real threat to existing suppliers. Both when it comes to competitive manufacturing of the phones, and when it comes to efficiently marketing and distributing them. Will Ericsson, and others, be able to maintain their competitiveness in the long run? If the terminal is an integral part of the network, the answer is probably yes.

## 5. Conclusions

What has become apparent during this study is that the strategic nature of decisions is determined by the consequences they give. When faced with a technological choice, we can only establish it as strategic if its implications are of a strategic nature. However, in a sense this leads us to a contradiction in terms, simply because strategic consequences, changing a firm's structure, market or technology base, are never caused by one single choice. Instead we must consider a number of choices, sequential and parallel, made over a period of time and influencing an outcome that we perceive to be strategically important.

As an example, let us take the discussion in this paper about future producers of mobile telephones, in chapter 4. Here we notice that Ericsson has reorganised in a way that indicates the strategic importance, for the systems suppliers, of the terminals in a mobile telecommunications system. This is not just a consequence of the decision to reorganise the company. It has its roots both in the market development, where new firms pose a potential threat to Ericsson, and in the technological competence, regarding development and production of mobile phones, that Ericsson has built up over several decades.

Discussing the strategic implications of technological choices, leads us to three important aspects of the choice - implication relationship.

Firstly, we note that technological choice is made at a different level of the organisation than the level at which the implications of these choices are observed. Researchers and product developers do not perceive the choices they make to have strategic implications, because at their level they are not in contact with customers and competitors.

Secondly, it is apparent that time has to pass before a certain decision leads to any noticeable effects. Expressed in an other way, the strategic implications we attempt to study always have a back-history. This back-history is partly defined by a number of unobtrusive technological choices, made over a long period of time. This becomes apparent in the case of data services in GSM. The design of these services must be seen as a process where many technological choices were made along the way.

Thirdly, the technological choices are always made in a context. This is the other part of the back-history discussed above, namely because the context for technological choices in itself changes over time. We can see this in both the case of data services in GSM and the possible overturn of the TDMA paradigm by CDMA. In fact, we can go as far as saying that the ever-changing context in which technological choices are made is what causes the unfortunate effect of lock-in.

# References

*Interviews*

Andersson, Jan-Erik. Ericsson Radio Systems. 31 Jan 1996.
Bergenlid, Lars. Ericsson Radio Systems. 19 Apr 1996.
Dahlin, Steinar. Ericsson Radio Systems. 28 Feb 1996.
Fagerstedt, Urban. Ericsson Radio Systems. 12 Mar 1996.
Gudmundsson, Björn. Ericsson Radio Systems. 2 Apr 1996.
Lundqvist, Åke. Formerly Ericsson Radio Systems. 16 Jan 1997 (discussion).
Stjärnvall, Jan-Erik. Ericsson Radio Systems. 14 May 1996.
Wedberg, Rolf. Ericsson Microwave Systems. 19 Jan 1996 and 26 Jan 1996.
Örnulf, Erik. Ericsson Radio Systems. 19 Feb 1996.

*Literature*

Ahlin, Lars & Zander, Jens (1992) *Digital Radiokommunikation - system och metoder*, Studentlitteratur, Lund.

Andersson, C., Ewald, L. & Holmgren, K. (1993) *Handboken i tele och data kommunikation*, Studentlitteratur, Lund.

Arthur, W. Brian (1994) *Increasing Returns and Path Dependence in the Economy*, The University of Michigan Press.

EITO, *European Information Technology Observatory 1995*, Frankfurt, Germany.

Eliasson, Gunnar (1995) *Teknologigenerator eller nationellt prestigeprojekt?: Exemplet svensk flygindustri*, City University Press, Stockholm, Sweden.

Ericsson, "Ericsson changes its organization", *Press Release*, 22 November 1996.

European Telecommunications Standards Institute (1995) *The State of the Art 1995: European Telecommunications Standardization and the Information Society*, Atalink Ltd, London.

Flichy, Patrice (1995) *Dynamics of Modern Communication: The Shaping and Impact of New Communication Technologies*, SAGE Publications, London.

Heimbürger, H. & Tahvanainen, K. V. (1989) *Svenska Telegrafverket: Del VI: Telefon, Telegraf och Radio 1946-1965*, Televerket, Materialavdelningen, Stockholm.

Helgesson, Claes-Fredrik & Ioannidis, Dimitrios (1994) "Företagande i en föränderlig politisk miljö - Telia och staten vid ett näringspolitiskt vägskäl", from *Företag och marknader i förändring - dynamik i nätverk*, Mattson, Lars-Gunnar & Hultén, Staffan (eds), Nerenius & Santérus Förlag, Stockholm.

Karlsson, Magnus (1995) "Nyordning och global reglering", from *Världens största maskin: Människan och det globala telekommunikationssystemet*, Karlsson, M. & Sturesson, L. (eds), Carlsson Bokförlag, Stockholm.

Meurling, J. & Jeans, R. (1995) *A switch in time: AXE - Creating a foundation for the information age*, CommunicationsWeek International, London.

Mouly, M. & Pautet, M.-B. (1992) *The GSM System for Mobile Communications*, Cell & Sys, Palaiseau, France.

Mölleryd, Bengt G. (1996) *Så byggdes en världsindustri - Entreprenörskapets betydelse för svensk mobiltelefoni*, EFI Research Report, Stockholm School of Economics, Stockholm.

Olsson, Hans-Inge "Tuffare marknad för GSM-telefoner", from *Dagens Industri*, p11, 27 June 1996.

*PCS Focus 96/97: The Directory of the PCS Industry*, IBC Business Publishing Ltd., London.

Post- och Telestyrelsen, Information Material, March 1996, Stockholm.

[1]See for example Arthur, 1994.

[2]Conférence Européene des Administrations des Postes et des Télécommunications.

[3]European Telecommunications Standards Institute.

[4]See ETSI's "The State of the Art 1995".

[5]Flichy, 1995:82.

[6]Karlsson, 1995.

[7]According to Post- & Telestyrelsen, Sweden's regulative authority.

[8]Helgesson & Ioannidis, 1994.

[9]An example of a new service that has appeared recently in Sweden is "call waiting".

[10]Mouly & Pautet, 1992:47pp.

[11]The concept is similar to that of alpha numeric paging.

[12]Mouly & Pautet, 1992: 56pp.

[13]High Speed Circuit Switch to Data.

[14]Time Division Multiple Access.

[15]Generalised Packet Radio System.

[16]I.e. the interface between the base station and the handset.

[17]Code Division Multiple Access.

[18]See Ahlin & Zander, 1992.

[19]See Ahlin & Zander, 1992.

[20]In fact the Global Positioning System, GPS, also uses CDMA signalling.

[21]See Ahlin & Zander, 1992.

[22]In terms of population potential for licensees that have chosen CDMA compared to licensees that have chosen other systems, or who have yet to choose. Source: PCS Focus 96/97, pp 74-85.

[23]The system standard using CDMA that has been developed mainly by Qualcomm is officially named IS-95. In daily use it is often, incorrectly, referred to as CDMA. CDMA is the access technology used in the air interface of the IS-95 system, in other words just a small part of the complete system.

[24]Interview with Steinar Dahlin.

[25]Interview with Björn Gudmundsson.

[26]I.e. with realistic assumptions of traffic load, etc.

[27]See Mölleryd, 1996.

[28]See Mölleryd, 1996.

[29]See Eliasson, 1996.

[30]Discussions with Åke Lundqvist, Ericsson Radio Systems, 16 Jan 1997.

[31]EITO, 1995.

[32]See Ericsson press release 22 Nov 1996.

[33]Discussions with Åke Lundqvist, Ericsson Radio Systems, 16 Jan 1997.

[34]See Mölleryd: 1996.

[35]Dagens Industri, 27 June 1996.

# 070

John Lew Cox
Department of Management/MIS
The University of West Florida
11000 University Parkway
Pensacola, FL 32514
USA
Office 904-474-2316
FAX: 904-474-2716
Internet: JCOX@uwf.edu


Marcia R. Howard
Office of the Dean of the College of Business
The University of West Florida
11000 University Parkway
Pensacola, FL 32514
USA
Office: 904-474-2348
FAX: 904-474-2716
Internet: MHOWARD@uwf.edu

**Title:**     **Technology, Virtual Life and Virtual Education:
Perhaps the Luddites Were Right**

**Key Words:** Technology, Education, Technology Management

**Topic:**     F.  Management of technology education; curricula, program evaluation and
unmet needs

**Category:**   1.    Conceptual or Theoretical

**Suitable for:** Oral Presentation

## Technology, Virtual Life and Virtual Education:
## Perhaps the Luddites Were Right

In the early Nineteenth Century, employed and unemployed workers banded together to riot against textile machines. These workers, called Luddites, were fighting the dramatic changes occurring in the workplace during the Industrial Revolution. And while change can represent progress and improvement, it can also signal a demise. To the Luddites, the textile machines signaled the demise of industry as they knew it; and, indeed, an industrial revolution did occur.

Education is on the brink of a similar revolution brought about by the application of technology to learning. And as one contemplates the potential change in the way education is offered via distance and virtual learning, one might also question if the Luddites were right.

Certainly, technology has much to offer the delivery of learning; and traditional delivery systems have not always been effective. "The structure of education and the way people access education is going to change" states the vice president for information systems at Virginia Tech (*Chronicle*, 1997, A26). Few educators would argue against the notion that education needs to change, but they must beware of "throwing out the baby with the bath water."

The introduction to *Technology, Open Learning and Distance Education* (Bates, 1995) states,

> Major changes are needed in the post-secondary and workplace training systems to meet the need for a higher skilled workforce, and for lifelong learning in an increasingly complex society. Recent technological developments provide an opportunity for radical change through the application of open and distance learning. Those countries that harness the power of telecommunications and computing to the education and training needs of the workplace will be the economic leaders of the 21$^{st}$ century. However, there are still justifiable concerns about the quality and cost-effectiveness of technological applications to teaching and learning. (i)

Karen Carr (1995) suggests a curious paradox in that

> virtual reality is hailed as an important advance in helping us to visualize and control more complex information, such as abstract computational data, when it does so by moving us "backwards" into our primitive subjective viewpoint, manipulating our perceptions so that we use an egocentric way of thinking. Virtual reality reduces the need for abstract, extero-centric thinking by presenting processed information in an apparent three-dimensional space, and allowing us to interact with it as if we were part of that space. (1)

445

And the title to the Editor's Note in the January 1997 edition of *Management Review* reads, "Watercooler Effect: Information systems are coming of age, isolating people just when organizations are promoting teamwork" (1).

There is a fine line between supporting education via technology and destroying the human portion of education through technology. Treading that fine line is difficult.

The purpose of this paper is to raise some issues and to stimulate inquiry as we ponder managing technology in the classroom in such a way that personal productivity is augmented and essential personal experiences are preserved. Furthermore, some considerations in the selection and management of technology to preserve the human element will be offered.

**Technology, Virtual Life and Virtual Education: Some Musings**

Technology has allowed us to experience many aspects of the human "experience" artificially (or virtually). We can "fly" virtual airplanes, "tour" virtual houses, "shoot" virtual villains, and carry out a host of other day-to-day activities in an artificial or virtual--as opposed to an actual--sense. Current technology enables us to do much the same thing with the educational process. We can have virtual instruction, distance instruction, teamwork without physical contact, and classes conducted without the necessity of professors and students being in the same geographical or physical location.

Technologically-enabled virtual education allows us a dramatic increase in academic "productivity." We can multiply the effects of one professor as many times as we have the technology to do so, but a question arises: Are we gaining anything by having people "experience" virtual life and virtual business through technology, rather than actually experiencing them? Or, are we making them calloused to actual human experience? Perhaps some light can be shed on the debate by looking at analogous situations.

One professor discusses similarities between the development of artificial intelligence and the development of artificial flight. His point is that no progress was made on man flying (artificial flight) until people moved away from the idea that a prerequisite for flight was feathers attached to appendages. In attempting to develop artificial intelligence, little progress was made until people removed themselves from the idea that the computer needed to look like the human brain. Will no progress be made in "artificial instruction" until people detach themselves from the idea that someone must stand in front of a room? Yet, the point of much of the enabling technology for virtual education seems to be the replication of the human being (professor) in as many dimensions as possible.

A good deal of the technology works toward making the "person" standing in front of the room more realistic by better communication between the home site and the remote site. The sense of reality is limited only by the amount of money the organization is willing to spend. The technology range on virtual education runs from e-mail (text only) through actual virtual meetings lacking only the third dimension and the visual/aural cues allowing the seer/listener to home in on the source of the conversation. But a major question becomes "Should the objective be to make the virtual professor more realistic, or should the objective be to facilitate learning?" The answer can have a great impact on the design and implementation of any distance learning system.

If realism is the major determinant, perhaps several microphones at the sending end can be hooked to the respective speakers/locations at the receiving end to allow speaker/listener to have a more immediate connection. Otherwise, when a voice is heard, the listener must look to see which mouth is moving to determine where in the image to look. In addition, the purchase of what currently are expensive projection devices (a la the digital light systems of Texas Instruments) may be necessary so that images can be adjusted to life-size. If one follows this line of thinking, it will soon be possible (for the proper investment) to have holographic images to add the third (now lacking) dimension. Will this add to the learning experience? It is likely it will add to the "experience" but perhaps not to the learning. Hence, the question already posed: "Should the objective be to make the virtual professor more realistic, or should the objective be to facilitate learning?"

Perhaps one of the major advantages of a static media distance learning class or classes is the fact it is replicative. That is, once a videotape is made, or once a CD is made, any number can be made in exactly the same image. If this version of "distance learning" is used, however, it loses the interaction and spontaneity of real-time two-way audio/video. Is this a detriment? It depends on whether the emphasis is on the technology and realism or on learning.

No matter how one may define "distance education," there are some things one cannot get through distance education. For example, human contact is missing in virtual education, and some human contact is essential.

Consider the possibility of a baby reared by virtual reality rather than actual reality. Would that baby's rearing be equivalent to actual reality? Currently, that answer must be "No." As technology develops, we may get closer; but until we get near the story lines and androids of Star Wars or Star Trek, the experiences provided by humanity cannot be replicated. No matter how imperfect they may be, humans still provide unique experiences.

The human information comes from the higher level sensory contacts other than virtual reality. In general, people can distinguish, at least for the moment, between the human voice and a computer generated voice. What is the difference in the touching of keys versus the touching of a person? Through distance education, one can get facts well. Can one get knowledge? The student can also amass or develop a mastery of things and technology, but is this education?

In his book *Cybercorp: the New Business Revolution* (1996), James Martin suggests, "For every operation in a cybercorp we need to ask, 'What should be done in-house and what should be done virtual?'" While the university may not consider itself a cybercorp, one must ask whether it should do so. In the beginning of *Cybercorp*, for instance, Martin defines a "cybercorp" as

A corporation designed using the principles of cybernetics. A corporation optimized for the age of cyberspace. A cybernetic corporation with senses constantly alert, capable of reacting in real time to changes in its environment, competition, and customer needs, with virtual operations or agile linkages of competencies in different organizations when necessary. A corporation designed for fast change, which can learn, evolve, and transform itself rapidly. (5)

In many cases, universities tend to react, as in Tom Lehrer's old lyrics, like ". . .ivy-covered professors in ivy-covered halls"; i.e., change comes very slowly. They may, in fact, get to the point of trying the usual distance education and teleconferencing at the point where corporations have already decided there are better alternatives and have moved on.

In the early days of personal desktop computers, many corporations and people bought computers because "everyone" was buying them. They then looked for things the computers could do. On the one hand, this was a great waste of corporate and personal monies. On the other hand, it provided an impetus for many thousands of people and corporations to be introduced to the personal computer, people and corporations who may not have become familiar with them until much later. Then, one asks, "Are we trying to do distance learning because it is better, or because "everyone" is doing it?"

**Preserving the Human Element**

Without question, technology can enhance the educational process. It can evaluate a student's needs and progress; outline a path by which a student achieves specific objectives; provide meaningful, individualized drill and practice; select a specific review program based upon an individual student's path through a program. All of these and more, technology can provide, perhaps more effectively and even with more pizzazz, than can the human instructor. But the human element is still essential to the educational process if students are going to be able to perform and interact successfully with humans in the real world.

Human beings comprise the real world. Ultimately, all communication between and among humans depends upon the use of the five recognized senses. In any encounter, each sense contributes a varying amount of the total information acquired. The most informative communication results from a combination of all the senses.

In the usual business or organizational environment, the majority of business is conducted via face-to-face meetings wherein each participant has the advantage of five senses. When the input of all senses is not available, some information is lost and the message may be faulty. Thus, the information conveyed and the information acquired will be different than if all sensory input were present. The management of virtual encounters in a virtual setting requires a different kind of expertise. Some of the major decisions to be made in the management of technology toward

**448**

virtual education, then, revolve around what is to be conveyed.

Many educators employ a model which is helpful in determining and designing meaningful educational experiences:

1. Recognize/identify the need
2. Draw up goals and objectives
3. Select and utilize the technique/delivery system which can most effectively meet the goals and objectives
4. Evaluate the experience to determine if goals and objectives were accomplished

Only when we have defined what the end should be can we determine which media most efficiently and effectively accomplish those ends. If education is to produce a "knowledgeable" citizenry, one which has the knowledge and the skills to interact in the real world, it must employ the best blend of media to meet those goals and objectives. Facilitating learning is the aim.

Do we want humans to look like birds? Or do we want them to fly? Only when we can shift the paradigm from our traditional image of instruction--a human in front of a classroom full of bodies--to a careful blend of media to accomplish varying needs will education be most productive. As the paradigm shifts, we need to retain what works well and draw in other means to augment and enhance the educational experience. But we must not throw out the baby with the bath water.

## Summary

Many current organizations conduct their business in locations dispersed around the globe. A 1995 issue of *Business Week* describes the current trend in typical large business organizations:

> Texas Instruments' high speed telecommunications chip may look like any other semiconductor. But it's the product of a world's worth of effort. Conceived with engineers from Ericsson Telephone Co. in Sweden, it was designed in Nice with TI software tools developed in Houston. Today, the TCM9055 chip is produced in Japan and Dallas, tested in Taiwan, and wired into Ericsson line-cards that monitor phone systems in Sweden, the U.S., Mexico, and Australia. (64)

Such is the way "modern" business is transacted. As early as the 1970s, electronic media were suggested as a means to enable physically close or geographically dispersed group collaborators. And students from universities must be cognizant of this type of business; they must be comfortable working in it. Thus, it would seem to make sense to impart some of the content of their degree programs using the same types of information technology.

However, in the final analysis, much of business is still conducted face-to-face--actually, not virtually. The education of our university graduates must include not only the facts, theories, and practices necessary for them to understand and apply tools crucial to their trade but also the skills which are vital to their being able to make decisions that are ethically sound in the human ramification.

Facts, figures, theories, and applications of them to practical situations may be practiced to some degree by virtual means. To really know how one will react in the same actual situation requires actual reality rather than virtual reality. Unless the students have to face the results of their decisions and understand the feelings in looking at a human, more Luddites may be running around with technological sabots (like viruses) ruining the machinery of business.

In *Reaching Learners through Telecommunications* (1993), the authors observe,

> It is commonplace for education at every level to use a "damaged goods" response to explain educational shortcomings. Each educational level suggests that the preceding level sent them damaged goods -- that is, ill-prepared learners. At the lowest educational level the source of the damaged goods is said to be learners' parents. No level of education and training can be wholly responsible for student preparation, nor can it be entirely without accountability for the adoption of practices that respond to social, economic, and cultural imperatives. (201)

This is a good observation as far as education is concerned, but it may not make the point that the same explanation or accusation is made of the outcomes of the educational system; i.e., the graduates, by the employers of these graduates. Education is accused of delivering damaged goods, goods that cannot perform in organizations, in the so-called "real world." Technology can augment the work of professors and teachers in imparting facts, techniques, and theories; but for the parts of the job that require interfacing with actual, rather than virtual, people, technology (at least current technology) may be inferior to live practice. Will education through technology face the accusation of delivering graduates who cannot interface with people?

Martin has also suggested that "mass production is being replaced by agile networks of producers..." (6). Perhaps the same should be true of education. The best education may be procured by each type of the current capabilities doing what it does best. Some facts and other techniques may well be learned best through the use of some type of machine (computer) that can generate an endless stream of examples on specific subjects or techniques, allowing the student to practice until his or her heart's content, and beyond, without trying the patience of a human teacher. Some types of other knowledge transfer may perhaps be passed on using technology that allows anonymous input and question asking. Some can be learned best (if at all) by face-to-face contact between real humans rather than virtual humans. Experiential education falls in this last category. Can the same learning occur where the experience is virtual, rather than actual? While one recognizes that some "virtual" experiences can evoke real emotion (some motion pictures, for instance), it is unlikely that enough widespread talent exists to build the same type of emotion-evoking experiences into virtual (distance) education.

450

If we make a continuum of education process, we can put "education" totally via technology at one end and "education" totally by the Socratic method at the other. Only reality can't be illustrated virtually.

This paper has served a heuristic function: it raises questions, presents issues, and hopefully stimulates inquiry. Certainly, much study is needed to determine the most effective and efficient use of technology to effect learning. Only time will tell, and as the future becomes the present, educators will face the results of their own decision making. Perhaps the Luddites were right.

## References

Bates, A. (1995). *Technology, Open Learning and distance education.* London: Routledge, Inc.

Blumenstyk, G. (1997, January 17). An experiment in 'virtual community' takes shape in Blacksburg, Va. *The Chronicle of Higher Education,* pp. A24, A26.

Burroughs, P., Bernier, L., and Engardis, P. (August 7, 1995). Texas Instruments' global chip payoff. *Business Week,* pp.64-66.

Carr, K. and England, R. (Eds.) (1995). *Simulated and virtual realities: Elements of perception.* London: Taylor & Francis.

Duning, B. Van Kekerix, M., and Zaboroweski, L. (1993). *Reaching learners through telecommunication,* San Francisco: Jossey-Bass Publishers.

Peak, M. (1997, January). *Management review.* Watercooler effect: Information systems are coming of age, isolating people just when organizations are promoting teamwork. 86:1, p. 1.

Martin, J. (1996). *Cybercorp: The new business revolution.* New York: AMACOM.

# 071

# TECHNOLOGY AND CYBERSPACE EFFECTS: THE 21ST CENTURY UNIVERSITY

Author
John Lew Cox, Ph.D.
Dept. of Mgt/MIS,Coll. of Bus., Dean's Off.
The University of West Florida
11000 University Parkway
Pensacola, Florida 32514 - 5752
U. S. A.
Tel:        +1-904-474-2313
Fax:        +1-904-474-2314

Co-author:
Parks B. Dimsdale, Ph.D.
The University of West Florida
11000 University Parkway
Pensacola, Florida 32514 - 5752
U. S. A.
Tel:.       +1-904 - 474 - 2666
FAX:        +1-904 - 474 - 2314

## ABSTRACT

Industries for the twenty-first century must undergo profound changes, and this is certainly true of the "university" industry. Whether traditional manufacturing or services, a common theme is the necessary and complete redefinition of the "product" and an equally dramatic reorganization of the distribution channels. Both the redefinition and the reorganization depend heavily on the use of cyberspace, as well as on the use and management of supporting technology.

At least three characteristics have been essentially forced upon twenty-first century universities by the availability, advertising, and promulgation of cyberspace. The characteristics are all related to the utilization of technology, and all involve their making great use of both the internet and intranets. These characteristics are (1) Virtual, (2) Micro-Wired, and (3) Macro-Networked, and each is elaborated upon below.

VIRTUAL. Universities must make services available to both current and potential students who may not be located AT the university. While these students may be PLACE-BOUND, that PLACE may not be the campus. Interaction will most likely be via virtual meetings, connoting the availability of continually updated communications technology (with "communications" defined in the broadest sense, including two-way voice, image, and data).

MICROWIRED. Universities must be micro-wired; i.e., the students must be able to access any of the services of the university from a remote location, whether that service is admissions, purchasing of books or materials, payment of fees, or accessing the library. In addition, they must have access to EACH OTHER in order to work as virtual teams. This connotes the technology allowing such access.

MACRO-NETWORKED. Universities must serve as throughways to the macro- environment of other universities and their libraries, industrial organizations and their data, and governmental entities and their data. This will be necessary in order for them to acquire the necessary information to perform in their programs of study as well as to pursue employment. Further, their knowledge in this area will allow them to live in the realm of continual virtual education.

The full paper will address how each of these characteristics requires the university environment and operations to be changed, and will discuss the ongoing impact on the task of managing the supporting technology that is needed for the changes to occur. Finally, the paper will offer alternatives on how to move forward in the best manner.

KEY WORDS: Technology, Education, Technology Management

Oral Presentation

# 072

# NATIONAL TECHNOLOGY POLICIES: US ADVANCED TECHNOLOGY PROGRAM

Author:
Spender J.C.
Dean, Sch of Mgt, NYIT,
POBox 8000 Old Westbury NY 11568
USA
Tel:        +1-516-686-7423
Fax:        +1-516-484-8328
Email:      spender@admin.nyit.edu

## ABSTRACT

Given the rising domestic and global economic and political
significance of technology-based industry, governments in mixed
economies see many reasons to intervene in their private sector's
R&D. But the theoretical justifications for government
intervention into the private sector are hotly debated and poorly
researched. The most widely accepted argument in favor of
intervention is that private R&D has substantial public payoff
and that it therefore behooves government to subsidize activities
which would otherwise fall victim to failures in the market for
infrastructural goods. For this reason, like many other
industrialized countries, especially those in Europe, the US is
experimenting with non-military technology R&D support programs.
We consider the Department of Commerce's Advanced Technology
Program (ATP), established in 1988 and considerably expanded
since. The peculiarly hostile political environment for this
program has surfaced new varieties of policy discussion. It has
proved important to move beyond the market failure argument above
into a richer analysis that reflects the interplay of interests
which this kind of program affects. The paper offers a
conceptualization which describes technology support programs as
promoting trajectories through an innovation space formed by
partnership between the US's three institutionally distinct modes
of scientific and technological innovation: scientific research,
private enterprise and public sector management of our society's
public goods.

# 073

# Functional Integration of R&D and Marketing in a Firm's Capability-Building Process: Case Studies of Drug Innovation Projects

Qing Wang
Science Policy Research Unit, University of Sussex, Brighton, United Kingdom

*Abstract*

A considerable number of studies have been assembled over the last decade on the management of the R&D/marketing interface in product innovation. Most of these studies focus on the R&D/marketing interface as a self-contained unit of analysis, offering little explanation of the interface's contribution to a firm's competence building in ways essential to innovation success. This paper demonstrates that the importance of the R&D/marketing interface lies in its dynamic capability in influencing the direction of product development projects towards enhancing existing, or building new, competencies. The case study results show that this dynamic capability is concentrated in three areas, i.e. corporate conceptual development (CCD), product conceptual development (PCD) and project implementation (Ip). The case studies evidence reveals that the performance of project teams during the implementation stage, is heavily dependent on *earlier* activities in the areas of CCD and PCD. This in turn indicates that the dynamic interface capability evolves over time, thus pinpointing the vital importance of learning-before-doing in the innovation process.

## 1. Introduction

The R&D/marketing interface is critical for new product success (Cooper & Kleinschmidt, 1987; Souder & Chakrabarti, 1978; Hauser & Clausing, 1988). The interface issue is central to the debate as to whether new product development should be driven by technology or market, since it represents the point where these two forces intersect. During the past ten years, the pace of research into the effects of R&D/marketing integration on both project and company-level success has accelerated. Most of these studies focus on the R&D/marketing interface as a self-contained unit of analysis, and address issues such as successful factors for effective R&D/marketing integration, communication channels and integrating mechanisms. A more recent study (Wang, 1996) revealed that changes in corporate structure (towards flatter and project-based organisations) and communication channels (the increased use of information and communication technology networks) in large firms have resolved some of the traditional interface problems such as lack of credibility of marketing information and lack of commercial awareness of R&D personnel. However, these changes at the same time have resulted in higher demands for cross-functional integration, flexible partitioning of tasks, and timely technology commercialisation. Each of these demands, in turn, presents a new challenge to the R&D/marketing interface. Against this background, this paper will argue that a deeper theoretical understanding of the R&D/marketing interface is best obtained from a perspective which has its basis in the knowledge and capabilities of the firm.

The starting point of the current research is the unique contribution of the R&D/marketing interface in linking product to market and an organisation to its technological and market environment. From a knowledge-based view, such a role can be interpreted as the dynamic capability that exploits a firm's existing technological and marketing capability in responding to the changing market and technological environment. This dynamic capability embedded at the interface involves both internal and external integration. In the current research this interface capability is shown to evolve over time, as the two functions of R&D and marketing build shared knowledge for the purpose of performing development project tasks. Since this shared knowledge is embedded in people and embodied in co-ordination mechanisms and new product development approaches, it goes beyond a firm's functional competence to form an essential part of the firm's core capability.

We use projects as a vehicle to study the relationship between functional integration of R&D and marketing and a firm's capability-building, and propose that the importance of the R&D/marketing interface lies in its ability to influence a project's direction towards enhancing existing or creating new competencies. This proposed linkage between a firm's core capabilities, development projects and the R&D/marketing interface emerges from literature on the nature of organisational competence. It is captured in the conceptual framework developed in this paper. Furthermore, recent field research conducted by the author on twelve new product development projects in the UK pharmaceutical industry has been used to test this framework. Owing to space limitations, only four project case studies are described in detail in this paper. However, the cross-case analysis and empirical findings presented in the final section are based on results of all twelve project case studies.

## 2. The R&D/Marketing Interface Literature

The need for managing flows across marketing and R&D boundaries was recognised as important in the 1970s (Rubenstein *et al.*, 1976; Block, 1977), became critical in the 1980s, and has continued to be important to firm success since then (Souder & Sherman, 1993). Research prior to this period, which assumed hierarchical corporate structures with separate functional groups, is being reassessed in the light of interfunctional innovations. The functions of marketing and R&D used to be centralised in a single person in the early era. However, as the firm grows larger, these two functional groups grow apart and become specialised only in their own fields. As integration and communication between these two critical functions decreases, their ability to combine knowledge and skills to develop successful products decreases, and the firm suffers.

Scientific evidence in the field of product development suggests that good communication between marketing and R&D enhances new product success, whilst poor communication results in new product failure (Cooper, 1983, 1984, 1990; Dougherty, 1990). This has led to further research attempts at identifying the states of the R&D/marketing interface, the barriers to communication and the causes of the interface problems. The main barriers to the effective R&D/marketing interface have been found to be related to perceptual, cultural, organisational and language factors. Firstly, Gupta, Raj and Wilmon (1986) found that marketing and R&D managers were similar in many traits, the main difference being in time orientation. This suggests that the true barrier may be a perceptual one of stereotypes rather than actual personality differences. Secondly, the cultural difference results from their different training and background (Gupta *et al.*, 1986; Souder, 1988). Thirdly, organisational barriers arise out of different task priorities, ambiguity tolerance and departmental structures. Finally, the language difference is such that, whilst marketing professionals speak in terms of product benefits and perceptual positions, R&D professionals speak the quantitative language of specifications and performance. Misinterpretation and incomprehension disconnect customer needs from engineering solutions, even though each group thinks they are talking about exactly the same thing . If each group does not understand customer needs at the level of detail that they need to do their job, they become frustrated with the communication process (Griffin & Hauser, 1996).

However, most of this research failed to drew a distinction between those interface barriers and problems that are situational and those that are non-situational to the external technological and market environment. Apparently, such a distinction is significant at least in practice for differentiated problem-solving. For example, in Souder's (1988) customer-developer-condition (CDC) model, according to the level of sophistication of customers[1] (a function of the market condition), and the level of sophistication of a firm's R&D[2] (a function of the technological condition), the interface can be divided into seven different states, each with distinctive interface tasks and problems, and thus different problem-solving mechanisms. The research results reported in this paper support the contention that the amount of integration required between marketing and R&D depends on the environment within which product development occurs.

The main achievement of the interface research so far has been a better understanding of the process of interfunctional communication and integration. However, the effect of this integration process upon the evolution of a firm's capability in new product development has not been examined. This paper argues that a study of this kind requires a knowledge-based perspective.

## 3. The Development of A Research Framework

The connection between knowledge and core capability[3] has been an important theme in recent work on the nature of organisational competence (Prahalad and Hamel, 1990; Leonard-Barton, 1992; Pisano, 1994). Research that focuses on the learning curve has documented the tendency for manufacturing performance to improve with cumulative production experience and has provided an empirical foundation for the concept of 'learning-by-doing' (Arrow, 1962). However, Pisano (1994) points out that the learning curve reflects only a narrow slice of the broader phenomenon of organisational learning. Firms routinely create and implement new organisational and technical processes through purposeful planning and R&D prior to the start of production. Kenney and Florida (1994) emphasise the economic and technical efficiencies that come from collaborative problem-solving and learning.

---

[1] Customers' level of sophistication is defined in terms of their need awareness and their ability to communicate their needs.
[2] R&D's level of sophistication refers to their understanding of products and their technical means to develop the products.
[3] Leonard-Barton (1992) defines a core capability as the knowledge set that distinguishes and provides a competitive advantage. Its content is embodied in (1) employee knowledge and skills and embedded in (2) technical systems. The processes of knowledge creation and control are guided by (3) managerial systems, whilst associated with the processes of knowledge creation and control are (4) the values and norms. Thus a core capability is an interrelated and interdependent knowledge system.

Apparently, the learning process occurring at the R&D/marketing interface is intrinsically social and collective. It comes about because of joint contributions to the understanding of complex problems, such as engineering design and customer need trade-offs, rather than merely through the imitation and emulation of individuals, as with teacher-student relationships. Consequently, this process results not only in new functional knowledge, but more importantly in new product development knowledge, which includes new product development approaches, co-ordination mechanisms and cross-functional climate. Their value to the organisation goes far beyond the boundaries of the two functional departments.

Previous studies (Souder, 1988; Wang, 1996) found that the amount of shared effort required from the two sides is not consistent but varies according to specific situations. Thus, in order to apply timely information and to adjust product development activity accordingly, an on-going dialogue and communication must be maintained between these two critical functions. From a knowledge-based view, this communication is more than the exchange of messages. Rather, it involves the development of a common horizon as a basis for learning to take place. This is because learning requires common codes of communication and co-ordinated search procedures. In this manner, knowledge accumulates on the basis of both external and internal stimuli in the joint area of R&D and marketing and expands to the entire organisation.

**Figure 1 A framework for studying the role of the R&D/marketing integration in building a firm's new product development capability**

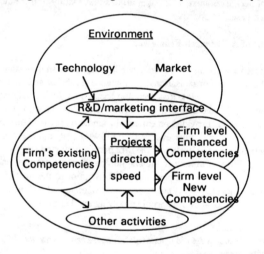

In this framework, a linkage between a firm's competencies, product development projects and the R&D/marketing interface is established. It postulates the vital importance of the R&D/marketing interface in influencing a project's direction ( in both conceptual development stage and implementation stage) towards enhancing existing or creating new competencies. Moreover, this interface capability evolves over time and strengthened by earlier activities.

# 4. The Research Population and Samples

## 4.1 Market Competition in the Pharmaceutical Industry

The most distinctive feature of the pharmaceutical industry is the co-existence of two layers of customers, namely doctors and patients. The industry is highly profitable and is thus attractive for potential newcomers. However, there exist substantial barriers to entry, and these include patents, R&D investments, marketing investments and company reputation. The pharmaceutical market can be subdivided into ethical pharmaceuticals and over-the-counter medicines. In the ethical pharmaceutical market, there are two types of product, patent-protected brands and generics. Business portfolios in the pharmaceutical industry vary a great deal from one company to another. Some companies have highly diversified businesses across most areas, including branded products, generic products and over-the-counter medicines, whilst some other companies concentrate only on ethical pharmaceuticals. It is necessary to note that even in the ethical pharmaceutical market, there exist as many as nine main therapeutic areas, including cardiovascular, anti-cancer, antiviral, anti-ulcerate, antibiotics, respiratory, central nervous systems, etc. Each area requires a distinctive set of scientific and technological knowledge and marketing expertise. Therefore, for companies who have decided to concentrate on ethical pharmaceuticals, they still need to acquire new technological and marketing knowledge (which may be unrelated to their existing expertise), if they want to extend their businesses to a therapeutic market they have not served before.

Overall the industry remains very fragmented. However, at the level of therapeutic area, the market share is much more concentrated in several major companies. For instance, the top three manufacturers of cardiovascular drugs, Merck, Bristol-Meyer Squibb and ICI controlled about 40% of the therapeutic market (abpi estimates). Drug innovation is a major competitive weapon, and companies are relying on "blockbusters" even more than before. Consequently, as sales of the largest-selling drugs become ever larger, it is increasingly difficult to achieve adequate size from sales in just one market, and international marketing scale becomes critical.

## 4.2 The Research sample

The four case studies are taken from a large scale investigation of twelve case studies of drug innovation projects. These cases are selected for theoretical rather than statistical reasons. They are cases of extreme examples and polar types in which the processes of interest for this research are as transparently observable as possible. These four case studies are largely representative in terms of project types[4] and company coverage. Since the 'Unrelated Technology and Unrelated Market' type of

---

[4] Among the twelve projects, four belonged to a "related technology and related market" (hereafter RT-RM) type of project, two belonged to a "related technology but new market" (hereafter RT-NM) type of project, three belonged to a "unrelated technology and unrelated market" (hereafter UT-UM) type of project, and three belonged to a "new technology and new market" (hereafter NT-NM) type of project. There is a clear distinction between "UT-UM" type of project and "NT-NM" type of project. The technology required for the former is new to the firm, but has been mastered by competitors; similarly, the project's target market is new to the firm, but is already a well-established territory of

project appears to be most problematic, we selected two of them ( a success and a failure) to compare. In order to ensure reliability of data, we applied multiple data collection methods, including archives, industry reports, interviews, a small-scale questionnaire survey and on-site observation. A total of forty-four people were interviewed during a twelve-month period. Every interview was carefully prepared and most companies provided detailed materials in advance, and many interviews were tape-recorded. The twelve drug development cases are analysed on the basis of the conceptual framework. The following aspects in particular are highlighted in the case studies:

(a) the technological, market and competitive environment of the project;
(b) the activities carried out at the R&D/marketing interface
(c) the effect of these interface activities upon a firm's competence building

**Table 1 Brief description of the twelve projects studied**

| Company | Project | Type | Degree of market success |
|---|---|---|---|
| Glaxo | **Zantac\*** | UT-UM | **Very high** |
| | Serevent | RT-RM | High |
| | Imigran | NT-NM | High |
| SmithKline Beecham | Tagamet | NT-NM | High |
| | Augmentin | RT-RM | High |
| | **Eminase\*** | UT-UM | **Very low** |
| ICI Pharmaceuticals | Tenormin | RT-RM | High |
| | **Zoladex\*** | RT-NM | **Low** |
| | Diprivan | RT-RM | Moderately high |
| Wellcome | **Zovirax\*** | NT-NM | **High** |
| | Lamictal | UT-UM | Very low |
| | Retrovir | RT-NM | Moderately high |

## 5. The Accounts of Four Individual Case Studies of The Drug Innovation Projects

### 5.1 Zantac Project (UT-UM)

Zantac project was initiated within Glaxo in 1976 for the purpose of finding an effective ulcer treatment. However, only several months after its initiation, a breakthrough in the same area was announced by SmithKline for its discovery of the first H2-antagonist - Tagamet - the first effective treatment for peptic ulcers. The research team members in Glaxo analysed factors including the size and potential of the new market and the performance of Tagamet, especially with regard to its high side-effects and frequent dosage needs. They came to the conclusion that there was still a place in the market for an improved anti-ulcer drug. Consequently, they made the crucial decision to switch their goal from finding a completely new agent to developing an improved H2-antagonist.

competitors. For the latter, the scientific knowledge and approaches required do not yet exist, and thus need to be developed from scratch; similarly, the project's target market is untapped virgin territory. Therefore, in the "NT-NM" type of project, the firm is both a technology leader and a market leader.

The timing of the Zantac project was crucial for its success. It came after the company's restructuring programme, which had led to the disposal of the company's non-ethical pharmaceutical businesses in order to fit the company's new corporate strategy. The strategy identified the ethical pharmaceutical market as being the market of greatest potential, and prioritised five therapeutic areas for its resource allocation. Some of these therapeutic areas were new to the company, and thus required very different sets of technological and marketing expertise and knowledge (anti-ulcer was one of them). As a result of the restructuring, communication had been improved and employees' minds had been focused. During the six years from 1970 to 1976, the company was searching and preparing for a suitable project to create new competencies.

In this climate, the R&D and marketing people worked together effectively both at the conceptual development stage and implementation stage of the project, despite the lack of previous experience in anti-ulcer drug R&D and marketing. Top management was present in most important decision-making at the project level. Influenced by R&D and marketing, the team applied a novel 'development-in-parallel' approach and a simultaneous world-wide co-ordination mechanism for the new drug's development. These approaches allowed clinical tests to be undertaken simultaneously rather than sequentially, thus significantly reducing the development time. The case study has revealed that a change towards using such new approaches to replace the old functional and local based co-ordination mechanisms was conceived *before* the Zantac project began. The Zantac project acted as a catalyst and a focal point for these approaches to flourish.

The implementation stage was also crucial, since Zantac's success largely depended on the extent to which customers could appreciate the additional benefit provided by an improved drug. This required a convincing translation of the new drug's technical advantages into major customer benefits. For instance, Zantac's major technical advantage over its rival, Tagamet, was its lower dosage requirement and lower side effects. One could argue that these advantages were minor, because peptic ulcers are not a condition for which patients need regular treatment. However, the project team succeeded in convincing customers of the drug's major benefit in prevention as well as treatment because of its lower side effects, which in turn had resulted in a market extension into the prevention market segment. This result had a major implication for the firm's competence building in that, not only had it created a new competence in developing new product in the ulcer *treatment* segment, it had, at the same time, extended this competence into the ulcer *prevention* segment.

The Zantac project has been regarded as a classical example of the success of heavyweight project management. Strong top management involvement during the project has thus been considered as the major success factor. However, empirical evidence from this research shows that the contribution of top management involvement at project level was more symbolic than real. The real contribution came from the successful application of novel approaches and mechanisms, which had evolved since the restructuring process, and were guided by meaningful corporate strategy.

## 5.2 Eminase Project (UT-UM)

Eminase was a heart attack treatment developed by Beecham. The company was new to the cardiovascular market and technology. The concept of Eminase was developed by the research people following an accidental discovery of a molecular association. The project began in 1983 and was launched by Beecham in 1989 during the process of merger.

Heart attack is caused by the formulation of clots in the blood circulation system. The question was how to make a drug which would bust up the clots faster and more directly. Time saving is regarded as being crucial in treating heart attack patients.

There already existed several heart attack treatments in the market. These included Genetech's Activase (TPA), costing £1,600, and streptokinase, an old drug, costing £200. Beecham's Eminase costs £1,200. Unlike the other drugs, Eminase was targeted at the GP market, rather than at cardiologists in the traditional hospital market. The competitive pressure was intense because none had a clear advantage over the others. Beecham attempted to differentiate Eminase from its rivals by emphasising the new drug's time-saving benefit. The company also faced a very demanding and difficult task of educating the GP market. Normally GPs did not treat heart attack patients. Instead, they gave them oxygen or a heart simulator and rushed them to hospital. Having no experience in this area, GPs were wary of making mistakes and facing negligence claims.

Despite these major obstacles to Eminase project, the company decided to go ahead with it. This decision was accompanied by a huge financial commitment due to the biotechnological nature of the new drug. Consequently, this project was given high priority, and top management was heavily involved at the project level in anticipation of the difficulties facing the project.

The R&D/marketing interface came later at the implementation stage. The interface activities included the investigation of consumer attitudes, product positioning and differentiation, and design of a massive education programme. Despite a strong push from top management, they found it difficult to perform these tasks satisfactorily. R&D people complained about the inconsistency and lack of reliability of marketing information, whereas marketing people were frustrated, and viewed their role passively as 'damage limitation'. Concern about being blamed for it was at the back of some team members' minds, especially since both R&D and marketing people were working in areas that were unfamiliar to them. As a result, co-operation was superficial and reserved. Therefore, despite top management's determination to create new competencies in developing new products in the cardiovascular area, the project team, particularly the R&D and marketing people, felt ill-prepared for the task and were overwhelmed by the problems.

The development project took six years and the drug was highly innovative technologically, winning the Queen's Award for Technology Achievement in 1990. However, despite strong top management involvement and a heavyweight project management style, the Eminase project was not commercially successful. Sales of Eminase were extremely low, especially compared to its high development cost and expectation. This case manifests the limited effects of heavyweight management and the importance of the R&D/marketing interface at the concept development stage. The project was set up to create a new competence in developing a product in a new therapeutic area. However, this target was not achieved, and the poor interface between R&D and marketing was one of the major causes for such failure.

### 5.3 Zoladex Project (RT-NM)

Zoladex was developed by ICI Pharmaceuticals. Prior to its conception, the company's corporate management had identified anti-cancer drug development as an important element in its long-term strategy. Having successfully developed an effective breast cancer treatment, the target was set for a lung cancer treatment, as it is the largest category in the cancer market. Zoladex, a new chemical compound for prostate cancer treatment, was discovered unexpectedly in 1976, and launched in 1987.

At the time when the project was initiated, the most common treatment in the anti-prostate market was surgical castration. Although this was effective, a number of patients felt that a kinder and less intrusive alternative would be welcome. Since other companies were also active in developing drug treatments for prostate cancer, ICI Pharmaceuticals was confronting both non-pharmaceutical and pharmaceutical competitors.

The new product concept was developed by research people in the laboratory. The interface between R&D and marketing started later at the implementation stage. This late involvement was particularly difficult for the marketing people. This was because the scientific knowledge needed for developing an anti-prostate cancer drug was related to the company's existing technological base, which had been built up and evolved since the company's earlier projects in the anti-breast cancer area. In contrast, the market knowledge required for the prostate cancer market, which mainly consists of males over 70 years of age, was entirely different from that for the breast cancer market, where all patients are women. However, little effort was made to address this knowledge gap, except for the establishment of a cross-functional team at the implementation stage. The R&D people were dissatisfied by the quality of marketing information and were suspicious of its reliability. Consequently, although joint effort was made in identifying the target market, developing promotional programmes and communicating the drug's benefit to the customers, the effectiveness was very limited.

The development speed was very slow, with the process taking eleven years. The drug was innovative. However, its commercial performance was not satisfactory. It had generated only £50 million in sales four years after launch. This case illustrates that one cannot assume that because the knowledge and skills required for developing technical functions and features of a new product are similar to the firm's existing technologies, the marketing knowledge and skills required for the project will also be the same as the existing marketing knowledge and skills. Instead, for the new product development, the firm should carefully identify the gap, not only between a firm's existing and required technological knowledge and skills, but also between its existing and required marketing knowledge and skills. Apparently this is an important task; its accomplishment requires the new product development project to be market-oriented.

### 5.4 Zovirax Project (NT-NM)

Zovirax was developed by Wellcome. The drug was the first effective treatment for shingles and herpes infection in the antiviral therapeutic area. Seven indications were developed and launched during a course of sixteen years. Antiviral research was extremely challenging scientifically, which partly explains why there is still no serious competition in this area even though Zovirax was first launched more than ten years ago. Zovirax was a biotechnology-derived drug with a highly selective mode of action and low side effects.

The project began in 1974, and had resulted from the company's then technological policy of pursuing scientific excellence when the company was owned by the Wellcome Trust. The new product concept was developed by scientists who looked into modified nuclear bases in the hope that the resulting compound would interfere with virus replication.

For the purpose of investigating the R&D/marketing interface and the firm's competence building process, we divide the Zovirax project into two distinctive stages. The first stage covers the period from the development of the new product concept in the research laboratory to the launch of the first product indication, an eye ointment for treating simple infection. It took seven years. The second stage covers the period from the launch of the first product indication to the completion of all six major product indications. The second stage lasted nine years and the six product indications included genital herpes treatment, intravenous serious herpes infection treatment, cold sores treatment, shingles treatment and chicken pox treatment.

At the first stage, the project was research-driven, with the purposes of exploring a completely new scientific area and developing a new class of product. The market was also completely new and there was no competition. Doctors were not adequately aware of patients' need for treatment, because of diagnosis difficulties and patients' reluctance in seeking treatment. As a result, it was difficult to evaluate the market size for this new drug, and the company's original forecast of £15 million annual sales was later proved to be a gross underestimation.

Because of the novelty and uncertainty of this project, there was no pressure either from the market or from the corporate management to complete the project quickly. The project team 'took its time' to develop the new drug, as both marketing people and R&D people were finding their way forward. They were overwhelmed by what were seen as their own functional problems: for R&D, it was the challenging scientific and technical problems; for marketing, it was the problem of estimating potential market size, pricing and stimulating primary demand in the market. Consequently, the R&D/marketing interface was almost non-existent until very near to the launch of the first product indication. This eye ointment was first to be launched because it had the same dosage form as an existing old treatment, which provided a basis for comparison.

In the second stage, the purpose was switched to exploiting the full benefit of this new product class and to finding as many applications for it as possible. In order to do so, the R&D and marketing departments had to work closely together to understand the specific needs of different market segments and to optimise the scientific and technical performance of their customised new product indications. However, since there was still no competition at this second stage, the main objective for their co-operation was to define the directions of the project (in terms of which market segments the project should be targeted) rather than on the speed. As indicated earlier, the development speed was slow. Zovirax's commercial success (it achieved sales of £471 million in 1990) was gradually built up over a course of nine years after the first launch in 1981. Top management strongly supported this project but was not directly involved in it.

This case illustrates the evolution of a project from being research-driven to being market-driven. More specifically, it shows the changing pattern of the R&D/marketing interface and the different types of competencies created. At the first stage, the project was research-driven and the competencies created as a result were scientific and technological. It created a new product class - the antiviral product class - which opened up a whole range of new product development opportunities in this area. On the other hand, the competence created at the second stage, i.e. the post-launch development, was in new product development in diverse market segments.

## 6. Cross-case Analysis, Important Findings and Managerial Implications

### 6.1 Shared R&D/marketing Tasks Performed in the Twelve Projects and their Effectiveness

Evidence from all twelve drug development projects suggests that R&D and marketing have co-operated to differing extents in accomplishing tasks in both conceptual development and implementation in one or more of the following areas:

(1) Corporate Conceptual Development (CCD): access to and identifying relevant sources of new information, especially with regard to technological and market information, and evaluating the value of this information for the company's long-term market opportunities;

(2) Product Conceptual Development (PCD): access to, identifying and using relevant technological and market information for current product development, including setting directions for clinical trials, market positioning and product differentiation, resolving technical design and customer need trade-offs, etc.;

(3) Implementation (Ip): designing and implementing new co-ordination mechanisms and approaches to ensure efficient communication between organisational sub-units and between the product development team and the customers, which in turn lead to the timely application of new information and fast development speeds.

Two instruments were used to measure and evaluate the effectiveness of the R&D/marketing interface in these areas of a particular project. The first is the measurement of the *actual* communication flow/barrier according to the frequency of communication, the timing of R&D (marketing) involvement and the type and adequacy of existing coordination mechanisms and structures. The second is the evaluation of *perceived* interface effectiveness. Managers were asked the following questions: (a) did you think it was necessary to cooperate with R&D (marketing) in general/in a specific event of the project? (b) What did you expect to achieve from this cooperation in general/ in a specific event of the project, and (c) to what extent has the expected level of cooperation been achieved? The combined use of these two instruments has provided us with relatively reliable indication of the interface effectiveness. Moreover, as these instruments were derived from the case studies, there exist implicit links between the evaluation of the effectiveness and the text of the case studies.

Next, the degree of market success refers to the actual sales of a new drug, taking into consideration of the company's expected/projected sales. It is worth noting that the degree of market success is simply a statement of facts. It is given out as a reference, and does not necessarily imply a causal link between the effectiveness of the R&D/marketing interface and the degree of market success. Since such a link is outside the scope of the research model. However, the results has indeed revealed a link between the interface effectiveness and enhanced or new competencies of a firm.

**Table 4: shared tasks performed by R&D and marketing and their effectiveness**

| Type | Project | CCD | PCD | Ip | Degree of market success |
|------|---------|-----|-----|-----|--------------------------|
| RT-RM | Serevent | +++ | +++ | +++ | high |
|  | Augmentin | +++ | +++ | +++ | high |
|  | Diprivan | ++ | +++ | ++ | moderately high |
|  | Tenormin | ++ | +++ | ++ | high |
| RT-NM | Zoladex | 0 | ++ | + | low |
|  | Retrovir | 0 | ++ | +++ | moderately high |
| UT-UM | Zantac | +++ | +++ | +++ | very high |
|  | Lamictal | 0 | + | ++ | very low |
|  | Eminase | 0 | + | + | very low |
| NT-NM | Imigran | 0 | +++ | ++ | high |
|  | Tagamet | 0 | ++ | ++ | high |
|  | Zovirax | 0 | ++ | ++ | high |

Notes: CCD: Corporate Conceptual Development carried out before development stage; PCD: Product Conceptual Development; Ip: Implementation. RT: related technology; UT: unrelated technology; NT: new technology. RM: related market; UM: unrelated market; NM: new market.
Effectiveness of R&D/Marketing co-operation: +++ = very close and effective; ++ = close and effective; + = not very effective; 0 = no interface

Table 4 shows that the R&D/marketing interface has been involved in both external integration in conceptual development and internal integration in implementation in drug innovation. *However, the degree of involvement and effectiveness varies across different types of projects.* Specifically, the results show that:

(a) in all the projects that belonged to the RT-RM type, a very effective R&D and marketing interface was present in all the projects and all the areas, and the market success of these projects was high;

(b) in all the projects that belonged to the NT-NM type, R&D and marketing performed shared tasks in only two areas, i.e. product concept development and implementation, however their degree of market success was still high;

(c) compared to the NT-NM type projects, those UT-UM type projects (Lamictal, Eminase) which had very similar interface levels to the NT-NM type projects had much lower degrees of market success.

## 6.2 Analysis of the results: the association of the interface patterns with types of project and their effect on the competence-building

The result stated in (a) has provided strong evidence that an earlier and continuous interaction between R&D and marketing, which derives from years of co-operative experience in a particular segment, is essential for achieving an effective R&D/marketing interface, which leads to the project's success, and enhanced competence in new product development. This is achieved either by sustaining the company's current position in a market segment, or by extending the company's position into another related segment, or both.

The most obvious explanation for the results stated in (b) is that *the required level of the R&D/marketing interface for the NT-NM type of project is not as high as that for the RT-RM type of project due to the lack of competition.* However, a deeper explanation is generated by applying the conceptual framework developed in the current research. The reason for the difference in the required interface level for different projects is the different types of competence that each project is aimed to create. In particular, the type of competence to be created in the NT-NM type of project is scientific and technological, which leads on to the creation of a new product class or a dominant design; whereas the type of competence created in the RT-RM type of project is in new product development. The Zovirax project case has provided an ideal comparison these two types of competence-building processes. From the discovery to the launch of the first product indication, the objective of the project was to create scientific and technological competence, which opens up a whole range of new product development opportunities in the area. However, after the launch of the first product indication, the main goal of the project was to create new competence in new product development by offering customised new product indications to meet the specific needs of different market segments. The R&D/marketing interface was crucial during the second stage.

Next, we will discuss in-depth the result stated in (c). Compared to the UT-UM type of project, which is aimed to create both scientific/technological competence and new product development competence, the NT-NM type of project is only intended to create new scientific/technological competence. Apparently, it is much more difficult to try to create two major sets of competencies at the same time. This helps explain why a larger number of UT-UM projects failed. Nonetheless, this does not imply that the UT-UM type of project has no chance to be successful (as illustrated in the Zantac project case study).

The case studies of the Zantac and Eminase projects, both UT-UM projects, have provided a deeper insight into this issue. The results show that both projects had adopted a heavyweight project management style with strong top management commitment. The obstacles in the marketplace seemed to be equally challenging. One was facing a major market and technological leader with a highly innovative drug that had commanded high customer loyalty; the other was facing strong resistance from the

GPs and strong competition from rivals. Both the Zantac and Eminase projects were aimed at creating two sets of new competencies, i.e. scientific/technological and new product development. However, the one major factor that seems to separate these two projects is *the presence of effective earlier activities in corporate conceptual development and product conceptual development both at the firm level (through the restructuring programme) and at the project level in the Zantac project, which contrasts with the absence of earlier such activities in the Eminase project.*

The evidence strongly suggests that the UT-UM type of project can be successful, provided the company had prepared for it strategically and operationally long before the project actually started. This preparation involves the development of new organisational structures and interactions among all employees within the company guided by a clearly stated corporate strategic direction. The Zantac project is a manifestation of the importance of such earlier activities for innovation success. Top management involvement and heavyweight project management can only be *based on* these earlier activities, and provide an *add-on* effect to the project. They alone could not make a project successful. This explains why when used in the Eminase project, the effect of top management involvement and a heavyweight project team was very different from that in the Zantac project.

## 7. CONCLUSION

This research has provided a theoretical explanation of the role of the R&D/marketing interface in a firm's competence-building process. The research findings show that the R&D/marketing interface plays an important role in a firm's competence-building process by exerting influence on both the direction and the speed of a product innovation project, which leads to an enhanced competence (as in the case of RT-RM and RT-NM types of project) or creates new competence (as in the case of UT-UM and NT-NM types of project) in product development.

Furthermore, the research findings indicate that this interface capability evolves over time. An effective R&D/marketing interface at the project level during the project implementation has its root in the earlier activities in conceptual development at both corporate level (CCD) and product level (PCD). The former usually involves a sustained period of company-wide strategic preparation, which may or may not be directly targeted at a specific project, whilst the latter refers to previous co-operative experience at project level. The evidence shows that, despite top management attempts to build an instant platform (e.g. by means of heavyweight project management), in the absence of such earlier activities, the effectiveness of this kind of platform has been far from satisfactory, because a 'quick fix' cannot lead to a sustained innovation process. 'Learning-by-doing' alone is not enough: successful innovation also requires 'learning-before-doing'.

The research findings show that the main contribution of the R&D/marketing interface is to enhance or create new competence in the area of *new product development*, rather than to create new competence in the area of *science and technology*. Nevertheless, when a project is aimed at creating both types of competence at the same time (as in the case of Zantac and Eminase), the R&D/marketing interface has a vital importance for the innovation success.

Finally, this study has some important implications for management practitioners, and is directly and specifically relevant to those who work in medium and large firms in high-technology environment. Firstly, it offers a new mind-set in thinking and planning product innovation. Managers can plan product innovation, in terms of the types of competence (scientific vs. new product development) they want to enhance or create, and linking this desired competence to the firm's existing scientific/technological base and earlier new product development experience. Secondly, the research provides managers with a new way of thinking, in terms of project-based competence-building, as opposed to functional-based competence-building. Finally, managers should carefully examine the state of the R&D/marketing interface both at the general level and at a project level, and assess the different interface requirements for the different types of projects, before giving a 'go-ahead' to a research project. For this purpose, the research results can be used as a basis for generating some simple and basic tools for managers in the innovating firms.

## Acknowledgement

I would like to express my thanks to Keith Pavitt, Nick von Tunzelmann and Mike Hobday, for comments on previous drafts of this paper.

## References

abpi Annual Report 1980-81, 1982-83, 1984-85, 1986-87, 1988-89, 1990-91. Printed by CW Printing Ltd, Sevenoaks, Kent.

Arrow, K. (1962) 'Economic welfare and the allocation of resources of invention', In National Bureau of Economic Research (ed.) *The Rate and Direction of Inventive Activity: Economic and Social Factors*. Princeton University Press, Princeton, NJ. 609-625.

Block, J. 'Recognizing the coherence of personality', *International Psychology: Current Issues and Future Prospects*, D. Magnusson and N. S. Endler (eds.). New York: Wiley, 1977.

Cooper, R.G. (1983) 'The new product process: an empirically based classification scheme', *R&D Management* 13(1):1-13.

Cooper, R.G. (1984) 'What distinguishes the top performers?', *Journal of Product Innovation Management* 2:151-164.

Cooper, R.G. (1990) 'Stage-Gate systems: a new tool for managing new products', *Business Horizons*, May-June:44-54.

Cooper, R.G. and Kleinschmidt, E. (1987) 'What separates winners from losers?', *Journal of Product Innovation Management* 4:169-184.

Dougherty, D. (1990) 'Understanding new markets for new products', *Strategic Management Journal* 11:59-78.

# 074

## SERVICES AND TECHNOLOGY TRANSFER TO ENTERPRISES AS UNIVERISTY FUNCTION

Author:
Edi Madalena Fracasso Prof.
Nucleo de Gestao da Inovacao Technologica (NITEC)
Programa de Pos-Graduacao em Administracao (PPGA)
Universidade Federal do Rio Grande do Sul (UFRGS)
Av. Joao Pessoa, 52 sala 11
90 040-000 Porto Alegre, RS, Brazil
Tel:        +55-51-316 36 50
Fax:        +55-51-227 10 36
Email:      fracasso@vortex.ufrgs.br

Co-author:
Marli Elisabeth Ritter dos Santos and
Dr. Paulo Antonio Zawislak
Same addres.
Email:      paz@vortex.ufrgs.br

## ABSTRACT

The increase in the relationships university-enterprises, that it is been hapenning in Brazil since the 1980ís, spurred many discussions in the literature about the nature and the legitimacy of these relations. One of the main focus of discussion is related to the fact that as main agents of the science and technology system, both universities and enterprises are joining forces to strenghten the competitive capacity of the country. By so doing a relationship of complementarity is established in which the university aims to transfer knowledge to the enterprises and they aim to present their problems and to test the solutions found in the universities. University and enterprises have been interacting through the traditional forms of teaching and research as well as through new forms such as services (technical analysis, consultantships, in house training), technology transfer (patent licensing), and joint research. Although the Federal University of Rio Grande do Sul (UFRGS) followed the trend of the main Brazilian universities by increasing its interactions with the enterprises this has been done mainly through the rendering of services rather than technology transfer or joint research. Is this predominance of services over other forms of interaction a peculiarity of UFRGS? Is this a permanent trend and services will be a university function as important as teaching and research? Or it will change over time? To answer these questions and based on the historical experiences of Stanford and MIT the authors developed a simple evolutionary model associating the technological stage of the enterprises with the forms of interactions. An empirical test of the model comprises data of UFRGS as a whole as well as data from six case studies. The results of the analysis intend to provide some guidance for improvement of

# 075

Michael Larsen.

M.Sc., Doctoral student

Department of Production, Aalborg University

Fibigerstraede 16, DK-9220 Aalborg Oest, DENMARK

Phone    until february 3rd +45 98 15 42 11-2983
         after february 3rd +45 96 35 89 91
Fax no.   +45 98 15 30 30
e-mail:   i9ml@iprod.auc.dk

Title of paper: Learning to control production chains
Key words:    Production chains, supplier relationships, SME,
              management, learning.
Topic:        G,  Methods in technology management
Category:     1.  Conseptual or theoretical
Suitable for: Oral presentation only

# Learning to control production chains.

## abstract

In a world were most firms are small suppliers to a few major corporations, two problems are facing SMEs that are a part of a production chain. The first is that the SME have limitations in its resources and the later being that the SME is to small to have the power to force it decisions on the other firms in the chain. The intuitive solution to this problem is to establish one common control-loop for the entire chain or most important part hereof. The rest of the paper is devoted to giving Lars Hansen Inc. a framework to achieve this control-loop. It starts with a mapping of the current production chain, of which Lars Hansen Inc. is part and then characterizes the participants in the chain and grade them in the SSI-model. Then the keyplayers are identified and a dialogue is initiated before Lars Hansen Inc. have to choose measures to manage the production chain. The paper ends with a conclusion and suggestions for future work.

## 1. Introduction: the small firm in the big environment

In a world where most firms are small suppliers to a few major corporations, there is considerable gain in viewing the firm as part of a network or process from raw material to end-user and attempting to manage the firm accordingly.

> Lars Hansen Inc. is a small family-owned Danish manufacturer acting as supplier to a small number of larger firms which, in turn, deliver products to wholesalers before the products reach stores and the customer. Lars Hansen Inc. delivers some of the most valuable component of the products but - despite the fact that Lars Hansen's immediate customers always have treated the firm well - Lars Hansen's management would like to be able to influence its own situation more. But how is this possible with much larger firms up-stream and a long way from the end-user?

Two problems facing firms like Lars Hansen Inc. are that there are severe limitations to what the firm might do because of limited resources /Jensen, 96/ and the firm has not enough power to force through its decisions in the network of which it is a part /Jarillo, 93/. Lars Hansen Inc. is a small player in an environment with major players all around.

Within this context, we will allow ourselves the simplification of concentrating of one of the most simple forms of a network: a chain of firms. We define a production chain as: "a chain of legally independent firms that produce a specific product or service. A production chain covers all stages from raw material to end user. For the purpose of producing the good or service, materials and information are exchanged throughout the chain at different control levels", /Larsen, 96a/. In our previous work, we have discussed the problems related to the way production chains traditionally have been managed, /Larsen, 96b/. In short, Lars Hansen Inc. will have problems in influencing its own destiny because a chain is traditionally managed so that each firm in the chain attempts to manage for its own benefit and not for the benefit of the entire chain and ultimately the end-user. /Larsen, 96a/ The well-known Forrester-effect is an example of this way of managing a production chain, where each firm maintains its own control-loop and suboptimizes the materials flow in the chain with devastating overall results to follow, /Forrester, 58/.

The intuitive solution - which we shall elaborate on how to reach in this paper - is to establish one common control-loop for the entire chain or the most important parts of it, /Larsen, 96a/. In the example of Forrester-effects, this corresponds to have one planning function for the materials flow in the entire chain as to avoid sub-optimization.

## 2. The intuitive solution?

*But what does it mean for Lars Hansen Inc. to establish a common control-loop for the entire chain?* Two examples may provide Lars Hansen Inc. - and others - with some valuable inspiration.

Example I:

Company D, a Danish producer of medical equipment, had developed a touch screen to a computer as a part of the medico-technical solutions. The production and the further development of the touch-screen was not seen by Company D as a natural part of their core competencies and a discussion of how to treat the touch-screen technology was initiated. The management decided to outsource the competence and they decided to offer it to supplier M. Supplier M is a important supplier to Company D and have a reputation for keeping promises and delivery dates. Company D had a management decision about not broadening the core competencies and a desire to tie some selected suppliers closer to the company.

Example II:

Company C, a Danish manufacturer of audio and video products, has outsourced many of its key competencies in order to maintain agility and save cost. Company C is an end product producer of the production chain which consists of six layers. According to Company C, their products are developed to be five years ahead of consumers' present wishes and demands.

But how does Company C make sure that all the firms in their production chain develop the necessary competencies for tomorrow's products?

Company C maintains a close relationship to its suppliers. For instance, Supplier A was founded by a former R&D manager from Company C with the active aid of Company C, in order to produce one of the key components of company C's product. In order to make this possible, Company C sold the necessary manufacturing technology to supplier A and made sure that the technology was transferred successfully. Company C is still aiding Supplier A in this respect by providing engineers and other kind of assistance. Furthermore, Supplier A is involved in product development projects at Company C. In this manner it is made sure that Supplier A knows which competencies to develop/buy in due time. Another way for Company C to ensure that suppliers A's competencies are developed is by forcing supplier A to serve other customers in other industries. These customers also make demands to Supplier A competencies and thus invites to further development.

The message of these examples is that it is possible to develop a shared vision of what the end-user wants through-out the entire production chain and, furthermore, to translate this to what each individual firm is to do in order to benefit the end-user and, hence, the entire chain. By doing so, Lars Hansen can suspend some of its problems related to limited resources and expand the strategic options of the firm. *But how is this to be done?* This is the subject of section 3.

## 3. A framework for managing production chains

In this section we will propose a framework for Lars Hansen Inc., and other SME firms, to reach a situation where the entire production chain is managed in an optimal manner for the entire chain.

For Lars Hansen Inc., the intuitive solution will be to map the production chain, so that he will identify the other firms in the chain. In order for him to do this, he needs to look at different aspects of the cooperation throughout the chain, such as: legal aspects, technological aspects, etc. After doing this, he will have to look at the firms individually and asses their performance in six different areas, such as price, value added by the firm, complexity, etc. On the basis of the results of these two tools, Lars Hansen Inc. is now able to place all the firms in the chain in the SSI-model. Based on the result from the SSI-model and the information about the firm, Lars Hansen Inc. can now decide which firms are important for the chain, and should be a decision maker in the chain, and which firms are not. After defining the keyplayers in the chain, Lars Hansen Inc. will have to go into a dialogue with these key players. In this dialogue Lars Hansen Inc. will have to, together with the other firms in the chain, make a choice of which measures to use in managing the production chain. To decide on the measures Lars Hansen Inc. can use the SAT-model, which defines Arche Types of supplier relationships, and clarifies how the company should treat them with regard to the areas described above.

If we expresses this as a Phase model, it will look like this:

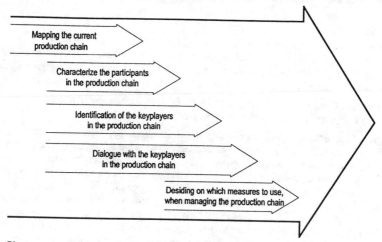

Phase one:    Mapping the current Production Chain

Phase two:    Characterize the participants in the production chain

Phase three:    Identification of the keyplayers in the production chain

Phase four:    Dialogue with the keyplayers in the production chain

Phase five:    Deciding on which measures to use, when managing the production chain

## 3.1 Mapping the current production chain

In the first phase Lars Hansen Inc. have to map the production chain in order to create an overview of the chain and the other participants in it. In order to map a production chain, a number of different perspectives may be applied:

- *Legal*. This area concerns the nature of a contract, what kind of papers can the supplier see, are there areas in the factory where they are not allowed and so on? Is there a signed contract or just a order confirmation?

- *Organizational*. How is the chain organized? Is it by on-line computer systems or a project organization with members from different firms within the chain or by correspondence? Who is responsible for the contact to the others members of the production chain? Who is representing the chain to the outside?

- *Economical*. How do the firms in the chain treat each other: Open calculations, so the supplier can see the firm's contribution margin or are the cheapest supplier chosen ? Does the firms feel that they are being paid according to there effort?

- *Strategy*. Does any of the firms in the chain use the price as buying strategy ? Does the chain need one or many suppliers to a specific product ? Do any of the firms develop their own products or do they cooperate with the suppliers and customers about it? Do the firms in the chain want to produce all themselves or do they want to outsource some of it?

- *Technology*. What is being produced in the chain and how? Look at the contribution from each firm. Is the supplier up to the firm's standard or should the firm make a transfer of the necessary technologies ? Do the suppliers have technologies that are not utilized? Is there a demand from the customer about a special technology? Is there a demand from the authorities to use a special technology? Which process technologies and administrative technologies go into production of the product/service of the chain?

- *Activities*. Which activities go into production of the product/services of the chain? Can the firm produce the product in one stage, or does the product need time to mature/settle etc.? Is the making of the product depending of e.g. the weather, time of the year etc.?

The mapping will aid in understanding the production chain and provide a basis for the preceding phases in the methodology.

## 3.2 Characterize participants

Evidently, not all participants in a production chain are alike /Riis *et al*, 96a/. Some are strategically important, because they posses skills that the firm does not posses, while others mainly deliver commodity items. In order for Lars Hansen Inc. to decide which participants to involve in production chain control, the author proposes that Lars Hansen Inc. characterizes the participants according to the following supplier status investigation model (SSI-model). Figure 2 illustrates the author's proposal of the SSI-model.

With the SSI-model Lars Hansen Inc. looks at the firm in the chain as suppliers to the next level in the chain. Lars Hansen Inc. will use Supplier status investigation look at the firms in different areas. As such, the model can be sued to characterize all of the participants in the production chain, i.e. everyone is a supplier to someone - except the end-user to whom everyone supplies. In figure 2 the Y-axis is the different types of suppliers. Grade A is full cooperation with for instance Research & Development (R&D) across company borders. This could mean transferring technology to the suppliers, in order for them to meet the company's demand. Grade F is companies ordering screws and bolts by picking up the phone and place an order with the cheapest supplier. The X-axis is the importance which the company places on the supplier. 0% means little or no importance, whereas 100% is when the company is fully focused on the area.

These areas mentioned above are:

- *The price as a strategic tool.* The direction of the line indicates that the companies are expected to look at the price with little importance, when working closely or have shared R&D.

- *The value added by the supplier.* This line indicates that the lower grades of suppliers (grade D,E,F) does not add much value to the product.

- *Where is the supplier located, where is the factory ?* This line is an indicator of how far away the supplier is located. It indicates an expectation of that the companies need to have the most important suppliers closest to the factory. /Roberts, 1981/ says the distance between those who communicate is inversely proportional to the value of the communication.

- *How complex is the product delivered by the supplier ?* The line shows the expectation of: the more complex the product is the more important is the supplier.

- *The amount of Research & Development (R&D) involved in the product.* The line shows an expectation of: the more R&D-intensive the product is, the higher the supplier is graded

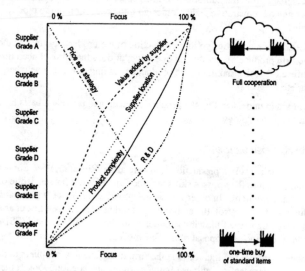

Figure 2: Tentative illustration of the SSI-Model.

When Lars Hansen Inc. have listed the individual firms in the chain in the SSI-model, they will have a good perception on the production of which he are a part and the players in it. Lars Hansen Inc. now have the information which is necessary to identify the keyplayers in the chain.

## 3.3 Identification of keyplayers in the chain

Lars Hansen Inc. can take the SSI-model and look at the different firms and their placement in the model, and hereby get an idea of, who the keyplayers are. It is very unlikely that a firm which have been graded as E or F will be a keyplayer in the production chain. A keyplayer will normally be placed as A, B or C in order to have a position in the chain that qualifies as a keyplayer. A way to identify the keyplayers, besides the SSI-model, is looking at who is strategically important to the survival of the chain, who is adding a lot value to the product and who have the core competencies to produce the product. If a firm is a keyplayer it means that it per definition has to have a shared competence development with one or more firms in the production chain. The SME will normally be a keyplayer or else he will be working on becoming one. The reason we can say that is that if a SME undertakes the task of mapping the production chain, it must have a certain size, in order to have the resources to do so. It must also have a interest in the production chain and the continued existence of the chain, and not just an interest is selling on a one time basis only. This characterizes a not so small firm, with a interest in optimizing the production chain.

The need for managing the production chain can be identified by considering the end-user of the production chain and how the production chain works to produce its good or service to this customer. In line with the work on integration of business strategy and competence development, see /Drejer, 95/, a methodology for identifying the need for internal changes within a firm has been proposed, /Drejer, 96/. This methodology can be altered to fit a situation, where an entire production chain is seen as "firm" towards the end-user. This makes it possible to re-use the existing work to a large extent, and focus the research on those phases most relevant to production chain control. A discussion of a methodology for identifying the need for internal changes within a firm can be seen in /Drejer, 96/.

## 3.4 Dialogue with participants

After Lars Hansen Inc. have found out which firms he would like to cooperate with in the production chain, he must initiate a dialogue with them. It is now up to Lars Hansen Inc. to convince the other firm that it is possible to create a win-win situation. In the production chain, the situation is rarely so that a firm can dictate to the other participants of its production chain how the chain should be controlled. If that was the case, the desirable integrated control loop would already be in place. First the firms must agree upon the SSI-model and the characteristic of their own firm, as it will form the basis for the further work.

In order for Lars Hansen Inc. to be successful in his venture he must have prepared different things. Lars Hansen Inc. must be aware of what his own interest in this negotiation is and have an idea about the interest of the other firms, so that it can be a negotiation of interests rather than on viewpoint. If you back down on a viewpoint, it is often seen as weakness, this situation is not the same concerning interest. /Jensen et al, 96/ The firms can serve their interest in many different ways. Lars Hansen Inc. must also have an idea about what possible conflicts there are and also what areas of synergy there are. These are some of the areas of which Lars Hansen Inc. must be aware, but exactly how this dialogue is to be organized and function has not yet been established. However this is a subject for recent research at the department, /Riis et al, 96b/

## 3.5 Choice of measures

After Lars Hansen Inc. have started on the dialogue with the other firms, he needs to look at measures to manage the production chain. For Lars Hansen Inc. it will be a good idea to choose measures in accordance with the results obtained in the other phases of the methodology. This can be done by the Supplier Arche Type (SAT) model. The model shown in table 1 is the author's proposal.

The SAT-model is a framework for rules and regulations on how Lars Hansen Inc. should treat the different grades of suppliers. When Lars Hansen Inc. have graded a supplier by the use of SSI-model above, the SAT-model in table 1 will give Lars Hansen Inc. a clearer look on how he should be treating the supplier in question. In table 1, Lars Hansen Inc. will be able to identify appropriate measures regarding different grades of suppliers.

This model defines Arche Types of supplier relationships, and clarifies how Lars Hansen Inc. should treat them with regard to specific areas. These areas are the ones used to map the production chain. These areas are set against the different grades of suppliers, obtained from the SSI-model.

The framework for the SAT-model is outlined in table 1.

| | Legal | Organizational | Economic | Strategy | Technology |
|---|---|---|---|---|---|
| A | Full insight | Cross organizational groups | Calculate prizes together | Common survival and expansion | Shared technology and common investments |
| B | | | | | |
| C | Only product specification | Involve the customer and maybe the end user | If the company can use it, the pay | Some degree of out sourcing | The company might have to transfer technology |
| D | | | | | |
| E | | | | | |
| F | No insight | Contact via Phone or fax | Meet specifications to the cheapest prize | Change every time some other can sell it cheaper | Low technology All mastered by the supplier. |

Table 1: This table illustrates the SAT-model. For illustration purposes Grade A, C and F are filled out.

A supplier who have been graded A will according to this SAT-model get full legal insight, which means that the supplier can see all or most of the contracts concerning this production chain whereas the supplier graded F will get an order confirmation and that is it. It will be natural for grade A to be a part of some cross organizational group concerning marketing, R&D, SWOT analysis and other areas where the chain can benefit from different experiences. Grade F will normally only have contact with a sales representative and grade F is to meet the specifications to the cheapest prize possible, where grade A calculate prizes together with the rest of the chain. The strategy for grade A is to secure the survival end expansion of the chain, and it can be done in the way of shared technology initiated by a shared view of the future, where the strategy for grade F will be to change to the cheapest supplier every time. Grade F is used for low technology tasks only and adds little value to the product.

## 3.6. Use of the framework

The proposed framework is based on a thorough review of the literature on Supply Chain management, e.g. /Sharpio, 84/, /Christoffer, 92a/, strategic alliances, e.g. /Jarillo, 93/, logistics, e.g. /Christoffer, 92b/, /Møller, 95/, organizational networks, e.g. /Savage, 90/, /Larsen, 86/ and management in general and represents an attempt to summarize the results of several different research areas in a manner which makes it useable for firms like Lars Hansen Inc. The overview, however, is created at the cost of detail. In other words, when using the framework one must remember that real life firms and real life situations are much more diverse and complex than any framework is capable of capturing.

# 4. Conclusion and further work

In this section a number of conclusions will be made and we will make a few suggestions regarding further work on the subject of controlling production chains.

## 4.1 Summary

In this paper we have been focusing on how small and medium sized firms may overcome two of their worst problems - severe limitations to what the firm might do because of limited resources and not enough power to force through decisions in the network of which they are a part. Since most firms are small suppliers to major firms closer to the end customer, we consider this a piece of very relevant research.

The intuitive solution is to establish one common control-loop for the entire chain or the most important parts of it, /Larsen, 96a/. In the example of Forrester-effects, this corresponds to have one planning function for the materials flow in the entire chain as to avoid sub-optimization.

The normative contribution of the paper is the proposal of a framework to achieve a common control-loop. The framework starts with a mapping of the current production chain, of which the SME is part and then characterizes the participants in the chain and grade them in the SSI-model. Then the keyplayers are identified and a dialogue is initiated before the SME have to choose measures to manage the production chain.

## 4.2 Value of research?

As already noted the proposed framework is based on a review of the existent literature from a number of different research areas, must notably Supply Chain Management, Logistic, Organizational networks, strategic alliances and Management in general. *But what is the value of such a framework?*

From a theoretically point of view, the research in this paper is a matter of synthesizing already existing research in order to make this research useable in industrial practice. Therefore, we feel that the real value of this work lies in confronting a number of theories with industrial practice - something that no management researcher of any kind can object to. The value of this research must be found in industrial practice. We therefore propose to test the framework in industrial practice in order to determine its value. This leads us to the issue of further work.

## 4.3 Further work

In our future work we plan to study production chain control in industrial practice. The purpose of studying industrial practice is two fold: 1. to describe how production control is done in order to see whether a framework like the proposed is at all useful and 2. to develop the proposed framework further in relation to a specific task of production control.

We will limited our work to the issue of competence development in production chains. Competence development in production chains constitutes a specific problem, because in the event of a technological solution being developed by a supplier, a certain amount of time is required for the passage of the desired need down to the supplier, and for the development to take place. Time, instead of material, will suffer from the Forrester effect. /Forrester, 58/ Furthermore, the individual firms are separated by organizational and legal boundaries, which normally make it impossible to manage competence development within the industry. /Pralahad & Hamel, 90/

# 5. References

Christopher, 92a
M. Christopher. *"Logistics and Supply Chain Management"*, Pitman Publishing, 1992

Christopher, 92b
M. Christopher. (Editor) *"Logistics - the strategic issues"*, Chapman & Hall, 1992.

Drejer, 95
A. Drejer. *"Integration of Business Strategy and Competence Development"*. Challenges for integration in manufactoring, IPS, 1995

Drejer, 96.
A. Drejer. *"Integrating Business Strategy and Competence Development"*. Proceedings of MOT V, Miami, USA, 1996.

Forrester, 58
Jay W.Forrester. *"Industrial Dynamics, a major breakthrough for decision makers"* Harvard Business Review, July-August, 1958, pp. 37-66

Jarillo, 93
J. C. Jarillo.*"Strategic Networks"*.Butterworth, Heinemann, 1993.

Jensen *et al*, 96
K.E. Jensen, T. J. Jensen & J-P. Virum *"Kvalitet i Professionelle Partnerskaber - et værktøj"* Industriens Forlag, 1996. (in Danish)

Jensen, 96
Eystein Jensen *"competence development by small firms in a vertically - constrained industry structure"* Dynamics of competence competition, edited by Sanchez, Heene & Thomas, Pergamon, 1996.

Larsen, 86.
B. Larsen. *"Fra Hierarki til Netværk"* Civiløkonomernes Forlag, 1986.

Larsen, 96a.
M. Larsen. *"Controlling Production Chains"* Development of Integration in Manufactoring. IPS. pp. 159-180.

Larsen, 96b
M. Larsen. *"New Approaches to Technology Forecasting"* Preceedings from The 1st Annual International Conference on Industrial Engineering Applications and Practice December 4-7, 1996, Double Tree Guest Suite, Houston, Texas, USA

Møller, 95
C. Møller. *"Logistics Concept Development"*. Department of Production, Aalborg University, 1995.

Pralahad & Hamel, 90
C. K. Pralahad & G. Hamel. *"The Core Competence of the Corporation"* Harvard Business Review, May-June, 1990

Riis et al, 96a
J. O. Riis, J. Johansen, J. Lythcke-Jørgensen & H. Hansen. *"Fremtidens Underleverandører"* Sant + Bendix, 1996. (in Danish)

Riis et al, 96b
J. O. Riis, A. Drejer, B. T. Møller & H. de Haas *"Experimental production system design"*, Education in engineering conference, San Diego, marts 1996

Roberts, 81.
E. B. Roberts. *"Generating Effective Corporate Innovation"* in Corporate Strategy and Product Innovation, ed. R.R.Rothberg, The Free Press, 1981.

Savage, 90
C. M. Savage. *"5th generation Management"* Digital Press, 1990

Sharpio, 84
R. D. Sharpio. *"Towards Effective Supplier Management"*. Working Paper, Harvard Business School, 1984.

# 076

TECHNOLOGICAL PROXIMITIES AND DOMINANCE OF
INTERNATIONAL MANUFACTURING FIRMS INSIDE THE TRIAD.

Cincera Michele
Universite Libre De Bruxelles DULBEA C.P. 140
Av. F.D. Roosevelt, 50 B-1050 BRUXELLES Belgium
Tel:          +32-2-6504151          Fax:          +32-2-6503825
email:          mcincera@ulb.ac.be

ABSTRACT

This paper aims at analyzing technological proximities as well as
technological dominance of large international firms among the countries
of the Triad and to what extent these characteristics are the source of
spillovers. The main international R&D-intensive firms in manufacturing
have been selected to perform this analysis. The sample is composed with
1500 firms and covers the period 1987-1994.
The first part of the paper is devoted to map technological proximities of
international firms which account a main part of industrial R&D. To what
extent are firms technologically close? Are technological proximities
influenced by geographic locations? Are there dominance relationships
between firms as far as we consider their geographic locations? In order to
give an answer to these questions a matrix based on average technological
proximities at the firm level among 22 manufacturing sectors and for the
three pillars of the Triad is constructed. The technological proximities are
performed by reference to the concept of technological space.
The second part of the paper has to deal with the question of technological
dominance. To what extent are the R&D activities performed by firms
concentrated in given geographic areas? In which technological fields are
countries better performing or are dominant? Here, the methodological
framework which allows us to give answers to these questions rests on data
analyses techniques. The first step of this methodology will consist in
determining the technological channels characterizing the countries inside
the Triad. In a second phase, a descriptive statistical analysis will
determine to what extent these technological channels are dominated by
firms belonging to a same geographic area. Yet, it is also interesting to
investigate the level of technological concentration that characterizes
these technological channels.
The third part of the paper tries to characterize the importance of
technological spillovers generated by firms through their R&D activities.
What is the magnitude of technological spillovers? In which industries are
these effects the most important? How higher are intra-industry spillovers
comparatively to inter-industry spillovers? For a given industry, do these
effects have the same magnitude inside the countries of the Triad or does
geographic location matter to capture technological spillovers?

key words: international firms; technological proximity, spillovers and
dominance

# 078

# Feasibility studies in Product Development
## – a key issue for successful product development projects

S. Ritzén, Royal Institute of Technology, Department of Machine Design
Stefan Nordqvist, Annika Zika-Viktorsson, University of Stockholm, Department of
Psychology

## Abstract
The objective of the present study is to analyse how feasibility studies are performed in industry today and by that conclude which factors affect the success of a feasibility study and what the prerequisites are for conducting one. The research in the study is empirical: Data was collected from five different Swedish companies by interviews which were analysed. The participating companies all declare that the feasibility study should be a general seeking of solutions, held on a broad scale. The result of a feasibility study should form the decision basis whether to accomplish a PD project or not and should also lead to instructions on how to proceed. The research project indicates important aspects on how to succeed in such processes, e.g. definition of goals, forms of co-operation, team characteristics and attributes of the project manager (functional and social). Difficulties and problems connected with the performance of a feasibility study are mainly a result of missing prerequisites as lack of resources. It is shown that both practical aspects, e.g. available tools, and psychological aspects, e.g. difficulties in team work, are of great importance for the efficiency of a feasibility study.

## Introduction and background
A successful industrial business is based on the companies' continuous renewal and improvment of products. Being competitive on today's international market demands an efficient product development (PD). More and more complex products, which better meet customers' demands and with a higher quality, should be developed in a shorter time than before. To be able to achieve this, it is important that the competence of different disciplines are integrated already in the early phases of PD.

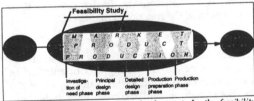

*Figure 1. A structure of product development. In the feasibility study the early phases are performed.*

### Models for product development
A trend towards a more frequent use of a systematic approach in PD is recognisable in industry today. This means most often that companies create their own models for the PD process. A theoretical basis for these models can be, for example one of the earliest by Pahl & Beitz "Engineering Design" [1], or one recently developed by Ulrich & Eppinger "Product Design and Development", [2]. Systematic design enhances the possibilities of developing complex products, meaning products involving numerous physical parts and solutions demanding use of several technical disciplines. However a systematic approach is not enough for meeting higher demands. Changed demands in quality and lead-time together with changes in product complexity require several competencies to take part in PD. "Integrated Product Development" describes PD as a systematic process in an organisational context, integrating market and production aspects with the more tra-

ditional product aspects, [3]. Integrated Product Development is based on two principles [4]:

- Activities in the PD process should be performed in parallel.
- Actors from different disciplines with different competencies should co-operate.

*Feasibility studies*

The diagram in figure 2 explains the importance of the early phases in PD are so important. The possibility of product changes decreases when the PD process proceeds. Simultaneously the total costs of the project increases, [5]. Therefore an increasing number of companies introduce feasibility studies (FS). An FS should be performed in order to show what the needs in further developed product features are and how they can be accomplished. It is important to find out whether a product is going to become profitable or not. A change in the performance of FSs has taken place in industry recently: more people are involved and more competencies are represented. The study also takes longer time though the total time of the project should not be prolonged. FSs are theoretically described as convergent processes: An iterative generation and reduction of concepts, [6].

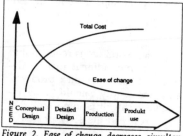

*Figure 2. Ease of change decreases simultaneously with the increasing costs. [5]*

*Organisation of product development*

The PD work is organised in projects in order to increase productivity and efficiency. Industrial PD can be organised in *functional organisation, project organisation* and *matrix organisation*, [7]. In *functional organisation* the project is performed in a department with the responsibility of the functional manager. In *project organisation* a project manager are responsible for the project which is performed with members from different departments. A *matrix organisation* is in between the former two, with a shared responsibility of the project manager *and* the functional manager.

*Project manager*

The role of a project manager is different from the leadership in a permanent organisation, mostly due to the limitation in time and the strong task orientation in projects. The role is very important with a strong relation to the performance of the project team, [8]. A project manager should have a solid technical knowledge and be able to understand and analyse the organisation, [9]. He or she should also have the capacity of making decisions and be able to create good relations with the members in the team.

*Project team*

Integrated PD means among other things PD in multidisciplinary teams. The team is another important factor for the result of the FS. A well functioning team is expected to perform better than the separate individuals. The performance are related to the character of the task, the social relations in the team and to individual benefits. A collective and individual responsibility is of vital importance for the achievement of the team [10]. A common goal view and a co-operation in order to establish a confidence in the team are also important. The team members should have required talents but also complement each other. A working climate that facilitates creative processes is imprinted of dynamics in the team. This is attained among other factors by involving *different* people [11].

*Purpose of the study*
The present study is a part of a research project, huMAN DEsign COmmunication (MANDECO), which aims to find possibilities and obstacles for achieving efficient PD. Within the MANDECO project Frisk, Nordqvist & Norell performed the study "The feasibility study – an important phase for efficient product development" in 1994 [12]. The FSs in two companies were investigated. A number of factors important to successfully perform FSs were pointed out in the study. Anchoring and support in the company were expressed among these, as well as creating common goals for the members in the project team. Other factors were the role of the project manager and the co-operation in the team.

The purpose of this study is to further investigate and analyse FSs on an empirical basis. The investigation is a mapping of planning and organisation of the feasibility studies, with the intention to identify characteristics for early phases of PD. The aim of the analysis is to find key factors for successful FSs, to clarify the prerequisites and to identify problems and difficulties in the process of FSs. The role of the project manager and the project team has been in focus in the investigation, initiated from results of earlier research.

By performing empirical research, based on interviews with people active in feasibility studies, a reliable picture is demanded with conclusions applicable in industrial PD.

## Research methodology
The study included five large manufacturing companies. The companies represent different lines of business and products, in order to increase the possibilities of achieving general results. Another criterion for choice of companies were that the companies should have developed their way of working with early phases of the PD process recently. A certain complexity in FSs, demanding the participation of several competencies was also required.

Data was collected by interviews with people experienced in FSs. The interviews were performed during 1996. 21 persons were interviewed in total: 5 heads of department, 6 project managers, 4 designers, 2 manufacturing engineers and 4 people from the marketing department.

An interview guide was created for performing the interviews which were tape-recorded and transcribed. A coding scheme was drawn up based on a selection of the transcribed interviews. All the interviews were coded according to the scheme and then analysed according to the principles of "*Grounded theory*", [13]. The coding were performed independently by the three authors.

## Results
The presentation of the results will follow the process of performing feasibility studies from an initiation to a closure of the study. Essentials for the proceeding of

the process, characteristics for a successful process, together with problems and difficulties will be described. The companies have been analysed jointly and only in specific matters will company wise features be described.

*Description of the feasibility studies*
A general definition of an FS can be formulated based on the interviews:

"A feasibility study is an investigation in which customer demands should be identified and the technical possibilities to realise the customer demands should be clarified."

The FS was in all companies described as an "open" process for seeking product solutions. It includes a market investigation and a technical investigation. The market investigation should answer the question "What?" (which functions, which performances, etc.) and the technical investigation "How?" (how will the product be technically realised). The following product development phases are referred to as *the project* by the interviewees. Figure 3 shows the main terms used in the interviews and the connection between the terms.

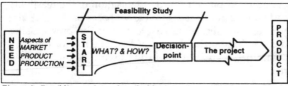

Figure 3. Feasiblity study as described by interviewees.

The interviews show that an FS differed from the following parts of the PD process in that an FS was a broader process with less formal management. The FS should be a creative phase while the following parts are "fulfilling" phases. The interviewed people had also experienced a change in how FSs were performed in the companies. The FS seemed to be more important than before with more resources together with an extension in time. The strongest motive for allocating more resources in the early phases of the PD process was the increased importance in fulfilling market demands.

*Initiatives to and start of feasibility studies*
A need for PD occurred in the companies when changes in customer demands were observed. Development of technology, internally identified needs for efficiency improvements, analysis of competitors and threats of new legislation were other reasons for starting PD processes. However market demands was clearly the most important reason to initiate PD in the investigated companies. The companies had different ways of starting an FS due to the differences in their company specific structure of their PD process. Three different cases can be pointed out in the analysed material.
1. The decision of performing an FS was taken in the company when a need of a new product series had been identified.
2. A brief investigation of the profitability in a new product was started when changed customer demands had been identified by a local market company. In case of possible profitability an FS was started.
3. A strategic planning based on an analysis of customers and competitors with an analysis of new legislation are managed in the company. When the need of PD is identified in the strategic planning an FS is started.

In the initial phase of the FS, the actors in the FS were organised. According to the definitions in "*Organisation of product development*" the investigated companies applied a matrix organsiation. The project organisation was then a parallel organisation to the functional organisation, figure 4.

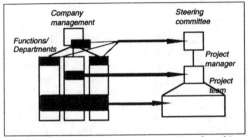

Figure 4. A complementary project organisation is formed in parallel to the functional organisation.

A steering committee was put together of mainly the managers of the affected lines of business. The steering committee's task was to continuously follow the development work and to manage resources and the time schedule. A project manager (PM) was selected in all the investigated FSs. In one company the PMs were employed as PMs but in the others they were employed in a technical department, mainly at the design department. All interviewed PMs had a technical background. The selection of the team members was managed by the PM. Participants were selected based on the need of different functions FS and of the competence of specific individuals. The availability of people was also reported as a basis for judgement. All project teams were multidisciplinary.

At the start of the FS the PM applied for resources to the steering committee. The needed amount of money was stated together with the need of tools and people. The same document stated a time schedule for the FS.

In all companies activities for emphasising the start of the FS took place. The so-called "kick-off" could vary from a cake at the coffee break to a meeting lasting for several days. A "kick-off" served as an indication on the importance of the project in the company. Interviewees claimed that a higher commitment is obtained in a team if the project is experienced as important. A meeting, preferably placed outside the company, served as an opportunity to let members get to know each other better and to start the work of creating a common picture of goals and purposes.

*Performance of feasibility studies*
The performance of an FS in the investigated companies started with the creation of a picture of goals and purposes. These were presented to the team members in form of overarching goals as well as concrete technical goals. A time schedule established in the team was reported as important to the participants. In one project the team jointly worked out a time schedule which was experienced as positive for establishing the goals. Deadlines were of great importance in the FS work but it was however possible to prolong a study. If a deadline could not be moved the complexity or functionality of the product were reduced. All interviewees considered the work with establishing common view of goals to be an important activity, both for the actual FS work as well as for the result of the FS. Goals should be high but realisticand they should be well defined and challenging. Difficulties in creating the common view lay mainly in the input of data to the team. Communication with the market department is then important, increasing the possibility of better understanding the customer demands.

Some of the interviewees claimed that valuable information was lost if there was an indirect communication between the market department and the FS team. This problem did not occur in the companies where the market department took active part in the FS work.

In general the project members gathered for meetings every two weeks. The meetings were meant for information or for solving problems in the project. The informal meetings between participants in the team were however reported as the most important ones. This could more easily be achieved if the project team had a room together. During the time of the project their working place should be in this project room, preferably with all the needed equipment. The interviewees claimed that the process of problem solving was more efficient, since there were better prerequisites for discussions in the project team, due to daily interactions between members. A special project room was also claimed to be important in the way that the status of the project was emphasised and for the team-spirit. Due to practical circumstances this was only realised in one of the investigated FSs.

*Project managers*
All of the interviewees thought that the PM was of great importance to the success of the FS. The tasks of the PM was to keep the team together in its work, to manage and urge the FS process. The PM should also manage the resources and the time schedule. In regard to resource management several of the interviewed PM's reported difficulties because of a well defined responsibility but a lack of power for performing the project.

Most of the interviewees claimed that a PM must not be a specialist in the technical field but rather a generalist. He or she should be able to have control of the technical development from a holistic view. Besides a basic technical skill and ability of handling administrative matters a PM should have managerial skills. A PM should manage the project in a way that the focus on the goal is maintained and that different paths of solving problems in the project are held open. In the same time it is the PM's task to make sure that the right path is chosen at critical points. More informal tasks of the PM were to encourage the project team and to create enthusiasm in the work. An environment open to new ideas was reported as important which was thought to be affected by the manners of the PM. It was also important that the PM let the participants work independently since there was a risk that the motivation decreased if the PM ruled to many details.

To be able to function well as a PM, according to the interviewed PMs, it was important that their role was well defined in the company and that the position had a certain level of status. The work of a PM was also affected in a positive way if the project had a high priority in the company.

*Project team*
There was a common opinion among the interviewees that FS participants ought to take part in the team on their full working time. Part time workers can not show the same commitment and are also torn between different tasks. In all the companies several FSs or development projects were performed in parallel and some of the participants took part in more than one project or kept working tasks from their

original position in a line of business. In these cases there was a risk that some tasks were given higher priority, on behalf of others and also that participants got a too high workload. In practice, part time workers are necessary because some competencies are required for only a limited part or during a certain phase of the FS process.

Whether marketing and manufacturing departments took part in the FS or not varied between the companies. In one of the companies, the market department took active part in the project for the first time. In the other companies the market department had the function of product orderer and provided the foundation for a specification of demands. The manufacturing department was represented in four of the investigated companies. The fifth company did not manufacture the product inside the company.

There was a common opinion among the interviewees that the multi-functional co-operation provided benefits in form of good solutions that were thoroughly dealt with. Also a commitment for the product was created in the whole company which facilitated both manufacturing and selling of the product. The multi-functional way of working also meant broader working tasks for some people which were experienced positively.

One of the important features of the participants was reported to be creativity. Other features were the ability of arguing for a possible solution in the team in combination with an intention to listen to and understand other participants' opinions. A dynamic team, created by participants with different age and experience, was also an important factor for a successful performance of the FS process.

*Support methods and tools*
Two of the companies in the study used QFD-analysis (Quality Function Deployment) during the FS. Both companies considered the method to be a support in structuring and quantifying the specification of demands. Since the analysis was performed jointly in the multi-funtional teams a common holistic view was created. This lead to a better understanding between departments and of customer demands. One of these companies also introduced "Process Mapping" and "Rapid Prototyping" in their FS work. The purpose of Process Mapping was to identify activities and interactions and to analyse disruptions and disconnects in their regular PD work. Process Mapping had a positive affect on the unity in the team and was a support for finding and avoiding earlier mistakes. Both QFD and Process Mapping had the negative features of being time consuming and taking effort from PD tasks. By Rapid Prototyping a prototype could be rapidly produced in the FS, providing a possibility for the team to see, feel and assemble the product. Contact with workshops and discussions with purchaser were then simplified.

*Results from FS*
The study clearly indicates what the FS should result in according to the interviewees' conception. An FS should result in a technical assurance meaning that the company should know what is required for realising the product and if this is possible with today's knowledge and available technology. In several companies one concept should be selected. The documents presented at the check-point after an FS

should also clarify costs for the product and for the continuing PD project together with the amount of time needed for the rest of the project.

In all investigated companies it was unusual that an FS lead to a closure of the PD project. In cases when requirements at the check-point were not fulfilled the FS was usually prolonged. However in most of the companies the FS should form a basis for decision of continuing the PD or not.

An examination of the produced documents and of the product concept(s) followed the FS. This meant that the concept, or suggestions to product solutions, were technically examined. The work process were in none of the cases evaluated. Transference of knowledge and experiences from a specific FS to other PD projects in the companies was totally based on the team members own initiative to evaluate and analyse the process. There was however an awareness of the value of a systematic evaluation of the working process. The interviewees saw a need in taking charge of the experiences and knowledge that existed in a project as well as in the individual team members. PMs also lacked a forum for discussions and exchange of experiences between each other.

## Discussion and conclusions

Though the investigated companies differ in type of product and organisation of PD process, there are several similarities in their way of performing an FS. The same development has taken place in the companies: more resources are used in the early phases, more departments take part in the PD and the time for FSs increases while the total time for a PD project decreases or remains the same. It is a common opinion in the companies that an FS contributes to "do right from the start" provided that the FS is a wide creative phase for seeking solutions. Also the fact that an FS is a part of performing a systematic PD is claimed to be important as this is considered to increase efficiency.

The performed study indicates distinctly that a successful FS is based on a well serving work process. The interviewees do not indicate any difficulties or problems related to finding technical solutions. It appears, as well, to be reasonable that obstacles in the technical development should be acceptable, for example due to too high costs or need of further research, etc. An non-serving working process should however not be acceptable. It is relevant to demand a well-serving and efficient process. Despite this it is the part that is less developed in industrial PD. Much more can be done for further stimulating an increasing efficiency regarding the work process.

The factors that control the working process are mainly goal management, co-operation in the project team with support from a well serving PM and an allocation of enough resources from the companies' management.

The product orderer must give distinct directions to the PM and the team. The company must also allocate the resources that are likely to correspond to the expected results. Distinct directions and reasonable resources indicates that the project are given a high priority which is important for creating commitment in the team. The project will also be considered to be a realistic task. Further distinct directions, as the input of data to the team, form a basis for the creation of a picture of goal in an early phase.

Forming a specification of demands put high pressure on the marketing department in a company. Information of customer demands must be transferred to the team. This could most easily be achieved if the marketing department takes active part in the FS. A prerequisite in the communication between the team and the marketing department is also a mutual interest in the understanding of each others work. The great importance in the marketing departments' participation in the FS is a result of the power of customer demands in PD.

Manufacturing departments participate in all projects where the product is supposed to be manufactured within the company. This is experienced as positive by manufacturing engineers as well as by the other represented functions. Manufacturing aspects are in this way considered early in the PD process which is considered to result in less changes at manufacturing start.

The reason for the importance of goals and goal management can be derived from the significance of co-operation between different competencies and different individuals. Goals do not play an important role if they are not common for the group members or relevant for all participating functions.

The possibilities of creating a common view and to achieve a climate suitable for co-operation must exist in an FS. That means in particular to see to that there is time for such activities and to accept that the results of the activities may not be distinct and concrete. Team-building activities give results continuously during the working process but may not be possible to measure.

All investigated companies make clear that a PM *should* be selected at the start of the FS. The role of the PM should be clear both in tasks and from an organisational point of view. PMs must be able to find support in the work, through co-operation with other PMs as well as with the steering committee. The PM should manage the project work and function as a co-ordinator in the group. Technical skill is a basic need but the role also requires different skills. The PM should be the prime mover and be encouraging but must not totally dominate the group. He or she must pay attention to all group members and lay the foundation to a feeling of safety in the group.

An informal co-operation during the FS is one major factor for efficient project work. This is stimulated when participants early find their different roles in the group, which can be stimulated by team-building activities. The placing of the participants is also essential from this point of view. Communication between participants is enhanced if their working places are close to each other. Also support methods can play an important role: When using certain support methods the process of performance affects the co-operation and a common view of the project could be more easily achieved.

The working process should be evaluated after a certain phase in the PD process, as the FS, has been closed. By finding out what have been successful and what have been complicated in the process, valuable information can be transferred from one project to another and the competence of running projects can be increased in the company.

It has not been within the limits of this study to verify whether the investigated FSs have resulted in PD projects with lower costs, shorter lead-time or increased quality. It is however clearly shown that there is a firm conviction that the present way of working affects the efficiency of the PD process. An increased integration of competencies in a project, as well as co-operation in the team, have a strong coupling to lead-time in product development.

## Acknowledgement

The project was financed by the Swedish Council for Work Life Research (RALF) and the Swedish National Board for Technical Development (NUTEK).

## References

[1] Pahl, G. & Beitz, W. (1977). *Engineering Design, a systematic approach.* ISBN 0-85072-239-X. London: The Design Council London.

[2] Ulrich, K.T. & Eppinger, S.D. (1985). *Product Design and Development.* ISBN 0-07-113742-4. New York: McGraw-Hill, Inc.

[3] Andreasen, M.M. & Hein, L. (1985) *Integrated Product Development.* ISBN 0-948507-21-7. London: IFS (Publications) Ltd.

[4] Hovmark, S. & Nordqvist, S. (1993). *Change towards more efficient product development: working methods and co-operation in five product projects.* Stockholm: Stockholm University, Department of Psychology. (In Swedish).

[5] Syan, C.S. & Mennon, U. (1994). *Concurrent Engineering, Concepts, Implementation and Practice.* ISBN 0-412-58130-2. London: Chapman & Hall.

[6] Pugh, S. (1990). *Total Design, Integrated Methods for Successful Product Engineering.* ISBN 0-201-41639-5. Cornwall: Addison-Wesley Publishers Ltd.

[7] Hayes, R.H., Wheelwright, S.C. & Clark, K.B. (1988). *Dynamic manufacturing. Creating the learning organisation.* New York: The Free Press.

[8] Levi, D., Slem, C. & Young, A. (1994). Team Work in Research and Development Organisations. In: G.E. Bradley and H.W. Hendrick (Eds.), *Human Factors in Organisational Design and Management - IV,* (pp 93-98). Canada: Elsevier Science B.V.

[9] Fabi, B. & Pettersen, N. (1992). Human Resource Management Practices in Project Management. *International Journal of Project Management,* Vol. 10, No 2, pp 81-88.

[10] Katzenbach, J.R. & Smith, D.K. (1994). *The Wisdom of Teams - Creating the High-Performance Organisation.* USA: McKinsey & Company, Inc.

[11] Ekvall, G. (1993). *Creativity in Project work: a longitudinal study of a product development project.* Creativity and innovation management, Vol. 2, No 1, pp 17-27.

[12] Frisk, E., Nordqvist, S. & Norell, M. (1995). *Concurrent Engineering – Strategies for Feasibility Studies in Product Development.* International Conference on Engineering Design, Proceedings Vol. 2. Praha, Czech Republique.

[13] Glaser, B.G. & Strauss, A.L. (1967). The discovery of grounded theory: Strategies for qualitative research. New York: de Gruyter.

# 079

**Dr. Luis Felipe Nascimento**
NITEC/PPGA/UFRGS
Av. João Pessoa, 52 sala 11
90.040-000 Porto Alegre, RS, BRAZIL
tel.: (55-51) 316 34 79 (direct) 316 3536 (message)
fax.: (55 51) 227 10 36
Email: felipen@vortex.ufrgs.br

Title: **ENVIRONMENT MANAGEMENT IN BRAZIL'S ENTERPRISE**

Categories: **d2** ("Technology for the sustainable society' and "Empirical and Experimental")

**This paper is suitable for Poster presentation only**

# ENVIRONMENTAL MANAGEMENT IN BRAZIL'S ENTERPRISE

## ABSTRACT

In Brazil, the environmental management is rarely known and practiced by SMEs. Although Brazilian laws on environmental protection and waste treatment are severe, many of Enterprise are still polluting the environment. A possible reason for this is because of the Enterprises lack of information about cleaner technologies or even the weak control performed by official agencies. A research conducted by Federal University of Rio Grande do Sul (UFRGS) has identified major difficulties of Enterprises of the metal-mechanical Sector in *Rio Grande do Sul*. The main results indicate the real situation of these firms, and revealed that there was a financial loss caused by waste. This paper, presents the environmental outline of the enterprises researched and suggests arrangements to improve the environmental performance and the productivity of them.


Key words: environment management, waste treatment, Brazilian enterprise

## 1. INTRODUCTION

For a long time there was a belief that economic grows would bring better life conditions for the hole society. The criteria to evaluate quality life were based fundamentally in the capacity of consumption of the group/country investigated. The consumption mentality developed, mainly, since the 50's, brought up the "discarded society". People were stimulated to waste, to use and discard. As Harman said (1990), "people started to be called as consumers instead of citizens".

The mentality of "use and waste", of consumption and the waste of prime material and energy, in excess and at ridiculous prices, infected also the management of industries. Allot of these industries changed from animal traction and man power to electric machines, starting to use the benefits of progress: "cheap and subsidized energy". The environmental cost of the production and consumption of electric energy stayed ignored for many decades. The prime material used in the production was considered a gift from nature, coming from a unfailing fountain. The pollution generated in the productive process was presented as the price of which society had to pay for the progress which was occurring in that region, in other words, the "progress" of one region started to be measured by the number of chimney existents.

The realization of international events like the meeting of the Roman Club in 1970 and the Stocolmo Conference in 1972 started the institutional organization in many countries, even in Brazil, with the agencies for environmental control. In 1973 was created

---

( * ) The author appreaciates the special help given by Angela Lemos and Erica Hiwatashi

the Company of Technology in Environment Sanitation (CETESB) in the state of *São Paulo*. Since 1975 appeared, in a national level, the first regulations to control environmental pollution.

The realization of many studies and international events in the decades of 80's and 90's, like for example, the essay of the Brundtland Commission (Our Common Future) in 1987 and the Conference about Environment and Development occurred in 1992 in *Rio de Janeiro* , and also the action well articulated by many "Non-Government Organizations" (ONGs), diffused the ecological consciences in Brazil. Becoming more and more difficult to export pollution, by the transference of technology that pollutes, or by products ecologically aggressive.

As MAIMON (1996), the Brazilian enterprises are adopting attitudes more responsible in relation to the environment. These attitudes changes occurred specially because of the environmental legislation matters and most recently by the international pressures and influences which helped financially projects of its potential for environment impact. It is possible to say that until then, in most of the cases, the enterprises acted almost only under external pressures. As estimated by some authors, the enterprises of many segments tend to assume a position pro-active, moved not any more by external pressures, but to attend to commercial barriers not taxed, imposed by ISO 14000 and to attend a market each day more exigent in ecological matters.

As so, environment quality of products passed to be incorporated in product quality. The disposability and diffusion of technological innovations permitted more and more the improvement of enterprises in environmental quality of theirs products and process. The innovation technology comes as a strategic factor for the solution of problems and the increase of competivity. In this sense, the problems of pollution started to be seen as needful of technological innovation.

In sector as the metal-mechanic, the EMS still configures as a long term objective, to be defined by the market impositions. Although, these impositions can came before the time that the managers of these enterprises thinks. As so, that makes it necessary to verify the environmental conditions existents in the enterprises of this sector, as well as their plans and conditions to implement a environmental management system, so saying, to better known the environmental outline of theses enterprises.

Although it has been done many researches to identify the environmental outline of enterprises of some sectors, there isn't one that describes us, deeply, this matter in the sector of metal-mechanic in the state of *Rio Grande do Sul*. The numbers and information accessible don't leads us to a good evaluation of the sector. Trying to fulfill this need, the Nucleus of Management in Innovation Technology of the Program of Graduate School in Business Administration- NITEC/PPGA of UFRGS, with the support of the Center of Studies and Research in Business Administration (CEPA) of the School of Business Administration/UFRGS develop this work to evaluate the environmental outline of the enterprises of this sector.

So, this research investigates the "externalities" of the productive process, as well as the motivations for the adoption of arrangements for environmental protection and of cleaner technologies. Verifies, not only, if the enterprises respect the actual environmental legislation, but especially, the actions and efforts developed in the sense to implement a Environmental Management System.


## 2. RESEARCH DESIGN

This research was done together with the enterprises of the metal-mechanical sector located in the State of *Rio Grande do Sul*. As already mentioned before, the choosing of this sector was because of the existence of studies which tells about enterprise strategy in relation to the environmental variable.


### 2.1 METHOD

The sample is restricted only to enterprises, of the metal-mechanic sector, that already obtained the certificate ISO 9000. As part in the Quality Comity of the Federation of Industries of Rio Grande do Sul (FIERGS), in April 1996, there were the registration of 61 enterprises in the state with the certificate ISO 9000. From these, 25 enterprises here from the metal-mechanical sector.

It starts out by the supposition that, the enterprises that have the certification of ISO 9000, are the enterprises of these metal-mechanical sector that are more concern about quality and that they do, systematically, the control of the non conformities occurred in the productive process. Although the certification ISO 9000 isn't a pre-condition for the planning of a Environmental Management System and for to get the certification on ISO 14000, it is consider that the enterprises already certified by ISO 9000 presents, potentially, the best chances to realize in a short future, these tasks.

By the investigation of enterprises located in different regions, that produces different products, and that attend the internal market and/or external, the research identifies the different types of problems existent on which is reflects the externalities of the productive process. This way, it was possible to conclude an environmental outline by the most advanced enterprises of the sector of metal-mechanic in terms of worries about quality, organization and of registration of proceedings.


### 2.2. THE RESEARCH EXECUTION

There were investigated 25 enterprises that already were certified by ISO 9000. It was used as a research instrument a questionnaire composed by 84 open and closed questions that were answered, in interviews with managers of sectors/departments of quality/security and environment of the enterprises selected. The questionnaire elaborated has section like: general information; the enterprise data; production and environment; knowledge about environmental management systems; information of the enterprise that did not implement and the ones that already implemented arrangements for environment protection; information about the quality control management of water, air and solid residues; accounting of the environmental cost; corporate actions and relations of the enterprise with the community. For the formulation of these questionnaire it was used, as an example, the research instruments used by the Society of Initiative and Support for Environment Management (*SIGA*), on which were made the necessary adaptations to the reality of enterprises of the sector of metal-mechanic of *Rio Grande do Sul*.

The questioner was presented and discussed in meetings of the Nucleus of Management for Innovation Technology -NITEC, and after that, it was done a first test in three enterprises as a sample. There was made some changes for better compression of the interviewed in relation to the questions asked, as well as to permit faster answers.

To facilitate the access to enterprises, the Coordination of the Research Project sent a direct mail to the enterprises explaining the objectives of this Research and another letter from the Coordination of the Quality Committee of FIERGS, of which these enterprises are part of. After all, the Research Coordinator, made a telephone contact, to verify if there was the acceptances of the enterprises to concede the interview and so to make an appointment to do the interview at the enterprise. The task of making clear the objectives of the research and the sensitization were very important, on what resulted in 100% acceptances from the enterprises of the sample of 25.

## 3. ENVIRONMENT MANAGEMENT IN THE ENTERPRISES OF THE SECTOR OF METAL-MECHANIC

Initially, was verified in the enterprises researched, the level of knowledge about "Environmental Management Systems". In the enterprises that already adopted arrangements for environment protection, is was tried to identify the motivations to adopt these attitude. Along the interview, were putted questions about management of air quality, water quality and management of the residues and about the accounting of environment costs. In the final part of the interview, were asked questions about the relation of the enterprises with the community on which it is inserted.

Further more is described each one of the topics shown above, presenting the main opinions of the interviewees of the 25 enterprises researched.

## 3.1. KNOWLEDGE ABOUT THE THEME ENVIRONMENT SYSTEM MANAGEMENT

The theme Environment System Management is known in greater or smaller level by enterprises researched. The opinions varies, although, about the importance and urgency of the implementation of a Environment Management System in the Enterprise.

The interviewees, in the majority, believe that the implementation of the environment management system is a world tendency which has to be done by the Brazilian enterprises. About this aspect, there are disagreements concerning the timing of its implementation. Some believes that the market (clients, competition) is who will force the enterprise to adopted a arrangements like the use of cleaner technologies and the substitution of prime materials trying to make the products more easily recyclable and "ecologically right".

The environment legislation of the state of *Rio Grande do Sul* was considered to much rigid, but necessary to force the enterprises to treat the residues generated.

The State Foundation of Environmental Protection (FEPAM), agency of environment control of the state, frequently criticized in the enterprise circle, had its acting evaluated in general as regular, been eulogized by some enterprises. Among the functions that should be done by FEPAM the ones most relevant are: to act as facilitator in the solutions of environmental problems and generate information by the organization of a data base system.

## 3.2. MOTIVATION FOR THE IMPLEMENTATION OF ARRANGEMENTS TO PROTECTION OF THE ENVIRONMENT AND THE ARRANGEMENTS ALREADY ADOPTED BY THE ENTERPRISE

The majority of the enterprises researched adopted arrangements of environment protection because of the exigency of agencies of environmental control, although some say that it was by their own initiative, it is visible the power of coercion by these agencies which leads many enterprise, even the ones that never were check by FEPAM, to adopt arrangements in these matter.

Among the arrangements done by the enterprises to reduce the environment aggressions, it is pointed out the actions in the sense to reduce the emission of liquid effluents and of the generation of solid residues. The less spoken were actions to reduce the consumption of energy and the reduction of gas and other emissions.

The enterprises, in general, are doing studies aiming to the utilization of prime materials or technologies less pollutant. In relation to the actions together with the employees, the enterprises initiative are, specially, the discussion about environment matters with them. It is each time greater the number of employees of the enterprises researched that participates in courses and trainings related to environment protection.


## 3.3. MANAGEMENT OF WATER QUALITY

The majority of the enterprises are located in regions were there are a great offer of water. Some of them point out the concerns about the increase of the demand of water because of the industrial expansion in the region. The water supply of the enterprise are done by the public system of treatment (water treatment stations) and water distribution. Few are the enterprises that have water artesian well with the capacity to supply its necessity.

The systems for treatment of liquid effluents are destined, in majority of the cases, to industrial refuse. The monitoring of liquid effluents is made because of the exigency of the agency of environment control. It's important to point out that some enterprises had made big investments in the treatment of liquid effluents, what permitted the implementation of close cycles, in other words, the reusing of 90% of the liquid effluents. This action resulted in significant economic gains. Although the environmental cost generally are not register and, when they are, they aren't accounted in the operational cost of the product.


## 3.4. MANAGEMENT OF AIR QUALITY

The enterprises already realized inventories to identify the fountains of emissions of air pollutants and they have equipment of atmospheric emission control. The efficiency of the equipment of atmospheric emission control are questioned by the Non-government Organizations (ONGSs). As these organizations say, the enterprises should invest priority in the substitution of polluted process, to process that use cleaner technologies.

The implementation of the equipment for atmospheric emission control occurred, in the majority of the enterprises researched, by the exigency of the agency of environment control. The efficiency, although, of the enforcement of the programs of checking the air's quality are much criticized by these non-government organizations.


## 3.5. MANAGEMENT OF SOLID RESIDUES

The solid residues are classified in three categories: Class I are residues considered dangerous that, because of its inflammable characteristics, also corrosive, reactivity, toxicant, and pathogenic can present high risk to the public's health. In Class II are found the residues considered non inherent that are not found in Class I. Are categorized as residues class III the ones that don't have non of the constituents soluble, in concentrations superior of the patterns defined.

In the enterprise researched was detected as solid residues class I: galvanic Ode, ganglia, oils, salts used in the thermic treatment. In class II are: packages, paper, plastic, residues of products from manufacturing, residues of rectification. As last, the residues of class III: paper in general, solid residues inherit, sand, domestic trash, etc.

The final disposition of the dangerous solid residues are thirdcerized, in other words, repass to another enterprise that stocks the residues. The residues class II are putted in industrial embankment. Few are the cases that the enterprise apply any measure aiming its recycling.


## 3.6. RELATIONS OF THE ENTERPRISE WITH THE COMMUNITY

The industrial activities promoted many effects upon environment and about the community that it surrounds. Critics about the noise, smell, gas emission, emission of effluents in water body, inadequate disposition of solid residues promote by the enterprises were, in the past, reasons of constant conflict between community-enterprise.

Because of many reasons, the enterprises started improving its environment performance and seeking to minimize the negative externalities. In this research it was tried to identify the actions realized and/or previewed in case of environment accidents because of the execution of theirs industrial activity.

The enterprises declared that, in case of environment accidents, their were seek to clarify the causes of the accident as well as permit the access of the community affected in the investigations of the causes of the accident and in the implementation of actions to restore the damage caused.

In the relations of the enterprise with the public entities, press, community and non-governmental organizations, is shown a good relation, in a informal way, with educational institutes and with the residence association. With the environmental control agencies and the other public institutions, prevail formal relations with conventions and agreements established with these agencies aiming to the present legislation and to the development of cooperated actions.

# 4. CONCLUSIONS

By the realization of these research it was possible to define the environmental outline of the enterprises of the sector of metal-mechanic of the state of *Rio Grande do Sul* that already obtained the certification ISO 9000.

The majority of the enterprises are characterized by an reactive posture, adopting only the measures exigent by the environmental legislation and that are checked by the environmental control agencies. Most of them, although, admit that the implementation of a environmental management system is a global tendency and that, in a brief future, they should be implementing it in the enterprise. Despite, because of high costs for the installation of liquid effluents station treatment and atmospheric emission filters, these actions are pos done, being part only of the future plans for the enterprise. In relation to the destination of the dangerous solid residues, the enterprises prefer to thirdcerized this services, without , getting rid of the responsibility of the final dispositions, like preview the environment legislation.

It is noticeable a great need for information about the possible implementation of cleaner technologies. The use of these technologies could reduce the losses (generation of residues and the liquid and gas emissions), improve environment quality of the products, establish a better relation with the community were it is inserted and with the agencies of environmental control and, at last, explore the ecological marketing that it gives when adopting these technologies.

Shows out also that the enterprises that already adopted actions concerning environment protection and that obtained economic gains because of the adoption of the arrangements, did not have the quantification of this gain. The lack of these information and the need for a methodology which analyses the negative externalities, which would be known and accepted by the environment agencies, makes it difficult to have an efficient environment accounting. There isn't, so far, precise data about the direct and indirect cost, return tax, etc. about investments in environment protection.

At last, it's important to point out the necessity of new researches in other enterprises of the sector of metal-mechanic and in enterprises of other sectors aiming to know the environmental outline of these enterprises, theirs necessities to then plan politics and develop actions aiming to the improvement in environment performance and the increase of competivity of these enterprises in the national and international market.

# 5 BIBLIOGRAPHY

BRESSAN, Jr. „Principais resultados da Política Ambiental Brasileira", **Revista de Administração Pública**, Rio de Janeiro, jan/mar, 1992.

CNI, Idealismo Pragmático. **Revista CNI**, Rio de Janeiro, jan/fev, p. 24-27, 1995.

COMISSÃO Mundial sobre o Ambiente e Desenvolvimento. **Nosso Futuro Comum**, Rio de Janeiro, FGV, 1988.

GLADWIN, T. N., KENNELLY, J. e KRAUSE, T. "Shifting Paradigms for Sustainable Development: Implications for Management Theory and Research", **Academy of Management Review**, v. 20, 1995.

HARMAN, Willis; HORMANN, John. **O trabalho criativo**. São Paulo: Cultrix, 1990.

MAIMON, D., Eco-Estratégia nas Empresas Brasileiras: Realidade ou Discurso?, In: **Revista de Administração de Empresas**, São Paulo, v.34, n.4, 1994.

STEGER, Ulrich. **Handbuch des Umweltmanagement**. Verlag C.H. Beck. München/Deutschland, 1992.

WELFORD, Richard. **Environmental and sustainable development - the corporate challenge for the 21st century**. London: Routledge, 1995.

# 081

# MANAGEMENT OF AN *ITRI* AS A LINK IN THE NATIONAL INNOVATION SYSTEM

Gideon de Wet
CSIR, P O Box 395,
Pretoria, 0001, South Africa

ABSTRACT: *Most countries in the world acknowledge the need for government to participate in the national innovation process. One of the policy instruments used by many governments is that of the Industrial Technology Research Institute or ITRI ( a generic name used, inter alia, by UNIDO), that is intended to acquire, adapt and deploy technology into the national innovation system. While such institutions could be highly specialised in First World countries, developing countries can normally afford only one or a few, placing severe demands on the effectiveness and efficiency of these organisations. In order to achieve these goals, governments tend to "commercialise" ITRIs, to ensure market orientation and demonstrate effectiveness through the willingness of private enterprise to pay "real" money for the products of the institution.*

*The two major strategic management issues that have to be resolved for an ITRI are first, the balance between government grant and contract income, to ensure a balance between the policy instrument role of long term capability building and serving the short term market demands and second, a reward framework to ensure effective transfer of technology against the resulting loss of continued contract income for the institution.*

*Although no formal design "theory" has been developed for an ITRI, some empirical observations about its design and management have been made, particularly by UNIDO. This paper provides some analysis of the dilemmas arising in the design of an ITRI, and offers some of the alternatives to be considered to achieve a feasible strategy in a specific national context. Learning gained over the last 10 years at the CSIR in South Africa is used as a case in point. It is illustrated that there seem to be critical relationships between business structure, the external context/market and reward systems that must be understood to ensure proper performance by an ITRI, from the establishment phase through the evolution to the mature phase.*

## INTRODUCTION - THE RAISON D'ETRE FOR AN ITRI

In general, the purpose of an Industrial Technology Research Institute or ITRI is to provide technology to industry - mainly in the country where the government that is the main stakeholder, provides the investment to create the "DNA-platform" for technology creation and deployment. Technology can be gained through external acquisition or internal research and development, or a mixture of both - one implicit assumption being that "science" is translated into technology in this way. It could be delivered to "customers" in a variety of ways, such as a "packaged" transfer, providing a service, delivering documentation and related "hardware items" or even the launching of a new venture. Historically the reason for having a local ITRI in many (developing) countries was to gain technology to support a national strategy of import replacement, in contrast to the more recent focus on international competitive advantage. The underlying grand strategy here is of course the economic prosperity arising from technology-based competitive advantage, either in providing products to the local market for which foreign exchange had to be made available previously, or in the global market to allow exports. There no longer seems to be any doubt about the contribution that technology could make towards the economic development of a country.

Why must government be involved in this technology acquisition process? The two main reasons that jump to mind are:

■ to provide critical technologies and/or inputs to many industries, because of lower levels of appropriability of such technologies - (human resource development and general education are part of this area);

- because government itself is a major beneficiary - either to enhance its own functional (regulatory/decision making) capability or to achieve strategic objectives in public health, defence, foreign policy and so on.

In general this is referred to as government doing what industry and business cannot do, or "common good" investment. To paraphrase the first reason above, government has to invest because certain activities in the national household (NHH) are not "profitable", or because government is "neutral" vis a vis competitive businesses. Private enterprise is either willing, or could be forced to provide government with information that it would never allow the competition to have access to. Once such information is aggregated and processed, it becomes vital to all the relevant competitors - national statistics is a typical part of this. That these considerations are not absolute, is demonstrated by the existence of private schools, colleges and universities on the one hand (demonstrating commercial viability of such "common good" activities), and the practice in Japan where a particular industry is chosen to do (government funded) pioneering R&D on a specific technology and is then required to share it widely, once it has reached a given level of maturity. (Illustrating that such work does not necessarily have to be done in a government institution. The Sematech joint venture for semiconductor technology in the USA is another case in point)

## A FUNCTIONAL MODEL FOR AN ITRI - A SPECTRUM OF CHOICE

Once the need for an ITRI has been identified, the next question tends to be about the functional form that it should take. Typically there are two extreme models for such a government policy instrument, i.e.:
- the "fire-brigade" model, and
- the state corporation model.

The fire-brigade model simply refers to a state-funded institution, where R&D is done on some or other area of interest to the nation at large or a particular sector of national activity. Historically in South Africa, the Leather Research Institute and Building Research Institute were examples of "mission-oriented" R&D activities, that provided the results of their endeavours free of charge to the relevant industries. In general the income of the institution has no direct relationship to the benefits conveyed into the national household and the underlying assumption is that, because it provides a common-good service, it is appropriate for government to "own" this activity.

The most serious problem arising in such a situation is the appearance of the ivory tower syndrome, where the scientists pursue avenues of research that are of more academic interest than of practical value to the intended beneficiaries, and government bureaucrats are not interested in/capable of steering the relationship towards a more satisfactory status. This is referred to as the fire-brigade model, to convey the notion of a service being made available, basically free of charge, to serve those in need of such a service, as and when they require it. However, unless there is some mechanism to ensure interaction between service to the client and reward to the institution, members of the fire-brigade could become more skilled in practising their hobbies than fighting fires. The S&T systems in the former Russian Empire, and to a large extent in South Africa, displayed similar tendencies. A second problem experienced by the state institution itself, is to justify the maintenance and possible increase in funding of the organisation - how does one confirm the extent to which the clients want, or are satisfied by the service offered and/or rendered? This is a familiar problem in many African countries.

The state corporation model, or fully commercialised model, refers to the case where the policy instrument is dependent upon generating its total income from contract work and receives no subsidy from government, apart from a possible initial endowment to create the facility. (Crown Research Institutes in New Zealand [1], Fundacion Chile [2]) In this model, if the institution survives, there is no problem to justify its existence or prove its utility to the client community, since this is measured in pure business terms - clients are willing to pay "real" money for its products. This model suffers from "short-termism" (to reduce risk and ensure income) and patently competes with similar enterprises in the private sector. It may also display "mandate creep", where the institution would pursue market opportunities rather than remain within the mandated area prescribed by government.

## AN OPERATIONAL MODEL FOR AN ITRI

Historically ITRIs were founded close to the fire brigade model, to support new areas of endeavour in given countries - areas such as mining, industrial materials, construction and building materials, etc. are typical of the former colonies of more advanced European countries. (Eg. CSIRs in British colonies, IPT in Brazil [3]) As these institutions (and their local industrial client base) mature, the question of commercialisation arises, mainly for two reasons: first, there is the need from government to ensure that the client community is actually being served properly and second, governments are finding it more and more difficult to provide funding for common good objectives. There seems to be neither an empirical international standard, nor a theoretical formula for the extent of commercialisation of an ITRI - or stated differently, what the ratio between government grant income and contract income should be. Both in South Africa and elsewhere there are examples ranging from one extreme to the other, depending on the local circumstances and level of maturity of the relevant industry. Typically a 50/50 ratio between government grant and contract income seems to be considered "healthy". [4]

While this ratio may be important, the more fundamental question to be addressed as the "fire brigade" is being commercialised, is that of the business model that should be implemented. Stated differently, the question is how to move away from the research laboratory type organisation to one that would be much more "market driven"? Again many alternatives are available with few formal criteria to guide the selection process - here one has to rely on experience gained elsewhere. In the case of CSIR in South Africa, wide consultation and intense internal debate led to the selection of a (relatively small) corporate office plus a number of strategic business units (SBUs) as the operational business structure. One of the major reasons for this choice was the extent of departure from the previous "R&D lab" model and the intensity of market focus engendered by this model. What was not appreciated fully at the time of the transformation, were the management implications of such a business concept for a policy instrument. Taking a closer look at the evolution of the management paradigm in CSIR (South Africa) could uncover some issues of interest.

### Managing the government grant

Historically the government grant was the income of CSIR. After the reformation towards being an ITRI in 1986/87, the treatment of government grant as income was maintained, although it was now understood that income had to be expanded by earning money on external contracts - getting to grips with the notion of "the Market". In order to distinguish between the two kinds of income, grant money was earned through "contract with executive" or CWE income, while non-grant income was labelled "external". Executive (or Corporate Management) could ensure the appropriate utilisation of grant monies by setting the value system according to which CWEs were allocated - typically including criteria like taking the long term view, scope of benefit to industry, non-subsidising of external contracts, CSIR mandate area, and so on, but of course, being a "business" now, return on investment (ROI) became a key criterion.

The next dilemma then for Executive was how to arrive at this ROI? They faced a situation where it was impossible to switch the classification of grant monies from "income" to "investment capital" - too many existing functional groups were not anywhere near the point where they could earn sufficient income from external markets, nor were they in a position to meet the requirements of the CWE criteria to qualify for investment funding. This was a critical dilemma for Executive, because it allowed the "abuse" of the process of investment allocation. This could be explained by understanding the discipline invoked by using an investment "filter" like CWE, that requires the recipient of investment funds to commit to a future return on such an investment. In normal business practice, investment funds are either shown as shareholder capital or long term loan capital and the business unit (SBU) receiving the funds is subject to the discipline that it either has to show a significant return on share equity or repay loans while earning more than the rate of interest on the loan. If "investment" is recorded as income however, there is no formal "trace" on whether the return promised via the original CWE submission was in fact achieved - and if there is no trace, there is no reason to be too "honest" when applications for investments are made.

While this reasoning is logically sound, it tends to be somewhat simplistic in the context of a real business and probably even more so for an R&D environment, where the linkages between a particular investment and eventual income are complex and income is spread out over a considerable time period. One is therefore forced to take a more aggregated view of investment and earnings, leading to a "portfolio" perspective for investments and consolidated figures for earnings. It does however not justify the relaxation of discipline to the level of using investment capital as income. As a result of the political transformation in South Africa after 1993, all government related institutions had to start submitting "business plans" to justify future funding and demonstrate "due diligence" in the use of past allocations of taxpayers' investment. This increased the need in CSIR to be able to trace the return on government grant funds and has lead to the development of a portfolio investment system known as IPT (Investment Process Tool). It overcomes the difficulty of the capital-as-income in the corporate accounting system, by taking grant fund investment "off-line" and treating it as a capital account, also referred to as the (Financial) Technology Balance Sheet. This not only provides the discipline on each SBU to live up to its promises at investment allocation time, but also provides a significant amount of additional information to manage technology and technology investments much more effectively than before.

While the IPT may be an enormous step forward in the management of investments, it does not remove the dilemma from the corporate accounts - there government grant monies are still shown as income - and there it could still be manipulated in many ways to "hide" shortcomings in external income activities.

## Managing external income

CSIR has managed to develop a robust, computer-based project management system, known as PMS, that is interfaced with the corporate accounts software and is recognised by the external auditors as an integral part of the auditing infrastructure required to meet the demands of the Reporting by Public Entities Act. External income, including interest and royalties, is thus captured and accounted for in a formal way.

The dilemma around external income is therefore not about the way such funds are brought to book, but about the behaviour of SBU management in securing external income. Two areas of concern are highlighted here, i.e.

- short term focus, manifested in the pursuit of sales that may not be exactly within the mandate of a particular SBU and/or in the longer term benefit of either CSIR or the intended stakeholders in the country;

- mono-SBU focus, manifested as a lack of enthusiasm among SBUs to participate in projects/contracts that require the capabilities of more than one SBU.

Overall there is the understanding that, as long as there is the "absolute" requirement for SBUs to meet the "bottom line" goals, these symptoms would be present. Furthermore, if the CSIR is to be run as a "market driven" organisation, this requirement can not be relaxed and it is therefore necessary that appropriate management measures should be in place to mitigate undesirable effects arising from this business paradigm. One such measure is the availability of government grant funds, that allow an SBU to create capability in the absence of an immediate client and thus be prepared for longer term market demands. But this does not necessarily address the collaboration among SBUs.

# THE BUSINESS MANAGEMENT INFLUENCE OF THE STRATEGIC CONTEXT

## Behaviour induced by the SBU model

If it is accepted that the organisational structure of a corporate office plus SBUs is an effective framework to emphasise the market orientation of a "non-profit" organisation, then the strategic management style has to ensure that the institution as a whole meets the other criteria set for a policy instrument - most importantly the longer term view and the willingness to take the risks involved in being the technology scout of industry. But SBU management, evaluated on "bottom-line" performance, will naturally tend to be more commercially oriented, be slow to react to urgent client demands and reluctant to get involved in projects involving other SBUs - not because they are poor managers, but because it is the nature of this kind of business. It arises from the fact that if an SBU management team wants to achieve its business goals, the value of contracts obtained from the market must lead (in time) the SBU capacity to deliver, by a sufficient margin to ensure that the work could be done and invoiced to reach the SBU business target at the end of the financial year. This means, first, SBU management has to ensure sufficient contract value available as early in the financial year as possible and second, there has to be some work in hand by the end of the financial year to lead into the next year.

This inherently leads to two "natural" consequences, viz.

- SBU management will tend to give preference to contracts that they could handle with the resources under their direct control, and
- any market demands arising after a certain point in the financial year will only be considered for execution in the next financial year, simply because resources would have been fully committed for the present year.

The first type of behaviour (typical of matrix organisations) leads to a "reluctance" to become involved in (especially short term) contracts that require joint participation of two or more SBUs. Tackling "multi-SBU" contracts therefore needs special management intervention. One such intervention in CSIR was the formation of Corporate Programmes, that required the involvement of a number of SBUs from the outset. The market segments assigned to these programmes are perceived to be long term in nature, justifying these special management arrangements. Short term, multi-disciplinary market needs are addressed mainly by way of "exhortation" from the Corporate Level, and sometimes when SBUs find it difficult to fill capacity from their "standard" market segments.

The second type of behaviour tends to exclude "targets of opportunity" that may often be small in business terms, but very important in strategic terms. Typically this could take the form of a short study to support decision-making for a government client or a potentially significant new client from the private sector. These market needs cannot be foreseen in any way other than say a typical percentage of the annual business of an SBU, but, since this tends to be less preferred type of business, this percentage would normally be on the conservative side if based on past experience. In terms of the fire-brigade metaphor, this would be seen by stakeholders as the fire-brigade ignoring "small fires" and only reacting when the "mayor's office" makes a special plea for action.

## Influence of the strategic context

The influence of a well-structured strategic context for a policy instrument, in the form of significant national programmes and objectives, can now be understood: first, because it provides longer term, wide scope strategic goals, that allow SBUs to plan over a time horizon of more than a single financial year and (mutatis mutandis) the opportunity and motivation to plan joint participation in meeting the more comprehensive market demands. Second, it provides credible (fully funded) and legitimate (formally established by all stakeholders) goals, the achievement of which will earn the SBU(s) acclaim among the relevant stakeholders, since it will be perceived as key contributions to the national development strategy and good value for the amount of resources used. Third, the more complex the assignment, the higher the perceived value addition, and thus the possible profit margin per unit of human resource hour, allowing the creation of a "buffer fund" to reserve a bigger percentage of capacity for targets of opportunity and thus enhance the image of a flexible organisation that is sensitive to urgent client needs.

Two important observations could now be made, ie.

- Some of the most important management "levers" to ensure the effective functioning of a business oriented policy instrument, are located outside the organisation - while the ITRI Executive has significant powers to ensure the quality of what is being delivered by the organisation and the efficiency of producing these products, ie. "doing things right", the identification of "doing the right things" is done externally. This is nothing more than the generic business/market relationship, but the fundamental difference is in the nature of the rules of existence for a private enterprise and those for a (market driven) policy instrument. If a private enterprise fails to interpret its market's needs, it will fail and disappear. Nobody else is responsible for its survival. If the market demands for a policy instrument are not articulated by its stakeholder community, it goes into a mode of being a government subsidised competitor with the private and tertiary education sectors - it will not necessarily fail and be closed down. This does, of course, not preclude the ITRI from participating in the generation of the "external" goals or market demands - the important distinction here is that the ownership of these goals is outside the ITRI.

- The "pricing policy" for a policy instrument has to be designed in a much more mature way than has been the general practice in most countries. This is a rather complex issue, discussed in the next section of this paper, but in general management language it comes down to the difference between cost-based pricing versus market value pricing.

## PRICING POLICIES AND REWARDS FOR AN ITRI

In the pure fire-brigade model, there is "no" charge attached to a product (including services). In the "commercialised ITRI" model, the price of the product is direct cost plus a small margin, as determined by the ITRI Board/Executive. The investment of government grant funds to create the capability to provide the particular product is normally not factored into the price. Compared to a private enterprise, an ITRI, treating government grant as income, therefore has a "hidden" subsidy on its products, amounting to "unlimited" amounts of investment capital at zero interest rate. Even though an ITRI may charge hourly rates comparable to those of the private sector, it may seldom show a higher margin than private enterprises, because of having to take higher risks (by virtue of its function) and experiencing a higher level of project failure (in a commercial sense) than private enterprise. It may also be paying higher average salaries and may be obliged to invest in more modern equipment.

By and large, this is the model accepted in many countries. In the light of the foregoing discussion, it tends to work better in countries where national market goals are articulated and funded better - where there is a clear understanding of the strategic context. What is not publicised at all well is the way these successful countries "compensate" their ITRIs for their achievements. There is the general statement by the Japanese that, once it has been decided what has to be done, the "necessary" funds are provided; there is the German model of the funding of the Fraunhofer Institutes, but typically the approach in many other successful countries is not fully understood.

The question that now begs an answer is whether there is a more fundamental argument around the compensation of a ITRI for delivering on national goals?

One basic problem in the R&D business is to relate outputs of an organisation to investment inputs. Because of the many-to-one relationships between outputs and investment, calculating return on R&D investment is a complex problem and thus an ongoing issue in the world-wide debates. (See eg. the work done by Edwin Mansfield [5]) The IPT-based approach developed by CSIR, and discussed in the foregoing, is a novel way of addressing this problem, because it does not attempt to establish a deterministic relationship between investment at the micro level and eventual single capabilities, but aggregates investments and capabilities into "thrusts" and, in turn, thrusts into technology competencies, aimed at specific market segments.

For the present argument, it is sufficient to accept that there is an approach like IPT at CSIR that will allow an ITRI to determine (rather than calculate) in a non-trivial way, the investments made in a "parcel" of technology that is ready for transfer, or being transferred to a "client".

The ITRI Executive now has a number of pricing options, where the cost of a product (or service) would consist of some aggregate of variable cost, some or all of (direct) fixed cost, and a small margin. Clients do not expect to be charged the cost of (prior) capability creation at the ITRI - private sector clients assume that the technology is acquired and developed for non-exclusive availability, otherwise they would have to contribute by way of a specific contract up front, and government clients assume that "government" should not pay twice for the same capability. But this tends to reinforce the implicit conflict of interest built into the business concept of a commercialised ITRI: having to earn an external income from the market implies that the ITRI should have technology that is of value to its clients, and the essential role of the ITRI is to transfer such technology to industry. But if it transfers the technology however, it actually loses future potential earnings. This leads to a reluctance to market "complete" transfer of the "money spinner technologies" and often leads to a "consulting" strategy, where the technology is retained to ensure future income and thereby failing in the essential function of its policy instrument role. This failure is in reality even more serious when there are multiple clients (remember the *common good* reason for having an ITRI in the first place) for the particular technology, in the sense that the ITRI would fail to study and try to find the optimal process of **transfer** of the technology.

Taking this to the logical extreme, unless the reward system would encourage actual technology transfer, the ITRI (and/or its SBUs), would tend to run shy of the major programmes and concentrate on the "small business", in order to ensure the maintenance of its external income. Two possible reward approaches that would encourage proper behaviour would thus be:

- compensation by way of an "investment recovery lump sum", determined by means of a mechanism such as CSIR's IPT system and provided by the government department that is the primary stakeholder in the national objective that is being served by the transfer, and/or
- the opportunity to "sell" the technology at a more mature stage, typically after its commercial viability has been verified and the "market" is able to place a value on the technology. This is one of the features of the model followed by Fundacion Chile. It is also the feature which is recognised by UNIDO as an essential part of the overall model of a "mature" ITRI [6], that will transfer the technology into a new venture, with or without an external partner and will only offer its share for sale after the viability of the venture has been demonstrated to the extent that private enterprises would express an interest to purchase.

Some of this thinking is being implemented in the CSIR "venture incubator", but the approach is still tentative rather than being encouraged by a host of enthusiastic stakeholders. If this activity is recognised to be a significant contribution in the national programme to create new ventures, plus, since it is happening at an ITRI, it is also the development of the process to be duplicated at every industry extension centre in the country, it becomes a major national programme! But then it must be resourced and managed as such.

While the forgoing discussion could be done in the context of technology transfer to industry, the problem of transferring technology to another government client should not be ignored. It is a problem in as much as government clients (other government departments in the same country) normally expect to be charged at a cost-based rate and in many cases even at a predetermined human resource cost rate. Quite often though the benefit to the country of transferring technology to a government client would be significantly larger than that of transferring technology of a similar "magnitude" in effort, to the private sector. It is therefore not a trivial problem, unless the idea of the investment recovery reward could be negotiated into the deal.

## VALUE ADDITION THROUGH SYNTHESIS

The general focus of the foregoing discussion was to demonstrate that, while the corporate structure of CSIR is more or less ideal for a commercialised ITRI, "ideal behaviour" will only be ensured by appropriate management - both at corporate as well as stakeholder (supra-corporate) levels. One aspect of the business, directly related to pricing policy and reward, that has not been discussed so far, is that of the "value of synthesis". This notion, well understood in the world of systems engineering, is not as familiar in other contexts. It is intended to convey the idea that the value perceived by the market of an integrated functional system is usually way beyond that of a complete inventory of the component parts of the system, and thus the "price" of the system that the market will consider to be reasonable or acceptable, is normally in excess of the "cost of inventory plus integration". While this has been at the roots of the motor car industry, it took many decades for this same industry to re-discover this and implement it at the next level of the system hierarchy, where the customer can now mix and match engine, body trim and spectrum of accessories - clearly at a price in excess of the cost of administration of the production line. Many companies in the weapons industry exist purely on this principle.

Translated into the ITRI context, it manifests in two primary dimensions, viz. the impact it has on the organisational structure and the impact on organisational behaviour. If, as in the case of other industries, systems engineering is a specialised value addition activity, then it could be practical to place this activity in a specialised business unit, but if products are delivered to the market at a cost-based price, and there is no possibility to reflect the higher perceived value in the "cost rate" of people performing systems integration, then the "systems house" SBU will fail. Therefore, unless the "system client" has a realistic perception of the value of the system product and is willing to pay such a price, the systems house will perish, regardless of whether the "component" suppliers are in the same enterprise or are external contractors, simply because the System SBU will not be able to offer the additional margin to be a favoured client. From the national perspective, especially in lesser developed countries, failure to mobilise the combined capability of the SBUs in an ITRI, would either result in the stakeholder community being "starved" of higher (systems) level products or the import of such products from more sophisticated contractors in other countries - thereby defeating the major object of having an ITRI in the first place!

In the case where the system product, perceived as a new market segment, turns out to be just the first application of a "new" **technology** (new for the particular organisation) that could be utilised by many users, then the business of the Systems SBU changes fundamentally. In fact it acts the role of a systems house for the first client (or first few clients), in order to understand the nature of the "new" technology, but in essence it performs the role of an intra-corporate ITRI, that gains the new technology and transfers it to one or more SBUs in the ITRI itself, that could then serve the clients in their market disciplines at a higher systems level than before. Once this has been achieved, the existence and mandate of the System SBU has to be formally reviewed - this may even lead to its dissolution.

## CONCLUSIONS

Having explored the role and functions of an ITRI, as well as some of the problems of implementing these in a practical and efficient way, it should now be possible to outline the "design logic" for such a policy instrument. This could be done along the lines of a 3-tiered strategy framework, as shown below:

## Grand Strategy

The Grand Strategy should define the functional role of the ITRI, ie. to gain and transfer technology to industry within a certain national context; delimit the technological areas/disciplines of interest; determine the mode of governance and identify the resource provision policy.

World-wide practice confirms that government, as major participant in the national system of innovation, should be a major shareholder, but the way in which this shareholders' interest is served by the Board of Directors, the executives and the legal framework of incorporation of the ITRI, is of cardinal importance. This aspect has not been addressed in the foregoing discussion, mainly because the present dispensation under which CSIR has been operating has proved to be highly effective and is generally similar to the UNIDO guidelines, allowing the grand strategy of the ITRI to be neither a "fire brigade" nor a subsidised "commercial competitor".

Finally the Grand Strategy should confirm the responsibility of the stakeholder community to identify strategic objectives and structure rewards for the achievement of such objectives, in order to ensure prime priority for achieving national goals, rather than to behave in a risk-averse, short term commercial way. For a more detailed list of issues at this level, see paras 1, 2 and 3.1 in the ITRI Checklist.[5]

## Executive Strategy

Although the selection of the corporate structure could be seen as a major element of Executive Strategy, it is of such importance in this case that it must be placed at Board level. Executive Strategy should specify the "force fields" required externally and internally to obtain effective and efficient behaviour by the SBUs in the organisation.

Effectiveness will be enhanced by clear, national, strategic goals covering a significant time horizon of 5 to 10 years and the assurance of appropriate rewards - both monetary and stakeholder recognition. Efficiency will be a function of the organisational structure, management processes and support systems established in the organisation, the level of training and quality of human resources and the skill with which leadership and management is performed. In addition, market segmentation that will drive the delimitation of SBUs, should include the consideration of "system house" SBUs, to address the opportunities of higher value addition through product integration. Similarly the reward system should allow the possibility to grow new ventures to the point where risks will be perceived to be in the commercial domain and the value obtained for the ITRI when such a venture is sold, would encourage repetition of the process. Finally the discipline in utilisation of government grant funds should be improved to the level where it would be one of the major items to gain recognition for management excellence among stakeholders. Clearly the full grant amounts could not be brought to book as investment capital, but at the same time if some part of it is not treated as capital, the discipline on investment returns is lost. Some further learning around this issue seems to be essential.

## Operational Strategy

Operational strategy is about doing "the business" - marketing, sales, information gathering, planning, procurement of inputs, acquisition of technology, adaptation/development of technology and technology deployment, management, administration and leadership. This happens within the context created by the grand and executive strategies, but it also influences those strategies.

## Summary

No attempt has been made here to arrive at the role and functions of an ITRI by way of an analysis of the national system of innovation (NSI) - this is still in the "pending file".[7] A number of perspectives need to be developed to obtain a more "basic" definition of the notion of an ITRI, and thus the considerations that are fundamental in its design as an element in the NSI. So the present discussion has been an "intuitive" approach, addressing a range of interrelated issues to discover some implicit constraints on an ITRI moving from the fire brigade phase into its next phase of maturity. Comparison of management and reward systems for ITRIs in many countries of the world indicates that for technologies (and their related industries) new to a country, government support and marginal pricing seem to be appropriate - they still need something close to the fire brigade. For more mature and advanced clients, charging market value rather than cost based prices seems to be acceptable. Government officials still find it difficult to accept the latter argument.

## REFERENCES

1    Ministry of Research, Science and Technology, **The Science System in New Zealand**, Wellington, New Zealand, August 1993.

2    Araoz, A, *Fundacion Chile - Technology Transfer and Diffusion through Demonstration Enterprises*, ICS Workshop on Managing Changes and Technological Innovations for Industrial Research Institutions in Developing Countries, Trieste, Italy, 5-9 December 1994.

3    Instituto de Pesquisas Tecnológicas, **IPT - Nine Decades of Technological Development**, IPT Publication 1825, São Paulo, Brazil, June 1990.

4    Clark, J B, *Comparison of Research Organisations*,   Internal CSIR Research Report, Pretoria, 1992.

5    Office of Science and Technology Policy, *Science and Technology - A Report to the Congress of the United States*, Washington DC, 1992.

6    Araoz, A, *Revitalisation of Industrial Technology Research Institutes in Developing Countries*, ICS Workshop on Managing Changes and Technological Innovations for Industrial Research Institutions in Developing Countries, Trieste, Italy, 5-9 December 1994.

7    Nelson, R R, **National Innovation Systems - A Comparative Analysis**, Oxford University Press, New York, 1993.

-----------oOo0ooo -----------

## BIOGRAPHICAL SKETCH

    Gideon de Wet has been director of the Policy Studies Unit (PSU) at CSIR for the four years 1992 -'95 and part-time professor in Management of Technology at the University of Pretoria. After official retirement from CSIR in 1996, he has remained with PSU under part-time contract.  His career includes lecturing in electronic engineering at the University of Stellenbosch, extensive experience in System Engineering, Programme Management, Operations Research and Technology Management.  He has been a consultant to major South African  and foreign  enterprises.  He holds a PhD in Electronic Engineering from the University of Stellenbosch.

# 082

Name            : Dilek Cetindamar Karaomerlioglu

Current Status  : Research Associate

Address         : The Center for Regional Economic Issues
                  Weatherhead School of Management
                  Case Western Reserve University
                  311 Wickenden Hall
                  Cleveland, Ohio 44106

Tel             : 1- 216- 368 5540
Fax             : 1- 216- 368 5542
E-mail          : dxk15@po.cwru.edu

Title           : Technology Policies and Economic Development
                  at the Regional Level

Keywords        : Innovation; Technology Policies; Economic Development

Topical Category: C and K

Paper is submitted for both oral and poster presentation and it is a theoretical paper using some macro data.

Abstract :

   The paper will discuss the benefits of studying the spatial dimensions of technology policies with respect to regional economic development. After exploring the Ohio economy, it will be shown that incorporating the main characteristics of the regional industrial clusters into technology policy may significantly improve observing some of the important elements of technology and industrial policies. This, in turn, facilitates to determine the actions needed to solve the failures or weaknesses of the regional economic development.

## TECHNOLOGY POLICIES AND ECONOMIC DEVELOPMENT AT THE REGIONAL LEVEL

The impact of technology policies on economic development at the regional level is one of the least studied topics in the economics literature, since the main focus has been the national level where the spatial dimensions of technological changes and innovation have been mostly disregarded. However, a few studies has recently attempted to establish the significance of the spatial context of technology by highlighting the distinguished effects of the characteristics of region on innovation.

Following the approach of these new studies, this paper will explore technology policies and economic development at the regional level. In that regard, first I will briefly introduce the relation between technology and regional development. Then, the focus will shift to discuss how to establish technology and industry policies at the regional level in order to build a successful environment for innovation and to foster economic development. To do so, I will propose a new approach and apply it to Ohio economy. By this example, I will show that incorporating the main characteristics of the regional industrial clusters into technology policy may significantly improve observing some of the important elements of technology policies. The paper will finish by discussing policy issues.

### 1. Technology and Regional Development

For a long time, the relationship between technology and development is ignored in the economics literature. This may be explained partly by the conceptualization of technology as a black box (Rosenberg, 1982), and partly by the dominance of national level analysis. Even though early studies which investigate technology and its impact on economic growth date to mid-1950s (Solow,1957), the studies with a concern on regions and technological processes are mainly carried on in the last fifteen years (Porter, 1990; Scott and Storper, 1992; Camagni, 1991; Beccattini, 1989; Harrison, 1992).

Two factors seem to play an important role in changing the course of the studies. First of all, economic development is increasingly decentralized with less central support which forced policy-makers to focus on the development of the local economy through creation of new enterprises and the enhancement of existing firms by increasing cooperation among state and local governmental agencies and nonprofit entities (Bingham and Mier, 1993). Emphasis is given to promote development from within region by using local capacities (Teitz, 1994: 1016). That is why these new development policies are called endogenous regional development (Romer, 1990).

This new approach in economic development is further strengthened with globalization, since it forces the individual parts of the economy to seek competitive advantage by attempting to mobilize all their assets in promoting the strengths of the regional economy as a whole and to take advantage of all possible economies (Vet, 1993). As Cooke (1995:5) describes : " The region becomes more specialized in its strengths, and more and more of a global force in those areas of specialization. The regional economic competitiveness in the 1990s rests on successfully interlinking regional networks with global networks of innovation and production." This strategy necessarily requires a good technological infrastructure inside the region and their integration into supra-regional economic networks are of central importance (Rosenfeld, 1995; Camagni, 1991). That is why technology become a significant part of regional economic development.

The second reason for the increasing concern of studies on technology and regional development issues is the recent challenges to neoclassical economics, and the rise of new disciplines such as evolutionary economics and the economics of technology. These new strand of studies affect regional studies by releasing the limitations imposed by neoclassical economics (Granstrand, 1994; Grabher, 1993; Nelson and Winter, 1982). Even within neoclassical theory, there are attempts to integrate geography into economics in new ways (Krugman, 1995).

Now, one of the main question in the literature is how to establish technology policies at the regional level in order to build a successful environment for innovation and to foster economic development. This question can only be answered if the relationship between technology and the industrial structure of the regional economy is understood thoroughly. In the following section, I will propose an approach to investigate this relationship.

## 2. Industrial And Technological Policies As A System

My model for studying of the relationship between technology policies and regional economic development is based on the fact that technology is an indispensable part of industrial structure. Therefore, technology policies must be combined with industrial policies. As Malecki (1991:257) points out "the link between science and industry now stretches the usual meaning of science and technology policy 'downstream' into industrial activity, and it pulls industrial policy 'upstream' into the source of competitiveness, technology." This interdependence between industry and technology necessitates an analysis of industries and technologies within a systemic approach. By using such an approach, governments can identify the actual relationship between their industrial and technological structures and based on this knowledge they can establish sound policies.

In order to understand why it is important to combine industry and technology policies, it is necessary to discuss the interdependence between these two policies. Many reasons account for their increased interdependence since the late 1980s. First and foremost, the production system has changed by shifting from mass production to flexible one which is information and technology intensive. This new system heightens the interdependence between industries and their technologies, since technology has become an important factor for high quality production and competition (Audretsch and Feldman, 1996). In the new production system, firms can not have all the complementary assets by themselves to introduce innovations continuously to compete successfully in market (Porter, 1990; Teece, 1992). Moreover, firms increasingly produce a variety of product items in different volumes with different due dates and with different production processes, which are carried out with different suppliers and producers (Scott and Storper, 1992). Because of these factors, having a network with producers, suppliers, and customers has become crucial for an efficient coordination of firm's production. Therefore, industries within a region may form a coalition in order to optimize the efficient coordination of a complex economic and technological system. Success in economic development is increasingly considered as a combination of having competitive industrial clusters, infrastructure capacities, and public private collaboration (DRI, 1995).

An another reason of increase in the interdependence of industrial and technological policies is related to the spillover effects. When industries which have similar technologies locate close to each other, their technological and industrial development speed up due to cumulativeness and transferability features of technology (Camagni, 1991). Accordingly, the cumulativeness of technology induces technological innovations to exist in groups. These groups affect each other and concentrate "in certain sectors and their surroundings" (Schumpeter, 1939:101). The emphasis on a group of certain sectors and their surroundings is very important, since it brings attention to the dependency between industrial and technological development. As Dosi (1984:12) points out : "The evolution of technologies through time presents some significant similarities and one is often able to define 'paths' of change in terms of some technological and economic characteristics of products and processes." Thus, it is necessary to understand the birth, growth, maturity and decline of industries and technologies simultaneously (Freeman et al., 1982:65).

Similarly, the transferability of technology leads to continuous technological flows among industries arising from transferable benefits of innovations to those products at technical proximity. These benefits mainly arise from learning-by-doing, economies of scope and sharing of input costs (such as labor and equipment) among a number of products. Firms from different industries employ these benefits and they use for their incremental technological development. In fact, this synergetic effect of technology flows is one of the main causes of technology clusters (Rothwell, 1994), which also affects the industrial structure.

One another reason for the increase of interdependency between industrial and technological policies is agglomeration economies. This type of economies reinforce the existence of industrial and technological clusters. Some of the sources of agglomeration economies may be listed as follows (Weber, 1929; Richardson, 1995; Harrison, 1992): a local concentration of customers which reduces overhead and infrastructure costs; economies of scale in production or distribution; sufficient demand which warrants the provision of specialized infrastructure; a deep and diversified pool of workers sufficient to realize a more specialized local division of labor; the usage of specialized equipment and services; opportunities for bulk purchasing; joint research; organized markets for finished products; reduced cost of negotiating and monitoring contracts; the existence of specialized brokers, and specialized machinery producers.

In addition to traditional static agglomeration economies, dynamic agglomeration economies have also strengthened the co-existence of industrial and technological systems.

These dynamic economies are related to the technological learning (not simply reductions in unit costs of production with a given technology); development and adoption of new technologies (Dosi et al., 1988; Lundvall, 1992); and acquisition of the synergy of different technologies and other elements of the system. Additionally, the technological infrastructure is highly determined by the industrial mix of the region (Porter, 1990). Thus, having a highly integrated web of industries leads to strong institutional connections and brings economies of scale for the establishment of the infrastructure required for technological advancement.

All the factors underlying the interdependence of industries and technologies as a system highlight that the emphasis should be to maximize the efficiency of the complete system instead of concentrating on improvements in the individual component industries or technologies (OECD, 1992:104; Teece, 1992). This necessitates the combination of both industry and technology policies. The next section will present how the industries and technologies are interdependent each other by using the case of Ohio.

## 3. The Industrial and Technological Systems of Ohio

The identification of which technologies and industries form a system requires decisions on two crucial factors, namely how to define an industry group (or cluster), and what criteria to use in order to match a technology to a group. According to the criterion chosen, the final sets of technologies and industries belonging to a system will be different

In this section, first I will give a list of industries forming clusters, then I will show a list of technologies belonging to each industries. By combining these two lists, I will try to show how industries and technologies form a system together. However, I will not go into details related to the determination of each lists, since my aim in this paper is to show empirically the investigation of interdependence between industries and technologies as well as how to use these information in forming policies. The empirical model discussed here is a tentative model and needs to be developed further.

The industries forming a cluster are selected by using an ad-hoc model based on input-output and employment data (Karaomerlioglu, 1997). According to this model, an industry belongs to a cluster on the basis of two criteria. First criterion requires the sum of three variables to pass a threshold [1]. These three variables are the employment share of the industry, the share of input purchased from industries other than itself, and the relative employment share of the industry in total Ohio employment with respect to that industry's share in total US employment. Second criterion is related to the number of industries which the industry has input-output relationships (this information is taken from the US national input-output table). Again, this criterion checks each industries' value with a pre-decided threshold. If the industry satisfies both conditions, then it is selected as the cluster member. The industries which have condense input-output (I/O) relationships with this main industry are included into the cluster. The cluster is called by the name of the main industry used to form that cluster.

---

[1] Thresholds are choosen after many iterations of try and error.

After the abovementioned procedure is applied to Ohio data, I selected five clusters in order to examine in this study. The selection is based on the total employment of cluster industries. These five clusters consist of nearly half of the employment in Ohio. The industries belonging to each clusters are given in Standard Industry Classification (SIC) codes[2] and are shown in Table 1. It is important to note that each industry belongs more than one cluster and its weight in each cluster change according to their relationship with the dominant industry of the cluster. As explained in Appendix A, the relationship between industries is measured by the multiplier.

Table 1. Cluster name and cluster industries.

| Cluster Name | Cluster Industries (SIC) |
|---|---|
| Industrial machinery and equipment cluster | 73,87,89,65,60-2,48-51,42, 33-7, 30,28,26, 15-7 |
| Fabricated metal products cluster | 73,87,89, 67, 48-51, 42, 33-7, 28, 15-7 |
| Transportation equipment cluster | 73,87,89,48-51,42, 33-7,30,28 |
| Primary metal products cluster | 73,87,89,48-51, 33-8,28,10, 15-17 |
| Rubber products cluster | 35-7, 30, 28 |

Once the list of industrial clusters is formed, the next step is to find out the technologies that belong to each industry group. In order to find these technologies, many different ways may be pursued. In this paper, I will use the CorpTech database[3] to find out the list of product technologies. This database consists of industrial and technological classifications of 40321 high-tech US firms, of which 1316 are in Ohio. As it has firm-level data, it has precise information about the industry classification and product technologies of the firm. The only problem with the data is that it doesn't include firms in services (except software services). Thus, the final list has only manufacturing industries. The assignment of a product technology to an industry is done according to the number of the firms using that technology [4]. When a technology is used by 20% or more of the firms, then it is considered as one of the main technologies of the industry. This list is given in Table 2.

Table 2. Industry and the main technologies of the industry.

| Industry | Main Technologies of the Industry |
|---|---|
| Industrial machinery and equipment (SIC 35) | Factory automation (FA), subassemblies & components (SC), computer hardware (CH) |

---

[2] For the detailed SIC codes and their names, refer to Appendix A.
[3] Corptech is a product of Corporate Technology Information Services, Inc. It has data from year 1995.
[4] The complete list of the main product technology classes are only 17 ( factory automation, biotechnology, chemicals, computer hardware, defense, energy, environmental, manufacturing equipment, advanced materials, medical, pharmaceuticals, photonics, computer software, subassemblies & components, test & measurement, telecommunications, transportation), but the total number of sub-classes are nearly 250.

| Fabricated metal products (SIC 34) | Factory automation, subassemblies & components, energy (E), manufacturing equipment (ME) |
|---|---|
| Transportation equipment (SIC 37) | Transportation (T), subassemblies & components |
| Primary metal products (SIC 33) | Advanced materials (AM), manufacturing equipment, subassemblies & components |
| Rubber products (SIC 30) | Advanced materials, manufacturing equipment |

As it can be seen in Figure 1, all five clusters are highly integrated with each other in terms of both their product technologies and buyer and seller relationships. The four industries, namely chemicals and allied products (SIC 28), industrial machinery and equipment (SIC 35), electronic & other electric equipment (SIC 36), and transportation equipment (SIC 37) exist in all clusters. Similarly, factory automation (FA), advanced materials (AM), manufacturing equipment (ME), and subassemblies & components(SC) are common technologies in all clusters. Clearly, any policy change regarding these industries and technologies will have a chain effect in other industries and technologies. Therefore, policy makers in Ohio should consider the relationships among all industries and technologies as I did here for a few of them before they build sound policies for long-term economic development in Ohio.

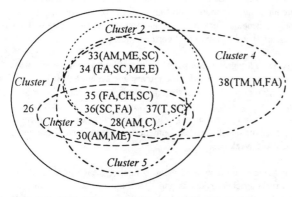

C - Chemicals; TM - Test and Measurement; M - Medical.
Figure 1. Clusters with their industries and technologies

## 4. Some Policy Remarks

Once the dynamics of a region based on its industrial and technological structure are observed as shown in the case of Ohio, then these information can be used to:

- prioritize policy options for working with firms in a given industry and technology;
- promote long-term cooperative linkages among industry firm;
- find out growth prospects for each industry and technology as well as diversification potential;
- forecast how recent national and global economic trends may affect the elements of clusters;
- highlight the elements most amenable to state action;
- solve problems related to the lock-in effect of path-dependent development;
- establish technology policies integrating the concerns of not only state but also firms and existing organizations (such as universities, trade associations, or intermediary organizations);
- induce more rapid diffusion of new technologies and techniques; and
- develop spillover effects and to benefit from synergies.

The existence of interrelated industrial and technological policies brings efficiency, since many factors (such as industrial linkages, infrastructure or workforce requirements, the strengths and weaknesses of industries and technologies in the state) are taken into consideration in a systemic view. But more importantly, these policies will help to increase the collaboration among intermediary organizations and industries. Thus, they will have better impact on the industrial and technological performance.

Furthermore, having an integrated industrial and technological policies can also helps firms to: see themselves within a broader framework and evaluate their functions and improve their operations by reorganizing their structure with the elements of a general system; cooperate with other organizations (both profit and non-profit organizations - universities, independent research organizations, trade associations, regional societies, government agencies-); take the benefits of environment or try to improve them; and identify their competence and weaknesses.

In short, the knowledge on different aspects of technology development and various industrial structures warrants a richer understanding of real life mechanisms for policy makers. After the dynamics of industrial and technological system is observed at the local level, the determination of the type of policies for economic development becomes easier and solid. This, in turn, improves the development of the region.

## Notes:

[1] There are a few studies which are worthwhile to note here. Even though they do not directly work on the issue of identifying industries and technologies within a system for the economic growth, they may ground the basic steps for this purpose. For example, a study is done by using data collected from both individual firms (5116 Austrian firms) and the Austrian patent database that classified technologies in 31 groups (Gassler et al. , 1996). By using the distribution of patent applications of firms broken down by industrial sector which a firm belongs, a technology matrix is built where the related technologies and industrial are identified. Another study is done by Jaffe (1989). He uses data gathered from 500 US firms as well as patents and NBER's (National Bureau of Economic Research) database. He first limits the technology classes given by the US Patent Office into 49 groups (such as organic chemistry, food, and medical). Then, he forms 20 industrial clusters based on the technological position of the firms by using the cluster analysis. The final matrix shows which industrial clusters are integrated with which technologies. For example, he finds that one of his industrial clusters is called "food and kindred products cluster" and it is in close relationship with the following technologies: food, carbon chemistry, refrigeration, organic chemistry, cleaning & abrading, metals & metal working, and receptacles & packages (Jaffe, 1989:92).

## REFERENCES

Audretsch, D. B. Feldman M. P. 1996. Innovative Clusters and the Industry Life Cycle. Review of Industrial Organization. 11: 253-73.

Beccattini, G. 1989. Sectors and/or Districts: Some Remarks on the Conceptual Foundations of Industrial Economics. Small Firms and Industrial Districts in Italy. E. Bamford, J. Saynor P., and Goodman. NY, Routledge, 123-35.

Bingham, R.D., Mier, R., 1993, (ed.) Theories of local economic development : perspectives from across the disciplines, Sage, London.

Camagni, R. 1991. From the Local 'Milieu' to Innovation Through Cooperation Networks. in (ed.) Innovation Networks: Spatial Perspectives. R. Camagni, 1-9. London, Belhaven.

Camagni, R. 1995. Global Network and Local Milieu: Towards a Theory of Economic Space. in (ed.) The Industrial Enterprise and Its Environment: Spatial Perspectives. S. Malecki, E. J. Oinas, P. Conti. Brookfield, Vermont, Avebury, 195-216.

Cooke, P. 1995. (ed.) The Rise of the Rustbelt. St. Martin's Press, New York.

Dosi, G. 1984. Technological Change and Development. London, Macmillan.

Dosi, G. , Freeman, C. , Nelson, R. , Silverberg, G. , and L. Soete. 1988. Technical Change and Economic Theory, London, Pinter.

DRI. 1995. America's Clusters, McGraw-Hill.

Freeman, C. Clark J. Soete L. 1982. Unemployment and Technical Innovation. Westport, Connecticut, Greenwood Press.

Gassler, H. Frohlich J. Kopcsa A. 1996. Selective Information on the National System of Innovation As an Important Input for the Technology Management of Firms. International Journal of Technology Management, Speical Issue on the 5th International Forum on technology Management, 11, no. 3/4: 329-42.

Grabher, G. 1993. Rediscovering the Social in the Economics of Interfirm Relations. The Embedded Firm: On the Socioeconomics of Industrial Networks. G. Grabher. NY, Routledge, 1-33.

Granstrand, O. 1994. Economics of Technology. Amsterdam, North-Holland.

Harrison, B. 1992. Industrial Districts:Old Wine in New Bottles?, Regional Studies 26 (5): 469-83.

Jaffe, A. 1989. Characterizing the "Technological Position" of Firms, with Application to Quantifying Technological Opportunity and Research Spillovers, Research Policy, 18: 87-97.

Jaffe, A. B. Trajtenberg M. Henderson R. 1992. Geographic Localization of Knowledge Spillovers as Evidenced by Patent Citations. NBER Working Paper 3993, Cambridge.

Karaomerlioglu, C. D., 1997 (forthcoming). The Rebirth of Industrial and Regional Clusters, REI Working Paper, Cleveland.

Krugman , P. 1995. Development, Geography, and Economic Theory. MIT Press, Cambridge.

Lundvall, B., 1992. National Systems of Innovation : Towards a Theory of Innovation and Interactive Learning. Pinter, London.

Malecki, E. J. 1991. Technology and Economic Development . Longman Scientific & Technical, London.

Nelson, R., Winter S. 1982. An Evolutionary Theory of Economic Change. Cambridge, Massachusetts, Harvard University Press.

Niosi, J. 1991. Technology and National Competitiveness: Oligopoly, Technological Innovation, and International Competition. Montreal, McGill-Queen's University Press.

OECD. 1992. Stuctural Change and Industrial Performance. Paris, OECD.

Porter, M. 1990. Competitive Advantage of Nations. New York, Free Press.

Richardson, H. W. 1995. Economies and Diseconomies of Agglomeration. in (ed.) Urban Agglomeration and Economic Growth. H. Giersch, Kiel: Springer.

Romer, P. M. 1990. Endogenous Technological Change. Journal of Political Economics 98(5), S71-S102.

Rosenberg, N. 1982. Inside the Black Box: Technology and Economics. Cambridge University Press, New York.

Rosenfeld, S. A. 1995. Industrial Strength Strategies. Aspen Institute, Washington, DC.

Rothwell, R. 1994. Industrial Innovation: Success, Strategy, Trends. in (ed.) The Handbook of Industrial Innovation. M. Rothwell and R. Dodgson, 33-53. Brookfield, Vermont, Edward Elgar.

Schumpeter, J. A. 1939. Business Cycles: A Theoretical, Historical and Statistical Analysis of the Capitalist Process. New York, McGraw-Hill.

Scott A. J., Storper, M. 1992. Pathways to Industrialization and Regional Development. London, Routledge.

Solow, R. M., 1957, 'Technical Change and the Aggregate Production Function', Review of Economics and Statistics. 29, 312-20.

Teece, D. J. 1992. Competition, Cooperation, and Innovation: Organizational Arrangements for Regimes of Rapid Technological Progress. Journal of Economic Behavior and Organization. 18: 1-25.

Teitz, M. B. 1994. Changes in Economic Development Theory and Practice . International Regional Science Review. 16(N. 1&2):1016.

Vet, J. M. 1993. Globalization and Local& Regional Competitiveness. STI Review.13:90-121.

Weber, A. 1929. Theory of the Location of Industries. Chicago, University of Chicago Press.

## Appendix A. SIC Codes

| SIC | SIC description | SIC | SIC description |
|-----|-----------------|-----|-----------------|
| 7 | Agricultural services | 33 | primary metal products |
| 10 | Metal mining | 34 | fabricated metal products |
| 12 | Coal mining | 35 | industrial machinery and equipment |
| 13 | Crude petroleum and natural gas | 36 | electronic & other electric equipment |

| | | | |
|---|---|---|---|
| 14 | Nonmetallic minerals mining | 37 | transportation equipment |
| 15,16,17 | Construction | 38 | instruments and related products |
| 20 | Food and kindred products | 39 | Miscellaneous manufacturing |
| 21 | Tobacco products | 40-2,44-7 | transportation |
| 22 | Textile mill products | 48 | communications |
| 23 | Apparel and other textile products | 49 | electric, gas, and sanitary services |
| 24 | Lumber and wood products | 50-7,59 | Trade |
| 25 | Furniture and fixtures | 58 | Eating and drinking places |
| 26 | Paper and allied products | 79 | Amusement & recreation services |
| 27 | Printing and publishing | 60-4 | Insurance |
| 28 | Chemicals and allied products | 65,67 | Real estate and dwellings |
| 29 | Petroleum refining and related products | 70,72,76 | Hotels. personal services, mic. repair services |
| 30 | Rubber and miscellaneous plastics products | 75 | Automotive repair and services |
| 31 | leather, and leather products | 73,87,89 | business services, engineering & management services, services, nec. |
| 32 | stone,clay, and glass products | 80,82-3,86 | Health, educational, social services |

# 083

# Subjectivity in Technology Evaluation

M.S.Dariel
Israel Atomic Energy Commission, currently on sabbatical at The Office of Technology Innovation, National Institute of Standards and Technology, Gaithersburg, Md.

Summary: The evaluation of innovations in technology is ideally based on technical expertise and scientific principles. A review of accepted practice in the field, however, shows that subjective judgment, intuition and experience still play a large role. This proposition was tested on a sample group of consultant evaluators and found to be essentially true. Reducing evaluator subjectivity in evaluations is desirable as it improves consistency. A multiple-review process is discussed which is in operation at The National Institute of Standards and Technology (NIST) and reviews 100 proposals made by individual inventors per month. This high-volume process was designed to deal with the great disparity in subject area and technological level of proposals submitted for evaluation. This process can be assumed to reduce the influence of subjectivity.
The evaluation criteria which are subject to the largest variations and their impact on the evaluations are discussed.

Keywords: Technology evaluation; resource allocation; analysis involving multiple variables; group consensus; OTI, Office of Technology Innovation at NIST; DOE, Department of Energy.

Congress established the Energy-Related Inventions Program (ERIP) to provide funds for new technology development. The underlying premise was that significant innovation can occur outside the boundaries of disciplined approaches characteristic of government-funded programs. This is a polite way of saying that there may be gold out there in the mud, waiting to be picked up. Results show that this somewhat daring idea is in fact being vindicated: inventions by "ordinary people" (outside the mainstream of corporate or government technology) constitute the bulk of innovations that have been successfully commercialized under the program. Energy savings resulting from these innovations amount to $10^{15}$ BTU or 150 million barrels of oil, with a current value of about $30 billion. This, incidentally, goes a long way to demonstrate that notwithstanding pessimists, traditional grass-roots American "inventiveness" is still alive and well.

There is, however, one small but significant problem with "grass-roots inventiveness": it may, by definition, appear in a multitude of less than conventional forms. The fecund stream of innovation proposals, encompassing all sorts of possible (and some impossible) ideas, taps sources from all strata of technical proficiency. Many are inventions that private venture companies may not want to touch with a 3.048 meter pole (that's 10 ft but we're going metric). Nevertheless, however tempting the notion of handling only homogenized and neatly formatted proposals may be, the last thing you want to do is stifle that sometimes unbridled inventiveness and regulate it to death. Yet you still need, day in and day out, to sift the (sometimes hairy) proposals in a reasonably consistent and unbiased way in order to extract the 2 to 3% that are worthy of encouragement. And remember that some really original and good ideas may come in, described in a very rudimentary form, along with others that are both practical and unpractical, couched in state of the art terms. This brings us to the basic problem of evaluation. Even with 100% hindsight it is sometimes difficult to rationalize the multiple choices that are required in making the decisions that lead to the successful introduction of new products to the marketplace. Listening to successful inventors or to businesspeople who have made it good in the commercialization of innovations, you are struck by the infinite variety of methods they cite as key to their success. These people, often blessed with outgoing personalities, finally leave you with the definite impression that nothing can replace intuitive judgment, experience and flying-by-the-seat-of your pants decision making. To many individuals and corporations who require the evaluation of a technology, this is indeed the only recourse available.

It is well known that it is easier to detect changes or differences in values rather than to establish their absolute magnitudes. A well-known example is the human eye's ability to differentiate between even slightly different intensities of color, for instance of colored solutions in glass vessels, placed side by side. This, for many years was the basis for several colorimetric methods for the determination of concentrations in analytical laboratories, before the advent of more precise instrumentation, with surprisingly reproducible results. The procedure consisted in preparing standard solutions of known, gradually increasing concentrations of chemicals, known as standard or calibrated solutions. To determine the unknown concentration of a solution of the same substance, all you had to do was to bracket the unknown solution between two standards, one of slightly less intense color and one slightly more intense than the unknown. The concentration of the unknown was then determined to be between the known concentrations of the standard solutions.

By analogy, evaluating things by comparing them with established standards is relatively easy. It is much harder to do so in the absence of standards or when the evaluated objects are so different as to make the comparison of little relevance, or as the saying goes, like comparing apples with whatever other fruit comes to mind. The great variety of proposals requiring evaluation of some kind virtually ensures that the comparison of different projects *as a whole* will yield small dividends in the way of, for instance, grading them as to expected performance. This is the essential problem encountered in the course of evaluating proposals, be it from the technological, marketing or any other aspect. This is also the main reason that subjective, intuitive judgment, sometimes based on long experience, is the accepted and probably the most commonly used method, in many cases where evaluation is done.

Since evaluation is a very basic aspect of all activities involving allocation of resources or priorities (competing for grants, competing for investment funds!), this is a problem that has invited many different approaches. A way of increasing the consistency of the process is by grading the different projects according to *common criteria*. The underlying assumption is that however different the projects may be, when treated as whole units, they invariably will have a number of common features. In several evaluation procedures, these are designated as *critical factors*. It is clearly apparent that the judicious definition of these factors is of crucial importance. It is also immediately obvious that the choice of these factors introduces a large amount of subjective, investing either in this circuitous route that reintroduces by the back door, so to speak, the intuitive type of decision making previously mentioned? The best answer is that judgment is probably easier when confined to much smaller, easier to encompass units of decision making.

As described below, expert consultant evaluators are utilized routinely in the NIST/ERIP evaluation process. The existence of evaluator subjectivity was tested as follows. Ten experienced evaluators were asked to attribute weights to the different factors listed in Table 1. These factors may be used to evaluate the commercial promise of projects. As the results show, the attribution of weights may vary widely, according to the individual views of the evaluators. The average deviation is about 38%. The interpretation of this variance is that subjectivity is present and the result of the evaluation may strongly depend on the individual consultant evaluator. One suggested remedy would be to subject the weighting of criteria to discussion in order to arrive to a group consensus that would henceforth be accepted as a standard, at least for a specific class of proposals. This in fact constitutes a step of educating or indoctrinating the consultant evaluators to reach a desired level of consistency in the process.

Table 1

| | | E | V | A | L | U | A | T | O | R | S | | | |
|---|---|---|---|---|---|---|---|---|---|---|---|---|---|---|
| | Factor [1] | 1 | 2 | 3 | 4 | 5 | 6 | 7 | 8 | 9 | 10 | Average | Std Dev | % |
| 1 | Technical Feasibility | 5 | 5 | 5 | 5 | 5 | 4 | 5 | 5 | 5 | 5 | 4.90 | 0.30 | 6 |
| 2 | Functional Performance | 5 | 5 | 5 | 4 | 5 | 4 | 3 | 4 | 5 | 5 | 4.50 | 0.67 | 15 |
| 3 | R&D | 2 | 1 | 4 | 4 | 0 | 2 | 0 | 0 | 2 | 5 | 2.00 | 1.73 | 87 |
| 4 | Technology Significance | 3 | 2 | 5 | 3 | 0 | 2 | 2 | 4 | 4 | 4 | 2.90 | 1.37 | 47 |

| # | Criterion | | | | | | | | | | | Mean | SD | % |
|---|-----------|---|---|---|---|---|---|---|---|---|---|---|------|------|----|
| 5 | Safety | 2 | 1 | 3 | 2 | 1 | 3 | 1 | 4 | 2 | 5 | 2.40 | 1.28 | 53 |
| 6 | Environmental Impact | 2 | 4 | 3 | 5 | 1 | 3 | 2 | 3 | 4 | 5 | 3.20 | 1.25 | 39 |
| 7 | Technology of Production | 4 | 4 | 5 | 4 | 1 | 4 | 3 | 3 | 4 | 5 | 3.70 | 1.10 | 30 |
| 8 | Tooling Cost | 3 | 3 | 3 | 4 | 1 | 3 | 4 | 2 | 2 | 5 | 3.00 | 1.10 | 37 |
| 9 | Cost of Production | 4 | 4 | 4 | 5 | 5 | 4 | 5 | 3 | 4 | 4 | 4.20 | 0.60 | 14 |
| 10 | Need | 5 | 3 | 4 | 4 | 5 | 3 | 5 | 4 | 4 | 3 | 4.00 | 0.77 | 19 |
| 11 | Potential Market | 4 | 4 | 5 | 4 | 5 | 4 | 3 | 2 | 3 | 3 | 3.70 | 0.90 | 24 |
| 12 | Trend of Demand | 3 | 3 | 3 | 3 | 5 | 3 | 2 | 1 | 2 | 4 | 2.90 | 1.04 | 36 |
| 13 | Duration of Demand | 3 | 2 | 4 | 3 | 5 | 3 | 2 | 2 | 2 | 3 | 2.90 | 0.94 | 33 |
| 14 | Demand Predictability | 2 | 2 | 2 | 3 | 1 | 2 | 2 | 2 | 0 | 3 | 1.90 | 0.83 | 44 |
| 15 | Product Line Potential | 2 | 1 | 3 | 1 | 1 | 1 | 1 | 4 | 0 | 3 | 1.70 | 1.19 | 70 |
| 16 | Societal Benefits | 2 | 2 | 2 | 4 | 1 | 1 | 2 | 4 | 1 | 3 | 2.20 | 1.08 | 49 |
| 17 | Compatibility | 2 | 2 | 3 | 3 | 1 | 3 | 3 | 3 | 1 | 3 | 2.40 | 0.80 | 33 |
| 18 | Learning | 3 | 1 | 3 | 0 | 1 | 3 | 4 | 3 | 1 | 4 | 2.30 | 1.35 | 58 |
| 19 | Visibility | 3 | 1 | 4 | 2 | 3 | 4 | 4 | 3 | 1 | 4 | 2.90 | 1.14 | 39 |
| 20 | Appearance | 2 | 1 | 2 | 0 | 1 | 3 | 1 | 3 | 0 | 3 | 1.60 | 1.11 | 70 |
| 21 | Function | 4 | 4 | 5 | 5 | 5 | 3 | 4 | 4 | 5 | 3 | 4.20 | 0.75 | 18 |
| 22 | Durability | 4 | 3 | 3 | 2 | 1 | 2 | 3 | 3 | 1 | 3 | 2.50 | 0.92 | 37 |
| 23 | Service | 4 | 3 | 5 | 2 | 5 | 2 | 4 | 3 | 2 | 3 | 3.30 | 1.10 | 33 |
| 24 | Price | 5 | 4 | 4 | 4 | 5 | 3 | 5 | 3 | 3 | 3 | 3.90 | 0.83 | 21 |
| 25 | Existing Competition | 4 | 1 | 5 | 5 | 1 | 4 | 4 | 3 | 2 | 3 | 3.20 | 1.40 | 44 |
| 26 | New Competition | 4 | 1 | 5 | 4 | 1 | 3 | 4 | 3 | 2 | 2 | 2.90 | 1.30 | 45 |
| 27 | Marketing Research | 3 | 1 | 2 | 4 | 3 | 3 | 5 | 2 | 2 | 2 | 2.70 | 1.10 | 41 |
| 28 | Promotion Cost | 2 | 0 | 2 | 3 | 1 | 4 | 5 | 3 | 1 | 2 | 2.30 | 1.42 | 62 |
| 29 | Distribution | 3 | 0 | 2 | 3 | 1 | 4 | 3 | 2 | 1 | 2 | 2.10 | 1.14 | 54 |
| 30 | Legality | 3 | 2 | 4 | 2 | 5 | 4 | 5 | 5 | 5 | 5 | 4.00 | 1.18 | 30 |
| 31 | Development Risks | 3 | 2 | 3 | 3 | 1 | 2 | 2 | 3 | 2 | 3 | 2.40 | 0.66 | 28 |
| 32 | Dependence | 2 | 2 | 4 | 3 | 1 | 4 | 3 | 3 | 2 | 3 | 2.70 | 0.90 | 33 |
| 33 | Protection | 4 | 2 | 1 | 5 | 5 | 4 | 5 | 4 | 1 | 2 | 3.30 | 1.55 | 47 |
| 34 | Size of Investment | 4 | 0 | 5 | 3 | 0 | 5 | 5 | 4 | 1 | 4 | 3.10 | 1.92 | 62 |
| 35 | Potential Sales | 4 | 4 | 5 | 4 | 3 | 5 | 3 | 4 | 3 | 4 | 3.90 | 0.70 | 18 |
| 36 | Payback Period | 4 | 4 | 5 | 3 | 5 | 4 | 2 | 4 | 1 | 4 | 3.60 | 1.20 | 33 |
| 37 | Profitability | 2 | 2 | 5 | 1 | 1 | 3 | 1 | 4 | 2 | 3 | 2.40 | 1.28 | 53 |
| 38 | Energy Impact | 5 | 5 | 5 | 5 | 5 | 5 | 5 | 5 | 5 | 5 | 5.00 | 0.00 | 0 |
| | | | | | | | | | | | | | 1.05 | 38% |

(1) Adapted from Dr. G.G. Udell, "Analysis of Product Evaluation and Venture Assessment", (1993) Innovation Institute. What is one to do when a *large number of individuals* is called upon to do *occasional* evaluations? This is precisely the problem that confronted the program, where the diversity of technologies to which the proposals relate is extremely large. This constraint required the formation of a pool of approximately 400 consultants, who are experts in their respective fields, in order to cover all the necessary areas with a high degree of technical expertise. These consultants are often recognized scientists from academia, full-time consulting engineers or experts who are retired from private or government sectors. As the quality of

527

their knowledge is the overriding factor in their selection, they may typically reside in locations far-removed from NIST. This explains why, usually, these experts are not amenable to or available for the phase of education in the process that is necessary to increase consistency. This problem compounded the difficulties inherent in the non uniform presentation, uneven clarity and overall large variability in the sources of proposals expected in a program that is *popular* (e.g., for the people, by the people . . . )

Consequently, at OTI a procedure had to be developed which allowed the inclusion of the highly specialized technical expertise of a very large number of consultants, without the penalty of added unevenness. The solution adopted increases the accuracy of analysis by using a multiple consultant review procedure, with the NIST staff evaluators making the decisions. This should have the effect of decreasing the impact of subjectivity inherent in diverse individual judgments.

Briefly described, the procedure consists of the following steps:
...submission of (unsolicited) proposal at any stage of development
...assignment to an NIST evaluator (senior engineer)
...first stage evaluation of the invention by two consultants - experts in the particular technology
...reassessment by NIST evaluator
...second stage evaluations for proposals that have been found promising in 1st stage (this consists of a comprehensive engineering report, detailing findings in a prescribed engineering report format)
...NIST evaluator reviews all three consultant evaluations and his own analysis. Only then decides whether the invention is worthy of recommendation to DOE.

More than 32,000 evaluation requests, principally from individuals, have been processed since the program's inception in 1975, and almost 700 recommendations forwarded by NIST to DOE. DOE provides support by funding market assessment, commercialization plan development and awarding a grant for appropriate developmental actions. The market entry after support by DOE is about 24%, better than that of the private *investment community.* This program strategy has resulted in identifying and supporting successful innovations that have, thru 1994, leveraged $48 million in grants into almost $1 billion in cumulative sales, creating or sustaining 4000 jobs. It has also saved one quad ($10^{15}$ BTU) of energy. By way of comparison, in 1990 the annual energy consumption in the US was 68 quads. We can safely assume that many of these innovations would not have found their way to the marketplace through the conventional systems of evaluations and grants.

I gratefully acknowledge critical remarks by G.P.Lewett, R.W.Bartholomew and H.Robb.

# 084

## INTEGRATIVE PRODUCT-PROJECT CLASSIFICATIONS: IMPLICATIONS FOR BUSINESS INNOVATION AND CROSS-FUNCTIONAL MANAGEMENT

Authors:
Gary S. Lynn, Aaron J. Shenhar and Dov Dvir*
Stevens Institute of Technology
School of Technology Management and Mareting
Hoboken, NJ 07030, USA
Tel:        +1-201-216 8024
Fax:        +1-201-216 8355
Email:    ashenhar@attila.stevens-tech.edu


*Tel Aviv University

## ABSTRACT

A traditional classification of innovation as either incremental or radical has often been mentioned in the literature of technological innovation. This view of innovation was rooted in earlier organizational concepts as products completely new to the firm, products innovations were considered minor changes to an existing product and were generally in the form of product modifications, upgrades, derivatives and line extensions. Researchers haft often argued that different types of innovation require dIfferent organizational practices. As our study shows, this dichotomized view of innovation is much too limited for describing the richness of today´s organizational efforts associated with product selection, creation and introduction. In this study we suggest a new way of classifying the product effort. It is based on a joint classification of the product and the project. The product classification impacts mostly the marketing function, the project classification affects the R & D function, while the joint classifications is directly linked to the marketing R & D cross-functional effort and interaction. Different types of product-project categories.

# 085

*First author:*

Cecilia Beskow
Machine Design
KTH
100 44 Stockholm
tel: 08 - 790 63 03
fax: 08 - 723 17 30
e-mail: cecilia@damek.kth.se


*Co-authors:*

Svante Hovmark
Dept. of Psychology
Stockholm university
106 91 Stockholm
tel: 08 - 16 39 43
fax: 08 - 15 93 42
e-mail:
shk@psychology.su.se

Margareta Norell
Machine Design
KTH
100 44 Stockholm
tel: 08 - 790 80 68
fax: 08 - 723 17 30
e-mail:
maggan@damek.kth.se

*Title of paper:*

Improving co-operation in project teams

*Key words:*

Product development, co-operation, project team, empirical research methods, dialogue conference.

## Abstract

A study, with the participation of four Swedish manufacturing companies, was performed with the purpose to explore and initiate changes to refine and improve product development work. The study included four dialogue conferences, two sets of interviews and one questionnaire. The dialogue conferences functioned as a forum for discussions and for generating ideas which in turn were incorporated into company operations. The conferences were also a means for collecting data. The participants in the study were designers, chief designers, manufacturing engineers and chief manufacturing engineers. The product development work in the companies was carried out in an integrated way with parallel activities, which has caused greater complexity and a greater need for collaboration between project members from different departments. The results show that the demand for collaboration necessitated a work organisation which facilitates communication and co-operation by means of personal meetings and effective technical aids for distance communication, for example. All the companies needed to make the development process clearer, and this need has given rise to activities for structuring the operations and to better define the working processes. Furthermore, bridges between different cultures and different views were needed to create a comprehensive view of goals as well as working processes. The participants thought that attending the dialogue conferences had introduced valuable ideas and experiences to the renewal of PD work.

## 1 Introduction

Being competitive in the international market today, put great demands upon the manufacturing industry. The development of products with a high complexity, requires companies to be more flexible to match the ever changing demands of the customer, e.g. higher quality, lower price, faster delivery and decreased environmental load. This often demands radical changes in the product development (PD) process.

### 1.1 The product development process

Introducing integrated product development (IPD) is one possible way to fulfil the customers' increasing demands. IPD implies that the PD activities are conducted in a more parallel way than in a sequential, which results in a shorter development time. By including more functions from the beginning of the development process, the competence spectra is widened throughout the entire process, which in turn increases product quality.

There are several models of the PD process, all of which are based on an integrated approach, e.g. [1, 2]. There are three main elements to consider for an efficient IPD: *Organisation, Methods and tools* and *Information management* [3].

A plain, structured PD process is an important part of an efficient product development. According to Ulrich and Eppinger [4] a well defined process is useful for:

- *Quality assurance:* Following a development process with wisely chosen phases and checkpoints is one way of assuring the quality of the resulting product.
- *Co-ordination:* A clearly articulated process defines the roles of each team member, when they are needed and with whom they ought to exchange information.

- *Planning:* The timing of the natural milestones in the process anchors the schedule of the overall project.
- *Management:* By benchmarking the process definition with the actual process the manager can more easily find problem areas.
- *Improvement:* The documentation of an organisation's development process often helps identifying improvement possibilities.

### 1.2 Project teams

It is getting more common to conduct PD in projects with cross-functional teams. The purpose is to increase the efficiency as well as the product quality. Therefore, the team's achievements are of critical importance and their effort is dependent on factors related to company, resources, technology, goals, psycho-social work environment and the competence of the team members.

The success of a project and the achievement of a team are complicated to measure and an evaluation should not focus merely on whether the team complies with the product goals and resources. According to Hackman [5] a team's achievement is related to the following three dimensions: *The character of the task, The social relations in the team* and *The members' well-being and growth.*

The composition of a group, regarding competence and qualifications of individual members, is of great importance to the success of the project. The criteria which usually control the choice of members are their competence, personality, representativity and their wish to work toward the goal [6]. The difficulties in composing a well-functioning team include both finding the most useful competence available and judging potential talents [7]. According to Belbin [8], the composition of a highly achieving team is a question of finding people with necessary talents, which complement these of the other members. People suited for team work are those who have the ability to alter their roles, limit their effort, create roles to others and do the work others will not.

### 1.3 Dialogue conferences

One means to improve the organisation is to participate in dialogue conferences. According to Gustavsen [9] should dialogue conferences be arranged as a series of discussions. The participants should be employees from four or five companies, who represent important pressure groups and have an interest in development work. The conference group should reflect the decision process in the company, if they are to practically realise the change proposals in the companies. The participants should also be cross-hierarchical - from upper management to non-managers.

### 1.4 Purpose

The purpose of the study was to contribute to the knowledge of product development work as well as initiate renewal processes in the participating companies. The study was focused on factors that affects co-operation between the companies' design and manufacturing departments in PD work. The intention was that the results also should be applied in companies which were not participating in the study.

## 2  Method

The study was carried out from June '94 to March '96, with the participation of four Swedish manufacturing companies. The research was conducted with an "action approach", which means that the participants actively take part in the research process and successively test the ideas that come up. The investigation contained several empirical research methods (see figure 1): four *dialogue conferences* - which were the main activity, two *interview sessions* and one *questionnaire*.

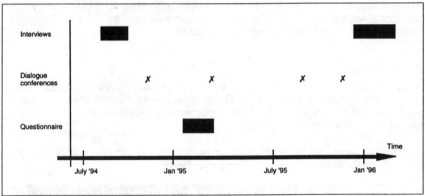

Figure 1. Research activities during the investigation period.

### 2.1  The dialogue conferences

Four conferences were held during a period of 14 months and the focus topic was: *co-operation between the design and manufacturing departments in PD projects*. The research group gathered four companies with geographically separated design and manufacturing departments. They were all active in developing their PD work and making it more efficient as well as interested in a set of conferences to exchange experiences with other companies. The participating companies were all from Swedish manufacturing industry.

Employees both from the design and the manufacturing departments, managers as well as non-managers, participated in the conferences. Each company was represented by four employees: one chief designer, one chief manufacturing engineer, one designer and one manufacturing engineer. The attendance was 87 percent on an average. From the research group five to seven people were involved in the dialogue conferences.

The conferences followed the principles described by Gustavsen [9]. The participants are usually discussing four question areas during a conference. The research group and the conference participants commonly agreed on discussing the following themes:
- Conference #1: Characteristics of and obstacles to a well-functioning co-operation between the design and manufacturing departments.
- Conference #2: Activities and tools to support a well-functioning co-operation.
- Conference #3: Team roles and changing tasks in PD.
- Conference #4: Team building.

The questions were first discussed in smaller groups and then the results were reported in a plenary sitting and more concrete proposals were established. After the conference each company modified and implemented selected parts of the proposals into their own PD process. The companies were then again brought together for a new dialogue conference to exchange experiences, with a following period of in-house renewal work and so on.

The last conference was dedicated to an evaluation. The participants' perspective is usually shifted from content to process [9]. In the beginning of the conference set there was a wish of structural changes in the company and by the end the main interest was *how* change work should be conducted.


## 2.2 The interviews

Prior to the first dialogue conference, the research group performed an interview session in the participating companies. The purpose was to describe the companies' organisation of PD, problem areas and improvement activities as well as their expectations of the forthcoming dialogue conferences.

Seven to ten people were interviewed in each company (compare table 1) - 32 persons in total - during August and September 1994.

| Table 1. Interviewees August - September '94. | Functional manager | Project manager | Designer/ Technician | Total |
|---|---|---|---|---|
| Design dept. | 4 | 8 | 9 | 21 |
| Manufacturing dept. | 3 | 2 | 5 | 10 |
| Other | | | 1 | 1 |
| | | | | Σ 32 |

After the last dialogue conference a completing set of interviews were performed, with the purpose to gather opinions on the conferences and evaluate any change in PD during the period. In total 22 people were interviewed this time, from December '95 to February '96 (compare table 2).

| Table 2. Interviewees December '95 - February '96. | Functional manager | Project manager | Designer/ Technician | Total |
|---|---|---|---|---|
| Design dept. | 4 | 2 | 6 | 12 |
| Manufacturing dept. | 4 | | 6 | 10 |
| | | | | Σ 22 |

The separate interviews had a semi-structured form and followed an interview guide with different question areas. All interviews were recorded and later transcribed. The written material was coded and analysed. After this the individual results were discussed and reported [10].

## 2.3 The questionnaire

A questionnaire was sent out to 127 employees in the four participating companies. It contained items concerning project work, communication, co-operation, work climate and background questions such as age, sex and education. The response rate was 79 percent. The results from the questionnaire served as background data in the study and are further reported by Hovmark et al [10].

# 3 Results

## 3.1 The product development process

All of the participating companies have, since the late 1980's, worked with improving their PD process. Their purpose has been to increase product quality and manufacturability, to shorten lead time and to design products which better met the customers' requirements and needs. The changes have caused a higher degree of complexity in the development work. Sometimes there has been a confusion of the contents of each phase, which in turn has caused problems in controlling the project concerning time schedules and costs. These problems have resulted in the need for a more structured and more carefully described process.

Each company had defined a model for their PD process prior to the start of the study. This model described the process and defined phases, activities, management and sometimes decision points. The number of phases, their content and the degree of details in the model differed between the companies. Some of them also had a handbook, which is one way of clarifying the process model to the people involved.

## 3.2 Cross-functional co-operation

The participating companies had actively been working with improving the co-operation between the design and manufacturing departments during the last few years. Co-operation was seen as a very important aspect to obtain a more efficient PD work.

One condition for a well-functioning co-operation in project teams, according to the participants in the study, is favourable prerequisites for the project in the organisation. The requirements and goals must be clear to all people involved. All of the participants should early in the PD process have access to all project information. There should also be anchored routines for the PD work. Rules and routines for administration, design briefings and drawings distribution ought to be well defined and followed up. It should always exist a time schedule which includes regular meetings and decision points.

The status of the project leader in the organisation is another important aspect to consider. Functional managers and the project's steering committee should show active interest in and keep themselves informed of the progress in the product development. The management's commitment gives status and priority to the project. Yet, neither functional managers nor steering committee should interfere in daily work. It is the project manager's responsibility to manage the project. He or she should have the ability to firmly establish the project's goals and to create participation in the entire project team. The project manager should also be able to communicate with all team members and combine their different wishes to a whole.

The project team should be characterised by openness and commitment. According to the participants of the study there must be "space" provided for both taking and giving criticism. The team should consist of people who have the skills to work with ideas and an ability to co-operate. There must be respect of individuals and routines and a basic understanding for each other, professionally as well as socially.

During the dialogue conferences important factors in cross-functional co-operation were discussed. Two types of factors were extracted from the discussions: *obstacles* to co-operation (see figure 2) and *activities* which support a well functioning co-operation. The individual obstacles which were discussed could be summarised as: fear of risk-taking, low degree of personal commitment, cultural differences, lack of holistic views and personal territories. The most disturbing structural obstacles were: lack of tools for preliminary concept review, hesitant acting on preliminary results, lack of a systematic transfer of knowledge, unrealistic time schedules and secrecy policies. A more general problem was the difficulties in combining short-term and long-term views in daily work.

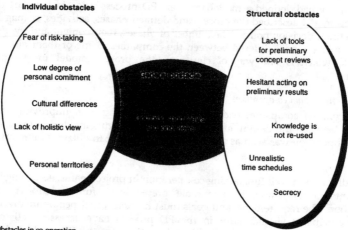

Figure 2. Obstacles in co-operation.

To change people's attitudes and views of their work is time-consuming and difficult and to overcome these obstacles several changes are required. In the discussions the group came up with the following ideas for *activities* to facilitate the growth of a well-functioning co-operation: team building, common project planning, job rotation, transfer of knowledge between projects, a designer's office at the manufacturing department and vice versa.

Geographically separated design and manufacturing departments demand special measures to obtain a well-functioning co-operation. However, an efficient dialogue could be supported with effective technical communication tools and frequent meetings.

### 3.3 Effects of the dialogue conferences

The evaluation showed that the conferences were successful in supporting the dialogue between the participating companies. The companies had meetings and discussed particular questions in between the conferences. They also planned to proceed these contacts after the completion of the conference set. The main part of the participants thought the conferences had been successful in supporting new ideas on how to improve PD work and found the time well-used.

The companies implemented some of the tools and working methods discussed during the dialogue conferences. One example is that several companies started using the "successive method", which is a planning tool supporting the estimation of project cost and time. An invited guest presented and discussed this method during one of the conferences. Another example is that two of the companies planned to install an office for a designer at the manufacturing department and vice versa. The companies also planned an increasing team building effort when initiating new projects.

## 4 Discussion

### 4.1 Dialogue conferences as a research method

The central part of the study was the dialogue conferences. The companies reported that the conferences had added valuable contribution to the renewal and improvement of PD work. The dialogue conferences worked as a catalyst and a drive for changes concerning the PD work. The benchmarking of the PD process between the companies resulted in an increased degree of reflection over and knowledge of their own process. By a dialogue with the other companies, they got an understanding that problems are seldom unique, which could strengthen their self confidence.

The implementation of new ideas found during the conferences was less extensive than the research group expected when the conferences started. This meant that the companies only could report limited practical experiences concerning these ideas. The reason could be that more time was needed to realise their specified renewal work.

The study was also carried through during a trade boom in Swedish industry and the running business demanded a big part of resources and power. The time span between the conferences was longer than planned from the beginning. The reason was that the companies wanted to reduce the number of conferences out of consideration for the running business in the companies, to be able to prioritise and have a motivation to participate actively.

The chosen approach was to tone down the role of the research group and their active participation, to stimulate a self-supporting change process in the company. The intention was to provide freedom and possibilities to independently formulate their need for changes. At the evaluation of the study some participants wished that the research group had presented more models or solutions to an efficient PD process. However, according to the chosen strategy the research group should not control the conference's content but only its form [9]. This provides better conditions for a long-term learning.

## 4.2 The renewal of product development work

The renewal of PD work in the participating companies was a change process which had been going on for several years and was planned to continue in the future. The activities in the companies are in accordance with the description of IPD by Karlsson and Åhlström [11]. They see the applications of IPD as a process of continuous changes, where the principles are setting the direction, and do *not* describe a state which is obtained after a certain time. In the companies there is an awareness of IPD and the need for a change. For a successful implementation of IPD a concordance around values, structure, processes and systems in PD [11] is needed. In the participating companies there were activities to increase the concordance and the participation in the dialogue conferences could be seen as a part of these activities.

## 4.3 Advice and recommendations

The problems in the companies seldom have a general solution. Conversely, each company must create their own solutions. The following advice should not be seen as a general and covering solution but should, however, be considered at the initiation of projects or organisational changes. The advice and recommendations are based on the results of the study.

Many of the changes in the participating companies concerned the clarification of the PD process. One way of defining the as-is process is to ask the people who are working in it. This could be done by *interviews* and/or *questionnaires*. By involving several persons in the change work, the anchoring of the new should-be proposals in the organisation is facilitated. *Benchmarking* could give new ideas for improvement of the process.

A lack of a holistic view and a confused opinion on which activities that are included in the phases of the project are common problems in industrial PD today. One way of informing the project participants is to have a so called *design briefing* at the end of each phase, where the entire design is examined commonly by the people involved - regarding aspects on both the product and the process. There should be *guidelines* for the proceedings of the briefing, so that nothing is forgotten.

When the different functions are geographically separated it is convenient with an *office for a visiting representative*. These offices should be furnished with telephone, computer and other tools which could be needed. Quick and robust *computer communication* is also an important asset in long-distance co-operation.

Besides formal meetings the company should encourage the team to have informal meetings. By establishing *project rooms*, where each project team could have prototypes, common documents, meetings, etc, team work is stimulated.

To get the project teams' attention concerning their and other team members' behaviour, *team roles* could be discussed in connection with the beginning of a new project. By *team building activities* the group could learn about each other and obtain a more efficient co-operation.

To establish the transfer of knowledge between projects, a *key person from an earlier project could join a new one*, either as a team member or as a reference person. A project ending with a thorough *documentation* of both positive and negative experiences from the work, is another way of transferring knowledge.

## 5 Acknowledgements

The study is a part of MANDECO (huMAN DEsign COmmunication), which is a project for empirical research with both a technical and a psychological perspective on PD work. The project was financed by the Swedish Council for Work Life Research (RALF) and the Swedish National Board for Technical Development (NUTEK).

The authors like to thank Pia Eneström (the Royal Institute of Technology) as well as Stefan Nordqvist and Annika Zika-Viktorsson (Stockholm University) for their valuable contribution during the study. The authors also like to thank the companies for their participation in the interviews and conferences.

## 6 References

[1] Mekanresultat 850208. *Integrerad produktutveckling - en arbetsmodell* (in Swedish). Sveriges mekanförbund. Stockholm, Sweden 1985.

[2] M M Andreasen and L Hein. *Integrated Product Development.* IFS (Publications) Ltd. U K 1987.

[3] M Norell. *The use of DFA, FMEA and QFD as tools for concurrent engineering in product development processes.* Proceedings of the International Conference on Engineering Design, ICED 93. The Hague August 17-19, 1993.

[4] K T Ulrich and S D Eppinger. *Product Design and Development.* McGraw-Hill Inc. USA 1995.

[5] R Hackman. The psychology of self-management in organizations. (In: M Pallak & R perloff Eds). *Psychology and Work.* American Psychological Assosiation. Washington D C, USA 1986.

[6] J Packendorff. *Projektorganisation och projektorganisering - projekt som plan och preliminär organisation.* Institutionen för företagsekonomi, Umeå universitet. Sweden 1993.

[7] J R Katzenbach and D K Smith. *The wisdom of Teams - Creating the High-Performance Organization.* McKinsey & Co, Inc. USA 1994.

[8] R M Belbin. *Management Teams - Så skapas framgångsrika teams* (in Swedish). IHM Förlag AB. Göteborg, Sweden 1993.

[9] B Gustavsen. *Dialogue and Development*. The Swedish Center for Working Life, Stockholm. Van Gorcum, Assen/Maastricht. Netherlands 1992.

[10] S Hovmark, S Nordqvist, C Beskow, A Zika-Viktorsson, P Eneström. *Produktutveckling i förändring: Förnyelse genom dialog och nätverk* (in Swedish). In press at the Stockholm university, Department of psychology, Stockholm, Sweden, 1997.

[11] C Karlsson and P Åhlström. The difficult Path to Lean Product Development. *Journal of Product Innovation Management, 13,* pp 283-295. 1996.

# 088

TITLE:    Life-Cycle HSE Assessment Model: A Military Technology Acquisition Decision-Making Tool

AUTHORS:   A. Szwilski, J. Hooper, W. McCumbee, A. Lodgher, H. Al-Haddad

## ABSTRACT

The life-cycle assessment model is an assessment tool that will evaluate the health, safety and environmental (HSE) impacts, performance and cost effectiveness, associated with the use of a technology or operational system. The HSE model (HSEM) is being developed to be a useful informational tool in the decision-making process of the military office of acquisitions [1]. The HSEM will be implemented using a software system, designed to be user-friendly.

## INTRODUCTION

The HSEM has a systematic set of procedures that will evaluate HSE impacts, performance and cost effectiveness of proposed and acquired technologies utilizing appropriate and relevant internal criteria, regulations, standards, codes of practice, scientific principles and guidelines. As technological innovation is rapidly decreasing the life-cycle of products and processes, assessing the performance and HSE impact features of the technologies needs to be rapid and unambiguous. The model is intended to assist management to focus on continuous improvement of technology and operational system use and associated HSE impacts. Since there is a myriad of factors and protocols to consider to assess the HSE impacts, the HSEM software system will guide the project manager in task choice, and from there to corresponding assessment protocols and technical help menus. Ideally, the technological products should be designed to optimize health, safety and environmental performance. A radical technological innovation and/or poor safety features can make a product obsolete [2].

The life-cycle assessment model assesses the potential HSE impacts associated with the use of technologies by compiling an inventory and evaluating of relevant inputs and outputs for each pertinent life-cycle step. There are Inherent limitations in the assumptions made in selecting the system boundary (life-cycle phase or sub-phase) , data sources and impact categories and indicators. Accuracy will depend on accessibility, availability of relevant, quality data. Four health, safety and environmental assessment tasks have been identified: (1) HSE impact assessment; (2) continuous product/process performance improvement; (3) compare competing technological products; (4) "what-if" scenarios. Tasks 1, 3, and 4 predict anticipated change in the environmental indicator; determine the magnitude of the change; apply a weighting (importance factor) to the change; analyze and assess impact significance of change. Task 2 continuously monitors HSE indicators and chooses an appropriate mitigating strategy. Designed to be user-friendly, the software system will facilitate and speed the assessment tasks, data management and decision making.  The software will also provide step-by-step guidance to accomplish the identified task. Other features include accessing existing databases on regulations, standards and codes of practice, scientific data, and integration with other protocols.

HSEM's life-cycle process tool (Figure 1) can provide management with reliable, objective and verifiable information concerning the HSE policy, objectives and targets [2]. The HSEM will be one informational tool in the decision-making process for use by the military office of acquisitions and others.

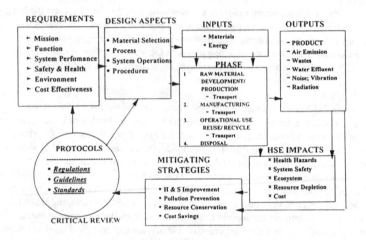

**Figure 1. HSE Life-Cycle Assessment System**

## ASSESSMENT OF TECHNOLOGY PRODUCTS AND SYSTEMS

The four HSE assessment tasks identified will assist military management in undertaking proactive initiatives to evaluate HSE impacts and identify opportunities for cost savings through effective resource management, and reducing pollution and HSE risks throughout the technology/product life-cycle. These four tasks are:

1. HSE Impact Assessment. Reduces the findings to a single result -- a Finding Of No Significant Impact (FONSI) or significant impact [4]. Impact assessment can be done for new or existing technology product/process. The software system supports the user to gather data from various sources, and build the steps of the phase levels and sub-levels. Once the phase level steps are entered, and the assessment table built, an evaluation process can be triggered.

2. <u>Continuous Process Improvement</u>. Identifies areas for improvement (mitigating procedures) --
for a selected technology product/process and to reduce HSE impacts and costs. The continuous
process improvement task can be applied to a technology, product, process or system procedure.
The software will provide tools for a user to change the various steps and change the assessment
values. This process is iterative, and thus may be performed an unlimited number of times until
a satisfactory result is obtained. The HSEM will assist military management to evaluate the
consequences of a proposed action within a defined system (life-cycle phase) boundary by
analyzing the indicators (HSEPIs) in the HSE inventory. For Task 2, the HSEPIs will be
continuously monitored and appropriate mitigating strategies chosen. Figure 2 shows the
relationship between the military management system, the evaluated health, safety and
environmental status, technology, product life-cycle impacts, and communication to interested
parties (stakeholders).

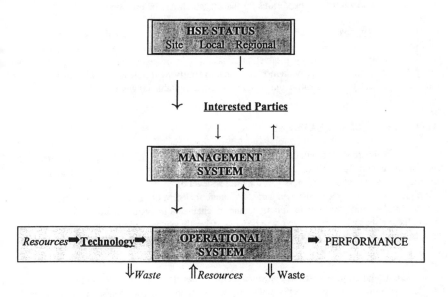

**Figure 2. Military HSE Management System**

Having defined the boundary of the HSE evaluation task and boundary, the HSEPIs will be
identified considering the inputs and outputs from the system. Depending on the nature of the HSE
evaluation, priorities for the HSEPIs will be set. Examples of HSEPIs are [3]:
    <u>Raw Materials</u>: Cost of recycled raw material used per unit of product; units of waste used

in process as raw material.

Energy: Energy units of each source of energy used; energy units of nonrenewable energy used per year.

Waste: Units of waste disposed of per year; units of waste recycled per year.

Maintenance: Number, types, amount of cleaning solvents used in routine maintenance ; number of spills from parts maintenance.

Effluent Discharge: Number of days with no spills, upsets or incidents; units of discharge, emissions.

Compliance with Laws and Regulations: Number of days in compliance with permit limits at all water discharge points; number of days in which no enforcement citations were issued.

3. Compare competing products: The software will allow the user to set up various parameters for comparison, including costs, and other HSE indicators. The software will compare the products and generate a comparison report, the various formats of which will be provided.

4. "What-if" Scenarios. Evaluates changes of design, process and operational procedures to reduce HSE impacts and costs. What-If scenario is a mechanism that will evaluate the effect (adverse or beneficial impact) of a technology, product, process or system procedural change during the product life-cycle. The software will provide mechanisms for identifying the steps where changes could be made. The process will be iterative until values within acceptable ranges are obtained.

## SOFTWARE DESIGN FEATURES

The software system will enable the military to manage the HSE procedures and protocols, and facilitate and speeds the decision making process of evaluating HSE impact, system performance, and cost effectiveness. At the highest level of abstraction, the software system will be designed to perform four tasks, comparable to the four HSEM tasks. For each of these tasks, the software will provide lower level functions and mechanisms to systematically guide the user to accomplishing the task. The software will be a user-friendly system and provide access to existing databases on regulations, standards and codes of practice, and integration with other protocols.

The design of the software is dependent upon the development of HSE protocols. However, the HSE protocols are being developed with the knowledge that a software system will be used for its implementation. Therefore, the use of the HSE protocol implies the use of the software system. The HSE protocol is quite large and detailed, and using the protocol without the software would be a very tedious and time-consuming task. The protocol "relies" on the software to make some detailed processes easier by providing templates, guidance, on-line help, etc. Thus, the overall design of the software reflects the overall design of the protocol.

### HSE Life-Cycle Software System Description

The main functional components of the overall system are: Tasks, Phase Support Planning,

544

Phase Levels, Data, Impact Analysis, Impact Report and Mitigating Strategies.

*Tasks:* The system gives the user a choice of four tasks. These tasks, which reflect the protocol tasks are: HSE Impact Assessment, Continuous Process Improvement, Compare Competing Technologies and Products, and "What-if" Scenarios.

*Phase Support Planning:*
Once the task is selected, the software will allow the user to enter, edit or review the phase support planning steps. The phase support planning component allows the user to decide the life-cycle assessment steps with respect to material selection, process, operations, and procedures.

*Phase Levels:*
This component divides the cradle-to-grave process into the four major phase levels: Raw Materials, Manufacturing, Operational Use, and Disposal. Each of these phase levels is then broken into sub-levels. The number of sub-levels will depend on the level of details the user decides for the product/process. According to the main task selected, the software will allow the user to build the levels, modify, or review the materials at that level.

*Data:* The task of building or reviewing phase level and sub-level steps, and impact assessment of each step will be one of the more "tedious" tasks of the protocol. The software will provide tools and mechanisms to assist in the step building and assessment process. A repository of phase-level and sub-level steps templates, categorized by product or process type, will be made available. Various editing facilities, which will include cutting and pasting steps from other products or processes, will be provided.

*Impact Analysis:*
The input and output impact value categories such as health hazards, system safety, ecosystem and cost will be recorded. To assist the user to determine and enter the values, various tools and on-line help will be made available. To record the HSEPI values, an assessment table will be maintained for each step. This table will be built by querying the user about the inputs into each step (such as, materials, energy, investment, etc.), and the outputs from each step (such as, air emissions, water effluent, solid waste, hazardous waste, etc.). If at a particular step in the phase level regulations, standards or codes of practice need to be addressed, it will be possible to "look-up" the appropriate on-line databases.

*Impact Report:*
The impact values at each life-cycle step under consideration will be collected and an overall impact determination made. A report of the impacts at various stages, could be generated.

*Mitigating Strategies:*
Having completed an impact assessment, several mitigating strategy options may be reviewed. These mitigating strategies could have an impact on the phase level and sub-level steps. The new impact values could be determined, and the process continued.

# HEALTH, SAFETY AND ENVIRONMENTAL COMPONENTS AND REQUIREMENTS

The principal objective of the HSEM is to fulfill the requirements, and facilitate effective implementation of a military HSE management program. The following aspects should be systematically defined and addressed when applying the HSEM [2]:

HSE Assessment Objectives:

- Systematically and adequately address the HSE consequences of using a technology, a product, from raw materials acquisition to final disposal.
- The detail and time for the HSE study dictated by the study goal and scope definition.
- The HSE assessment scope, assumptions, data quality parameters, methodologies and output to be definitive, understandable, comprehensive and transparent.

Scope:

- Objectives and scope of the HSE assessment clearly defined and consistent with the intended application.

Goals:

- Intended application -- select an appropriate assessment task
- Intended audience -- to whom the study results will be communicated

HSEM Components:

- New technology, a product, process
- System
- Function of the system
- System boundaries
- Allocation rules (for multiple products) for manufacturing and system use
- Scale, type and methodology of the HSE impact assessment
- Assumptions and limitations
- Initial data quality requirements
- Type and format of the report required of the study
- HSEM critical review

Data Quality Requirements: Needs to be defined to meet the goals and scope of the HSE study with respect to:

- Precision, completeness, and representativeness of the data and the data sources
- Consistency & reproducibility of the protocols used
- Sources of data
- Variability & uncertainty of the information and protocols/methodology

Reporting Requirements:

Continuous learning and improvement are critical in high-tech development and utilization. Thus it is important that the extent and detail of the reporting requirements should be defined in the scope phase of the study. The results, data, methodology, assumptions and limitations should be transparent and in sufficient detail to allow the reader to comprehend and use the result and interpretation in a manner consistent with the goals and study.

HSEM report format:
1.  Goal and scope definition: goal, scope, data quality requests, critical review (if required)
2.  LCA inventory analysis: data collection and calculation procedures
3.  HSE impact assessment: nature and extent of impact
4.  Interpretation: results, methodology data related limitation, data quality assessment
5.  Critical Review
    - Protocols consistent with regulations, guidelines and standards
    - Procedural and testing protocols are scientifically and technically valid
    - Interpretations reflect the limitations of the study
    - HSE study is transparent and consistent
6.  Internal review
7.  Expert review
8.  Review by interested parties

Note: Provisions should be made in the HSEM to respect confidentiality and proprietary matters, and incorporate new scientific findings and improvements in the state-of-the-art methodology.

## CONCLUSIONS

The HSEM is a life-cycle assessment tool that will help identify and evaluate potential HSE impacts and performance a technology or product used by the military. This is done by using appropriate and relevant internal criteria, regulations, standards, codes of practice, and scientific principles and guidelines. The HSEM can provide military management with reliable, objective and verifiable information concerning its HSE policies objectives and targets, and a useful informational tool in the decision-making process for technology acquisitions. The HSEM can be a useful tool in fulfilling the requirements and effectively implementing a military HSE management program. The HSEM implemented using a user-friendly software system that can provide templates, guidance, access to existing databases, and on-line help.

## REFERENCES

1.  Final Report, Phase 1: Development of a Health, Safety & Health Protocol For The United States Navy, U.S. Gov. Contract No. 51-96-S-022-A, 1996.

2.  Betz, F., 'Strategic Technology Management', McGraw-Hill, Inc. 1993

3.  Draft Text for Annex F, Environmental Performance Evaluation (EPE), ISO/TC207/US SUBTAG 4(EPE), 1996

4.  Environmental Impact Statement (EIS), National Environmental Policy Act, 1969, 42 USCA 4321, 40 CFR (NEPA) Part 1500.

# 089

# THE DYNAMICS OF THE DIVERSIFIED CORPORATION AND THE ROLE OF CENTRAL MANAGEMENT OF TECHNOLOGY

Author:
Jens Froslev Christensen, Associate Professor,
Department of Industrial Economics and Strategy,
Copenhagen Business School, Nansensgade 19, 6,
1366 Copenhagen K, Denmark
Tel:       +45-38-152535
Fax        +45-38-152540
E-Mail:       jfc@cbs.dk

## ABSTRACT

During recent years there is reported evidence of widespread "downswing" efforts within headquarters of large multi-divisional corporations. This tendency has also involved downgrading of corporate R&D (i.e. in the form of corporate labs), and decentralization of R&D to (divisional or business unit levels. These dynamics have stimulated motivation and entrepreneurship at decentral level]s and a stronger market-orientation in technological innovation on.

However, a likely negative implication of this downsizing of central R&D may be increasing corporate fragmentation which may contribute to undermine core competence, reduce inter-divisional synergy and increase duplication of efforts. Moreover, technological innovation may become strongly biased in the direction of increinentalism and short-terms at the expense of long-term exploration of new opportunities.

This paper discusses how management of technology can contribute to counter these negative implications and play a critical role in promoting corporate coherence in large - and highly decentralized - multi-divisional corporations. Corporate coherence is defined as the corporate capacity to exploit and explore synergies from a diversity of capabilities, competence's and other resources. I will focus on both the vertical relations (between corporate level R&D and management of technology and divisional level R&D and innovative efforts), the horizontal relations between divisions and business units, and the relations to external parties. Apart from literature studies, case studies of one or two Danish industrial corporations will provide significant input to the paper.

# 090

## DOMINANT DESIGN AND MODULARITY

Author:
Jong-Tsong Chiang (Ph. D. of MIT)
Associate Professor
Director, Ph. D.. Programs in Technology Management and Strategic
Management, College of Management, National Taiwan University,
50, Lane 144, Keelung Road, Section 4, Taipei, Taiwan.
Tel:        +886-2-3630231x2864  Fax:        +886-2-3634103,

ABSTRACT

Limited to relatively complex assembled products, the concept of dominant
design has important technological, economic and organizational
implications. A dominant design has the effect of enforcing standardization.
Therefore, the emergence of a dominant design also implies the prevalence
of a collection of related standards. On the other hand, system architecture
refers to the interfacing standards, which coordinate the related parts or
modules to function as a whole. The notions of system architecture and
modularity are thus closely associated with the dominant design concept.
And the competition between and the control of the critical interfacing
specifications, standards and mechanisms are crucial for the ultimate
success of the different parties making a living based on a dominant design.
In this regard, there are three generic patterns, the first and the second
relating to internal modularity and the third to external modularity.
(1) The main structure of modularity is designed by the system integrators
and the critical interfacing specifications and mechanisms are largely the
system integrators´ proprietary assets. Then the system integrators rather
than the upstream suppliers tend to capitalize more on the dominant
design. (In the meantime the system integrators compete against each other
along the converging or similar design paths.)
(2) The main structure of modularity is designed by the system integrators
but the critical interfacing specifications and mechanisms are largely open
standards because of the availability of standard constituent components
from the markets or the de jure standardization by industry or government.
Then the system integrators need to have competitive advantage in
proprietary key modules or system designs in order to have an upper hand
over the upstream suppliers and the producers of compatible products - to
whom the entry barriers are fairly low.
(3) If there are strong network externalities, the focal products and the
external complementary products should be thought of as constituent
modules of higher-level systems.  In this case, those who can enlarge the
installed base (if necessary, through licensing production provided that the
intellectual property protection regime is tight) and control the interfacing
mechanisms (like the development tools for complementary products) tend
to  win in the dominant design competition  Moreover, it is likely that the
winner takes almost all. This pattern covers the competition between and
within the so-called "platforms" and extends the conventional concept of
dominant design, if defined broadly.

# 092

## COMPETITIVE TECHNOLOGY AND KNOWLEDGE TRANSFER - THE APPROACH OF THE STEINBEIS FOUNDATION FOR ECONOMIC PROMOTION (GERMANY)

Prof. Dr. J. Löhn, Prof. Dipl.-Virtsch.-Ing. A. Voegele   Steinbeis Foundation for Economic Promotion, Stuttgart   Germany

ABSTRACT

Nothing is more permanent than change . This classical bon mot characterizes the nature and work of the Steinbeis Foundation, which, in its thoughts and actions, has been developed over the years from a "*partner for technology transfer*" into a "*full service solver of problems*" Within this philosophy, the Steinbeis Foundation is ready at any time to discuss new, complex market concepts, overall company structuring and efficient technology transfer. The main aim of this Foundation, set up in 1971 and organised within the private sector, is to bridge the gap between science and economy The intention is for small to medium-sized companies in particular to profit from the extensive know-how potential of the Steinbeis Foundation. The *actual transfer* work is done in more than *about 250* different and specialized Steinbeis*Transfer Centres (Transfer Network)*-independent, flexible, decentralized and close to its customers.

*Thechnology transfer* as we know it consists of *three elements*, source, recipient and method. A source of technology or know-how may be a research institute but it could also be a highly industrialized country or a technology-oriented company. The recipients of technology transfer are usually companies and in particular small and medium-sized enterprises. The methods used to convey know-how, and in particulate technologies, from the source to the recipient, are extremely varied In order to give some structure to this variety, we classify technology transfer into the following *four categories:* Information transfer, Strengthening transfer, Pre-competitive transfer and Competitive transfer.

There are existing *ten axioms* which characterise the Steinbeis Foundation and are reflected in all *of its activities,* f.e. making use of the established R&D infrastructure, benefit for the customer, availability and adaptability, holistic approach, decentralisation and flat hierarchy, financial independence, internationalisation.

"Transfer of Transfer" is the product of years of work in the field of technology transfer Steinbeis has managed to implement a *technology transfer model* whose principles are unique of their type in the world and which forges links between industry, research and government. The aim of the "*Transfer of transfer*" project is the successful implementation of a technology transfer model to be developed for the recipient country through the application there of the basic principles of the Steinbeis Foundation. Rather than simply copying the Steinbeis model, this involves systematic adaptation to the existing infrastructure in the recipient country. For this reason a strategy is developed at the evaluation phase in collaboration with all those involved and interested in the technology transfer and then applied in the subsequent phases. This strategy is based on the so-called "*EOC Principles*". Executive and Operational Training, Company Coaching. Meanwhile this new method/product is carried out throughout the world from South-East-Asian countries over India and East-Europe up to South America.

# 093

# University-Industry Technology Transfer: A Learning Perspective

Michael P. Hottenstein, D.B.A, and Abdelkader Daghfous
The Pennsylvania State University
University Park, PA USA

## ABSTRACT

This paper presents the results of an empirical investigation of how learning activities and prior knowledge contribute to the benefits to that firm from university-industry technology transfer projects. A conceptual model and a set of hypotheses were developed and tested using a research design that consisted of a large mail survey. A significant positive relationship was found between the learning activities performed by the firm during the development and implementation stages of the technology transfer project and the benefits to that firm from the project. In contrast, prior knowledge of the firm about the existing technology was found to have only a marginal contribution to the project benefits. However, further exploratory analysis based on high and low levels of technical and organizational uncertainty revealed some provocative relationships.

(*Keywords:* Technology Transfer, Organizational Learning, Prior Knowledge, Uncertainty, Learning Benefits)

## INTRODUCTION

The main research question in this study is: how do learning activities and prior knowledge of the recipient firm contribute to the benefits to that firm from a university-industry technology transfer project? More specifically, this study seeks to address the following three questions: (1) how does the prior knowledge the recipient firm has about its existing technology and the organizational context where the transferred technology will reside relate to the benefits of the transfer project? (2) how do learning activities undertaken by the recipient firm increase the benefits of the technology transfer project? and (3) how does uncertainty associated with the technology to be transferred and the organizational impact of that technology affect the relationships between prior knowledge, learning activities, and the benefits of the transfer project?

## MODEL AND HYPOTHESES DEVELOPMENT

The conceptual model of the study, shown in Figure 1, is based on the following propositions:
(1) The model proposes that the better the firm understands its existing technology and the corresponding organizational context, the greater will be the operational benefits of the technology transfer project.
(2) The learning activities that the firm undertakes during the project will influence the achievement of technical and non-technical benefits from that project.
(3) In addition to the operational (i.e., technical) benefits that are usually used to assess the outcome of a given transfer, there may be other important learning consequences. These learning benefits may be independent of the operational ones. That is, a project may be considered a failure in terms of fulfilling the intended operational benefits and goals, yet provide valuable lessons to the recipient firm. Hence, this study emphasizes such a distinction and proposes that both types of benefits have different antecedents.
(4) High levels of uncertainty increase the need for prior knowledge and of learning activities to achieve the project outcomes. Technological uncertainty is related to the level of familiarity the recipient firm has with the features and science underlying the technology being transferred. In contrast, organizational uncertainty is related to the company's familiarity with the potential impact of the new technology on the organization, its existing set of skills, and technologies. However, both types of uncertainties are expected to have similar effects. That is, if there is a high level of uncertainty, the firm will need to develop high levels of prior knowledge and institute learning activities in order for the project to achieve high operational and learning benefits.

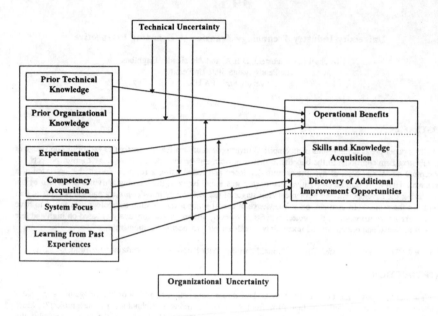

Figure 1. The Conceptual Model

**Prior Technical Knowledge**

Bohn (1994) presented a creative conceptual framework for understanding and evaluating the technical knowledge the firm has about its production process. He proposed an eight stage scale to measure the technical knowledge the firm has about a particular input variable's ($Xi$) impact on the output (Y) of the production process. To illustrate the importance of prior knowledge, Bohn explained that General Motors' \$40 billion investment in automation in the early 1980's never worked properly mainly because the firm lacked adequate process knowledge. The firm automated a large, complex, and poorly understood manufacturing process. The result was a large, complex, poorly understood, and unreliable automated manufacturing process. Bohn stated: "If workers do not understand a process, they cannot handle unanticipated situations, nor can they do much to improve the process, even if they are motivated." A high level of prior knowledge, then, permits the formulation of appropriate project specifications that reduce the likelihood of delays and increase the likelihood of achieving effective technical solutions. That is, in order to achieve significant technical improvements, the firm should enter the project with an adequate level of knowledge about what is to be improved. Therefore:

**Hypothesis 1 :** During the project specification stage, the greater the prior technical knowledge the recipient firm has about its existing technology, the greater will be the operational benefits from the university-industry technology transfer project.

However, Cohen and Levinthal (1990) found that a firm's absorptive capacity is less important in cases where external knowledge can be assimilated and exploited without any specialized expertise. They defined absorptive capacity in terms of the firm's ability to recognize the value of new knowledge, assimilate it, and exploit it. Prior related knowledge, which can be increased though in-house R&D, contributes to this ability. Therefore, the contribution of prior related knowledge to operational benefits can also be expected to vary according to the complexity and the newness of the new technology being transferred. Hence, we can expect technical uncertainty, defined in terms of technical newness and complexity, to affect the strength of the relationship between prior technical knowledge and operational benefits. The technical complexity and newness of the new technology are captured here by the construct *technical uncertainty*. However, since uncertainty decreases as the project progresses, the construct refers to the level of uncertainty as it is perceived by the recipient firm at the beginning of the project (i.e., at the project specification stage). Hence:

**Hypothesis 2 :** If, during the project specification stage, the recipient firm perceives that there is high uncertainty about the technology to be transferred, then it is even more important for the firm to understand its existing technology in order for the transfer to achieve expected operational benefits.

**Prior Organizational Knowledge**

Managers often make assumptions about the organizational context into which the new technology is introduced. The organizational context here refers to the local environment and infrastructural support within the firm where the new technology will reside. For instance, Duimering et. al. (1993) studied the implementation of JIT and CIM in a number of firms. They found that organization structures that are highly functional and do not emphasize cross-functional teams are likely to exhibit poor communication and coordination of interrelated organizational tasks. In contrast, some factories may have already grouped individuals (or departments, units, etc.) according to individual products or broadly defined product families that require highly independent tasks. Organizations may also rely on certain types of communication systems (computerized or otherwise) to generate, disseminate, and process information. Duimering et. al. (1993) noted that if information is "soft" (i.e., cannot be easily codified), then computerization may not help to generate, disseminate, or process useful information and subsequently useful knowledge.

Leonard-Barton (1988) addressed the value of knowledge about the organizational context during the project implementation phase. She emphasized the value of continuous, ongoing mutual adaptation of technology and organization during the implementation of new technology, since the new technology never exactly fit the user environment. Leonard-Barton also emphasized the value of the original definition phase of the project. During this phase, she argued, a better understanding of the user environment would decrease disruption and the cost of adaptation cycles. Iansiti (1995) also argued that technology integration during product development projects involves the integration of deep knowledge of the existing environment (context specific knowledge) with the specification of project tasks.

The model depicted in Figure 1 proposes that, similar to technological knowledge, firms must attain a certain level of knowledge about the organizational context of the technology transfer project in order to acquire the appropriate technology and to be adequately prepared to integrate the new technology into the organization. Therefore:

**Hypothesis 3 :** During the project specification stage, the greater the prior technical knowledge the recipient firm has about its existing organizational context where the transferred technology will reside, the greater will be the operational benefits from the university-industry technology transfer project.

**Hypothesis 4 :** If, during the project specification stage, the recipient firm perceives that there is high uncertainty about the organizational impact of the technology to be transferred, then it is even more important for the firm to understand its existing organizational context in order for the transfer to achieve expected operational benefits.

**The Role of Learning Activities**

This study introduces a secondary technology transfer outcome. This outcome goes beyond adoption and implementation of new technology and beyond the characteristics of the transfer process. This study argues that it is useful and insightful to evaluate the outcome of a technology transfer project in terms of learning benefits. Learning benefits (also referred to here as *non-technical* or *spillover* benefits) include: (1) the acquisition of new skills and knowledge, and (2) the discovery of performance gaps, which present opportunities to explore other improvement initiatives. The recognition of these benefits is based on Tyre and Orlikowski's (1994) conception of events which are viewed as windows of opportunities that must be recognized and exploited quickly.

## The Role of Experimentation

The construct experimentation is widely used in the literature on organizational learning, innovation, and technological change to denote an activity whose aim is collecting information and knowledge that does not already exist. In the technological innovation literature, this activity has also been called *learning by doing*, *learning by trying*, *learning by using*, and *trial and error*. In this study, the term *experimentation* is chosen, as it is used to denote a learning activity by Garvin (1993) and by Yeung et. al. (1996).

The construct experimentation is operationalized in terms of the learning activities proposed by Chew et. al. (1991). These activities are: (1) formal and informal efforts to learn from the experience of other groups or firms with similar technology, (2) construction of an artificial model of the new technology to run experiments, (3) building a small scale prototype of the new technology in a controlled environment to identify potential problems and opportunities, and (4) examination of a full-scale working model of the new technology under actual conditions.

Moreover, the higher the levels of technical and organizational uncertainty experienced by the firm in the beginning of the project, the more knowledge the company needs to acquire through experimentation (Daghfous and White, 1994). Although experimentation may result in learning benefits, this study focuses primarily on the operational (or technical) benefits. Hence:

**Hypothesis 5 :** The greater the experimentation undertaken by the recipient firm during the university-industry technology transfer project, the greater will be the operational benefits from that project.

**Hypothesis 6 :** If, during the project specification stage, the recipient firm perceives that there is high uncertainty about the technology to be transferred, then it is even more important to undertake experimentation in order for the transfer to achieve expected operational benefits.

**Hypothesis 7 :** If, during the project specification stage, the recipient firm perceives that there is high uncertainty about the organizational impact of the technology to be transferred, then it is even more important to undertake experimentation in order for the transfer to achieve expected operational benefits.

### The Role of System Focus

System focus is viewed as a learning activity wherein the organization purposefully: (1) relies on cross functional organizational arrangements to solve important product and process problems, and (2) takes into consideration the impact of design choices on other existing technologies within the organization. System focus is expected to increase the spillover effects of the technology transfer project. More specifically, as the recipient organization uses cross-functional teams and other cross-functional arrangements and takes into consideration the impact of product and process design choices on other existing technologies within the organization, non-technical spillover benefits can be expected.

Technology transfer projects involve technology acquisition, assimilation and adaptation of the new technology by the recipient organization. University-industry technology transfer projects, where the recipient firm has a high level of system focus, are expected to reveal to that organization: (1) areas of weaknesses in product or process development procedures, (2) better ways to manage collaborative projects with a university, (3) additional opportunities to benefit from a university as a source of knowledge, (4) areas of potential improvement in product design, production technology, or production management, and (5) the need for additional competencies to keep up with state-of-the-art science and technology.

These spillovers are additional improvement opportunities that follow the technology transfer project or are discovered during the project. Borrowing from Tyre and Orlikowski's (1994) idea of window of opportunity, the university-industry technology transfer project can be considered as an event that can trigger new spurts of adaptive activity. Hence, the project can be considered as an "interruption" or a "disruption" that organizational actors can benefit from through improvements in other parts of the organizations. To recognize and exploit potential areas of improvement, the recipient firm must have the system focus that can be expected to provide the broad perspective that allows the firm to look beyond the narrow technical boundaries of the project. Such a firm can be expected to benefit from the project's spillovers significantly more than firms that lack such system focus, ceteris paribus. In addition, it is expected that the more organizational uncertainty associated the project, the broader will be the scope of that project. Hence, a system focus would be greatly needed to address challenges and opportunities that go beyond the technical focus of the project.

**Hypothesis 8 :** The greater the system focus undertaken by the recipient firm during the university-industry technology transfer project, the greater will be the discovery of additional improvement opportunities as spillover from that project.

**Hypothesis 9 :** If, during the project specification stage, the recipient firm perceives that there is high uncertainty about the organizational impact of the technology to be transferred, then it is even more important to develop a system focus so that additional improvement opportunities might be found.

### The Role of Competency Acquisition

Firms develop both individual and group skills and knowledge by promoting learning at every level. Nevis et. al. (1995), reported that the EDF company had been developing both individual and group skills. Whereas EDF employees followed individual training programs for certification and promotion, teams learned by using simulators. The acquisition of cutting-edge and relevant knowledge may accelerate teams' and individuals' capability to assimilate more new knowledge and subsequently develop innovative new products and processes (Cohen and Levinthal, 1990).

Competency acquisition is considered here as an organizational learning activity that aims at augmenting the skills and knowledge of individuals and teams. A firm acquires new competencies and enhances existing ones by encouraging individuals and teams to do so and by demonstrating a commitment to such forms of learning (Yeung and Ulrich, 1994). This can be done by making competency acquisition as a part of the firm's business strategy.

However, knowledge is often tacit and cannot be transferred through blueprints and documentation (Leonard-Barton, 1995). This type of knowledge is usually transferred through informal processes and communication channels. Hence, it is quite difficult to focus on a specific way or a set of activities that all firms can perform or use to acquire new competencies during a technology transfer project. Instead, the main focus here is on the strategic intent and commitment by the firm to acquire competencies during the technology transfer project.

**Hypothesis 10 :** The greater the commitment by the recipient firm to the creation of a nurturing environment for the acquisition and development of competencies, the more will skills and knowledge develop during the university-industry technology transfer project.

**Hypothesis 11 :** If, during the project specification stage, the recipient firm perceives that there is high uncertainty about the technology to be transferred, then it is even more important for the firm to create a nurturing environment for the acquisition and development of skills and knowledge.

### The Role of Learning from Past Experiences

Product and process development projects, as well as other organizational change initiatives, often fail. Whether they succeed or fail, these experiences offer valuable learning opportunities for the firm. Often, though, firms use only informal and ad hoc procedures to learn from the past successes and failures. Garvin (1993) described a variety of systematic ways in which some renown firms review and assess past experiences, then record and disseminate these lessons. Garvin also made the very important distinction between a productive failure and an unproductive success. He defined a productive failure as one that "leads to insight, understanding, and thus addition to the commonly held wisdom of the organization." Hence, procedures (formal or informal) aimed at learning from past experiences are a valuable process of knowledge acquisition and accumulation. Such a process converts internal stimuli into new knowledge and firm-specific competencies, which are central to the enhancement of the firm's competitive advantage. High levels of uncertainty magnify such stimuli and provide a bigger opportunity for learning. In addition, highly uncertain projects are more risky and, hence, the relative degree of success or failure can be expected to be quite high in either direction. Therefore:

**Hypothesis 12 :** The greater the learning from past experiences in regards to university-industry technology transfer projects, the greater will be the discovery of additional improvement opportunities during the current transfer project.

**Hypothesis 13 :** If, during the project specification stage, the recipient firm perceives high uncertainty about the organizational impact of the transferred technology, then it is even more important for the recipient firm to have systematic mechanisms for learning from past experiences so that the current transfer project will result in the discovery of additional improvement opportunities.

**Hypothesis 14 :** If, during the project specification stage, the recipient firm perceives high uncertainty about the technology to be transferred, then it is even more important for the recipient firm to have systematic mechanisms for learning from past experiences so that the current transfer project will result in the discovery of additional improvement opportunities.

## METHODS

The unit of analysis in this study was technology transfer projects from the Pennsylvania State University to companies. During the Summer of 1996, a survey questionnaire was sent to 465 informants who were believed to be the most knowledgeable about transfer projects in their firms. After a second mailing, usable responses were received from 120 projects. Multi-item scales were developed to measure the constructs used in the conceptual model shown in Figure 1. Nine of the eleven measurement scales used in this exploratory research are newly developed. The items used to measure *competency acquisition* and *operational benefits* are the only ones directly derived from the empirical literature. A total of 36 items were developed to measure the eleven constructs used in the conceptual model. These items were submitted to reliability and validity analyses. While reliability measure the degree to which a measuring procedure yields the same results on repeated trials (Carmines and Zeller, 1979), construct validity determines the degree to which an instrument measures the construct it was intended to measure (Sakakibara et. al., 1993).

The reliability of each scale was assessed using the internal consistency method by calculating the coefficient alpha (Cronbach's alpha). Cronbach's alpha was calculated before and after performing the factor analyses. Hence, reliability was checked before and after validity (Sakakibara et. al , 1993). That is, unreliable scales were changed to ensure reliability. Then, to ensure their validity, these scales were changed again based on a principle component factor analyses with varimax rotation. The third and final step was to recalculate Cronbach's alpha for the resulting scales as a second and necessary check for reliability of the scales which were used in the subsequent hypotheses tests. Only the final alpha values, however, are reported. After subjecting the original items and scales to reliability tests and factor analyses, the variable "system focus" was dropped from the study. In addition, two items were dropped and changes were made to the original item groupings of the scales.

The hypotheses developed above were, then, adjusted to reflect the factor analyses results. The items used to measure the new scale "training and cross functional teams" was dominated by the original "competency acquisition" related items and included two items from the "system focus" scale. Therefore, while hypotheses 1 through 7 remained unchanged, hypotheses 8 and 9 were not tested and the following are the revised hypotheses related to skills and knowledge acquisition:

**Hypothesis 10A:** The greater the commitment of the recipient firm to training and the greater the use of cross functional teams during the development and implementation of the university-industry technology transfer project, the more will skills and knowledge acquisition develop during the project.

**Hypothesis 11A:** If during the project specification stage, the recipient firm perceives that there is high uncertainty about the *new technology* to be transferred, then it is even more important for the firm to create a nurturing environment and adopt cross functional teams for the acquisition and development of skills and knowledge.

556

**Hypothesis 11B:** If during the project specification stage, the recipient firm perceives that there is high uncertainty about the *organizational impact of the technology* to be transferred, then it is even more important for the firm to create a nurturing environment and adopt cross functional teams for the acquisition and development of skills and knowledge.

Canonical correlation analysis was first performed to explore the general relationships among the two sets of independent variables (i.e., prior knowledge and learning activities) and the set of dependent variables (i.e., operational benefits, skills and knowledge acquisition, and discovery of additional improvement opportunities). These dependent variables were, subsequently, used separately to perform hierarchical regression analyses to test the hypothesized relationships and explore new ones. Split sample analysis was also used to explore how the direct effects might change for projects with high and low levels of technical uncertainty and high and low levels of organizational uncertainty. This was performed by splitting the sample at the median into two groups of *high* and *low technical uncertainty*. The same split sample analysis procedure was also performed for *organizational uncertainty*. The results of split group analyses were, subsequently, tested by recoding technical (and organizational) uncertainty into a binary variable (also split at the median). Hierarchical regression was performed on the full sample (N=120) to determine the significance of the interaction terms between the uncertainty variable and the four independent variables of interest (i.e., Prior Technical Knowledge, Experimentation, Training and Cross Functional Teams, and Systematic Learning from Past Experiences).

**MAJOR FINDINGS**

The results of the hypotheses were summarized in Table 1. Although some hypotheses were not supported, exploratory analyses of the data revealed several provocative relationships among the variables. Table 2 summarizes the results related to the influence of learning activities on project benefits and the impact of uncertainty on these relationships.

This research found that the use of organizational learning activities by the recipient firm during the development and implementation stages of a technology transfer project increases the benefits to that firm from the project. Of the three different types of benefits, operational benefits was found to be the most influenced by organizational learning activities. All three learning activities had a significant impact on operational benefits. However, the significance of the impacts of these learning activities changed as the level (high or low) and type of uncertainty (technical or organizational) experienced by the firm at the project definition stage changed.

For projects characterized by high technical uncertainty, experimentation was found to be the only rewarding learning activity for operational benefits. In comparison, for projects with low technical uncertainty, systematic learning from past experiences was found to be the only rewarding learning activity on operational benefits. However, systematic learning from past experiences was found to have a significant negative effect on operational benefits during projects characterized by high organizational uncertainty. In these projects, training and cross functional teams were found to have a significant positive impact on operational benefits. For projects with low organizational uncertainty, experimentation and systematic learning from experiences were found to have a significant contribution to operational benefits. In addition to these learning activities, prior technical knowledge that the firm has about its existing technology was found to have a significant positive contribution to operational benefits in projects characterized by a high level of organizational uncertainty.

Operational benefits are usually the focus of a technology transfer project and, hence, considered the most important benefits. However, this study showed that firms reported other important spillover benefits, which are *skills and knowledge acquisition* and *discovery of additional improvement opportunities*. All three types of benefits (i.e., operational and learning benefits) were found to be significantly correlated with the financial benefits of the project.

For projects with high technical uncertainty or high organizational uncertainty, training and cross functional teams were found to have a significant contribution to skills and knowledge acquisition. While systematic learning from past experiences did not contribute to this learning benefit, it was significantly and positively affected by experimentation for projects with low organizational uncertainty. The other learning benefit, namely *discovery of additional improvement opportunities* was significantly affected by training and cross functional teams for high levels of technical and organizational uncertainty.

| Table 1. Results of Testing Hypotheses | | |
|---|---|---|
| Hypothesis | Relationship | Results |
| 1 | Prior Technical Knowledge and Operational Benefits | Rejected |
| 2 | Technical Uncertainty *moderates* Rel. between Prior Technical Knowledge and Operational Benefits | Rejected |
| 3 | Prior Organizational Knowledge and Operational Benefits | Rejected |
| 4 | Organizational Uncertainty *moderates* Rel. between Prior Organizational Knowledge and Operational Benefits | Rejected |
| 5 | Experimentation and Operational Benefits | Supported |
| 6 | Technical Uncertainty *moderates* Rel. between Experimentation and Operational Benefits | Rejected |
|  | *High* Technical Uncertainty *moderates* Rel. between Experimentation and Operational Benefits | Partially Supported |
| 7 | Organizational. Uncertainty *moderates* Rel. between Experimentation and Operational Benefits | Rejected |
| 10A | Training and Cross Functional Teams and Skills and Knowledge Acquisition | Supported |
| 11A | Tech. Uncertainty *moderates* Rel. between Training and Cross Functional Teams and Skills and Knowledge Acquisition | Rejected |
|  | *High* Technical Uncertainty *moderates* Rel. between Training and Cross Functional Teams and Skills and Knowledge Acquisition | Supported |
| 11B | Organizational. Uncertainty *moderates* Rel. between Training and Cross Functional Teams and Skills and Knowledge Acquisition | Rejected |
|  | *High* Organizational. Uncertainty *moderates* Rel. between Training and Cross Functional Teams and Skills and Knowledge | Supported |
| 12 | Systematic Learning from Past Experience and Discovery of Additional Improvement Opportunities | Rejected |
| 13 | Tech. Uncertainty *moderates* Rel. between Systematic Learning from Past Experience and Discovery of Additional Improvement Opportunities | Rejected |
| 14 | Organizational. Uncertainty *moderates* Rel. between Systematic Learning from Past Experience and Discovery of Additional Improvement Opportunities | Rejected |

The strategic importance of the project to the recipient firm was the only contextual variable that had a significant impact on the results of this study. However, strategic importance played a role quite similar to the one played by organizational uncertainty. That is, the greater the strategic importance of a project, the greater the organizational uncertainty seems to be. Moreover, the prior performance of the recipient firm was not significantly correlated with the learning activities, hence providing no evidence that past success acted as a "tranquilizer" and a barrier to organizational learning.

In addition, the study did not produce conclusive evidence about the effect of prior organizational knowledge and frequency of interactions with the university. Prior organizational knowledge apparently was not adequately measured. Similarly, frequency of interactions should be adequately measured in future studies. The literature on strategic alliances (e.g. Parkhe, 1993), for instance, provides usable instruments and empirical results that would help researchers explore the impact of the frequency of interactions on project performance.

**Table 2.** Summary of which Levels and Types of Uncertainty Influence the Relationships between the Learning Activities and the Technology Transfer Benefits

| | Operational Benefits | | | Training and Cross Functional Teams | | | Discovery of Additional Improvement Opportunities | | |
|---|---|---|---|---|---|---|---|---|---|
| | Expr.[a] | TCFT[b] | SLPE[c] | Expr. | TCFT | SLPE | Expr. | TCFT | SLPE |
| All Cases (N = 120)[d] | (+) | | (+) | (+) | (+) | | | | |
| High Technical Uncertainty | (+) | | | | (+) | | | (+) | |
| Low Technical Uncertainty | | | (+) | | | | | | |
| High Organizational Uncertainty | | (+) | (−) | | (+) | | | (+) | |
| Low Organizational Uncertainty | (+) | | (+) | (+) | | | | | |

[a] Experimentation
[b] Training and Cross Functional Teams
[c] Systematic Learning from Past Experiences
[d] This row shows the direct effects after controlling for strategic importance and for uncertainty.

## CONCLUSIONS

Although the nature of this study is exploratory, the results obtained provide valuable prescriptions for more successful technology transfer projects. While firms are usually told to implement a variety of organizational learning activities at all times (i.e., the more the better), this study showed that some activities should be emphasized over others in certain conditions. This is because learning activities were found to play a different role under different conditions. These conditions relate primarily to the degree and type of uncertainty perceived by the firm at the beginning of the project. This study suggests the following:

(1) High technical uncertainty: In these projects, firms should emphasize experimentation to increase operational benefits, while also emphasizing training and cross functional teams to acquire new skills and knowledge and discover additional improvement opportunities.

(2) High organizational uncertainty: In these projects, firms should establish training programs and cross functional teams to increase operational benefits, enhance skills and knowledge acquisition, and discover additional improvement opportunities. However, in these projects, firms should also identify counter-productive lessons and "unlearn" them. Firms can also enhance operational benefits by starting such projects with a high level of prior technical knowledge about the existing technology.

(3) Low technical uncertainty: In these projects, firms could increase their operational benefits from the project by having a systematic procedure for learning from past experiences. Given that projects involving incremental technological change are generally more frequent than radical ones, firms should establish a systematic way of learning from past experiences for these projects. In addition, these firms should continuously re-evaluate the lessons learned to eliminate (i.e., unlearn) the counter-productive ones.

(4) Low organizational uncertainty: In these projects, firms should emphasize experimentation to increase operational benefits as well as skills and knowledge acquisition. Systematic learning from past experiences, however, would only contribute to the operational benefits.

In general, firms should understand what type of knowledge the learning activity is intended to create. This understanding, combined with an understanding of the type and level of uncertainty faced at the beginning of the project, would permit the firm to emphasize and enhance the appropriate learning activities to achieve a high level of the desired benefits. For instance, if at the beginning of the project a firm determines that it is facing high technical uncertainty and low organizational uncertainty, then that firm should emphasize experimentation as the primary learning activity. This can be achieved, for instance, by acquiring adequate simulation skills and technology to run useful experiments.

In comparison, if at the beginning of the project a firm determines that it is facing considerable organizational uncertainty, then that firm should plan for extensive training and the establishment of cross functional teams, while unlearning dysfunctional lessons and poor ways of doing work. Moreover, the firm should verify that project definition choices are made based on a high level of technical knowledge about the existing technology. Although this study found prior organizational knowledge to have non-significant effects on any of the project benefits, Chew et. al. (1989) and Grant et. al. (1991) explained the considerable value of "organizational prototyping," which is a tool for the anticipation of potential organizational challenges and opportunities. This tool considers prior organizational knowledge as a key ingredient for informed and knowledgeable prototyping and diagnosis. However, following the results of this study, such prototyping may be unnecessary in all situations.

Perhaps the most important contribution of this research is that it is one of few empirical studies on organizational learning. This research also presented empirical evidence of the value of learning activity and prior knowledge to technology transfer projects, thereby bridging the gap between the technology transfer and organizational learning fields.

**Statistical Evidence and Tables are Available Upon Request.**

**References are Available Upon Request.**

*Biographical Sketches of the Authors*:

*Michael P. Hottenstein* is a Professor of Operations Management at Penn State University. He received his D.B.A. from Indiana University. His research is focused on manufacturing strategy and the management of advanced technology. He is co-director of the inter-college masters program in Quality and Manufacturing Management and associate director of the Center for the Management of Technological and Organizational Change.

*Abdelkader Daghfous*, is a Ph.D Candidate at Penn State University's Department of Management Science and Information Systems. He received his B.S. in Industrial Engineering from Penn State, and his M.S. in Industrial Engineering from the University of Pittsburgh, Pennsylvania, USA. His current research interests include technology management, technology transfer, and innovation.

# 094

## MECHANISMS FOR COMMERCIALIZING UNIVERSITYRESEARCH: A STUDY OF SELECTED UNIVERSITY PROGRAMS IN THE U.S.

Author:
Sarfraz A. Mian, Associate Professor, School of Business,
State University of New York at Oswego, Oswego, NY 13126 USA.

Co-Author:
Walter H. Plosila, Executive Director, State of North Carolina's Alliance
for Competitive Technologies (NC ACTs) at Research Triangle Park,
Durham, NC 27709, USA.

ABSTRACT

The mission of modern entrepreneurial universities go beyond
their primary responsibilities in teaching, research and public service to
include transfer and commercialization of research results to the
industrial sector. Major breeding grounds for new technology are the
research activities occurring at universities and how competitive a
country remains in the world's economy will depend in part on how
efficiently new technology is developed and commercialized through
universities. University technology transfer and subsequent
commercialization in a very complicated process warranting teaming up
with various industrial and governmental actors.
In the U.S, commercialization of university research is one of the
most important and controversial approaches to technology transfer.
However, there are new mandates from the national and state
governments to promote technology transfer by supporting
technological entrepreneurship as a way of rebuilding economic
competitiveness, and of recouping -- in more direct way -- something
from the public's massive investment in education and research.
This research was initiated to examine the organizational and policy
mechanisms for achieving the optimal commercial value from the
university research results in the United States. Several mechanisms
have been employed for this purpose including: licensing office, spin-off
companies, incubators/ science parks, equity/ venture capital,
technology ferreting and information dissemination. There are 2 key
questions the research will address (1) what are the various mechanisms
which have been employed for supporting the commercialization of
university research results, and (2) what are the emerging trends in
program design. The study method comprises of a survey of the selected
programs using a questionnaire followed by personal interviews. Where
ever necessary the data will be augmented through secondary sources.
The article after reviewing the various selected university
research commercialization models will take stock of the determinants of
success of each mechanism studied. The conclusions on more popular
mechanisms will serve as a guide in program design and improvements.

Key Words: university research results, commercialization mechanisms

# 095

## THE ECONOMIC EVALUATION OF TELEMATIC PROJECTS: PROBLEMS AND METHODS

Author:
Enrico Scarso
Istituto di Ingegneria Gestionale- Univeristy of Padova
Viale X Giugno, 22  I-36100 VICENZA   Italy

Co-Author
Bolsisani Ettore
Istituto di Ingegneria Gestionale- Univeristy of Padova
Viale X Giugno, 22   I-36100 VICENZA   Italy

## ABSTRACT

The advent of the advanced manufacturing technologies (i.e. CAD, CAM, FMS) has triggered in the early eighties a deep revision of the traditional economic evaluation techniques, *in primis*  DCF analysis. Starting from the well know deficiencies showed by the conventional thinking" in evaluating new technologies (Scarso, 1996), many alternative approaches have been searched for. Even if not yet completed, these efforts have till now yielded appreciable results, as the vast body of theoretical and empirical literature (Liberatore, 1990 Proctor and Canada, 1992) confirms.
At a distance of fifteen years, similar or more complex questions seem to arise again about the evaluation of large telematic investment projects, like for example Electronic Data Interchange (EDI) Systems. Actually these applications have strong strategic implications, and imply a deep organizational re-engineering so that their costs and benefits can be very difficulty evaluated. In addition their effective implementation involve a large number of different and autonomous economic agents, whose features and behavior influence the investment's success.
This paper aims at analyzing and discussing the main problems Ir' the evaluation of telematic projects, with a particular focus on EDI systems. Issues that should be taken into account in the appraisal of costs and benefits of these projects, as well as the key decision variables that should be considered, will be singled out. A critical examinafion of advantages and limits of traditional and non-traditional methods (e.g. multiattribute and multicriteria techniques, options pricing, and so on) in evaluating these kind of projects will be also carried out.

# The Economic Evaluation of Telematic Projects: Problems and Methods

## 1. Introduction

The advent of advanced manufacturing technologies (i.e. CAD, CAM, FMS) has triggered in the early eighties a deep revision of the traditional economic evaluation techniques, *in primis* DCF analysis. Starting from the well known deficiencies shown by the "conventional thinking" in justifying new technologies (Scarso, 1996), many alternative approaches have been searched for. Even if not yet completed, these efforts have till now yielded appreciable results, as the great deal of literature in this area confirms.

At a distance of fifteen years, similar or more complex questions seem to arise again with regard to the evaluation of large telematic projects, for example Electronic Data Interchange (EDI) systems. Telematic applications, in fact, not only have strong strategic implications, but also involve deep organizational changes; not to mention that their effective implementation entails a large number of different and autonomous economic agents, whose features and behavior influence the project's outcomes. They are all facts that make the economic justification of telematic systems a very intricate process. Without doubt, some useful indications to face this issue could be drawn from the literature concerning the strategic value of Information Systems/Information Technology (IS/IT) investments: but the involved questions and resulting difficulties are not precisely the same.

In light of these considerations, the paper analyzes and discusses the main problems a decision maker is confronted with when evaluating telematic projects. A specific attention on EDI systems is devoted. In particular, it aims at investigating the factors that should be taken into account in the appraisal of costs and benefits of these projects, and examines the decision criteria and methods that can be employed. The paper is organized as follows: section 2 recalls the primary features of EDI projects and focuses on the central questions the justification of EDI technologies raises. Section 3 highlights the shortcomings of conventional techniques and the necessity of formal justification analysis. Section 4 makes a critical examination of advantages and limits of two quantitative evaluation methods (*Analytic Hierarchy Process* and *Option Pricing Theory*) when appraising complex telematic investment projects. Section 5 draws some summarizing indications about the critical issues and the open challenges in the assessment of EDI projects.

## 2. Features of an EDI network and critical aspects in economic evaluation

Electronic Data Interchange is a particular type of Interorganizational Information System (Barrett and Konsinsky, 1982) that allows the direct computer-to-computer information exchange of standardized messages without the need of human intermediation. EDI communication requires a complete agreement not only on the content and meaning of electronic messages, but also on the modality of using the exchanged information (Brousseau, 1994). Even if the benefits of this technology have often been associated to the money and time savings deriving from the dematerialization of documents, the main feature of EDI is that it allows the automation of business transactions among trade partners. This offers considerable strategic opportunities to adopting firms but, at the same time, has a deep strategic and organizational impact.

In the last years the problem of evaluating the effects of EDI has been widely addressed in literature (Mukhopadyay, 1993; Kokuryo, 1994; Mukhopadyay *et al.*, 1995). These studies have contributed to understand the real nature of benefits and costs associated with this technology. However, an open challenge still remains concerning the quantitative *ex-ante evaluation* of EDI investments that should constitute an effective basis for management decisions. The various empirical studies currently available on EDI experiences all over the world (for a survey see e.g. Gottardi and Bolisani, 1996) are sufficient enough to underline some of the critical aspects in the ex-ante evaluation of this technology. It is on the basis of these studies that we will examine the different features that characterize an EDI network (according to the specific conditions and decisions of interconnecting firms) and identify the critical elements that affect the economic justification of the various options that can be adopted by firms.

## 2.1. EDI projects characteristics

*A. Network configuration and project leadership* (fig. 1). The simplest EDI connection is a bilateral linkage between two firms (TEDIS, 1992): for example a buyer and a supplier. The leadership in the project can be assumed by one of the participants, depending on the relative contractual power. When projects involve many partners, the network configuration can assume various forms. In manufacturing sectors, the most diffused and effective one is the so-called "hub-spoke" network, characterized by a leader firm (the hub, in general a large firm, e.g. a buyer) intending to establish a connection with a number of selected partners (the spokes, e.g. suppliers). In this situation the project is almost entirely designed and governed by the hub, capable to sustain the major costs of the system and to diffuse or impose it to the partners.

| Key characteristics | Possible options | |
| --- | --- | --- |
| NETWORK CONFIGURATION | - bilateral communication<br>- hub-spoke networks | - community projects<br>- open projects |
| EXCHANGED MESSAGES | - administrative documents<br>- logistic-operational documents | - financial notes<br>- commercial documents |
| EXTENT OF USE | - from door-to-door EDI to full-scale solutions | |
| MESSAGE STANDARD | - private standard<br>- sectorial standard | - public standard |
| SCOPE OF COMMUNICATION | - administrative efficiency<br>- communication speed<br>- inventory reduction | - market information<br>- customer service<br>- control over partners |

*fig. 1. Key characteristics of an EDI network*

We will limit our analysis to these two cases, where a leading subject that promotes and implements the system can be identified. We will consider the justification problem from the point of view of that subject; this allows us to face a reasonable degree of complexity of analysis. It is worth noting that EDI projects can also assume other configurations, where an evident leadership cannot be identified; in such situations the evaluation complexity grows. This is the case of *cooperative projects* when decisions regarding the system must be made under the direct involvement of all participants: *community projects*, with a large number of heterogeneous participants, promoted typically by a "super partes" organization (e.g. a trade association), and the so-called *open projects* promoted by public organizations in order to improve communication in particular business sectors.

*B. Exchanged messages*. Different types of electronic documents can be exchanged: administrative (e.g. invoices); logistic-operational (orders, order plans, stock levels); financial (payments, debit/credit notes); commercial (price lists, offer enquiries); and others. The exchange of each type of document has a different organizational impact. For example, the management of electronic invoices mainly concerns the administrative procedures, but the automatic transmission of orders or stock levels strongly impacts the purchasing procedures and the operations management routines. Furthermore, the "electronization" of business messages requires a

564

predefinition of the message content and a standardization of operational routines among interconnected partners. This can imply high costs and a long learning process especially when high volumes of EDI messages are exchanged among various partners.

*C. Extent of use.* Obviously the more extended is the use of EDI, the more complex is the system and its economic appraisal. Extent of use can be associated to: 1. the number of interconnected firms; 2. the range of exchanged electronic documents; 3. the volumes of "EDI-zated" transactions; 4. the penetration in the internal organization. At a minimum, an adopter can use a "door-to-door" connection with one or few partners: there is no connection with the internal information system, and a simple PC is used to receive the electronic messages that are then printed, and *viceversa* these are manually digited and transmitted. This is the easiest and less expensive type of EDI connection, and in general it is used by the smaller "spoke" firms especially in the initial steps of the project. Of course, door-to-door EDI does not allow the exploitation of the effective advantages of automated transactions (Riggins and Mukhopadyay, 1994). Instead, in a full-scale EDI system a significant volume of transaction documents with a number of partners are automatically exchanged and managed by the internal information system, thus by-passing the human intermediation.

*D. EDI message standard.* The automatic communication requires a complete agreement among partners on the structure, content and meaning of electronic messages. There exist various options in the definition of the *EDI message standard*. A *private standard* is defined as an exclusive communication within a closed group of partners, and therefore it is best targeted to the specific needs of a given network. However, the costs of standard development entirely weigh on network participants (in particular, on the hub-firm); furthermore, a targeted private standard reduces the flexibility of the network to future changes, and strongly limits an eventual interconnection with other networks. In order to avoid such problems and reduce the costs of implementation, *sectorial standards* (e.g. ODETTE for the European automotive sector) are developed through cooperation of various EDI groups. A sectorial standard constitutes a framework for EDI use in a specific sector and favors interconnection of different networks. In any case, an adaptation process is required within the specific network of users. By extension, the so-called *public standards* (e.g. EDIFACT for Europe, ANSI X.12 for the U.S.) should represent a general framework for the development of totally compatible EDI networks in all trade sectors, thus favoring the development of connections even for the smaller firms. However, the possibility of defining a general-purpose EDI standard is questionable, also conceptually (Brousseau, 1994); therefore public standards can only represent a sort of "metastandards" (David and Foray, 1994) that facilitate the process of standard definition by single users groups.

*E. Scopes of EDI communication.* Different kinds of aims can be pursued:
- administrative efficiency: dematerialization of documents reduces office time, costs and errors;
- communication speed: times between the various activities are shortened;
- inventory reduction: the rapid information and automation of transactions permit a more accurate planning of supply and delivery; a more rapid stock rotation can also be obtained;
- market information: more accurate and timely sales data can be collected and made available for decisions at various levels;
- customer service: this could derive from a reduction of errors and delivery times;
- control over partners: the EDI connection, in that requires a high inter-organizational standardization, can be used by a hub-firm to make relations with partners more stable.

Benefits and costs associated to each aim are different, as much as the evaluation problems that rise. For example, administrative efficiency can be measured on the basis of office costs reduction; but this kind of benefit is actually less significant than the others. More relevant advantages, like inventory reduction or better customer service, even if they can be estimated on the basis of costs and times decrease, are very difficult to assess in advance (Mukhopadyay *et al.*, 1995).

## 2.2. Critical aspects in EDI evaluation

As we said, various works have studied and classified the different costs and benefits (fig. 2) that would be associated with EDI implementation and use (Banerjee and Golhar, 1994; Scala and McGrath, 1994; Mukhopadyay *et al.*, 1995; Riggins *et al.*, 1995).

| COSTS IN EDI DEVELOPMENT AND USE | POSSIBLE TYPES OF BENEFITS |
|---|---|
| - *building (or adapting)* *the application infrastructure* - *purchasing hardware and software* - *telecommunication services* - *development of EDI message standard* - *development of internal expertise* - *training of users* - *organizational reengineering* - *(inter)organizational implementation* *and management of the network* - *network maintenance and development* | - *reduced costs and times in document* *generation and transmission* - *reduced errors in document handling* - *improved speed of communication* - *inventory reduction* - *better customer service* - *improved information on the market* - *quick response to the market* - *better control on the supply* - *improved relations along the value chain* |

*fig. 2. Costs and benefits associated to EDI*
*(various sources)*

A quick examination is sufficient enough to highlight how much complex the evaluation may be. In particular, the following critical aspects can be identified (fig. 3).

*Strategic dimension.* As aforementioned, the implementation of EDI should imply a strategic evaluation of competitive EDI worth. A medium-long term perspective should be considered. Various studies (e.g. Holland *et al.*, 1992; Brousseau, 1994) argue that, due to its nature, EDI cannot be used for occasional trade relations in the short term; on the contrary the technology implies relatively stables links among interconnected partners. In some sectors (a well-known case is automotive) EDI constitutes a fundamental support for the implementation of wide strategic programs, e.g. Just In Time or Efficient Customer Response. A strategic assessment is therefore a necessary element of an EDI project evaluation (Mukhopadyay, 1993).

*(Inter)organizational impact.* One of the main problems in EDI evaluation derives from the organizational impact. The deep reengineering of internal procedures and external inter-firm relations that EDI requires raises several problems for a correct evaluation of costs and benefits.

*Costs/benefits interdependence.* The specific characteristic of this technology must be taken into account when it has to be evaluated how costs and benefits are (or should be) shared among interconnecting firms. A first problem regards the benefits that can derive from participating in an EDI network; in principle, these benefits, just like all telematic technologies, could be associated to positive externalities for the interconnecting firms. The traditional concept of "critical mass" states that payoffs for participating in a network should increase with the number of previous participants. However, this seems to be at least in part inapplicable to EDI (Wang and Seidmann, 1995). In fact, effective EDI connections can be used also among few participants; in many cases, this number is willingly limited. Instead, other elements seem to have a more significant weight, e.g. the volume of exchanged messages between partners and the role and identity of each of these participants. Another relevant question is how costs and benefits

566

should be subdivided among partners. In a hub-spoke project, the major costs of project definition are sustained by the leader firm. But also the spokes have an adoption cost and, if the benefit for these subjects is not really significant, they can be reluctant to accept the connection. In this case incentivation policies must be adopted by the hub (Wang and Seidmann, 1995; Riggins *et al.*, 1994), but this implies additional costs to be considered and evaluated.

*Learning and uncertainty.* As we said, given to the deep strategic and organizational impact of the technology, a standard "market" solution for all the possible needs of potential users is quite impossible. Each EDI solution is implemented through a step-by-step process that can last various years, starting from a pilot application that generates scarce economic results, but is necessary for testing the potential of the technology and for developing the adequate network solutions. A learning process is activated, in consequence of the final network configuration and the results that are obtained can be significantly different from those expected in the starting phase. For this reason a high uncertainty necessarily affects the ex-ante design of an EDI network.

*Tangible versus intangible costs/benefits.* The *identification* of the sources of costs and benefits, and the *quantification* of their possible economic value, are affected by various problems. Some costs and benefits can be easily evaluated, e.g. costs of equipment and telecommunication or benefits deriving from a reduction of paper use. However, this can solve only a small part of the problem. The majority of costs, e.g. the organizational reengineering, are difficult to identify and evaluate; similarly, benefits deriving for example from the strategic use of EDI can in part be identified and are very difficult to evaluate.

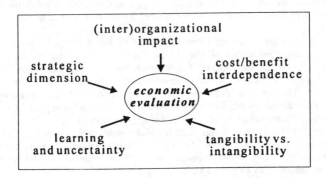

*fig. 3. Critical elements in economic evaluation of EDI*

## 3. EDI projects evaluation: limits of traditional methods and need of a formal analysis

As previously said, given the strong similarities between the two technologies, referring to the literature on the economic value of IS/IT may be a good starting point for facing the justification of EDI projects. Studies in this field, in fact, have deeply considered this topic, even if not always under the same perspective that we have assumed. A quite recent and comprehensive bibliography on the literature about the strategic and economic value of Information Technology can be found in Banker *et al.* (1993).

Generally speaking, almost all the IS/IT studies start from the pitfalls that the traditional capital budgeting techniques exhibit when applied to the evaluation of this kind of project. The various authors substantially agree on the fact that current capital budgeting practices may understate the business value of IT investments (Kriebel, 1993) to such a point that induces the firm not to pursue them. This is not the place to discuss all the criticisms, and we only remember the most important ones, according to the critical aspects described in figure 3.

The first point is that, since conventional techniques concentrate almost exclusively on tangible financial criteria, they are unsatisfactory in identifying and quantifying all available benefits; they also do not (or incompletely) address organizational and behavioral factors (Bacon, 1992). Secondly, the fact that these techniques require the exact knowledge of all the data, i.e. time and amount of cash flows, makes them totally ineffective in dealing with uncertainty and risk. The third point is that they treat projects as isolated investment opportunities about which a decision must be made immediately; thus, they do not allow a full appraisal of benefits deriving from the active management of projects. Moreover, they implicitly assume the existence of the "null alternative", i.e. the maintenance of the *status quo*: this is not only a glaringly naive assumption, as Clemons and Weber (1990) affirm, but also an unreasonable and hazardous hypothesis, especially because to effectively take advantage of EDI opportunities, change must place in the way of doing business activities or using information (Ward *et al.*, 1996).

All these shortcomings make this analysis not very helpful in evaluating projects as telematic investments, just because they generally yield benefits that involve changes inside the firm and its position in the industry (Toraskar and Joglekar, 1993; Post *et al.*, 1995). Nonetheless, difficulties in justifying an investment for which the value now seems indisputable should not be surprising. All summed up, in fact, basic problems with standard DCF analysis do not stand in its rationale, but in the fact that future benefits and impact on competitiveness are difficult to forecast in a dynamic environment, made even more turbulent by the nature itself of the technology under evaluation.

Starting from these considerations, the literature has developed two opposing views in considering quantitative analysis (Bacon, 1992). The former is that this analysis is neither feasible nor useful, given the insurmountable difficulties linked to an acceptable quantification of intangible benefits. The latter imposes a measurable approach, thus partially denying the reality of soft benefits. The resulting dichotomy implies the choices between accepting that IT and telematics investments are not different and standard techniques are applicable, or admitting that they are very different and new methodologies must be developed.

Our propensity, instead, is for a intermediate view, which puts together tangibles and intangibles, and tries to make the best use of the currently available evaluation techniques. More specifically, we think that important investments, as the adoption of telematic technologies, have always to be subjected to a rigorous justification process.

Investing, in fact, cannot be an act of faith (Kaplan, 1986), especially when huge sums are concerned. If it is accepted, according to Clemons and Weber (1992), that large IT investments like EDI projects may produce both big losses and gains, the whole decision cannot be driven by managerial feelings or generic strategic imperatives. Secondly, performing a formal evaluation of an EDI project: a) helps a preliminary identification of all the factors affecting the project outcomes; this seems a crucial issue according to what we discussed in the previous section; and b) puts the basis for a more effective audit of the investment results. Hence, we claim the exigency of a formal analysis, following the suggestions of authors like Bacon (1992) who underlines that "there is an increasing need to more rigorous analysis and justification, comparable to that undertaken for other investments".

In any case, a key question remains the selection of the "right" method or approach that can be used for evaluation. Powell (1992) affirms that the existence of many methodologies suggests that the field is already a little crowded and that a "new" method would likely add little. If this statement is shared, the matter is to investigate the available appraisal techniques in order to find the most appropriate one relating to the specific problem under evaluation. This is the reason why in the following section we will analyze two quite recent quantitative approaches that could support a formal evaluation of EDI projects. It is worth noting that they are general approaches, in the sense that they have not been specifically developed for evaluating IT or telematic projects. In this sense, they can be part of the common appraisal toolkit of a decision maker.

## 4. Quantitative approaches for EDI evaluation

In the light of the questions raised in section 2, we think that there are two methods which could positively support the appraisal of EDI projects. The first is the Analytic Hierarchy Process (AHP), which seems particularly useful when one has to consider several and interdependent difficult-to-quantify benefits (the right side of figure 3). The second is the Options Pricing Theory (OPT), which has been suggested by the investment appraisal literature as a tool able to take into account the strategic dimension of the project, and its uncertainty content (the left side of figure 3). It is worth noting that the interorganizational impact of the technology is not explicitly taken into account by the two methods; in any way, we think that it requires the evaluation of highly specific elements that must be dealt with in a "case-by-case" approach.

*AHP.* The *Analytic Hierarchy Process* is a complex and formal method for representing and quantifying intangible factors. It describes the problem in a hierarchical form, and helps the decision maker in weighing investment attributes by means of systematic comparisons (Saaty, 1980). In substance, the problem is broken down into levels, where the first represents the overall objective and the second is the criteria (attributes) conceived as important in achieving the overall objective; the set of alternatives to be evaluated are on the bottom level. Then the decision maker's preferences (i.e. the input data) are obtained by pairwise comparisons in which there is a comparison of items at the same hierarchical level regarding their relative importance with respect to a specific item at the next highest level. This quite apparent simplicity hides some pitfalls. In particular, no theoretical framework exists for structuring problems into hierarchies, so that two decision makers evaluating the same problem may arrive at different hierarchies. Additional shortcomings concern the questions asked in making comparisons, their number, the suggested scale for measuring them, and the nature of the normalization process that leads to the final outcome (whose logic is not transparent), which produces the rank reversal phenomenon when the introduction of a new alternative causes reversal in the rank of the old ones.

AHP has proven to be both a quite user-friendly and flexible tool, able to deal with different problems (as the rapid growth of practical applications testifies). Referring to our question, AHP seems to be especially useful when one has to resort to subjective judgments (which can be given only in a relative way), or when the assessment requires an extensive and detailed analysis involving a great number of different and heterogeneous factors. These situations characterize EDI projects, whose costs and benefits, as aforementioned, are many and difficult to identify and evaluate, like most of the elements shown in figure 2 are. As we said, it can be argued that AHP would possibly represent a way for facing the key elements in EDI evaluation described on the right side of figure 3, that are: the problem of evaluating intangible and interrelated costs and benefits. In any case, AHP primarily helps in structuring the decision problem (i.e. recognizing and organizing all the elements that affects the final decision), so that its main value lies in its process of formalizing the decision analysis rather than in the resulting outcomes.

*OPT.* In 1984 Kester used the term *growth options* to denote future growth opportunities that each new investment project carries out. Afterwards, the option concept was more often suggested for issues as uncertainty and flexibility, where the latter means the ease to modify a project during its execution with the aim of adapting it to changed business or technical conditions. Hence, this conceptual device has provided several analytical and explanatory aids in the field of technology investments selection, being able to account for uncertainty and irreversibility, and to explicitly recognize that time affects the investment value.

According to the option framework, the investment decision is treated as the decision to exercise a financial option, in that the new investment is evaluated on the basis of the present and future opportunities it discloses. An obstacle of the actual use of this procedure is that the majority of the applications are till now essentially limited to investment projects whose cash flows are based on quoted resource prices. Hence, financial models can be applied in only limited situations (and for very specific options), that is when market values of the investment project are obtainable. Also the simplified binomial pricing model does not allow overcoming some of these limits. Moreover, it is still a little known tool, and consequently it may be subject to great misunderstanding: the risk is to over-estimate the option (or strategic) value of the project with respect to its "traditional present worth".

Beyond all limits, this approach shows some promising properties. First, it may resolve some of the questions raised by traditional techniques, as the choice of the risk adjusted discount rate and the difficulties connected with considering all the possible cash flow outcomes. Second, it provides an opportunity for the evaluation of the flexible character of new technologies and of the learning processes involved in their implementation. Although, the most important feature of this approach is its logical coherence with the firm's economic value. In fact, it is accepted that the project does not produce only cash flows but also future business opportunities. The "options thinking" brings a new view of uncertainty and risk: while the old perspective favors a prudent behavior, this one forces to profit from uncertainty. Lastly, when the adoption of a new technology is considered, the option approach may be the correct framework within choosing the adoption timing, which is an absolutely important question of strategy (Scarso, 1996). In this way one can avoid the mistake that Clemons and Weber (1990) underline, that is to overlook the timing value when evaluating IT investment.

OPT has found several applications in the field of IT investments evaluation (e.g. Do Santos, 1991; Kambil et al., 1993; Kumar, 1996), which can be referred to the case of complex telematic projects like EDI. In particular, OPT can be considered a good framework when projects are realized in several steps. This particularly fits EDI projects, that are implemented through subsequent stages (starting from a pilot application) and require a long development process. In any way, this approach helps in highlighting the intrinsic *strategic nature* of telematics and EDI investments, thus favoring their appraisal. Finally, OPT could be proposed for facing the critical elements in EDI evaluation reported on the left side of figure 3, that are the strategic dimension of this application and the high level of uncertainty that derives from a complex learning process. They are issues whose implications are difficult to estimate in advance.

## 5. Conclusions

Establishing the economic value of telematic projects is a challenge with no simple answer. This evaluation, in fact, is very problematic both because the costs and benefits are hard to identify and quantify, and the strategic potential of telematic systems like EDI is a controversial issue. These facts raise big questions, especially when one wants to apply the conventional evaluation techniques, as DCF analysis. Nevertheless, the need to conduct a formal and rigorous economic analysis is not negated: on the contrary, given the dimension of the involved sums, the development of a systematic and rational planning process for telematic investments can be considered to be an imperative. If it is so, the question shifts to the methods which are the most adequate to perform this kind of assessment. The present paper shows that AHP and OPT can be useful techniques, in that they allow to take into account some of the main characteristics of EDI projects. In particular, it implicitly suggests a combined use of these methods, as a way to overcome the different kinds of evaluation difficulties. The previous considerations, however, do not exhaust the question. On the contrary they claim further research, aiming to empirically verify the previous methods in order to evaluate their practical applicability in real cases of EDI projects appraisal.

## Acknowledgments
This study arises by the research project "Nuove tecnologie dell'informazione e distretti industriali" supported by a contribution from CNR (National Research Council)

## References

Bacon C.J., 1992, "The Use of Decision Criteria in Selecting Information Systems/Technology Investments", *MIS Quarterly*, September

Banerjee S. and Golhar D.Y., 1994, "Electronic data interchange; Characteristics of users and nonusers", *Information & Management*, No. 26

Banker R.D., Kauffman R.J. and Mahmood M.A. (eds.), 1993, *Strategic Information Technology Management: Perspectives on Organizational Growth and Competitive Advantage*, Idea Group Publishing, Harrisburg

Barrett S. and Konsinsky B., 1982, "Inter-Organization Information Sharing Systems", *MIS Quarterly*, Special Issue

Brousseau E., 1994, "EDI and inter-firm relationships: toward a standardization of coordination processes?", *Information Economics and Policy*, Vol. 6, No. 4

Clemons E.K. and Weber B.W., 1990, "Strategic Information Technology Investments: Guidelines for Decision Making", *Journal of Management Information Systems*, Vol. 7, No. 2

David P.A. and Foray D., 1994, "Percolation structures, Markov random fields and the economics of EDI standards diffusion", in Pogorel G. (ed.), *Global Telecommunication Strategies and Technological Change*, North-Holland, Amsterdam

Dos Santos B.L., 1991, "Justifying Investments in New Information Technologies", *Journal of Management Information Systems*, Vol. 7, No. 4

Gottardi G. and Bolisani E., 1996, "A critical perspective on information technology management: the case of electronic data interchange", *International Journal of Technology Management*, Vol. 12, No. 4

Holland C., Lockett G. and Blackman I., 1992, "Planning for electronic data interchange", *Strategic Management Journal*, No. 13

Kambil A., Henderson J. and Mohsenzadeh H., 1993, "Strategic Management of Information Technology Investments: An Option Perspective", in Banker R.D. *et al.* (eds.), *Strategic Information Technology Management: Perspectives on Organizational Growth and Competitive Advantage*, Idea Group Publishing, Harrisburg

Kaplan R.S., 1986, "Must CIM be justified by faith alone?", *Harvard Business Review*, March-April

Kester W.C., 1984, "Today's options for tomorrow's growth", *Harvard Business Review*, March-April

Kokuryo J., 1994, "The impact of EDI-based quick response systems on logistic systems", in Pogorel G. (ed.), *Global Telecommunication Strategies and Technological Change*, North-Holland, Amsterdam

Kriebel C.H., 1993, "Formal Models in Research on IT Investment Evaluation", in Banker R.D. *et al.* (eds.), *Strategic Information Technology Management: Perspectives on Organizational Growth and Competitive Advantage*, Idea Group Publishing, Harrisburg

Kumar R.L., 1996, "A Note on Project Risk and Option Values of Investments in Information Technologies", *Journal of Management Information Systems*, Vol. 13, No. 1

Mukhopadyay T., 1993, "Assessing the Economic Impacts of Electronic Data Interchange Technology", in Banker R.D. *et al.* (eds), *Strategic Information Technology Management*, Idea Group Publishing, Harrisburg

Mukhopadyay T., Kekre S. and Kalathur S., 1995, "Business Value of Information Technology: A Study of Electronic Data Interchange", *MIS Quarterly*, June

Post G.V., Kagan A. and Lau K., 1995, "A Modeling Approach to Evaluating Strategic Uses of Information Technology", *Journal of Management Information Systems*, Vol. 12, No. 2

Powell P., 1992, "Information Technology Evaluation: Is It Different?", *Journal of Operational Research Society*, Vol. 43, No. 1

Riggins F.J. and Mukhopadyay T., 1994, "Interdependent Benefits from Interorganizational Systems: Opportunities for Business Partner Reengineering", *Journal of Management Information Systems*, Vol. 11, No. 2

Riggins F.J., Kriebel C.H. and Mukhopadyay T., 1994, "The Growth of Interorganizational Systems in the Presence of Network Externalities", *Management Science*, Vol. 40, No. 8

Saaty T.L., 1980, *The Analytic Hierarchy Process*, McGraw Hill, New York

Scala S. and McGrath R., 1993, "Advantages and disadvantages of electronic data interchange. An industry perspective", *Information & Management*, No. 25

Scarso E., 1996, "Timing the adoption of a new technology: an option-based approach", *Management Decision*, Vol. 34, No. 3

TEDIS, 1992, *Technical, Organizational and Managerial Aspects of Implementing EDI - Results and Experiences of 12 EDI Pilot Projects*, Commission of the European Communities

Toraskar K. and Joglekar P., 1993, "Applying Cost-benefit Analysis (CBA) Methodology for Information Technology Investment Decisions", in Banker R.D. *et al.* (eds.), *Strategic Information Technology Management: Perspectives on Organizational Growth and Competitive Advantage*, Idea Group Publishing, Harrisburg

Wang E.T.G and Seidmann A., 1995, "Electronic Data Interchange: Competitive Externalities and Strategic Implementation Policies", *Management Science*, Vol. 41, No. 3

Ward J., Taylor P. and Bond P., 1996, "Evaluation and realisation of IS/IT benefits: an empirical study of current practice", *European Journal of Information Systems*, No. 4

# 097

**Author**
Lisbeth Crabo Ljungman
Informatics and Systems Science
University of Stockholm
Vinkelvägen 7A
135 50 TYRESÖ, Sweden

Tel: +46 8 422 0122 or +46 8 712 2887
Fax: +46 8 712 2870

Title of paper:

## Meta systems in a disaggregated industry
will strongly influence product innovation

### Abstract

The paper also points to the necessity to develop processes that will administer and distribute products along with product development especially in the case of incremental and substantial inventions.

The paper deals with complications that will affect product and process development as companies decide to source products and include them in their product portfolio, and also complications that will occur due to outsourcing of functions.

Such complications and development will also have to be taken into account before a decision to start product development.

### Key words
disaggregation, discontinuous, environment, incremental, innovation, meta system, process

I believe the paper is best suited for oral presentation

Topic letter: E, category 3

# 098

# Competitive Advantage as a Link Between Technology Management and Customer Satisfaction-A Conceptual Framework Based on the Experiences on the Product Development of the Manufacturers of Energy Related Electronics Applications

A paper for the sixth international conference on management of technology, 25-28 June 1997, Gothenburg, Sweden.

Ari Maunuksela*
and Simo Keskinen^

*University of Vaasa, Production Economics
P.O. BOX 700, SF-65101 VAASA
FINLAND
Tel. +358-6-3248476
Fax +358-6-3248467
E-mail: ari.maunuksela@uwasa.fi

^Vaasa Institute of Technology, Electrical Engineering

Keywords: technology, customer satisfaction, and competitiveness

## From transactions to customer relationship management

The markets for the energy technology products are demanding. The products are often capital goods and the technical knowledge required in business is high. Depending on the products the length and content of the customer relationships are varying. Frequently the sales and marketing are operating with the same customers from year to year. Besides of the basic product there are also markets and needs for different supporting products (education, analysis, maintenance, operation control..). In the world class companies the business is global. The role of distribution and sales networks are important. The knowledge has to be available to different parties along the value chain with often customised requirements. This paper analyses the concepts and methods related to technology management and customer satisfaction from the perspective of the competitive advantage of a firm. Specially the product development processes in the companies are discussed within the industrial electronics equipment manufacturers as a part of the energy industries. *The objective is to analyse the management of the product development as a part of business organisation. Basic assumption in this paper is that the company specific technology management is implemented in the product development.* As a basic framework of this paper the concepts of customer satisfaction and competitive advantage are considered as relevant management constructs which have important role in the area of technology management. By positioning the discussion into the R&D area of management (specially product development) the idea is to analyse the implementation of the technology management in the firms. Competitiveness is based on markets and from the perspective of this research the suggested change from the transactions based marketing to the relationship approach (Grönroos 1990) is theoretically appropriate way to describe the nature of the specific markets (Picture 1).

**Figure 1.** Change from transactions based marketing to the relationships marketing (Grönroos 1990)

### In search for the new markets and products-Continuing challenge for the R&D

Product development is perhaps the most vital activity of a firm. In the industries where the pace of technological change is fast and uncertain the resources and tasks of product development are very closely related to the competitiveness of a firm. It is possible in fact that the technology strategy of a such firm is used as a competitive strategy for the creation of the competitive advantage to the firm (Porter 1983).

In order to manage product development as a part of the whole R&D it is appropriate to distinguish between different types of objectives (product project, technology assessment). If the R&D activities are managed strategically with the business strategy of a firm it may be appropriate to develop technical strategies for this need. Strategically technology is horizontal and therefore is affecting through the different business processes (Adler and Ferdows 1990, Porter 1983).

A broad synthesis development capability is needed in order to integrate and classify the R&D activities appropriately into a business plan-like approach which is needed if the technical strategies are indeed being used for the competitive management of a firm. Bridging the future technology prospects against the unarticulated customer needs is an example of the issues that must be considered from the skill and capability creation perspective which is eventually the practical side of the technology management. One possible solution to this is to divide the risky and strategic elements of markets and technology into "front-end" processes and the more mature development and performance elements into "back-end" processes which finally deliver the products to the customers (e.g. Meyer-Zack 1996). Following picture presents a synthesis from the recent ideas by Prahalad and Hamel 1994, Klein and Hiscocks 1994, Meyer and Zack 1996 and Miller 1995.

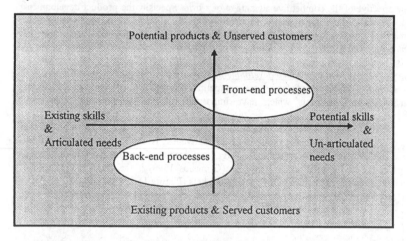

**Picture 2.** A proposed framework for the strategic classification of the R&D activities

Intuitively, competitive advantage is often understood and presented within the context of front-end processes and the creation of the product platform. The customer satisfaction performance is better described with the back-end processes, including the product family performance and related services.

**Customer value management and strategic use of technology**

Elements of the products and processes can be described with quality parameters and costs but the problem is that eventually all such constructs are immaterial and subjectively perceived by the different people. This kind of problems of conception, description and understanding are even more of importance when discussing R&D activities. In many high-tech industries the level of the knowledge exploited in the production is not necessarily high (Bohn 1994). If a firm is developing a totally new-to market product it has also the task of developing the words and concepts describing the new idea in functioning and while being used. On a long run the new terminology is going to be part of the customer satisfaction analysis. This example is just one perspective to the linkages between technology management and customer satisfaction. Without technological content the structure of the knowledge of customer satisfaction and competitive advantage is likely to be invaluable for practical purposes.

*Technology management approach should provide the company with the necessary concepts and structures in order to obtain real knowledge from the customer satisfaction surveys and competitor analysis.*

## Customer satisfaction and competitive advantage

It may be difficult to separate the various factors affecting on customer satisfaction and competitive advantage from each others. By comparing the basic concepts one may argue that competitive advantage has a more absolute effect. Another example of the common features describing competitive advantage and customer satisfaction is that neither of them is likely to change very fast. If we want to craft some type of forecasts with these issues it may be stated that the competitive advantage has more robustness. Competitive advantage places the product of a firm into a relative comparison against possibly competing products. But it is also possible to have other equally important sources of competitive advantage as products. *It might be possible to argue that the competitive advantage of a firm is more often understood through the image of the firm or the products of the firm, emphasising the linkage of the competitive advantage to the firm. Customer satisfaction on the other hand is more often understood through the products and customer groups of the firm.* Both concepts are possible success factors for the firms and perhaps it is one reason why these concepts are often used interchangeably. This implies that the practical meaning of competitive advantage and customer satisfaction is very dependent on the definition. The impact of awareness/perception-factors is important both for the analysis. "We had always assumed that inbound and outbound marketing needed to work from the same segmentation model. We re-examined this assumption and realised that we could use different segmentation models for inbound and outbound marketing as long they were consistent. For example, a factory could build products for the availability/performance segment, while outbound marketing would craft a mainframe-downsizing program for specific industry or application segments (Schnedler 1996: 90-91)."

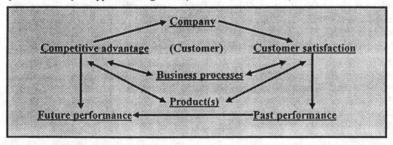

**Picture 4.** A proposed framework for the comparison between competitive advantage and customer satisfaction

## Measurement and analysis of customer satisfaction

Practises of customer satisfaction analysis have been recently critized for many reasons. Two major types of analysis (but inherently very different) are customer satisfaction surveys and the analysis of customer feedback. Customer satisfaction surveys are conducted more on annual bases as the customer feedback is a continuos source of information. Some problems of the customer satisfaction measurement are due to the weak conceptual validity of the constructs (e.g. Wetzel and Maul 1996).

Practically there seldom exists a relevant integration mechanism for the analysis of customer information (Goodman, DePalma and Broetzmann 1996). Another problematic area is to able to link the firms internal performance to the external data. Rosenberg presented five common myths about customer satisfaction: 1) Customer satisfaction is objective, 2) Customer satisfaction is easily measured, 3) Customer satisfaction is accurately measured, 4) Customer satisfaction is quickly and easily changed and 5) It is obvious who the customer is (Rosenberg 1996). It might be argued that the presented critique applies as well to the analysis of competitive advantage.

_Considering the analysis and measurement of customer satisfaction from the perspective of technology management it might be more appropriate to enlarge the content to the analysis of customer value._ First, "customer value analysis-or any other analysis of competitive position-must include any small foreign competitors with new technology" (Gale and Wood 1994). Second, as Miller (1995) pointed out with an example of early prototype testing with several stakeholder groups the concept of customer value management is a more appropriate concept if we prefer to discuss the forthcoming events in product development (customer involvement). _When analysing customer satisfaction concerning product development it is better to emphasise the performance evaluation objectives._ For example, the learning capabilities of an organisation can be indirectly measured by analysing the development of the continuos improvement efforts and results of a firm ( Wetzel and Maul 1996). Some possible metrics concerning product development might be for example: cycle times from idea to customer, and time through R&D (Ellis and Curtis 1995).

_What is the role of the tacit knowledge in the customer satisfaction analysis?_ Eventually much of the critique towards the analysis of customer satisfaction can be explained with the fact that there are too few cases when customer feedback or survey results are directly linked to corrective actions. "Voice of the customer process should yield a specific course of action. Often the failure is to be able to track the impact of the corrective action resulting from the same process (Goodman, DePalma and Broetzman 1996)." Few strategically important issues can be described about "how to proceed in a customer satisfaction analysis". First, start with in-depth interviews with key customers. Second, use a broader survey only when the preliminary work has been done and the problems are defined in sufficient manner (Rosenberg 1996). _Simple criterias of actionability like communicability, deployability and actionability may also be useful._ Finally, there are three customers for the firm to address when measuring satisfaction: consumers/end users, distribution chain customers and downstream operations in their own company (Ellis and Curtis 1995).

**Integration of customer satisfaction and strategic use of technology**

In the analysis of competitive advantage through customer satisfaction and technology management the challenge is to create a synthesis between two different types of management approaches. For example the value based quality paradigm according to Gale and Wood (1994) and the typology of the strategic use of the technology by Morone (1989). In both the core is to focus the appropriate challenges. The next picture describes the two models underlying the following discussion.

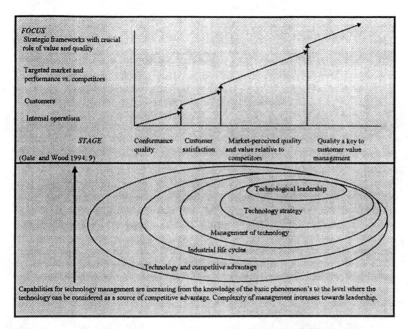

**Picture 5.** Theoretical frameworks of customer value management and technology management (Gale and Wood 1994; Morone 1989)

## Integrated strategic management of the electronics manufacturing firms -Consideration of the Product Development Environment Contingency Factors

This paper limits the strategically important areas to two closely related strategies. First, technology strategy is supposed to be an important part of the strategic management of a firm competing in the world energy equipment markets. Second, the manufacturing strategy is inherently important to the electronics manufacturing companies specifically discussed. "Manufacturing processes are critical enablers of the competitive performance in the electronics industry where technologies and manufacturing processes are being developed and exploited rapidly (Danielsson 1995)." The following excerpt from a product development process description is an example how early in the product development processes the manufacturing issues are already considered.

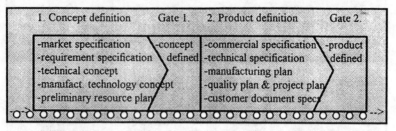

| 1. Concept definition | Gate 1. | 2. Product definition | Gate 2. |
|---|---|---|---|
| -market specification<br>-requirement specification<br>-technical concept<br>-manufact. technology concept<br>-preliminary resource plan | -concept<br>defined | -commercial specification<br>-technical specification<br>-manufacturing plan<br>-quality plan & project plan<br>-customer document spec | -product<br>defined |

**Picture 6.** An example of the content of the energy related electronics equipment product development process

*In practise the technology strategy and manufacturing strategy are likely quite integrated in the energy industries, specifically in related to electronics design and manufacturing. Based on this it is possible to present a hypothesis that the integration of technology and manufacturing strategies may offer some strategic advantages for the firms.* Based on the preliminary results from the research with firms in energy industries this proposition seems very promising. The analysis of product development activities is carried out with the environment contingency factors (factors describing the issues typical to R&D activities in a certain industry) in practise related to the presence of integrated strategic management approaches.

If technology strategy and manufacturing strategy are integrated in the management practise then the content of the technology strategy is broader than it would be otherwise. Technology strategy can be considered as the primary point of interest in this analysis because the more generic nature as opposed to the basically functional approach of the manufacturing strategy. It may imply that the main technological dimensions (Steele 1988) usually included in the strategy are products, manufacturing processes and equipment and also information systems. The analysis of product development in electronics can not be approached with too general assumptions of different success factors. *By comparing the product development processes of electronics in the consumer electronics industries against the energy or industrial electronics it is possible to see that manufacturing is generically included quite early into the processes but it may appear that in the energy industries the firms are actually competing with new technology development capabilities.*

**Management of product development**

What is not necessarily considered as a technological matter is organisation. It is important to analyse the organisation as a purposeful entity which is designed to specific tasks (Drucker 1992). Miller (1995) described the features of the 4th generation R&D practises where the main sources of new competitiveness are based on organisational and personal innovations. *It seems that an ability to manage by a structure (product concept, platforms or strategic architectures) is becoming an important skill for the product development management.* "Human capital, with the capability to acquire knowledge, is the asset that increasingly determines customer satisfaction and competitive advantage (Miller 1995: 26)."

If technology management is being implemented through product development it should be done so that the success factors or similarly critical issues and objectives of company specific technology management are included in the product development management. The divisioning between front-end and back-end processes may offer some guidelines for the selection of the relevant development priorities. The same idea can be found in the classification between platform projects and other types of product development projects (Miller 1995, Saaranen and Keskinen 1997). Meyer and Zack (1996) have also proposed specific platform efficiency measures which enables the evaluation of the platform concepts developed. The evaluation of the product and process platforms (Meyer and Zack 1996) is also accomplished with the customer satisfaction information analysis.

Market-winning product competitiveness is a key success factor for the product development. Success also requires that the company has complementary assests which are needed to benefit from the innovations developed (Teece 1986, Hobday 1994). How the various assets have effect on the customer satisfaction or to the competitive advantage is important. *The linkage between R&D and customers is very challenging. It is not likely that knowledge of the customer requirements and values is evenly analysed, disseminated and discussed in the various parts of the product development processes.* Nor it is clear that it even should because the mixture of technical skills in design and customer requirements has to be managed strategically. The specialisation in technical competencies has to be somewhat independent from the direct customer response. There are many reasons for that. For example the real development of new technology and products is not based solely on the customers whom on the contrary need often to be educated and taught in order for them to understand and use the new innovations from product developers.

According to Brown and Eisenhardt (1995) the main themes of the research in product development can be classified into three areas: product development as a rational plan, communication web and a disciplined problem solving strategy. Product development environment contingency factors seem to be less focused than product and project based success factors and their relationships. Team based organising is found to be perhaps the most successful principle in the product development. Also the roles of project leaders and senior management are emphasised. Communication processes the product development is another crucial factor. As the new "knowledge creation"-type principles are becoming the main stream of the product development research it is suprising to notice that the linkages between learning and decision making is not really discussed. Also the environmental context of product development is often missing, too.

According to the study of Brown and Eisenhardt (1995) the main performance indicators used in product development are developing from the financial success measures (profits, sales, market share) into more operational success measures like speed and productivity. This change is parallel with the increasing importance of knowledge creating capabilities of the organisation. *In practise the learning organisation must employ mechanisms which are linking the operational events to the markets and customers. This may imply that the increased usage of performance measurement systems is needed also in product development.* The relationship between technology management and performance measurement is relevant for the management (Maunuksela 1997).

The following model by Brown and Eisenhardt describes the major factors found affecting the success of product development projects.

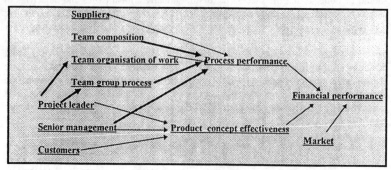

**Picture 7.** Factors affecting the success of product development projects (Brown and Eisenhardt 1995: 346)

### Technological leadership as a source of a competitive advantage

The role of electronics is becoming more and more important in the applications of energy technologies. In this context the role of product development of energy related products is becoming more divergent as before. The scope of the technological dimensions in the new product development is more wider than before. During 95-96 a specific survey was carried out in the Vaasa county. Based on the results (n=26) of the companies a simple classification for the companies according to the relationship to electronics was developed. The respondents were classified as electronics manufacturers, electronics applicators and potential applicators. The nature of the competitive advantage of the different groups is described in the following picture.

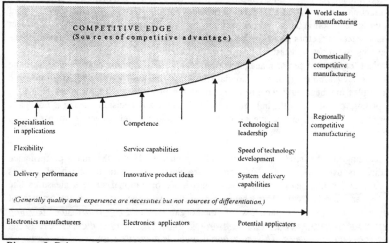

**Picture 8.** Drivers of competitive edge of the groups of companies in the Vaasa county (Spring 1996)

Various sources of competitive advantage are practically applicapable. Strategic focus should be set according to the main competitive priorities (For discussion on priorities see research on manufacturing strategy. For example Kim and Arnold 1996.)

**Applying technology management in the analysis of customer satisfaction**

"Developed and upgradeable roadmaps, descriptions, concepts, simulation and other models with specifications are necessary tools for constructing optimal platforms, products and product generations. The following picture presents the mentioned tools and for their information systems common and generally usable checklist. Its items can be divided into many groups, that can be used modularly like products. This versatile and well-structured framework can be seen as a platform for formulating document and information systems and media. It can be used continuously for various product areas both for internal and external applications at various levels (Saaranen and Keskinen 1997)."

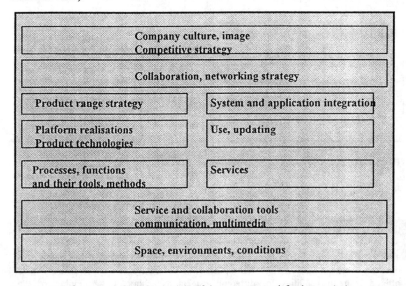

**Picture 9.** A framework for the criteria's of the customer satisfaction analysis (Saaranen and Keskinen 1997)."

**Analysing product development with a new integrated framework which combines elements of technology management and manufacturing strategy**

Some case interviews were carried out with a theoretical framework which integrates some elements of technology management and manufacturing strategy. Manufacturing strategy research has pointed out the importance of manufacturing competence (Cleveland, Schroeder and Anderson 1989, Kim and Arnold 1992). The discussion on the different dimensions of the manufacturing performance has also shown that different trade-off problems are important for manufacturing because it is not possible to be truly competitive in many ways (Leong, Snyder and Ward 1990; Miltenburg 1996).

The main performance dimensions of manufacturing can be called competitive priorities representing the different ways in which manufacturing can create competitive edge for the firm (Skinner 1969; Wheelwright 1978). These concepts are also valuable when analysing technology management (Maunuksela 1997). _One may argue that the competitive priorities may be specifically valuable when implementing or operationalizing technology management._ The following picture presents the suggested framework.

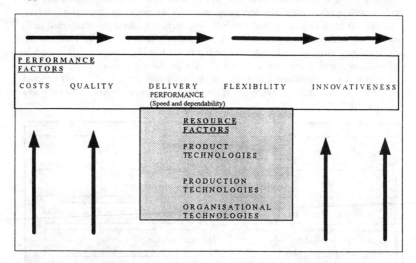

**Picture 10.** A CSCP-model, concurrent strategies lead to concurrent processes

### Results from the company interviews

Analyses of product development activities with the presented framework pointed out that it is possible to find out clear differences between companies. Three interviews were carried out with representatives of different firms. Some earlier interviews were also used as supportive material. Respondents were mainly working in major firms operating internationally. They were positioned differently in the companies which offered some possibilities for different insights even though the number of the interviewed people is low. But besides of the special interviews carried out for this purpose the writers have previously worked with some of the companies so the results are also based on the researchers preunderstanding of the subject area. Description of the results is descriptive and the argumentation is based both on the use of the qualitative analysis and to some part also on the use of action science based approach.

Customer satisfaction was increasingly important factor for the firms. The practises variate between companies but the trend may be from the firm level customer satisfaction analysis to the project level customer satisfaction measures. Practical results from the questionnaire describing the theoretical framework were promising but not very strong. Considering the different performance dimensions it was possible to draw some conclusions: a) organisational issues seem to affect the delivery performance of a firm, b) manufacturing issues seem to affect also to the delivery performance,

c) products are more often designed with the perspective for manufacturing, d) product issues are important for the cost performance and innovativeness. *Process management is considered quite important in product development. The impact of process or team management principles on the delivery performance of product development should be analysed more.*

Product development was considered as a key business process of a firm. The organisational structure of product development was different in the firms interviewed. Also the responsibilities were defined differently. Some units had global responsibility for the specific product areas inside the international firm. This may imply that the competitiveness of a certain product is not only dependent on sales and marketing but also from the suppliers capabilities for technology transfer in some markets. The special resources needed for international technology transfer operations seemed to be very important factor. "The role of research and development activities is changing from the traditionally supportive provider of technical support to an active participant in the sales and marketing (Miller 1995)". In this kind of environment the development of specific strategies may be very useful in order to co-ordinate the transfer of the appropriate technologies to customers.

All interviewed companies were mainly concentrating their product development efforts within defined product families. Use of product platform is also increasing but the concept of process platform was not yet evidently showing. Management principles are mainly based on the application of project management. The use of planning or R&D teams is increasing. Management evaluation of the performance is based on projects, teams and processes. The evaluation of process performance is increasing as a new area as compared to project or team evaluation. The increased impact of the software components in the products is showing. This may in fact be a very important change driving technology which strongly effects on the development between successive product generations. This kind of driving technology may actually be crucially important. Then the key technologies of the future products may offer some ideas for the priorities and methods suitable for the technology management of a firm.

**Conclusions**

Practising managers seemed to be more up-to-date about technology management (also core competence) than manufacturing strategy. There is an increasing need to be able to measure product development activities. It would seem that the common base of experiences in performance measurement may usually be based on customer satisfaction analysis. The need to be able to measure product development could lead to the situation where customer satisfaction practises are just transferred to R&D without further considerations. But it is important to emphasise the role of technology management and customer value analysis. As a response to the industry specific features in electronics manufacturing in the energy industries it can be said that the integrated model of technology management and manufacturing strategy seems very promising. This kind of a more broader approach to the content of technology management implies new possibilities to manage and measure basically technological phenomenon's. The following picture describes the proposed relationship between customer satisfaction, competitiveness and technology management.

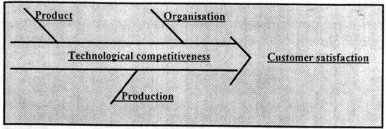

**Picture 11.** Technological competitiveness and customer satisfaction

REFERENCES

Kim, Jay. S.; Arnold, Peter. (1996). Operationalizing manufacturing strategy-an exploratory study of constructs and linkage. International Journal of Operations & Production Management. Vol. 16. pp. 45-73.

Saaranen, Jarmo; Keskinen, Simo. (1997). Improved customer focus concept. Proceedings of the Sixth International Conference on Productivity & Quality Research. ICPQR-97. Houston, Texas. March 16-19.

Keskinen, Simo; Takala, Josu. (1995). A new concept for the the technology strategy. Proceedings of the 13th International Conference on Production Research. ICPR-95. Jerusalem, Israel.

Drucker, Peter. F. (1992). The New Society of Organisations. Harvard Business Review. September-October. Published in the book "The Learning Imperative". Edited by Robert Howard.

Brown, Shona. L.; Eisenhardt, Kathleen M. (1995). Product Development: past research, present findings and future directions. Academy of Management Review. Vol. 20. No. 2. pp. 343-378.

Miller, William L. (1995). A Broader Mission for R&D. Research, Technology Management. November-December. pp. 24-36.

Gale, Bradley T.; Wood, Robert. Chapman. (1994). Managing Customer Value. Free Press.

Goodman, John; DePalma, David; Broetzmann, Scott. (1996). Maximising the value of Customer Feedback. Quality Progress. December. pp. 35-40.

Wetzel, David K.; Maul, Gary P. (1996). How to measure continuos improvement. Quality Progress. December. pp. 41-48.

Rosenberg, Jarrett. (1996). Five myths about customer satisfaction. Quality Progress. December. pp. 57-64.

Lynn, Ellis W.; Curtis, Carey C..(1995). Measuring customer satisfaction. Research, Technology Management. September-October. pp. 45-48.

# 099

THE ROLE OF PROCESS PLANT CONTRACTORS IN TRANSFERRING
TECHNOLOGY: A CASE STUDY OF THE MARKET DIMENSION

Author:     Derrick F. Ball, Emeritus Professor   De Montfort University
Leicester School of Business   The Gateway Leicester LE1 9BH   England

Co-Authors:James D. Mueller   Department of Management and
               Marketing   College of  Charlston  South Carolina   USA
Alan W. Pearson   R&D Research Unit   Manchester Business School   UK

ABSTRACT
Process plant contractors implement and bring to fruition capital
investment programs in such sectors as chemicals, energy and metals. In
undertaking a contract they perform all or a number of the following: plant
design and engineering, supply of process technology, procurement of
equipment, supervision of construction, plant commissioning and the
arrangement of project finance. Specific characteristics of the industry are
the variety of functions undertaken by the contractor and operation on a
world-wide basis (1). The nature and extent of contractor involvement in
transferring technology is determined by a complex interaction of a number
of commercial and technological factors (2). Investigation of these factors
has concentrated upon the circumstances in which companies choose to
use contractors as opposed to design and construction in-house (3), and
upon contractor-client preferences once a contract has been agreed (4).
A dimension which has received scant attention is the market This paper
describes the factors which are important in determining the success of
Western contractors in securing orders and thus in transferring the
technology available to those contractors. It focuses on a recent study of
identifying factors critical for contractors seeking to win projects in the
former Soviet Union (FSU) and in Central and East European countries
(CEECs). This draws upon an empirical analysis of over 1000 capital
investment projects and over 100 interviews with government and
industry officials from Russia, Poland, Hungary, Bulgaria, the Czech
Republic and Slovakia to identify key variables stemming from each
country's reform agenda. This was followed by a questionnaire study which
compared the contractor selection criteria as perceived by client firms
within the FSU and CEECs with that of Western contractors seeking
contracts in those regions.

(1) See for example: J D Mueller et al, The role of process plant
contractors in the energy supply industry, Applied Energy, September,
1996.
(2) A Grieve and D F Ball, The role of process plant contractors in
transferring technology, R&D Management, 22, 2, 1992, 183-193.
(3) E G Jones et al, The role of the process plant contracting industry in
technological change, R&D Management, 13, 3, 1983, 155-167.
(4) D F Ball and AW Pearson, The role of process plant contractors in
transferring technology into the Peoples´ Republic of China Process
Economics International, 7, 1988, 134-140.

# 100

## KSB-AJAX PUMPS - RESISTANCE TO CHANGE.

Author:

Dr. Dianne Waddell
Monash University
Department of Management
Clayton Campus
CLAYTON, Victoria, 3168
AUSTRALIA

Tel:      +61-3-990-55402
Fax:      +61-3-990-55412
Email:      dianne=waddell@vut.deu.au

## ABSTRACT

Preliminary research has identified that although resistance is perceived as negative by many managers, in fact resistance has been used to successfully implement change processes in organizations. This paper aims to challenge preconceived notions that resistance is an impediment to change by producing evidence identifying inconsistencies within the theory and highlight the lack of consideration about its constructive role within organizations.

As part of a larger research study on the topic of positive resistance, which included a national survey, five case studies on the behavior of management and employees in Australian manufacturing industries was undertaken The five case studies were developed as a qualitative exercise, a form of descriptive research in order to induce or generate hypotheses rather than testing them in a survey The five Australian manufacturing companies were from different industries and would have undergone different change processes It became obvious that there were inadequacies in thinking and an absence of any measurement procedure. This led to the recognition of individual differences and the need to be aware of the mulitifaced nature of resistance, in both attitude and behavior.

As a result there was a need to accurately measure the nature of resistance within the organization and a questionnaire was developed to identify the type of resistance that existed within a particular environment The paper' will include the results of the testing instrument for the measurement of resistance at a particular manufacturing company: KSB-Ajax pumps (Australia).

The result leads to the conclusion that any change process is dependent on an identification of the type of resistance prior to any change strategies being planned. Therefore it is crucial to redefine resistance before redesigning an organization.

# 101

# Human Resource Management for Different Types of R&D Professionals: A Korean Case

**IAMOT**
**Technology Management Conference 97**
**in Sweden**

**Youngbae Kim**

Associate Professor
Graduate School of Management
KAIST
373-1 Kusong-dong, Yusong-gu
Taejon 305-701
Korea
Tel: +82-42-869-4322
Fax: +82-42-869-4310
e-mail: ybkim@ms.kaist.ac.kr

suitable conference topics:
E. cultural differences in technology management or
I.   industrial technology management

suitable for oral or poster presentation

# Human Resource Management for Different Types of R&D Professionals:
## A Korean Case

## Abstract

This paper empirically examines various personal characteristics and reward preferences of 1,333 R&D professionals in Korea. It identifies different patterns of reward and career development needs associated with four types of R&D professionals, who are categorized by personal characteristics: personality and attitude. A productive leader type shows active personal traits (which encompass high scores of professionalism, localism, need for achievement, and risk-taking propensity) and positive attitudes (which include high scores of job satisfaction, organizational commitment, and motivation level), while a cynical bystander type exhibits passive personal traits and negative attitudes toward a job. A passive adapter, who has passive personal characteristics but positive attitudes, and a frustrated champion, who is active in personality but negative in current job attitude, lie in between them. These four different types of R&D professionals show differences in their age, education and position level, and technical performance. They also reveal different perceptions of their work environments and their preferences in reward structures and career development paths.

Based on these findings, this study suggests a contingent type of human resource management in terms of selection and staffing of R&D professionals, performance appraisal, incentive systems, and career development plans.

Key words: R&D professional, Human resource management system, Korea

# I. Introduction

As Korea has been progressing from a Developing Country toward a Developed Country, it becomes a growing concern how to develop and exploit its technological capability to sustain an economic growth and competitive advantage in the world market. Facing an increasing rate of technological and market changes and rapidly eroded competitiveness in the labor intensive industries, together with emerging protectionism of technology assets in Developed Countries, many industrial firms in Korea have striven to strengthen indigenous technological competence through heavy investment in in-house R&D activities as well as strategic alliance with other foreign technological sources.

It thus appears to be one of the most important strategic issues for them to manage technical professionals effectively. Given the paucity of talented technical people and their peculiar nature of personality, however, human resource management systems in Korea, which have predominantly emphasized efficiency for non-professional workers over the past two decades, are in need of change to attract and motivate creative technical professionals.

It has long been recognized that technical professionals have many distinctive characteristics in terms of goal orientation, value system, need structure, and their behavioral patterns (Badawy, 1988). Compared to other organizational members, they are more likely to have expertise, to prefer autonomy, to have a strong commitment to their profession, to feel professional ethics, and to maintain collegial standards (Miller, 1986; Raelin, 1985; Von Glinow, 1988).

However, Allen (1984) noted marked differences between scientists and engineers in their goal orientation, communication behavior, and nature of technical works. Certainly, technical professionals are not identical in their personal characteristics and attitudes towards their job. According to their personal traits and attitudes, technical professionals exhibit different patterns of technical behavior and performance levels and demand different work environments and job characteristics (Keller & Holland, 1979; Pelz & Andrews, 1966). Many studies have attempted to reveal the matched or congruent relationships between personal characteristics and organizational environments, which may produce higher performance results (Holland, 1984; Ostroff, 1993; Terborg, et al., 1980).

Personal traits or personalities represent those characteristics of an individual which account for consistent patterns of behavior (Pervin, 1984). People can be differentiated by a series of individual personal traits such as need structure, risk-taking propensity, and other value systems. Among personal traits that have been found to be powerful predictors of behavior of technical professionals are professionalism (professional career orientation), localism (managerial career orientation), need for achievement, and risk-taking propensity.

Since Gouldner (1957), many studies have explored the relationship between goal or career orientation of professionals and their behavior or performance (Baugh & Roberts, 1994; Allen & Katz, 1992; Gerpott et al., 1988). They found that technical professionals tend to have two different career orientations -- managerial and professional -- and R&D people with strong managerial orientation are more likely to be concerned with movement into positions of managerial responsibility, while those with strong professional orientation have a primary concern in seeking recognition from their professional peers by technical knowledge and achievements. They also reported that R&D peoples with strong managerial orientation tend to achieve higher organizational performances, while those with strong professional orientation produce better technical performances. Recent empirical studies, however, found that these two dimensions are not mutually exclusive, but independent with each other in various cultural contexts (Gerpott, 1987; Gerpott et al., 1988, Aryee & Leong, 1991). That is, an individual can have a strong aspiration to be promoted as a higher-level manager in the organization and, at the same time, to grow as a top notch scientist or engineer in his/her technical field.

Need for achievement is defined as behavior toward competition with a standard of excellence (McClelland, 1953). An individual with high need for achievement prefers to assume personal responsibility for task performance, sets moderately difficult goals and tends to be preoccupied with task accomplishment (Daft & Steers, 1986). Hall & MacKinnon(1969) found that creative professionals are more likely to have a high need for achievement.

Risk-taking propensity is another personal trait required for achieving innovation tasks, given the chaotic nature and inherent uncertainty in the innovation process. Presumably, R&D people with high risk-taking propensity is willing to challenge the innovation project with high risk of failure but high rate of return. Scarpello and Whitten (1991) showed that entrepreneur type of technical people tends to have a high risk-taking propensity and pursue new venture out of technical innovations.

An attitude may be defined as a predisposition to respond in a favorable or unfavorable way to objects or person in one's environment (Daft & Steers, 1986). While the above personal traits remain stable to some extent, attitudes can be subject to change by external stimuli in the relatively short time period. For attitude variables of R&D professionals, job satisfaction, organizational commitment and motivation level have received much attention in prior researches.

Job satisfaction is defined as a pleasurable or positive emotional state resulting from the appraisal of one's job or job experience (Locke, 1976). Pelz and Andrews (1966) found that satisfaction of an individual was positively related with technical performance such as the number of publications and patents.

Organizational commitment refers to the degree to which an individual identifies with a particular organization and its goals, and wishes to maintain membership in the organization. This variable contains two underlying dimensions: organizational loyalty and turnover intention.

Lee (1971) reported that highly committed individuals were more productive, better motivated, and more satisfied than are their less committed co-workers.

Motivation level means the extent to which an individual makes an effort to achieve task goals (Van de Ven & Ferry, 1980). Professionals with high motivational level, a personal characteristic of creative problem solvers, generally place relatively greater value on "job interest" versus such extrinsic rewards as salary or status (Steiner, 1965).

Basic premises of this study are there must be some distinct but recurring patterns of personal characteristics among R&D professionals and these different types of professionals exhibit different preferences in work environments and human resource management systems. Specifically, research questions addressed in this study are following:

1) Are there different types of R&D professionals in terms of their personal traits and attitudes toward a job ? If yes, what are they ?

2) Are there differences in their demographic factors such as age, education and position level and technical performances among different types of professionals?

3) What are their preferences for performance appraisal and reward schemes and career development paths ?

To address these questions, this study empirically examines various personal characteristics of 1,333 R&D professionals and their preferences for human resource management systems in Korea. It first identifies different types of R&D professionals based on their personal traits and attitudes toward their job and organization, and then compares differences in preferences for effective performance appraisal and reward schemes and career development paths among them. Finally, several directions for effective human resource management of R&D professionals in Korea are suggested.

## II. Methods.

Samples:

This study has been undertaken as a part of a research project which attempted to change its human resource management system to encourage R&D professionals and build organizational environments conducive to technological innovations. The sample firm, a large electronics company in Korea, has several R&D laboratories in HQ and each business division with approximately 8,800 technical people. Initially, 189 teams were selected from 9 R&D laboratories and 1,600 questionnaires were administered to their leaders and members. Data from 1,333 R&D professionals were obtained and a response rate was about 83%. 21% of respondents were postgraduates and 65% were undergraduates. The average age was 30.3 years and the average tenure in the organization was 5.0 years. 99% of respondents were men.

Measurements:

Goal orientation (managerial and professional orientations) was measured by an instrument used in Gerpott et al. (1988). This study used a seven-item scale adopted from Edwards (1971) to measure need for achievement and a four-item scale in Jackson (1976) to measure risk-taking propensity.

As for attitude variables, job satisfaction was measured by a seven-item scale (Van de Ven and Ferry, 1980), while nine items were developed based on related scales of Van de Ven and Ferry (1980) and Pelz and Andrews (1966) to measure work motivation. Organizational commitment and turnover intention were measured by Cook & Wall(1980)'s abbreviated version of OCQ (Organizational Commitment Questionnaire).

Table 1 shows the means and standard deviations for the variables in the study. To examine internal consistency of multi-item scales, Cronbach's Alpha coefficients were also presented. The alpha coefficients of all variables were found to be acceptable according to criteria suggested by Van de Ven and Ferry (1980).

---

Table 1 here

---

For performance appraisal criteria, a review of related literature reveals 11 items under four different categories: performance result, skill and ability, attitude and behavior, and seniority (Von Glinow, 1988; Nathan et al.,1991). Other 11 items for incentive schemes under categories of financial, organizational, career, and professional rewards were delineated from prior research (Von Glinow, 1988;Gomez-Mejia et al., 1990; Jauch, 1976; Koning 1993). Table 4 and Table 5 present performance appraisal and reward items.

## III. Results

Four variables of personal trait - professional and managerial orientations, need for achievement, and risk-taking propensity – were used for cluster analysis to develop a taxonomy of R&D professionals. It produced two different types: assertive (high values on all personality variables) and passive (low values on all variables). The cluster analysis of four attitude variables also resulted in two distinct types: positive (high values on all attitude variables) and negative (low values on all variables).

Four types of R&D professionals were delineated by combining these two aspects of clusters: "productive leader (assertive personality and positive attitude)," "passive adapter (passive personality but positive attitude)," " frustrated champion (assertive personality but negative attitude)," and "cynical bystander (passive personality and negative attitude)" types. As shown in Table 2, 36% of technical people belong to productive leader type, while 24% of people are classified into passive adapter. 18% are regarded as frustrated champion, whereas 22% are cynical bystander type.

---
Table 2 here
---

Table 3 presents other demographic profiles of four types of R&D people. There is a significant difference in their age, education and position level. Productive leader is found to have highest scores on position and education level, age, and tenure among four types, while cynical bystander shows the opposite. In terms of technical performance, productive leader also produces larger number of patents (both of domestic and international), yet there is no difference among four types in their publication results.

---
Table 3 here
---

Different types of R&D professionals exhibit different preferences in performance appraisal criteria, reward schemes and career development paths. For performance appraisal criteria, as shown in Table 4, frustrated champion strongly insists that technical expertise, coaching skill and publication must be emphasized, but the value of organizational loyalty and personal relationship with supervisors ought to be reduced. Cynical bystander also exhibits a similar pattern of preference in performance appraisal criteria. R&D people with a negative attitude, compared to people with positive attitude, are more likely to oppose the current performance appraisal system, since they seem to feel their performance results might be undervalued due to subjective judgments by direct supervisors. On the contrary, passive adapter expresses a modest level of need for change in the current performance appraisal criteria.

---
Table 4 here
---

For reward schemes, as Table 5 reveals, productive leader tends to place priority in career and professional rewards, while passive adapter wants to receive recognition in the organization. Frustrated champion is more concerned about the career reward to experience diverse jobs and to challenge internal venture projects. Cynical bystander, however, does not show a particular pattern of preference in performance reward systems.

---
Table 5 here
---

As to career development paths, as shown in Table 6, professionals with active personality prefer to have a diverse job experience in business areas and want a strictly differentiated dual ladder with distinctive evaluation and reward systems. Specifically, they advocate a professional ladder which emphasizes technical ability and contribution to technical performance and has more autonomy and a merit-based pay system. Passive adapter, however, recognizes a need for dual ladder system but does not want so much distinction between two ladders as active people. Again, cynical bystander has lowest scores on all the items of dual ladder system.

---------------------------

Table 6 here

---------------------------

Four types of R&D people also prefer different types of R&D project. In response to a question, whether they are willing to participate in a strategic project with high risks of failure, almost half of productive leaders answer yes, while other types of professionals are more reluctant to take risks for performing R&D projects (see Table 7).

---------------------------

Table 7 here

---------------------------

### IV. Summary and Discussion

In a nut shell, the results of this study can be summarized as follows:

**1)** There are four different types of R&D professionals in terms of their personal traits and attitudes toward a job, who have different need preferences in human resource management systems: productive leader, passive adapter, frustrated champion, and cynical bystander.

**2)** Productive leader type of R&D people, who has aggressive personal characteristics and positive attitudes, is more likely to be found in the senior group, to produce more patents, to emphasize negotiation and coaching skills for performance appraisal, to prefer professional and career rewards, and to participate in a risky but more important R&D project.

**3)** Passive adapter, who shows passive personality but positive attitudes, achieves a relatively good performance and prefers to have an organizational recognition but does not want to change drastically the current human resource management system,

**4)** Frustrated champion with aggressive personal traits but negative attitudes seems to be frustrated by the current work environment and thus demands most radical changes in performance appraisal system. This type of R&D people emphasizes publication results, technical knowledge, and managerial skills as important performance appraisal criteria and demands to clearly differentiate the performance criteria and reward schemes between managerial and technical ladders. They appear to choose their career between 1) promotion on technical ladder for technical contribution and professional rewards and 2) pursuing other functional jobs or championing internal venture projects.

5) Cynical bystander type, passive personal traits and negative attitudes, tends to be lower level of technical people and does not exhibit an explicit pattern of preferences in human resource management system. However, it seems to be most cynical to current R&D organizational situation.

Based on above results, this study proposes a contingent type of human resource management system for different types of R&D people in Korea.

1) A dual ladder system should be designed to accommodate different preferences of career development paths among different types of technical people.

2) Each ladder must have different evaluation criteria for performance appraisal and promotion. Managerial ladder emphasizes administrative, negotiation and coaching or mentoring skills, while technical ladder considers technical knowledge and performance as primary evaluation criteria.

3) Different types of technical people must be assigned to different jobs, of which the requirement must fit the nature of people. For instance, it would be better for a passive adapter to be assigned to a technically routine but commercially important project team where organizational recognition would be much higher, while, for a productive leader, radical R&D project might be preferred.

4) It would be very important to encourage "frustrated champion" type of technical people for better R&D performance. Besides aforementioned recommendations, regular job rotation across functional areas and internal venture programs must be seriously considered for them. Technical peoples with strong goal orientation and achievement need are more likely to pursue diverse work experiences and to challenge a new venture out of their technical output.

5) There seems to be no logical answer to empower a "cynical bystander" type of technical people. So, the firm would rather screen this type of technical people out, if possible, in the early stage of recruitment. Accumulation of empirical results to classify different types of professionals, as attempted in this study, may be helpful to identify personal characteristics which account for their behavioral patterns and performance levels in R&D settings.

Finally, given the limited sample of this study and fragmented results of related studies in Korea, further research is required to rigorously identify R&D professionals with different abilities and need structures and to examine matched relationships between different types of professional and work environments, including career paths, project assignment, and leadership style.

## References

Allen, T.J., *Managing the Flow of Technology*, Cambridge, MIT Press, 1984.

Allen, T.J., & R. Katz, "Age, Education and the Technical Ladder," *IEEE Transactions On Engineering Management*, Vol.39, No.3, 1992, pp.237-245.

Aryee, S., & C.C. Leong. "Career Orientations and Work Outcomes Among Industrial R&D Professionals," *Group & Organizational Studies*, Vol.16, No.2, 1991, pp.193-205.

Badawy, M.K., "What We've Learned Managing Human Resources," *Research Technology Management*, Vol.31, No.5, 1988, pp.19-35.

Baugh, S.G., & R.M. Roberts, "Profesional and Organizational Commitment Among Engineers : Conflicting or Complementing?", *IEEE Transactions On Engineering Management*, Vol.41, No.2, 1994, pp.108-114.

Cook, J, & T. Wall, "New Work Attitude Measures of Trust, Organizational Commitment and Personal Needs Nonfulfillment," *Journal of Occupational Psychology*, Vol.53, 1980, pp.39-52.

Daft, R.L., & R.M. Steers, *Organizations: A Micro/Macro Approach*, Scott, Foresman and Company, 1986.

Edwards, A.L., *Edwards Personal Preference Schedule*, New York, The Psychological Corporation., 1971.

Gerpott, T.J., "Karriereorientierungen von Industrieforschern: Ein Beitrag zur Konstrukterfassung," *Zeitschrift fur Arbeits- und Organisationpsychologie*, Vol.31, 1987, pp.44-54.

Gerpott, T.J., M. Domsch, & R.T. Keller, "Career Orientations in Different Countries and Companies: An Empirical Investigation of West German, British and US Industrial R&D Professionals," *Journal of Management Studies*, Vol.25, No.5, 1988, pp.439-462.

Gomez-Mejia, L.R., D.B. Balkin, & G.T. Milkovich, "Rethinking Rewards for Technical Employees," *Organizational Dynamics*, Spring, 1990, pp.62-75.

Gouldner, A.W., "Cosmopolitans and Locals: Toward an Analysis of Latent Social Roles," *Administrative Science Quarterly*, Vol.2, No.4, 1957, pp.281-306.

Hall, W.B., & D.W. Mackinnon, "Personality Correlates of Creativity Among Architects," *Journal of Applied Psychology*, Vol.53, 1969, pp.322-326.

Holland, J.L., *Making Vocational Choices: A Theory of Careers(2nd ed.)*, Englewood Cliffs, NJ., Prentice-Hall, 1984.

Jackson, D. N., *Jackson Personality Inventory*, Goshen, NY, Research Psychologists Press, 1976.

Jauch, L.R., "Tailoring Incentives for Researcher," *Research Management*, 1976, pp.23-27.

Keller, R. T., & W. Holland, "Toward a Selection Battery for Research and Development

Professional Employees," *IEEE Transactions on Engineering Management*, Vol.26, No.4, 1979, pp.90-93.

Koning, Jr., J.W., "Three Other R's : Recognition, Reward and Resentment," *Research Technology Management*, 1993, pp.19-29.

Lee, S.M., "Organizational Identification of Scientists," *Academy of Management Journal*, Vol.14, No.2, 1971, pp.213-226.

Locke, E.A., "The Nature and Causes of Job Satisfaction," in M. D. Dunnette(ed.), *Handbook of Industrial and Organizational Psychology*,Chicago, Rand McNally, 1976.

McClelland, D.C., "The Calculated Risk : An Aspect of Scientific Performance," in Tylor, C.W., & Barron, F.(eds), *Scientific Creativity Its Recognition and Development*, New York, Wiley, 1963, pp.184-192.

Miller, D.B., *Managing Professionals in Research and Development*, San Francisco, California, Jossey-Bass, 1986.

Nathan, B.R., A.M. Mohrman.Jr, & J. Milliman, "Interpersonal Relations as a Context for the Effects of Appraisal Interviews on Performance and Satisfaction : A Longitudinal Study," *Academy of Management Journal*, Vol.32, No.2, 1991, pp.352-369.

Ostroff, C., "The Effects of Climate and Personal Influences on Individual Behavior and Attitudes in Organizations," *Organizational Behavior and Human Decision Processes*, Vol.56, 1933, pp.56-90.

Pelz, D.C., & F.M. Andrews, *Scientists in Organizations : Productive Climates for Research and Development*, New York, Wiley, 1966.

Pervin, L. A., *Personality: Theory and Research(4th ed)*, New York, John Wiley & Sons, Inc., 1984.

Raelin, J.A., "The basis for the professional's resistance to managerial control," *Human Resource Management*, Vol.24, No.2, 1985, pp.147-175.

Scarpello, V., & B.J. Whitten, "An Exploration of Critical Personalities in Research and Development Organizations," *The Journal of High Technology Management Reseach*, Vol.2, No.2, 1991, pp.151-168.

Steiner, G., *The Creative Organization*, The University iof Chicago Press, 1965.

Terborg, A.R., P. Richardson, & R.D. Pritchard, "Person-Situation Effects in the Prediction of Performance : An Investigation of Ability, Self-Esteem, and Reward Contingencies," *Journal of Applied Psychology*, Vol.65, No.5, 1980, pp.574-583.

Van de Ven, A.H., & D.L. Ferry, *Measuring and Assessing Organizations*, New York, John Wiley & Sons, 1980.

Von Glinow, M.A., *The New Professionals: Managing Today's High-tech Employees*, Cambridge, Mass., Ballinger Pub., 1988.

# 102

## PROBLEMS OF DEVELOPMENT OF THE NATIONAL INNOVATION SYSTEM IN ESTONIA

Rein Küttner, Professor, Vice-Rector of Tallinn Technical
University, Vice-Chairman of the Estonian Innovation
Foundation   Tallinn   Estonia

Jüri Lichfeld, Executive Director of Estonian Innovation
Foundation   Tallinn   Estonia

## ABSTRACT

Estonia has made some progress in the economic development. To further raise its growth potential, an effective national innovation system (NIS) is needed.

A NIS refers to all parts and aspects of the economic structure, research institutions and universities as well as R&D activity in the firms, a system for diffusion and use of modern technologies, which are located or rooted within the borders of a nation state. To develop a clear market-oriented NIS, a framework program is needed. The main features of this program are presented in this report.

The proposed programme consists of two main parts:
1. Development of innovation-support infrastructure.
2. Special subprograms/projects.

Financing the innovation activities is one of the most important problem to solve.

Two solutions are feasible.

- to fund innovation activities mainly by government,
- to establish almost self-financing institutions and have moderate or only little government intervention.

To support the innovation process, the Estonian Innovation Foundation was established in 1991 as a governmental institution under the Ministry of Economic Affairs. In the West, a shift from public to private financing of innovation is dominant and it is considered the main direction of development. Customers, universities and R&D institutions, are an important source of product-innovation ideas in firms. In Estonia, there is a lack of large R&D-intensive firms and effective communication between smaller firms and R&D institutions must compensate this weakness. R&D has a dual role: to develop new products and to help maintain a market position, and also to develop the capacity of firms to learn to anticipate and follow future developments.

In Estonia, there are practically no effective institutions for facilitating the diffusion of information between the business and scientific communities, for transfer of technologies. According to the higher education and science system reform programme, different kinds of technical service and information centres (Technology Competence Centres and Innovation Centres) are planned to be developed. In many industrial policy recommendations, the role of the public sector is to create an environment which supports private domestic firms. The practical content of public policy and governmental responsibility is discussed.

# PROBLEMS OF DEVELOPMENT
## OF THE NATIONAL INNOVATION SYSTEM IN ESTONIA

Rein Küttner
Jüri Lichfeld

Estonia has made some progress in development of its economy. To increase its growth potential, an effective national innovation system is needed. This report discusses some aspects related to the current state of Estonia's innovation system and offers guidelines for future development.

## 1. Estonian economy and innovation system, current situation

Estonia, like other former Soviet Republics and Eastern and Central European countries has been seriously affected by the economic recession. In five successive years compared with the preceding year, industrial output decreased, by 0.2% in 1990; 9.0% in 1991; 36% in 1992; 18.7% in 1993; 3,0% in 1994, but increased by 1,9% in 1995.

Estonia's economic reforms can be characterised by a radical and rapid introduction of a market-oriented economy accompanied by a high social cost.

Despite its recent progress, Estonia faces several problems in its transition to a market economy. For instance the need for long-term strategic thinking concerning technological change has not been recognised by public authorities and businessmen, and contacts with educational and research bodies, which could act as sources of innovation are scarce. Estonia's gross domestic ratio on R&D in GDP was in 1993 - 0.6% and in 1994 - 0.7%. For 1997-2000, the estimated value of the ratio is expected to rise to 0.7 - 1.1%.

During the first years of transition, the most widely used paradigm of competition was based mainly on low production cost. Cost-based paradigm is characterised by low wage rates and focused production. In the last years manufacturers have shifted their paradigm of competition to that based on the quality of products. In the next five years this quality paradigm is planned to be the main feature of industry and in the innovation programme must be planned the corresponding supporting measures.

Today many manufacturers are competing through an increased variety of products and services. This variety-based paradigm of competition seeks to satisfy the varied needs of customers by providing them with a wide variety of products to choose from. However, it requires implementation of a flexible production system, Just-In-Time (JIT) techniques, needs more investment, higher level vocational training, and better co-operation of industry with the R&D institutions, etc.

To day some manufacturers tend to push the leading edge of competition into the new frontier, time-based competition paradigm. This paradigm argues that if an enterprise can reduce its response time in getting a product onto market, it can gain a significant competitive advantage. The development of the competition paradigm is a key factor for success in industrial production in the near future. The research and the preparatory work required to implement these paradigms in the future must be also planned into the programme.

Economic recession has had marked effect on the R&D activities.
In 1990, the Estonian government established the Estonian Science Council (current name Estonian Research and Development Council) and three goal-oriented funds: the Science Foundation, the Innovation Foundation, and the Information Fund.

The main role of the Estonian Research and Development Council is to advise the government on science and technology policy.
The main tasks of the Estonian Science Foundation are to support basic research. The Foundation provides grants and other forms of assistance in the natural, exact, medical, agricultural, engineering, and social sciences and humanities.
The Estonian Innovation Foundation supports financially technical research and development, improvement of production technology and product quality. The Foundation can provide grants of up to 50% of project costs or loans of up 75% at the interest rates generally lower than those at commercial banks. Priority is given to projects in the area of energy saving, restructuring of production, using local know-how and raw materials, medical and veterinary technology, and plant protection.
The resources of the Estonian Innovation Foundation are relatively small - allocations from the state budget were 13.25 million Estonian kroons (MEEK) in 1994 and in 1995, only 9 MEEK in 1996, and for 1997 20 MEEK is planned. Additionally, resources for project financing have been acquired from payback of previously given loans and interests - 6.6 MEEK in 1994, 10.7 MEEK in 1995, 8.9 MEEK in 1996, and 14,3 MEEK is expected in 1997.
The Information Fund supports the R&D and implementation of these results in the field of information technology.

Despite multiple efforts to improve co-ordination of research towards social and economic goals, progress is still needed to identify and implement joint priorities for R&D and innovation, to develop co-operation between different organisations including the above-mentioned funds.

To improve the legal status of the R&D activities and institutions, several new laws have been prepared and adopted. In 1995, the Law on Universities and the Law on Research and Development were passed by the Estonian Parliament. Legal changes are still needed to improve the status of researchers and further reform of the funding system. Projects have been launched to achieve the standards of excellence needed for participation in the European and international scientific system. Centres of Strategic Competence have been established in materials science, gene- and biotechnology, information engineering and environmental engineering at Tartu University and Tallinn Technical University.
To support the implementation of technologies, the Tartu Science Park and the Tallinn Technology Park were established in the late 1980s.

## 2. Main trends of innovation policy in other countries

According to / 1 /, over the past few years a marked changes have taken place in the international arena of science and technology (S&T) policy. For Estonia, the most interesting trends are:

1. Governments clearly attach great importance to S&T, they see it as a means of overcoming their economic difficulties.

2. A large number of countries show a shift in policy emphasis towards support for technology, with governments allocating funding to innovation in order to maintain economic competitiveness and to stimulate growth.

3. Governments have made serious efforts to streamline their research and development systems. They have restructured administrative bodies and taken measures aimed at setting clearer priorities and concentrating resources on the sectors viewed as strategic to their policy objectives and their perceived strengths and weaknesses.

4. There is a growing emphasis on directing S&T towards meeting the needs of society.

5. Scientific education and technical training are increasingly causing concern. This concern has led to educational reforms, particularly at the university level. These reforms have a number of objectives. Of these, provision of greater autonomy to universities as public non-profit legal institutions. Another objective is to overhaul technical training in the higher education system. Several countries have launched major programmes aimed at increasing the number of doctoral students, setting up new graduate schools specialising in the areas corresponding to the perceived technological and commercial needs.

6. Collaboration between the university and industry sectors continues to draw attention. The emphasis is on strengthening university centres of excellence and on co-operation among universities, firms, and the authorities.

7. International co-operation is becoming increasingly important and accounts for at least 10% of government expenditure on R&D in some countries.

There are important differences among countries with respect to the distribution of their effort on different types of technology ("high", "medium", and "low") and the intensity of their research investments. The observed differences among countries are related to their economic situation, and industrial specialisation, and their position in world trade. Only a few countries have spread their research efforts broadly over the whole set of industrial sectors.

According to the GREEN PAPER / 3 / the main obstacles for the development of innovation in the EC are those affecting the co-ordination of efforts, human resources, private or public financing, and the legal and regulatory environment. There is too little industrial research and lack of anticipation of new trends in Europe.

The EC follows a policy mainly diffusion-oriented, helping the diffusion and exchange of knowledge, enabling, then to produce innovations.

In case of EC programmes, especially small- and medium-sized companies, participating in the programmes, take the opportunity to increase their effort in R&D, to enter into a research-intensive and knowledge-intensive industry sector, activating potential to further development.

## 3. Innovation and national innovation system
Innovation involves not only new technologies and new products but also new services, new methods of production, distribution and marketing, and the introduction of new techniques in the organisation of work.

A national system of innovation refers to all parts and aspects of the economic structure, research institutes and universities as well as R&D activity, system for diffusion and use of modern technologies which are located or rooted inside the borders of a nation state and affect the innovation process.

No single model exist to determine the subsystems, social institutions and processes that are most important and should be included into the programme. Besides theoretical and economic considerations, a social and historical analysis is also needed. The importance of different parts, concerning their role in the process of innovation, may change over time and may vary during different periods.

According to Porter / 5 / four stages of competitive development are distinguished:
1. Factor-driven stage
2. Investment-driven stage
3. Innovation-driven stage
4. Wealth-driven stage.
For the next five years, the investment-driven and innovation-driven stages are recognised as the main measures to increase the competitive advantages of Estonian industry. The supporting measures for motivating the firms to shift their activities from today's dominating factor-driven stage towards investment-driven and innovation-driven stages must be included in the programme.

## 4. Main principles of the development the innovation system in Estonia
In shaping our innovation policy, we cannot take into consideration only examples of the respective systems of the developed countries, but must additionally take into account the local conditions and requirements.
The general objective of the innovation policy can be formulated as the one which optimises the legal, organisational, individual, and financial conditions of the technological development of an economy. The objectives of the innovation policy must fit naturally into the purpose and tasks of the transformational process of economy.

To develop the main principles of the innovation policy for Estonia, the following conditions must be considered:
- Estonia is a small country and has a limited domestic market;
- Estonia has oriented to an open economy;

- the competition paradigm of industry is changing in time horizon of the programme;
- Estonia's economy is highly dependent on foreign trade;
- to raise the quality of workforce skills is needed.

The objectives can be achieved only if they fit into the long-term requirements and the economic possibilities.

According to the programme, the objectives of the national competitive advantage could be characterised by the willingness and ability of the firms to expand their activities by investing aggressively in modern efficient production technologies. The firms must be motivated to acquire the best technologies available in the market. Foreign technologies are not only applied but also improved for a firm's own purposes. Those basic ideas of development of the competitiveness are similar to the investment-driven stage of development. In the investment-driven stage, the competitive advantage can typically be achieved in the industries, which are characterised by scale economies, standardised products, low service content and easily transferable technologies / 4 /. In this stage, the public policies are selective - particular branches of industry are favoured at the expense of others. Industrial investments are in a key position in this stage. There are different problems to solve, mainly how to reach national consensus in the selection of firms or branches, how to motivate firms to invest in the Estonia's conditions characterised by lack of resources and the accepted of open economy and free market.
In the innovation-driven stage, firms not only adopt and apply innovations produced elsewhere but innovate themselves. Competitive strength is based on specialised and advanced factors, highly educated labour and on the implementation of R&D results. Firms compete in the market with differentiated products. The role of public polices is clearly different from that in the investment-driven stage. Subsidies, restricting competitions, protection of markets and selective industrial polices incompatible with this stage of competitive development. Indirect policy measures like, enhancing innovativeness through creating and upgrading advanced factors by improving education and research, encouraging establishment of new SMEs, enhancing domestic competition and demand sophistication, are appropriate in this stage. The programme must support firms to shift their activities into the direction of the innovation-driven stage.

Today, Estonia should pay special attention to small business development. As a result of the structural changes, a large number of well-educated and experienced engineers and managers were dismissed from former large state-owned enterprises and research institutions. They are to be engaged in small businesses.

## 5. National programme of innovation
Many countries have begun to apply the concept of a national innovation system and to develop corresponding programmes. In the following we

describe briefly the main features of the planned Estonian innovation programme.

The most important features of the innovation system are the financing system, innovation process management systems and methods, as well as educational and research systems.

Two parts of the innovation programme are planned:

- development of the activities of the public sector to support the innovation process and development of the infrastructure;
- sectional innovation (sub)programmes and projects.

The whole innovation process must be activated through regional, sectional, national programmes, and international initiatives.

The programme includes different projects to be carried out co-operatively by different bodies (companies, research institutions, universities, etc.).

The proposed strategy time horizon for the programme is planned for five years. The academic institutions usually have a five years or a longer horizon. The time schedule for technology suppliers and end-users of innovation must be linked to the rapid technological development that excludes longer planning terms. They have a yearly operative plan included in a longer strategic plan, to be reviewed at the end of each year.

## 5.1 Actors in innovation policy

According to / 2 / the improvement of technological and related capabilities is mainly based on the co-ordination between groups of companies and governments. The weakness of administrative capabilities in economies in transition is the main innovation policy problem of post-socialism. The effectiveness of policy in industrial and technology restructuring cannot be separated from the effectiveness of the administrative institutions. Important is the building-up of an institutionally rich system of government-business relations.

The conception of co-ordination comprises a wide range of informal mechanisms such as consumer and producer associations, university-industry associations, restructuring committees, etc, most of them existing already in Estonia to-day.

R&D has a dual role in an innovation process, it is required new product development, in maintaining a market position, and also for developing the capacity of firms to learn to anticipate and follow future developments.

In Estonia, there are practically no effective institutions which could facilitate the diffusion of information between the business and scientific communities, for transfer of technologies. According to the higher education and science system reform programme, different kinds of technical service and information centres (Technology Competence Centres and Innovation Centres) are planned to be developed.

Since there is a lack of large R&D-intensive firms in Estonia, effective communication between smaller firms and R&D institutions must compensate this weakness. SMEs are above all outstanding sources of innovation and economic development, they need better access to the contemporary technology, more productive relationships with the research community, and a reduction in the bureaucratic barriers to trade and investment.

Better quality skills of workforce, small and medium-sized batch production of specialised products, development of flexible production systems, support of the implementation of quality, time and variety based paradigms, are key factors in the advancement of Estonia's industry.

Science and technology parks are good means for promoting technology development in small and medium-sized companies, and they were a significant feature indicating the boom in local technology initiatives in the early 1980s, although subsequent years have seen a broadening of regional technology strategies in which the potential of science parks as seed beds for regional innovation and industrial growth has proved questionable. However, in less developed countries like Estonia, where the development of infrastructure is a priority, plans to develop such parks are remarkable resources for regional development.

The manufacturing industry has to strengthen its competitiveness through innovation and improvements in its business processes. The development and application of information and communication technologies (ICT) is regarded as a key element to make this happen. Like the steam engine age and electrification in previous centuries, the ICT is all pervasive and is modifying most aspects of economic, social and industrial life. The speed of dissemination of ICT stems largely from the economic advantages they deliver.

### 5.2. The role of state in the development of the innovation system
While a general goal is to reduce the previously extensive state interference, it follows from the nature of the socio-economic transformation that state's active participation is temporarily necessary in the areas of legislation, education, maintenance and development of an infrastructure, funding research, establishment and support of international relationships, attraction of foreign resources, etc.
The ultimate aim is to establish an institutionally rich system of government-business relations, and of self-organising mechanisms within business which will help correct failures of both markets and governments.

In Estonia a need exist to harmonise and reduce the regulatory barriers, which currently prevent the competition. The legal framework concerning standards, certification, quality control and insurance is of crucial importance and should be made more favourable to innovation. Several actions could be planned to promote the better use of the protection rules of intellectual property, development of patent information services, etc.
Of great importance is the creation of an industry with an export potential based on the international standards and quality systems corresponding to

ISO 9000. Work has started on approving the calibration and certification activities according to the European standards of series EN 45000.

Education is a key factor for economic growth and technological development. The main objectives of education and research policy are:
- to maintain an extensive and high level of education in order to promote the intellectual growth of the nation;
- to improve the quality of research;
- to upgrade vocational skills and promote employment.

The Estonian Research and Development Council is attaching increasing importance to the provision of funding for individual researches and their groups through programmes. At the same time, the council is engaged in institutional reorganisation with respect to co-ordinating mechanisms. Changes have to be made in the management of research and innovation.

Some countries have undertaken major initiatives to encourage the development of technological and commercial services (innovation centres). We have planned similar activities and currently the Innovation (Technology Transfer) Centre at Tallinn Technical University (IC) is being established. IC is considered to be an instrument for implementing Estonia's innovation policy. IC shall provide research and consultancy services for the development of products, production processes and services, promote extensive utilisation of international technological knowledge, co-operation, and technology transfer.

### 5.3. Innovation (sub)programmes and projects
Each nation goes through its own unique process of development / 5 /. National economy contains a range of industries with widely different sources of competitive advantage.
According to the / 5 /, the resource-poor nations have started from a position of international success in labour-intensive final consumer goods industries. For the Estonia it means industries such as textile and apparel, food-related products, products of engineering industries, including manufacture of machines and equipment, chemical products, etc., which were more successful in development of its export in last years.
It is necessary to introduce formal procedures for defining technology and innovation policy priorities and the corresponding activities in these and other promising for Estonia sectors (clusters) of industry. It must be accompanied by the creation of mechanisms designed specifically to forecast development trends in research and technology and plans of development R&D in priority areas.

The R&D part of the programme covers the so-called pre-competitive area leading to technological innovation: the development of new knowledge and methodologies, the development of the prototypes for new products and technologies. R&D planning in the programme follows mainly the top-down approach. A critical aspect is to push knowledge top-down to activate the transfer activity toward an industrial innovation.

Similar to the EUREKA, a mechanism is proposed for industrial innovation: development and implementation of the pilot solutions and transfer results from the technological innovation to the industrial innovation. Following the bottom-up approach, it is oriented to support technology leaders (innovators) involved as partners of development activities.

From 1993, for the projects financed by the Innovation Foundation, the following fields of priorities were established: energy saving, restructuring of production using local know-how and raw material, medical and veterinary technology and plant protection, transportation technology, and environmental technology.

In the field of engineering sciences, the Council of Research and Development declared the following priority areas:
• environmental engineering;
• information technology;
• material engineering;
• bio/genetechnologies.

The final decision upon the priorities of technological development for the following 5-10 years must be taken and the corresponding support measures implemented. In 1996 the Centres of Strategic Competence have been established to integrate the activities of different universities and research institutions in these areas.

### 5.4. Financing of innovation activities

Financing the innovation activities is the central issue. Two extreme solutions can be distinguished:
• to fund innovation activities mainly by government,
• to establish almost self-financing institutions and have moderate or only little government intervention.

Government funding for technology research is primarily planned to be provided via national technological research programmes. These programmes generally cover generic technologies (biotechnology, material science, information technology, etc.), the technologies in which countries have specialised for various reasons (food production, microelectronics, agriculture, transport, etc.) or technologies relating to the environment.

Because the implementation of the Innovation Programme needs much more financial support than our state budget can offer. We seek proper way of inviting more private resources to support the programme.

In most Western countries a shift from public to private financing of innovation has been a major trend.

While the unpredictability of innovation makes investments inherently risky, the situation based on the private financing is described by a trend towards short-term, high-return investments and the inability of firms to offer the guarantees demanded by investors. New measures are needed at national level to encourage private investment through insurance or guarantee systems and improved access to information for both the investor and the innovator. Furthermore, unlike our competitors tax incentives are not used in

Estonia, but must be considered as an effective financial tool in the future. The new regulatory mechanisms for tax incentives must be implemented.

## CONCLUDING REMARKS

It is through the development of the national system of innovation that the future of Estonia is created. The usefulness of the concept of an innovation programme is that innovation is understood as a process integrating various parties spurring the innovation: between researchers and firms, between firms and customers or suppliers.

The national system of innovation is facing the same kind of challenges as society as a whole. Decisive factors in the future will be how well the national system of innovation and the rest of society interact and how well relevant innovation management works. In this respect, it is of vital importance to improve the overall level of education, reallocate resources to activities which are the most important for development of Estonian economy, develop infrastructure for supporting knowledge development and implementation, ensure quality to attain top international standards in an increasing number of areas.

### References

1. Science and Technology Policy. Review and Outlook 1994. Organisation for Economic Co-operation and development. Paris, 1994.
2. B. Berg, K. Kilvits, M. Tombak. Technology Policy for improving Competitiveness of Estonia, Series C 73. Helsinki, 1996. Pp. 236.
3. Green Paper on Innovation. European Commission, 1995.
4. National Industrial Strategy for Finland. Ministry of Trade and Industry Publications 3/1993. Finland, 1993.
5. Michael E. Porter. The competitive Advantage of Nations. The Free Press, NY, 1990.

# 104

## Two DELPHI Studies About Management of Technology (MOT) Issues

**Dr. George Scott**
Professor, Operations and Information Management
School of Business, U-41OPIM
Storrs, CT 06269-2041
U.S.A.
Telephone: (860) 486-4176 or (860) 486-5295
Fax: (860) 486-4839
E-Mail: SCOTT@UCONNVM.UCONN.EDU

Topic Letter: F or I
Category: 2

Keywords:
Country Differences in MOT Issues/Problems
Strategic Planning for MOT
MOT Issues/Problems Research
DELPHI Issues Methodology
Organizational Learning About Technology
Technology Core Competencies
Importance of MOT Problems/Issues

This paper is suitable for Oral Presentation only.

# Two DELPHI Studies About Management of Technology (MOT) Issues

*by George M. Scott*                                    *University of Connecticut*

## ABSTRACT

This paper discusses two DELPHI Issues Questionnaire studies that use multiple questionnaires in sequence to define and rank the importance of MOT issues/problems. Study 1, completed, ranks twenty-four issues in order of importance. The Number One issue is found to be Strategic Planning for Technology Products. Other findings of Study 1 also are presented.

Study 2, in process, is a detailed DELPHI study of the Number One problem as established by Study 1. The twelve top sub-issues of this problem are presented in rank order, but these ranks are noted to be only preliminary findings of Study 2.

## INTRODUCTION

This paper explores the findings of two Management of Technology (MOT) studies, one of which is completed. The second study is about two-thirds completed and provides preliminary results which are examined in this paper; this second study will be completed in April 1997. The purposes of the paper are to:

1. Present an overview of the conclusions from the first study, which used DELPHI Questionnaire methodology to explore and rank twenty-four MOT issues (with "issues" defined as "unresolved problems");

2. Indicate the nature of the second DELPHI issues study now in process and present preliminary findings of this study; and

3. Suggest the need for further research in defining, ranking and examining MOT issues.

Although DELPHI Issues Methodology has been used previously in other fields to rank management issues (Scott; Branchau and Janz) this methodology has not previously been used in the MOT field. Indeed, only one survey of management problems in the MOT area is known by this author (Thurlings and Debackere). That study provides useful insights but does not rank the importance of MOT issues and is based on a one questionnaire (non-DELPHI) survey that establishes eleven "trends" in R&D.

## STUDY 1

Over a one year period spanning 1995 and 1996, one DELPHI Questionnaire study of MOT issues has been completed and a second one initiated. The first, here called Study I, involved three sequential DELPHI Questionnaires that examined MOT issues and ultimately placed the top twenty-four Issues in a rank order of importance relative to each other. The first questionnaire was used to help identify, clarify, and refine MOT issues and included fifty-nine MOT issues for experts to define, rank and evaluate. The top ranked twenty-three issues, along with comments by the participants about each, as well as several additional issues suggested by the participants, composed the second questionnaire which was sent to the participants of the first questionnaire as well as to a number of other potential participants. Ninety-eight experts from seventeen countries (a 32% response rate) participated in this second DELPHI questionnaire; nearly half not only evaluated each issue but also provided comments about specific issues. The lowest scoring issues were dropped and the remaining highest ranked twenty issues, along with the summarized participants' comments about each and several new issues suggested by participants were sent to all participants of the second DELPHI questionnaire as well as to several additional possible participants suggested by participants in the second round. Sixty-three responses were received to the third DELPHI questionnaire, for a response rate of 56%; as with the previous two DELPHI Questionnaires, extensive comments about each issue were provided.

The primary purpose of the study was to identify and rank MOT issues in terms of their importance so that industry technology managers and senior managers, experts in national laboratories and government technology agencies, and academic researchers can focus attention directly on the most important problems. In the process of doing this, the comments provided by participants (which were circulated back to the participants of each next-round) apparently led participants to reconsider their views so that a greater consensus about issue importance was achieved (this is a sought for result of the DELPHI Issues Methodology). These comments additionally form a rich reservoir about the nature of participants' concerns about each issue; additionally, in many instances suggestions were provided by participants about methodologies, practices, or directions to pursue that will help to deal with each issue. (The full results of the study, including statements of the major themes of these discussion comments is available in workpaper form from the author at the Management Issues Survey and Studies Institute — "MISSI.")

The three major findings and conclusions of this first study are presented below and discussed briefly in the following paragraphs.

1. Twenty-four MOT issues are placed in rank order of importance. A decreasing standard deviation of participants' responses for nineteen of the twenty issues from the second to the third questionnaires indicate that the agreement increased about the importance level of the issues (with one exception) during the study.

2. Overwhelming agreement is found that the Number One MOT Problem is "Strategic Planning for Technology Products."

3. There are significant areas of disagreement between academic and non-academic participants about the importance of specific MOT issues.

4. Indicators are found that the importance of particular issues varies among world regions and countries.

## THE RANK ORDER OF IMPORTANCE OF MOT ISSUES

One value of this ranking is that academic and industry education programs can place greater emphasis on the most important MOT problems. Another value is that researchers have a basis for focusing their activities on issues known to be among the most important. Also, technology managers and senior managers in industry can be alert to each "high-importance issue" as a possible trouble area within their company.

The final ranks and mean scores of these twenty four issues (based on 10 points, with "10" being "Most Important") are shown in Exhibit 1.

### NUMBER ONE ISSUE: "STRATEGIC PLANNING FOR TECHNOLOGY PRODUCTS"

Although no evidence was uncovered prior to the study that this issue ranked as more important than any other, the participating experts evaluated it as the most important MOT problem overall on all three DELPHI questionnaires. Indeed, the gap between it and the second-ranked issue increased by three-fold from the second to the final questionnaire and this gap is far greater than the distance between any other two issues. It is probable that this finding will spur attention to this as a research issue as these results become known. The statement of this issue as it appears in the final questionnaire is:

**Strategic Planning for Technology Products.** Issues associated with strategic and long range planning for technology-product development, such as aligning high-tech strategies with business strategies (or vice-versa if the technology strategy should be dominant), new product introduction strategies, strategic decision-making processes, lack of understanding of technology and its roles among corporate strategic planners, lack of coherent corporate level planning for high-tech management, failure to identify the critical success factors of a company's technology activities, and establishing the corporation's technology climate.

| Evaluations: | Academic Participants' Average | 8.000 | Overall Average | 8.180 |
|---|---|---|---|---|
| | Industry Participants' Average | 8.360 | | |

Several themes relating to this issue are of concern to the participating experts. Because this was so dominantly the top issue in importance, the author decided to conduct a second DELPHI study of this issue, which is discussed later in this paper, and these themes are incorporated into that study's statements of issues.

### AREAS OF DISAGREEMENT BETWEEN ACADEMIC AND NON-ACADEMIC PARTICIPANTS

While both academic and industry participants ranked the Number One Issue highest, there is significant disagreement between them about other issues. The greatest disagreement is with respect to the issue "Organizational Learning About Technology," ranked third overall but second by academic participants and a distant sixteenth by non-academic participants. This extreme mismatch suggests that academic participants are far more likely to give research attention to this issue than non-academic participants would prefer. This issue is stated in full below:

**Organizational Learning About Technology.** Issues related to organizational learning and institutional memory about new technology and new product development, including how to conduct training, how to provide updating educational opportunities for technical personnel, how to accelerate organizational learning, how to accumulate and preserve organizational learning, how to systematize and maximize core competence and core technology learning that is based on experience rather than education and training, how to measure the level of core technology knowledge and increases/decreases of this level, and how to develop education and training programs for special needs such as for design for manufacture.

| Evaluations: | Academic Participants' Average | 7.935 | Overall Average | 7.288 |
|---|---|---|---|---|
| | Industry Participants' Average | 6.640 | | |

On the other hand, the issue that is ranked fourth overall "Technology Core Competencies," is ranked second by industry technologists but is ranked eighth by academic participants. In this case, industry participants seem likely to prefer that academics focus strongly on this as a research topic, but it may be lower in the research priorities of academics. The full statement of this issue is shown below:

**Technology Core Competencies.** Issues involving identification and development of technology core competencies.

| Evaluations: | Academic Participants' Average | 7.000 | Overall Average | **7.220** |
|---|---|---|---|---|
| | Industry Participants' Average | 7.440 | | |

## DIFFERENCES IN RANKINGS AMONG COUNTRIES AND AREAS

In general, the number of participants from a particular country, geographic or economic region probably should exceed ten for statistics about the importance of each issue to become indicative rather than only suggestive. Only the number of participants from two countries (the U.S.A. and the United Kingdom) and one region (Europe, including the United Kingdom) exceed this arbitrary threshold of ten. Examination of these three groups suggests certain interesting differences, which may be the consequence of MOT education differences, country economic, cultural or regulatory environment differences, or only the small numbers of participants in each group. Significantly, all three of these groups evaluated "Strategic Planning for Technology Products" as their Number One Issue.

Among the top ten issues in importance, the major differences found among the three geographical groups are:

1. U.S.A. participants ranked "Organizational Learning About Technology" (7.550) much higher than did those of the U.K. (6.615) or Europe (excluding the U.K.) (6.708).

2. With respect to "Technology Core Competencies," both the U.K. participants (7.461) and those of Europe (7.667) are much higher than those in the U.S.A. (6.450).

3. "Creating a Conducive Culture" is highest for the U.S. group (7.700) and much lower for the U.K. group (6.231) with Europe in the middle (6.792).

4. The U.S. representatives view "Involvement of Marketing Groups" as much more important (7.684) than do the U.K. (6.308) or the European (6.375) groups.

5. For "New Product Project Selection," both the U.K. (7.538) and Europe (7.541) contingents view the problem as more important than does the U.S. group (7.000).

A follow-on study will attempt to focus more directly on specific countries by seeking larger numbers of participants in each of several countries. This seems especially feasible in Sweden, France, Canada and Germany, in each of which several participants already have participated.

## PRELIMINARY FINDINGS OF STUDY II: "STRATEGIC PLANNING FOR TECHNOLOGY PRODUCTS"

Because of its preeminent overall position as the Number One Issue ("Strategic Planning for Technology Products) of Study I, a second study was initiated and at this writing is in process. The researcher reviewed the literature relating to technology strategic planning and in so doing encountered two major problems with this literature:

1. The research and writing on the topic is sparse (relative, for example, to the research and writings about strategic planning for information systems usage in companies); and

2. No description of the technology strategic planning processes was found in the literature.

Both of these findings suggested that the need for issues research on the topic is all the more important. The second of the above suggests there may be no conception of the "how to do it" technology planning processes (i.e., no "best practices") against which to test the importance of issues or sub-issues. As many of the potential concerns about technology strategic planning might relate to process, but apparently there is no commonly understood process model, the researcher's Round One DELPHI Questionnaire study was divided into two parts:

Part 1. An eight page, single spaced planning vignette was developed which described the planning processes of a fictitious company. At the end of this vignette are listed in questionnaire form forty-three DELPHI issues which are framed in the context of specific strategic planning practices of the company in the vignette.

Part 2. An independent, standard DELPHI Questionnaire consisting of sixty-nine technology strategic planning Issues was developed. There was little overlap between the issues in the two questionnaires.

A relatively small number of expert potential participants were randomly sent either Part 1 or Part 2. Twenty-two have been returned, thirteen of them for Part 2. Round Two has now been distributed. It is expected that three rounds of DELPHI Questionnaires will be used.

The preliminary importance evaluations results of Round One are shown in Exhibit 2. These results are based on the evaluations of both the Part 1 and Part 2 Questionnaires. It is stressed that these are preliminary results, and the importance of issues relative to each other is very likely to change after the Round Two questionnaire. No conclusions should be made or actions taken on the basis of the information in Exhibit 2.

## IMPLICATIONS OF THIS RESEARCH

There are implications of the research of Study 1 and Study 2 for academics, companies and government agencies.

*Academic Research Programs.* Academics are particularly well positioned to undertake MOT research activity as their interests and their perspectives span companies and industries, and often even nations. The academic activity of systematically identifying MOT issues and their importance has been begun with the studies described herein.

However, the present studies should be considered only the beginning. Academics should confirm or reject these studies' results, and should extend or elaborate on them, as useful. Academics should pursue research dealing with particular issues among those evaluated as most important, and in the absence of reasons to the contrary, should tend to focus their attention on these "most important" issues. Academics can use a variety of research approaches to examine these "most important" issues.

*Corporate MOT Programs.* Each company is in a position to search for and deal with any MOT issues found in the company. The examination of this MOT issues research, and all that follows it to establish the nature and importance of the issues should precede efforts by individual companies. An "Issues Audit" methodology can be developed to assist with this search and the search can establish the specific nature and severity of an issue in a particular company. Standard benchmarking techniques can be used to establish how other companies deal with an issue area and to help establish "best practices." Changes can be implemented as needed, and corporate education programs can be established.

*Government Agencies.* The extent to which a country's companies deal effectively with MOT issues can be heavily influenced by government agencies. Agencies can conduct, encourage, or sponsor MOT research programs. In doing so these agencies can reference this issues research for guidance; ultimately agency research grants may be based in part on issues research.

Government R&D laboratories can conduct their own internal investigations of MOT issues, conduct benchmark tests, and even implement in their own environment the "best practices" they have found for MOT issues to serve as showcases for these practices.

*Professional Associations.* MOT professional associations, such as the International Association for the Management of Technology (IAMOT) can perform or assist with many of the MOT research activities. MOT issues research can provide valuable insight to IAMOT and other such associations which may assist, as examples with setting conference agendas and establishing criteria for acceptance of presentation papers.

### REFERENCES

Branchau, J.C. and D. Janz. (1996). Key Issues in Information Systems Management: 1994-95 S/M DELPHI Results, *MIS Quarterly*. June: 225-242.

Scott, G.M. (with P. Troberg). (1980). *Eighty-eight International Accounting Problems in Rank Order of Importance—DELPHI Evaluation*. Sarasota: American Accounting Association: 1-118.

Thurlings, L.F.G. and K. Debackere. (1996). *Trends in R&D*. Philips Research (Netherlands).

EXHIBIT 1
OVERALL RANKS OF THE TOP TWENTY-FOUR MOT PROBLEMS

|  |  | AVERAGE/MEAN |
|---|---|---|
| 1. | Strategic Planning for Technology Products . . . . . . . . . . . . . . . . . . . . | 8.180 |
| 2. | New Product Project Selection . . . . . . . . . . . . . . . . . . . . . . . . . . . . . | 7.297 |
| 3. | Organizational Learning About Technology . . . . . . . . . . . . . . . . . . . . | 7.288 |
| 4. | Technology Core Competencies . . . . . . . . . . . . . . . . . . . . . . . . . . . . | 7.220 |
| 5. | Cycle Time Reduction . . . . . . . . . . . . . . . . . . . . . . . . . . . . . . . . . . . | 7.076 |
| 6. | Creating a Conducive Culture . . . . . . . . . . . . . . . . . . . . . . . . . . . . . | 7.063 |
| 7. | Coordination and Management of New Product Development Teams . . | 7.056 |
| 8. | Technology Trends and Paradigm Shifts . . . . . . . . . . . . . . . . . . . . . . | 7.034 |
| 9. | Involvement of Marketing Groups . . . . . . . . . . . . . . . . . . . . . . . . . . . | 7.010 |
| 10. | Customer/Supplier Involvement . . . . . . . . . . . . . . . . . . . . . . . . . . . . | 6.967 |
| 11. | Senior Managers' Involvement in Technology . . . . . . . . . . . . . . . . . . | 6.936 |
| 12. | Soft Skills for Technical Personnel . . . . . . . . . . . . . . . . . . . . . . . . . . | 6.912 |
| 13. | Organization Structure for R&D . . . . . . . . . . . . . . . . . . . . . . . . . . . . | 6.857 |
| 14. | Alliances/Partnerships Between Technology Companies . . . . . . . . . . . | 6.757 |
| 15. | Within-Company Technology Diffusion and Transfer . . . . . . . . . . . . . . | 6.732 |
| 16. | Using High-Tech for Competitive Advantage . . . . . . . . . . . . . . . . . . . | 6.644 |
| 17. | Involvement of Manufacturing in New Product Development . . . . . . . . | 6.639 |
| 18. | Globalization of Product Development Processes . . . . . . . . . . . . . . . . | 6.553 |
| 19. | Resource Allocations to High-Tech Activities . . . . . . . . . . . . . . . . . . . | 6.352 |
| 20. | Establishing a "Technology Vision" . . . . . . . . . . . . . . . . . . . . . . . . . . | 6.213 |
| 21. | Productivity of Product Development Activities . . . . . . . . . . . . . . . . . . | 5.967 |
| 22. | Rewarding and Educating Technical Personnel . . . . . . . . . . . . . . . . . | 5.893 |
| 23. | Project Continuance/Discontinuance . . . . . . . . . . . . . . . . . . . . . . . . | 5.779 |
| 24. | Oversight of High-Tech Activities . . . . . . . . . . . . . . . . . . . . . . . . . . . | 5.627 |

## EXHIBIT 2
## ISSUES OF STRATEGIC PLANNING FOR TECHNOLOGY PRODUCTS
## PRELIMINARY RESULTS OF DELPHI ROUND ONE

The issues which follow are merged from the two separate questionnaires of Round One. They are placed in order according to their numeric rating on one of those questionnaires, with the first listed having the highest rating, and so on.

1. **A Focus on Short-Term Product Planning.** Issues associated with a tendency to emphasize short-term rather than long-term technology planning. The strategy issue of "What advanced technology products should we be marketing now" should instead be a long-term issue of "What technology competencies should be increased in order to provide which products in the long run?" *Average Score from Round One — 8.71*

2. **Linkage Between Corporate and Technology Strategic Planning.** Issues that arise because companies do not have good procedures for establishing an explicit linkages between technology strategic planning and corporate strategic planning. *Average Score from Round One — 8.60*

3. **Linkage of Corporate R&D Strategic Planning with Business Unit Product Development Planning.** Issues associated with failure to link corporate technology planning and research with business unit planning for product development. Too often there is no explicit linkage between levels of planning activities, or the linkage is weak. Failure to make the linkage reduces overall coordination and may mean that product development projects that are good for the company overall may not be undertaken by any business unit. *Average Score from Round One — 8.50*

4. **Need for Extensive Communication and Interaction Among Technologists.** Issues associated with promoting communication among technologists and the role of this interaction in strategic planning. A variety of means of exchanging ideas and transferring technology knowledge among technical personnel and among technology managers (especially among those in different organization units) helps to create an environment that is conducive to effective technology strategic planning. Companies that do not explicitly encourage and provide for these interactions and technology knowledge transfers may have less effective technology strategic planning and less coordinated technology plans across business units and product lines. *Average Score from Round One — 8.50*

5. **Roles of the Chief Technologist in Establishing Overall Technology Direction.** Issues associated with the leadership role of the chief technologist and the procedures used to establish the company's future technology directions, such as bringing together technologists and senior managers for discussions. These critical leadership activities that are so necessary for successful strategic planning are not as likely to take place without the leadership and initiative of a CTO or other chief technologist. *Average Score from Round One — 8.50*

6. **The Influence of Technologists and Technology Managers on the Nature and Structure of Strategic Plan Guidelines.** Issues associated with not empowering technical personnel and technology managers to critique technology planning guidelines, technology objectives, and strategies in a manner that may lead to their substantial modification. *Average Score from Round One — 8.43*

7. **The Senior Technology Leader as a Senior Manager.** Issues associated with the chief technologist's role as a senior manager and the effects of this on technology strategic planning. Companies where the CTO or other chief technologist is not a respected senior manager who can represent the technology group and technology strategic planning well to the most senior managers are likely to have less effective technology strategic planning. *Average Score from Round One — 8.29*

8. **Short-Term Operations Problems Compromise Long-Term Technology Strategic Plans.** Issues that relate to preoccupation with current operating problems to the exclusion of long-term planning for technology. Even if a solid technology strategic plan is in place, it may be compromised by short-term operating considerations, especially if the company has a financial downturn that might seem embarrassing or inconvenient for senior managers, or might diminish the stock market performance of the stock, if technology costs (such as R&D costs) are not cut. *Average Score from Round One — 8.20*

9. **Overall Framework for the Strategic Plan and Strategic Plan Development.** Issues related to the absence in the management of technology discipline of an overall and generally accepted framework and methodology that is designed for technology strategic management and for the technology strategic planning processes. Other areas of companies (e.g., finance, marketing) have effective strategic management frameworks and planning processes tailored to them, yet the

technology management processes used in companies tend to involved fragmented and piecemeal approaches to technology strategy. One result of this fragmented and piecemeal approach may be that elements of approaches from other areas of activity may tend to be substituted for good technology management processes (e.g., forms of financial analysis that are inappropriate for technology planning). *Average Score from Round One — 8.07*

10. **Technology Intelligence Activities for Strategic Planning.** Issues pertaining to devoting too little attention to gathering information about the research status and future prospects in the marketplace of the technologies that are relevant to a company's product lines and to devoting too little attention to analysis of technologies used by competitors in competing products. *Average Score from Round One — 8.00*

11. **Strategic Leadership via Technology Strategic Planning.** Issues revolving around using technology strategic planning activities and processes as a means to assist managers to think and act innovatively and strategically rather than to only prepare technology strategic plans as a "bureaucratic exercise." *Average Score from Round One — 8.00*

12. **Developing and Selling the Technology Vision.** Issues associated with failure of senior managers and technology managers to jointly develop a vision of the role of technology in a business unit and failure to disseminate and sell this vision throughout the unit. *Average Score from Round One — 8.00*

# 105

# Managing R&D as an Important Element of Business Systems

Hiroyuki Yamasaki*, *MIAMOT, SrMIEEE, MIEE*, Kenneth G. Pechter**, *MIEEE*,
Fumio Kodama**, *MEAJ* and Jun'ichi Baba***, *SrMIEEE, MEAJ*

\* ULSI Laboratory, Mitsubishi Electric Corporation, Hyogo, Japan
\*\* Research Center for Advanced Science and Technology, University of Tokyo, Tokyo, Japan
\*\*\* Mitsubishi Electric Corporation, Tokyo, Japan

## Abstract

In order for a business to survive, it must have distinctive business concepts. This distinctiveness is expressed in the business's products, the business system, and the ideas and vision of top management (which we call the three dimensions of products, systems and ideas). While products alone among these three dimensions refers to concrete objects, the objects by themselves are not enough to gain a broad perspective on the business. On the other hand, the ideas dimension is an abstraction and thus can only be interpreted equivocally. It is the systems dimension that brings together the other two dimensions, and thus in the competition between businesses it is the business system that determines survival.

We believe that business systems tend to converge to a fairly common set of objectives, which maximizes:
- the utility to the customers
- the consideration of the stakeholders
- the profit of the business

The reason for this convergence is that all businesses must comply with the law of the market: "Without profit, you die." Therefore, this set becomes the objective of R&D as well.

In light of the situation outlined above, we describe four concrete examples of Mitsubishi Electric Corporation's new wave of innovation management:
(1) Incorporation of the Semiconductor Device Development Center into the responsibility of the Strategic R&D Planning Group
(2) Establishment of new concept information technology laboratories in the Boston area
(3) Establishment of the Power System & Transmission Engineering Center as the mediator between R&D and business operations
(4) Establishment of an in-house Institute of Technology to construct a corporate network of engineers and thus foster a collective field of vision

## 1. Introduction

The scientific and technological output of industry laboratories receives high praise from academia. There are few areas where this output does not contribute to company success. However, an effective laboratory is not the same thing as a productive laboratory. This fact indicates the importance of R&D management to the company (Yamasaki and Baba, 1996a). Regardless of the company, all laboratories are undoubtedly encountering the transformation from an effective laboratory to a productive one. In Mitsubishi Electric, R&D planning was transformed in 1965 when the Central Laboratories were put in closer contact to the Business Groups by Ichiro Shibayama, General Manager of the Central Laboratories. According to the literature (Myers, 1996), Xerox began rethinking the relationship between research and the company in 1986.

The fundamental objective of R&D management is to ensure that R&D plays a central role in the strategic and administrative management of the company. Also, since R&D is concerned with the future, it is accompanied by technological uncertainty and uncertainty in the market. R&D can play an important role in the organizational learning of the company.

## 2. The Business System of the Twenty-First Century Company

The most fundamental objective of the company is survival. To accomplish this objective, the company must possess distinctiveness. Distinctiveness, which is not an individual product service, is expressed comprehensively by the business system. How to create distinctiveness depends on the understanding of the total business process.

The total business process:

(1) The representative players in the business are the sellers and buyers of goods and services. Sellers and buyers negotiate with each other through the market.

(2) Traditionally, companies have attempted to do everything from R&D and design to production and distribution, but this has become both infeasible and uneconomic. Companies therefore are increasingly outsourcing production and distribution. The outsourced supplier companies can be considered stakeholders of the outsourcing companies.

(3) The stakeholders are not limited to the suppliers of goods and distribution services; they also include stockholders, employees, the government, universities and local communities.

(4) Modern society is inundated by artifacts produced through the development of science and technology. Businesses cannot ignore the tangible and intangible effects of these artifacts on the environment.

(5) External business forces influence the business system. These external forces come from such sources as science and technology, environmental considerations, government, ethics and law.

Viewing the business process in this way, we see that companies make profits by selling goods and services while customers satisfy their needs by demanding the utilities of goods and services (in consideration of the cost-performance ratio). Since we cannot do business without considering stakeholders and the natural environment, it is safe to say that they are part of the infrastructure of business activities. Stakeholder relations are fostered through the development of mutual trust over long periods of time. Through such relationships, companies interact with their stakeholders not only formally but informally and even tacitly. In the future, stakeholder relations will become even more important (Kaku, 1995). This importance is evident in the way that companies often contribute considerable amounts of money to universities and local communities and thus foster a sense of gratitude toward the companies.

Companies have to build distinctive business systems in order to grow in the market through a balance of supply and demand and within the stakeholder relationship based on mutual trust. As shown in Fig 1, the core objectives of the business system are to maximize:

- the utility to the customers
- the consideration of the stakeholders

- the profit of the business

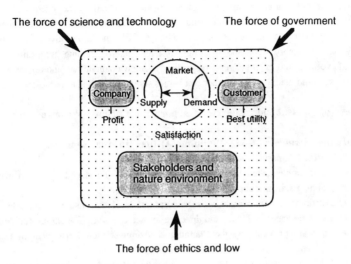

The force of science and technology        The force of government

Market

Company    Supply    Demand    Customer

Profit                          Best utility

Satisfaction

Stakeholders and
nature environment

The force of ethics and low

Fig. 1 Total Business Process

## 3. Attaining Dynamic Stability

R&D is a critical activity to the achievement of growth under the three objectives described above. However, R&D activity is usually accompanied by uncertainties in technology and the market. Management cannot allow itself to become befuddled by these uncertainties, so that it can focus on the attainment of stable growth and ensure the company's survival. The attainment of stability is accomplished through change management; that is, dynamic stability (Boynton, 1996). Knowledge and trust are essential factors for possession of dynamic stability.

### 3.1 Knowledge

There are two kinds of knowledge, general knowledge and specific knowledge. General knowledge is that knowledge contained in books and periodicals, and is thus shared by many people. Although it contributes to the individual's fundamental knowledge base, it cannot contribute to the differentiation of the company. Differentiation is dependent on specific knowledge. Specific knowledge is accumulated through learning in such everyday activities as design, manufacturing, and marketing. Knowledge about a specific customer is one example of specific knowledge. Close communication between R&D and business units is necessary for the acquisition of specific knowledge.

Specific knowledge is a useful tool for differentiation. A system of specific knowledge which is shared throughout the company forms a knowledge platform. The contents of the knowledge platform will be revised according to the developments of science and technology, but for the most part will remain unchanged for a given period. An easily accessible knowledge platform contributes to good communication among business units, which will further improve productivity.

### 3.2 Trust: The Community of Practitioners

In this age of rapid change, all members of an organization must work together as a team to overcome difficulties. This requires good communication and the creation of communities of practitioners, where engineers and managers can exchange skills and know-how informally. Small group activity on the factory floor and meetings of managers for training are examples of the communities of workers and of managers, respectively. Such communities should be open, and university professors and managers from other companies should be invited to participate.

## 4. Examples of Mitsubishi Electric Corporation's New Wave of Innovation Management

### 4.1 Role of the Strategic R&D Planning Office in the Semiconductor Device Development Center (Yamasaki and Baba, 1996b)

New business is implemented based upon excellent ideas introduced by top management (CEOs), but the planning staff that supports the CEOs is also important.

Mitsubishi Electric has laboratories at both the corporate level and business groups level. Four corporate laboratories are located in Japan, and three are located overseas. The administrative services for these laboratories are provided by the Planning & Administration Department of Corporate Research & Development.

Expenditures during the development stage are higher than those during the research stage due to the increased need for human resources and capital for product development. More capital is therefore invested in the R&D activities of the business groups. Each business group has a development laboratory where research and development aimed at future business opportunities are promoted. The research budgets for each business group are raised from the profits made by the group.

The Semiconductor Group has three development laboratories, ULSI Laboratory, Optoelectronic & Microwave Devices Laboratory and System LSI Laboratory. It was thus necessary for this group to have a standing organization to correlate laboratory plans, and to oversee and coordinate research and development activities so that overlaps of activities and insufficient activities in a specific field could be avoided. For this purpose, the Research & Development Planning Department was established as the planning department of the Semiconductor Group.

In this modern era where information and environmental technologies are of great importance, it is not correct for corporations to act solely on their own interests, indifferent to social and economic activities. If a particular company's research and development were to be planned solely taking into account trends in science and technology, the resulting activities would be unbalanced and incomplete. Proper research and development require full projection over all areas, which means that movements in the market and economy must also be taken into account. Corporate research and development must now be conducted based on a wider frame of reference including living creatures, society, economics, culture and so on. In consideration of this fact, the Research & Development Planning Department established the Strategic R&D Planning Group to collect and analyze vast types of information, and then draft high-quality strategic plans.

### 4.2 Promotion of a Transnational R&D Organization

Mitsubishi Electric is currently promoting development of its businesses by way of applying a global flat-organizational strategy that concentrates core competence in the direction of the customer. The globalization of operations throughout Mitsubishi Electric continues to progress at a rapid pace, and in June 1995 the entire corporate organization was restructured to support the company's transformation into a truly transnational entity.

The main pillar to support this change is the foundation of a trilateral R&D base in the USA, UK and Europe for the purpose of bringing together R&D and business strategies. This base consists of:

(1) Mitsubishi Electric Information Technology Center America , Inc. (Boston, Massachusetts, USA)
(2) Visual Information Lab., which is developing image-information technology for digital broadcasting technology (London, UK)
(3) Telecommunications Lab. of Mitsubishi Electric Technology Center Europe, B. V., which is developing telecommunications technology focusing on mobile communications technology (Rennes, France)

These new R&D laboratories interact with existing works, factories and sales networks, the Information Technology R&D Center and ten other laboratories in Japan, and Mitsubishi Electric Research Laboratories (MERL) in Boston. In consideration of such interaction, these new R&D laboratories were established in strategic locations in order to intensify the development activities of multimedia technology and create new business opportunities worldwide.

The meaning of "transnational company" in Mitsubishi Electric is "a company that utilizes a strategy that promotes extension of the company's business groups (business units and products alike) on a worldwide basis, taking R&D and manufacturing operations to the most effective and efficient locations to serve the global market."

## 4.3 New Business Development by Responding to Customers' Needs and Desires

Next we have an example involving power systems business creation, which originated in Mitsubishi Electric Corporation through collaboration with customers and competitors.

After an interval of approximately thirty years, laws governing the power supply business in Japan were modified in 1996. Competition for supplying power will soon begin in this newly deregulated business field. This event has also sparked activity in the existing power generation industry, as companies that have been supplying electricity must focus on reducing costs in order to maintain competitiveness in the market. At the same time, regulations regarding environmental impact have become stricter, and uncertainty in the future direction of business is growing.

These facts suggest the need to expand engineering capabilities within the power utilities. However, contrary to this need, companies are reorganizing their corporate infrastructures and downsizing their engineering staffs. To compensate for this weakness, manufacturing companies should enlarge their engineering scope to support power utilities and participate in future power systems development focusing on the following two fields:

1) Power systems planning and operation
2) Electrical equipment design for possible future applications

Under these circumstances, Mitsubishi Electric Corporation established the Power System & Transmission Engineering Center in 1995. This center is in charge of consultation and collaboration of engineering projects with power utilities. Its scope covers both short- and long-term business objectives as do other business fields in the company. In other words, the center surveys both customer needs and desires, and performance is evaluated by customer satisfaction.

As an example of a long-term objective, the center provides planning tools and analysis support systems, and coordinates consultation with power utilities for planning systems. Through this process, it becomes possible to locate potential problems in each of the utilities in advance. After analyzing these future problems, the company proposes countermeasures to resolve the difficulty before it occurs, and in doing so indirectly participates in the original business.

One of the center's short-term business objectives is characterized by globalization. Domestic and overseas substation engineering, previously independent business fields, have been merged together. Overseas component supply and overseas outsourcing are tools which will soon be applied to the domestic market as well.

The center is planning to accumulate and store vast engineering knowledge through collaboration and exchanges with numerous electric utilities, and thus become a knowledge creation organization.

### 4.4 Establishment of In-House Training School (Yamasaki and Baba, 1996b)

Those people who understand the technologies of the entire company are the ones capable of providing positive feedback during the business innovation process. To foster this concept among employees, Mitsubishi Electric has established an Engineering Forum (affiliated with various Mitsubishi Electric engineering societies) and a Technology Training Camp, both part of the in-house Institute of Technology.

#### a. Engineering Forum

In a era where product technologies are becoming increasingly complex and fusing together, personal networks are vital. How much people "give and take" through these networks is the key to whether or not success will be attained. Known by the more common name of "Mitsubishi Electric Institute of Engineering," the Mitsubishi Electric Engineering Forum is contributing to the creation of a company-wide network of engineers.

The Engineering Forum was established in 1978 as a place for engineers in the corporate crossroads to go for self-education, self-training and exchange. It presently has fourteen technical societies and each society has an average of five or six special sub-societies. Activities in each technical society include such things as study meetings, presentations, lectures and the publication of a society bulletin. Recently, the utilization of teleconferencing systems between Tokyo and Osaka is on the increase. This allows engineers in each city to give their presentations together. Furthermore, lectures intended for broad engineering fields are being delivered via communications satellites on predetermined dates.

In the future, greater effort will be made to exchange information via E-mail. By utilizing E-mail, development propositions can be discussed on the network. We believe that by utilizing E-mail, more young engineers will be exposed to the opportunities of technological exchange, thus more effectively promoting the transfer and development of technologies through generations.

#### b. Technology Training Camp

A system in which engineers are trained as managers is well established at Mitsubishi Electric. The company created the "Technology Training Camp," in which the general manager, or members at the management level of the company's various works and labs, lecture and teach the concepts and philosophies of technology management to young engineers (around thirty years of age) who will be the future leaders of the works. This is the very reason that Mitsubishi Electric has consistently turned out presidents whose backgrounds are in technical fields.

The Technology Training Camp is located at the Central Education Center in Kobe, Japan. It accepts only forty-two young engineers each year, twenty-one in the spring and twenty-one in the fall. Each participant has been recommended by the general manager of works/labs. Upon entering the program, an engineer attends twelve lecture sessions, one each month for a year. Each session is six days long. The participants enter the training center on a Sunday evening and remain there until the evening of the following Saturday. The lectures cover all business fields, from energy conversion and electronic devices to materials.

The number of graduates from the Technology Training Camp now totals five hundred, and the members have formed an alumni association called Hishi-juku-kai. They frequently use E-mail to exchange information.

## 5. Conclusions

This paper analyzed R&D management as an important element of the business system. Based on this perspective, the paper then discussed various management innovations implemented by Mistubishi Electric Corporation. Key observations of this paper include:.

(1) The most fundamental objective of the company is survival, and for this the company must possess distinctiveness. Distinctiveness is expressed comprehensively by the business system.

(2) R&D activity is usually accompanied by uncertainties in technology and the market. Management cannot allow itself to become befuddled by these uncertainties, in order that it can focus on the attainment of stable growth and ensure the company's survival.

(3) The critical type of knowledge for the operation of the company is specific knowledge, since specific knowledge contributes to differentiation. Specific knowledge is accumulated through learning in such everyday activities as design, manufacturing, and marketing.

(4) Working together as a team requires the creation of communities of practitioners, where engineers and managers can exchange skills and know-how informally.

(5) We described the following examples of management innovations in Mitsubishi Electric Corporation: the role of the Strategic R&D Planning Office in the Semiconductor Device Development Center; the policy for the promotion of a transnational R&D organization; new business development by responding to customers' needs and desires; and the establishment of a private engineering school in order to foster professional engineers.

## References

Boynton, A.C. (1996) "Achieving dynamic stability through information technology," Engineering Management Review, vol. 24, no. 2.

Kaku, R. (1995) "Extending the guidelines for internationalization to the firm", Nihon Keizai Shimbun (The Japan Economic Newspaper), morning edition, January 19.

Myers, M.B. (1996) "Research and change management in Xerox," in Engines of Innovation, edited by Richard S. Rosenbloom and William J. Spencer.

Yamasaki, H. and Baba, J. (1996a) "General manager's role and responsibilities in a research and development center," Proceedings of the Fifth International Conference on Management of Technology, pp. 478-487.

Yamasaki, H. and Baba, J. (1996b) "New wave of managing innovation," IEEE Engineering

Management Society, International Conference on Engineering and Technology Management IEMC96 Proceedings, pp. 761-765.

## Acknowledgements

Many of the ideas and examples for this paper came from conversations between the authors and Dr. Hiroshi Suzuki, General Manager, Power System & Transmission Engineering Center, Mitsubishi Electric Corporation. We are grateful to Dr. Suzuki for his insight.

## Biographical Information of the Authors

**Hiroyuki Yamasaki** was born in Hyogo, Japan, on September 9, 1956. He received B.Eng. and M.Eng. degrees in electronics and a Ph.D. in electronic science and technology, all from Shizuoka University, Hamamatsu, Japan, in 1980, 1982 and 1985, respectively. His doctoral research was in the area of functional solid-state imaging devices.

He joined Mitsubishi Electric Corporation (Tokyo, Japan) in 1985. His career in the company is outlined as follows: 1985-1987, senior engineer of Advanced VLSI Design Group; 1987-1991, senior engineer of Novel VLSI Circuit Design Group; 1991-1993, assistant manager of Strategic R&D Planning Group of the LSI Laboratory (Hyogo, Japan); 1993-1995, assistant manager of R&D Planning Office, ULSI Laboratory (Hyogo, Japan); 1995, manager of R&D Planning Office, ULSI Laboratory; presently he holds the post of manager of Strategic R&D Planning Group, ULSI Laboratory.

Dr. Yamasaki received the Takayanagi Memorial Award for "Research on Novel Solid-state Imaging Devices with Inherent MNOS Memory" in 1986, and the Meritorious Person Award from Sanda City (Hyogo, Japan) in 1993. He lectured at the Graduate School of Engineering, Shizuoka University, in 1991. He is appointed a visiting associate professor, Center for Joint Research, Shizuoka University, in 1996. He is a senior member of IEEE, belongs to the IEEE Management Society and the IEEE Electron Devices Society. He is a member of IAMOT, IEE (Chartered Engineer), and the Japan Society for Science Policy and Research Management, and the Institute of Television Engineers of Japan. He is a member of the Board of Directors, and Editorial Committee Board of the Japan Society for Science Policy and Research Management, and is a member of committee 149 of the Japan Society for the Promotion of Science.

**Kenneth Pechter** is Faculty Research Associate of Science, Technology and Policy at the Research Center for Advanced Science and Technology, the University of Tokyo. His research interests include innovation studies and international technology policy and management.

In addition to this research, Pechter has been active in various commissions focusing on technology and policy issues involving the U.S. and Japan. He was a member of the U.S. Congress's Office of Technology Assessment team that produced the July 1995 report, International Partnerships in Large Science Projects. He was a rapporteur and editor for the September 1996 conference Technology Policy in a Borderless World Economy, under the auspices of the Engineering Academy of Japan and the transnational Council of Academies of Engineering and Technological Sciences. He is a research staff member for the US-Japan Joint Task Force on Corporate Innovation under the auspices of the Japan Society for the Promotion of Science and the U.S. National Academies of Science and Engineering. He has worked for Japan's Research Institute for Telecom Policies and Economics, has served on the Programming Committee of the Japan-America Society of

Southern California, and has consulted to various Japanese companies.

Pechter received B.S. (magna cum laude, 1987) and M.S. (1988) degrees from the University of California, Irvine, in Electrical and Computer Engineering in the area of signals and controls, and was a University of California Chancellor's Fellow in the School of Engineering from 1988 to 1993 researching policy-relevant aspects of industrial engineering. In addition to Electrical and Computer Engineering, he also held a research position in the University's Institute of Transportation Studies. From 1988 to 1990 Pechter was a Ministry of Education Monbusho Scholar at the Tokyo Institute of Technology's Department of Industrial Engineering and Management, and has been an invited fellow at both the MIT Japan program (1991) and the Stanford-run Inter-University Center in Japan (1993-94). Pechter has also worked as an engineer in both the U.S. and Denmark.

**Fumio Kodama** is Professor of Science, Technology and Policy at the Graduate School of Engineering in the University of Tokyo. He is also Director of the Socio-Technological Research Department at the Research Center for Advanced Science and Technology (RCAST). Previously, he taught at the Department of Industrial Engineering and Management in the Tokyo Institute of Technology (1993), and at the Graduate School of Policy Science in Saitama University (1984-1993). In addition to teaching, he has worked as Director-in-Research of the National Institute of Science and Technology Policy at the Science and Technology Agency (1988-1991).

Kodama was Visiting Professor of the Kennedy School of Government at Harvard University in 1991-1992, teaching in the Program on Science, Technology, and Public Policy. In 1992-1993 he was Visiting Professor of Mechanical Engineering at Stanford University, teaching in the VTSS (Values, Technology, Science, and Society) Program. He is a graduate of the University of Tokyo, where he received B.S. and M.S. degrees in mechanical engineering (in 1964, 1967), and earned a Ph.D. in Engineering in 1974. He had been an administrator at the Ministry of International Trade and Industry (MITI) in 1964-65, a Research Fellow at Institute of Systems Research at Heidelberg in 1967-1969, and a Fulbright visiting professor at Hamilton College's Government Department in New York in 1978-79.

Kodama is a member of the Engineering Academy of Japan and serves as a director on its board. He also serves on several advisory committees of Japanese Government agencies such as MITI, the Science and Technology Agency, and the Economic Planning Agency. He is the author of many articles on science and technology policy. One of his works is "Analyzing Japanese High Technologies: The Techno-Paradigm Shift", (Pinter Publishers, London, 1991), the Japanese version of which received the 1991 Sakuzo Yoshino Prize. He is also a recipient of the 1991 Science and Technology Minister's Award for Research Excellence. His journal publications include "Technology Fusion and the New R&D" (Harvard Business Review, July-August 1992). His most recent book "Emerging Patterns of Innovation: Sources of Japan's Technological Edge" was published in April of 1995 by Harvard Business School Press.

**Jun'ichi Baba** was born in Osaka, Japan, on January 29, 1926. He received B.Eng., M.Eng. and Ph.D. degrees in electrical engineering, all from the University of Tokyo, Tokyo, Japan, in 1947, 1949 and 1954, respectively. His doctoral research was in the area of insulation for equipment in power-generation systems.

He joined Mitsubishi Electric Corporation (Tokyo, Japan) in 1952. His career in the company is outlined as follows: 1973-1977, general manager of Planning Department, Power & Industrial

Systems Division (Tokyo, Japan); 1977-1981, general manager of Central Research Laboratories (Hyogo, Japan); 1981-1985, director and general manager of Corporate Engineering and Manufacturing (Tokyo, Japan); 1985-1996, advisor to the board of directors (Tokyo, Japan); 1996-Present, consultant to Mitsubishi Electric Corporation (Tokyo, Japan).

Dr. Baba received the Prize of Progress from the Institute of Electrical Engineers of Japan for "Research on Interconnection Equipment for Power Systems" in 1980. He lectured at the Department of Business Administration, Kobe University, in 1987. He is a senior member of IEEE. He is a member of the Board of Directors of the Academic Association for Organizational Science.

# 106

# 'New Korea Net' R&D Program
# for
# Korean Information Infrastructure

*Seong Youn Kim\*, Choong Young Jung\*\*, Sung Kyu Kim\*\*\**
\*   Head, Information Infrastructure Planning Section, ETRI, Korea
\*\*  Senior Researcher, Information Infrastructure Planning Section, ETRI, Korea
\*\*\* Director, Information Infrastructure Research Center, ETRI, Korea

Information society makes fundamental changes in social, economic, cultural styles and even in sociopolitical systems and structures. Advanced nations recognize technology as the core competency for sustainable economic growth and endeavor to build the information infrastructures to grasp the leadership in the 21st century. Korean government is building the Korean Information infrastructure (hereafter abbreviated as KII) to enhance the national competitive advantage and to raise quality of life. Unfortunately, Korea is not one of the advanced nations in the field of information and telecommunications technology, therefore it is inevitable to have the nation-own technology strategy, so that we should necessarily set up technology planning system which will be used to get the technological competitiveness.

In this article, we will present the overview of KII and the strategic technology planning model based on critical functionality for 'New Korea Net' R&D Program for the second phase[1] of KII.

## 1. Overview of KII

The KII is a broad concept enhancing changes even in the economic and social systems like NII. The main purposes of the KII are to realize citizens to enjoy the benefits of information society, and to enhance the national competitive advantage in the new century. The concepts of KII can be broken down into the following four categories: (1) information transmission layer, (2) information distribution layer, (3) information application layer, and (4) information society layer. The information transmission layer means the physical networks and includes the construction of new multimedia network infrastructure over which information data will be carried, such as Internet, broadband integrated service network(B-ISDN), wireless digital packet data network, integrated services digital satellite network, and CATV network. The information distribution layer includes the dissemination of information platforms, servers and databases. The information application layer includes the development and operation of various contents and application services. The information society layer includes efforts to foster a social, political, regulatory and cultural environments encouraging the active use of information services and applications. This 4-layered model is summarized as follows.

---

[1] The second phase is from 1998 to 2002

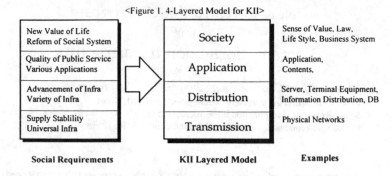

<Figure 1. 4-Layered Model for KII>

| Social Requirements | KII Layered Model | Examples |
|---|---|---|
| New Value of Life / Reform of Social System | Society | Sense of Value, Law, Life Style, Business System |
| Quality of Public Service / Various Applications | Application | Application, Contents, |
| Advancement of Infra / Variety of Infra | Distribution | Server, Terminal Equipment, Information Distribution, DB |
| Supply Stablility / Universal Infra | Transmission | Physical Networks |

The action plan for KII will be implemented in three major fields. First, KII aims to construct the physical high-speed government and public information networks. Second, KII includes the plans for developing key technologies and establishing test-beds and pilot demonstration projects as the integration and utilization of developed technologies. Third, KII action plan will also comprise the enhancement of public awareness and restructuring of environmental frameworks such as the reformation of current laws and regulations for open telecommunications services market.

KII will be built through the three phases; (1) first stage (1995-1997) is the groundwork phase, (2) second (1998-2002) is the diffusion stage, and (3) third (2003-2015) is the completion stage.

The construction of the government network is to focus on the improvement the efficiency of government and public services. It will support key users in the government and public sectors leading the advancement of newly emerging multimedia services and applications. The public networks will take the initiative of the establishment and exploitation of Fiber-to-the-home(FTTH) by 2015 through interconnecting companies, households, and general users via optical fiber cables. Universal multimedia information and telecommunication services will be available through facilitating wide-ranged, two-way, and digitized telecommunications.

## 2. Strategic Technology Planning Model for 'New Korea Net' R&D Program

Technology development is the crucial factor for the creation of KII. As shown in table 1, Korea has 3.2years technological gap in comparison with the advanced nations, therefore many core technologies are heavily dependent on advanced nations[2]. It is urgent to upgrade the level of IT technologies which are necessary to build KII with for the accomplishment of the planned objectives of KII.

<Table 1. Technology Gap in comparison with Advanced Countries>

| Technology | Telecommunications | Information | Components | Average |
|---|---|---|---|---|
| Gap (years) | 3.4 | 2.9 | 3.3 | 3.2 |

---

[2] In 1994, the deficit of technology trade balance was 1,165.6million dollars.

Under these circumstances, it is inevitable to strategically make a plan to take up a position as one of the top-class nations in information and telecommunications technology area in the near future, thus setting up the strategic technology planning process in prior to the identification of core technologies for KII is a starting point. Generally main purposes of technology planning are maintaining the technological core competencies and creating the technological advantage through innovation and efficient acquisition of distinctive competitive advantage using the internal and external technical capabilities. Technology planning can be considered as the system to transform the objectives and strategies into core technologies and R&D priorities. Therefore strategic technology planning process should have the characteristics such as consistency, flexibility, direction, completeness, and integration[3].

The incumbent technology planning has some problems and weakness in the following contexts. First, there is little concern on users' perspectives to decide the requirements of the system to be developed. Second, there is no temporal considerations on the time between the technological hierarchy, that is, applications and services, networks, equipment and technologies. Third, one of the most important objectives of R&D is to transform the technology into the input of the industry or firm. So the process of industrialization of technology which is not considered in existing technology planning should be taken into account in the strategic technology planning. Fourth, most plannings have overlooked the fusion in technology selection and target-setting.

To overcome the above problems and to get the most adequate technologies for KII, we established three essential technology selection principles for KII : (1) technology fusion-oriented R&D, (2) diffusion-oriented environment and (3) system-focused approaches to identify core critical functionality.

Technology fusion is very crucial and important phenomena in information and telecommunications technology. However most of technology planning used breakthrough approach so that they ignored the possibilities of fusion[4]. That is, breakthrough approach has limitations to efficiently identify newly emerging functionality. Fusion reflects the complexity and advancement of users' requirement. So strategic technology planning process should have the process to analyze and evaluate the market demand and the factors related to competitiveness in order to articulate the fusion. Also technological target-setting as the goals should reflect the fusion, first. For example in networked multimedia application, the technological goal should reflect the fusion(e.g. multimedia networking) first, and then set up as breakthrough(e.g. higher resolution).

KII is the national plan to build the new network infrastructure for the future. So diffusion strategy can be one of the most important technology strategy. Technology planning process must have the review process on the diffusion or technology transfer because the objectives of R&D are to increase social return and to have the competitive advantage of the industry through the product embedded with the technology. Especially under time-based competition the speed of technology diffusion is recognized as the most important factor[5]. Also this principle will give the new innovation incentives to the industry.

Finally, system focused approach is necessary to identify new functionality or new research project items. Technology cannot have the synergy effects itself. Especially IT technology has the hierarchy on applications - services - systems - technologies. To become an efficient

---

3 Boar, B.H., *The Art of Strategic Planning for Information Technology*, John Wiley & Sons, Inc., 1993
4 Kodama, F., Technology Fusion and the New R&D, *Harvard Business Review*, Jul.-Aug. 1992
5 But this does not always mean first-to-the-market strategy. Sometimes second entrant strategy will be used.

technology planning, and to identify core critical functionality the conceptual framework which is normatively conceptualized plays very important role in our planning model. That means conceptual frameworks have the hierarchy on the technology system within the target technological functionality as we will state in detail later. In our case, the conceptual framework is very enormous one because KII has the full functionality in IT. So we made 4 frameworks in relation with each other, which are analysis frames on users' perspectives, application concepts for newly emerging applications to be consistent with the evolving users' perspectives, service framework to support the applications, and network architecture for the services and applications identified.

Under these principles, five staged strategic technology planning model for KII as in the figure 2 is established, (1) constructing the KII conceptual frameworks, (2) situation analysis around the KII, (3) identification of technology opportunity through the critical functionality anaysis, (4) target-setting the technological goals through technology evaluation and assessment, and (5) making the technology acquisition strategy. We will introduce each step in short.

<Figure 2. Strategic Technology Planning Process for New Korea Net R&D Program>

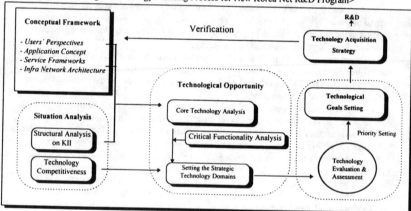

## Constructing Conceptual Frameworks

In most technology planning in information and telecommunications, planners consider technology hierarchy between applications, systems, and technologies in terms of time, but the identification of what applications are thrust by users is very difficult. In the past this step was disregarded because most engineers and researchers were accustomed to the follow-up mode in R&D. Under the follow-up or catch-up strategy they didn't need to make the original framework for the next-generation technologies, since there already existed market analysis and the technological model of leading companies or nations. They did just imitate advanced nations' model. But at these times highly severe competitions caused by globalization do not allow this kind of practice. So conceptual framework by normative approach for the future becomes more and more important.

Especially in the national program for constructing new networks accompanied with huge investment, the analysis of users' requirement is critical to the success of the program. The conceptual creation of new services/systems and of new technology concepts derived from the users' perspectives is main issue in this step. So the conceptual framework will be used as the analysis baseline through the entire process. The conceptual services/systems means the desired technology system with the expected value and utilities of users, and the conceptual technology means the new technological functionality that is necessary to implement the conceptual services/systems. This step has the point of view from future to present, that is, Out-In perspective on the time dimension of strategic technology planning process. Also this step uses very normative approach for the implementation.

Actually in this stage visionary models such as Applications Vision, Service Framework, and Integrated Infra Network Architecture for interoperability and seamless services are constructed to make the analysis on KII. First, for application vision, we identified five key applications[6] with the factors on intrinsic business attractiveness[7] and strategic impacts[8] for Korea as the key applications for KII. Second, service framework and integrated network architecture are established to extract and classify the technological requirements for KII.

## Situation Analysis

In this step, we introduce the generic strategic analysis. At this phase general situation analysis methodologies practiced by firms are used to identify the factors on threat, opportunity, weakness, and strength[9]. Thus the main activities consist of the analysis on environmental and internal factors affecting research and technology policy. The technology development scenarios (technology roadmap) are built on the analysis affecting technology strategy, the assessment of current technology status, and market value chain with the structural analysis on KII and identification of technology competitiveness. In this phase, the strategic options to proceed the strategic positioning in competitiveness for the future should be derived, too. This step has the point of view from present to future, that is, In-Out perspectives.

And the other important activity is to make the technology roadmap - in our case, we made application and service roadmap, terminal equipment roadmap, and technology roadmap - through the scenarios for strategic positioning and the foresight on technology development. The roadmap will be used as the guidelines for critical functionality analysis.

## Identification of Technological Opportunity

This stage is the most important one in this model. The purpose of this step is to identify critical technologies needed to implement the conceptual models, to verify the roadmap, and to look for the opportunistic technological options. Therefore the integration of previous two steps in the view of time horizon is done in this stage.

---

[6] Electronic Commerce, Virtual School, Distributed Business, Smart Factory, and Tele-Government are selected as five key applications for the promotion of KII.

[7] Industrial business potential and fitness with Korean competitiveness are used as variables to identify business attractiveness.

[8] Benefits for the industry and for the society as major factors are measured by brainstorming and experts interview.

[9] Especially National Information Infrastructure programs progressed in other advanced nations and strategic alliances between the leading companies of the world are core threat factor. On the other hand these become considered as the opportunity factors, too. The strength factors are unit people and strong government, the weakness factors are low-level technology, lack of highly-qualified human resources in engineering and research fields for the KII.

In order to pull out the important and necessary technologies, it must be carried out core technologies analysis (exploratory approach) on the basis of marketability, relevance, and the transition of technological gap level through the present and future R&D plan. Also the planner should evaluate and verify the technology roadmap constructed in the previous stage with the information from technology forecasting and conceptual framework. In addition, we should extract strategic technologies from the core critical technologies. Strategic technologies are defined as core technologies that we should acquire and possess to accomplish the specific desired objectives. In our study they were the bottleneck technologies which should be acquired by government R&D fund to complete the second stage of KII, because bottleneck technologies accompany with market failure in general.

The most important activity in this step is identifying the strategic technology domains(hereafter STDs) according to the critical functionality. These STDs will be guidelines for R&D programs.

Through this process we will be able to rearrange the unit technologies into the well-organized strategic technology domains that allow us to get various technological options for services/systems development.

## ❑ Strategic Technology Domains with Critical Functionality

Strategic technology domains are defined as sets of core competent technologies for the sustainable competitive advantage of the nation or organization. But how to identify core competent technologies becomes the major problem. What are frequently used to find them is through the core technology analysis, but that is only simple breakthrough approach. In fact, new technology or innovation has been selected in a single fashion in most technology planning system, that is, the choice was in the hand of engineers or scientist to make breakthroughs in that field. But this kind of selection is very ineffective to meet the users' requirement in the progress of fusion. For example, multimedia technologies have been evolved and will be evolving through the fusion.

Microscopic view of technology usually used in research community emphasizes breakthroughs, but macroscopic view concentrates on the fusion of technologies with new functionality and performances.

Therefore it is needed to introduce a new concept to overcome the limit of the methodology. Critical functionality is one of the significant alternatives to substitute the old plain one. Critical functionality is the functionality which is the newly emerging technology capability required in the market, and which is the technology function in the usage or utilization characteristics that will be a source of future sustainable competitive advantage of the country or organization. It can be derived from the point of view of implementing the key applications concept within the designated period. The important thing to take into account the criticality will be the degree of improvement of the given technology system in terms of time, performance, effectiveness, and other system-specific factors to measure the performance level.

STDs should include the core competencies to be able to have sustainable competitive advantage and national or structural competitiveness in the specific technology area. Therefore STDs will play a significant role of acquiring the national or organizational competitiveness through the core competency.

## ❑ Extraction Procedure of Strategic Technology Domains

STDs are the very critical problem in technology selection and adoption in national innovation system in developing countries because of the limit of resources[10] and lower level of core technological capabilities to accomplish the objectives of national science and technology policy. Unfortunately we have no well-defined procedures of STD to facilitate an efficient R&D investment.

The procedures to identify STDs are as follows; (1) establish the functionality model for the specific technology on the designated time domain, (2) analyze the newly emerging critical functionality from the technological functional model, (3) extract critical technologies to become bottlenecks in implementing the conceptual framework within the target period, recognizing competitiveness factors for national sustainable competitive advantage, (4) define STDs with the characteristics of the technology, and reorganize the critical technologies according to the characters of STDs.

<Figure 3. Extraction of Strategic Technology Domains by Critical Functionality>

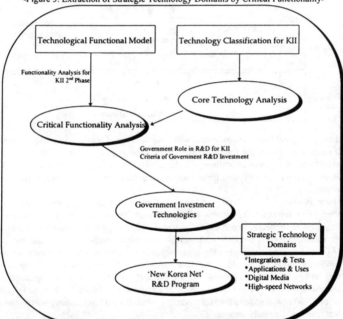

In order to find the STDs, what should be done first, is the analysis on core technologies with the factors on marketability, technical impacts, and gap analysis in terms of current status and future positioning through the comparison of the own technology plans and benchmarked ones. The result from this analysis will be used to verify whether the critical technologies of the next step is right ones.

Second, strategy planners should identify and define the functionality from technological

---

[10] National R&D investment of Korea in 1994 was 9.83billion dollars that was equal to one-seventeenth of US, one-twelfth of Japan.

requirements, and identify bottleneck technologies according to the functionality to implement in a specified time period. In KII we modeled functionality model as seen in figure 4, and analyzed and extracted critical technologies for implementing the functions according to contents creation, information management, information processing and packaging, networks, information appliances, navigator, common applications and field-specific applications.

<Figure 4. KII Technological Functionality Model>

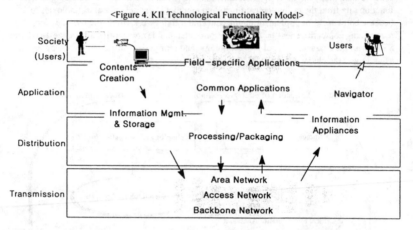

KII technological functionality model will have the crucial role as a baseline of technology infrastructure considering the value chain of information and telecommunication market. Critical technologies would be bottleneck technologies, but not strategic technologies. These technologies come from the technological importance, that means no strategic variables are not applied yet.

So there is a necessity to classify and regroup these shopping list of critical technologies by a certain criteria, for example, strategic areas or national technology policy. This will make enable qualitative modeling to recognize the sustainable competitive advantage factors. Critical issues in sustainable competitive advantage modeling are concerned with demand and supply sides of the technology system. For the efficiency, several questions should be considered. What kind of applications should be provided and when will it be possible? What are the necessary technologies for the provision of the applications and what technologies are critical technologies in the time? How can we acquire the necessary technologies, own or influence, make or buy? Who will acquire the technologies, national research institute, telcos, equipment providers, service providers, academia?

For the market side, a planner must consider technology and service market size, market growth rate, spin-off effects, and other critical issues, and also count the integration of technology and market, that is, service/technology mapping, optimum volume of demand and supply for the creation of demand in the investment.

By this process we need to set the strategic technology domains for R&D with similar technological functionality from the analysis. The strategic technology domains[11] are functional clusters of critical technologies for building the sustainable competitive advantage in the future,

---

[11] STDs selected for KII are as follows: Integration and tests, Applications and uses, Digital media, and High-speed networks.

and will be used as project baselines.

## Target-setting Technological Goals

To set up performance level necessary to satisfy the functionality and to solve the bottlenecks in designated period, we should first establish priority setting for technology development. Relevance analysis on technologies and conceptual services is the most crucial process in this step. This means that we should estimate whether the conceptual services or systems with the required performance level can be implemented by the critical technologies.

Usually we can determine technological goals for the STDs through market analysis considering the speed of technology development. We can express the goals with targeted time varying with service or provision time, and technological specification in minimum. We should make the hierarchy of the objectives or goals such as long-term, mid-term and short-term responding to the performance level because it is inevitable to reorganize the technologies in STDs by the technological alternatives in order to implement the conceptual services or systems.

If possible, we would like to recommend to conduct technology assessment to get the maximum effectiveness of the innovation and to give the early warning accompanied with the provision or use of the technologies before the setting technological target.

## Making Technology Acquisition Strategy

After the setting the target we should take into account how to acquire the desired technological goals. Technology acquisition strategy is very important part of technology strategy. In this step, we analyze the strategic alternatives for the acquisition of the targeted technological goals. And the trade-off analysis between the strategic alternatives is carried out to select the optimal acquisition strategies. Generally 'doing it alone' or 'looking for the unique technological solution' is very dangerous in technology planning.

Traditionally R&D and outsourcing are the major alternatives. But 'Own' or 'Influence' is rising as another issue in technology acquisition. In order to make an effective decision on strategic alternatives and to compare the feasibility of the alternatives, we would be able to do the enablers and barriers analysis which can identify what are the driver factors and what are the barriers to accomplish the goals.

After the selection of the acquisition strategy we should do priority setting for resource allocation to select optimal strategy for R&D. In this case, we have to recognize this need not be the same as strategic technology domain. Priority setting is concerned with the policy term, whereas strategic technology domain is just the technological classification to get the desired technological goals.

We should also take into account technology deployment and diffusion as one of the efficient acquisition strategy, to get the synergy effects between the R&D entities.

So this is necessary phase to maximize the effectiveness of acquisition on where and how to get the desired core strategic technologies with the given resources.

## 3. Conclusions

So far, we have discussed about strategic technology planning process for New Korea Net R&D programs based on critical functionality. The most important one in this model is constructing the functional model to draw out the critical technologies within the functionality. As previously stated, strategic technology domains represent new functionality, consistency to technology policy and strategy, and efficiency in R&D resources allocation on the focused area. We should carefully set up these strategic technology domains to be used as subprograms to get the maximum effectiveness of the planning, because the extracted strategic technologies are just the shopping list of the critical technologies.

We are sure that this technology planning process model which aims at KII can also be applied to different technology areas if it is slightly modified, and that although this model is established for the public R&D planning, it will also be efficiently used by the private firms.

# References

1. Betz, F., *Strategic Technology Management*, McGraw-Hill, Inc., 1994
2. Bitondo, D. and Frohman, A., Linking Technological and Business Planning, *Research Management*, Nov. 1981
3. Boar, B.H., *The Art of Strategic Planning for Information Technology*, John Wiley & Sons, Inc., 1993
4. Boden, M., *The Identification of Technology Priorities for European Research and Technology Development: A Review of Technology Mapping and Related Techniques*, MONITOR-SAST ACTIVITY, 1992
5. Burgelman, R.A. and Maidique, M.A., *Strategic Management of Technology Innovation*, Irwin, 1988
6. Gover, J., Corporate Management of R&D - Lessons for the U.S. Government, *Research · Technology Management*, Vol.38 No.2, Mar.-Apr., 1995
7. Iansiti, M., Real-World R&D: Jumping the Product Generation Gap, *Harvard Business Review*, May-Jun., 1993
8. Kodama, F., Technology Fusion and the New R&D, *Harvard Business Review*, Jul.-Aug. 1992
9. Koerner, E., Technology Planning at General Motors, *Long Range Planning*, Vol.22 No.2, 1989, p.p.9-19
10. Mitchel G.R., The Changing Agenda for Research Management, *Research · Technology Management*, Vol.35 No.2, Sep.-Oct., 1992
11. Roussel, P.A., Saad, K.N. and Erickson, T.J., *Third Generation R&D - Managing the Link to Corporate Strategy*, Boston, Harvard Business School, 1991.
12. Schoemaker, P.J.H., How to Link Strategic Vision to Core Capabilities, *Sloan Management Review*, Vol.34, Fall 1992, p.p.67-81
13. Werther, W. B. Jr., Berman, E., and Vasconcellos, E., The Future of Technology Management, *Engineering Management Review*, Fall 1994

# 107

# Integrated Competence Development

## A Concept for Company and University Coordinated Research

**Bengt-Olof Elfström, Ola Isaksson, Rosmarie Lunde**

Volvo Aero Corporation, 461 81 Trollhättan, SWEDEN

## Abstract

A framework for competence development involving universities and company in tight co-operation is being developed at Volvo Aero. A process oriented view and a concept for learning organisations are key factors for the company's competence profile and thereby it's competitiveness.

Experience from ongoing co-operation programs is presented. The objective is to transfer scientific knowledge into technical knowledge and at the same time stimulate university education and research.

The concept is based on PhD students and professors associated to both organisations and working in multi disciplinary teams. As a result, the level of interaction and communication between the university and the company have been significantly enhanced.

Advantages and disadvantages of this tight coupling between university and company are discussed.

## 1    Background and Introduction

Strategies and methods for efficient product development are popular issues in today's industry. Integrated Product Development (IPD), Concurrent Engineering (CE) and Integrated Product/ Process Teams (IPPT) are only some of the labels frequently mentioned. IPD (e.g. Conaway, 1995) will be used in this article for convenience. The fundamental ideas are the same in all concepts and the explicit techniques used all aims at obtaining an efficient and enthusiastic work environment where the right things are done in the right way and in the right time.

The title 'Integrated competence development' reflects on the apparent similarities between the concept to be described for competence development and the issues addressed in IPD. No unified definition of what is included in IPD exists although the concept (CE) is becoming firmly established (Couchman and Badham, 1996). Typical features are;

- identified customers with early and tight involvement
- tight communication with suppliers and partners
- use of structured support methods (e.g. QFD, DFM, FMEA)
- parallel activities
- cross-disciplinary teams
- efficient and intensive use of digital simulation tools (CAD, FEM, CFD, MSA)
- emphasise target definitions, objectives, aims, etc.

These features hold true not only in efficient product development but also in the concept of competence development at Volvo Aero in Trollhättan.

### 1.1 General driving forces in a competitive environment

The business environment is rapidly changing and companies have to be able to meet new situations faster and more often to stay competitive. Wheelwright and Clark (1992) identified the driving forces for industrial development as:

- Intense international competition
- Fragmented, demanding markets
- Diverse and rapidly changing technologies (which increases the variety of possible solutions)

To meet these tougher business situations the companies can either emphasise on

- rapid adaptation to new circumstances or
- more focused business strategy (by liaison, globalisation, outsourcing)

Both alternatives are frequently used, but in this paper the former will be in focus, i.e. when companies want to develop competence for a competitive organization.

In figure 1, an alternative description on how the company's complex situation forms the requirement on it's organisation and individual co-workers is illustrated.

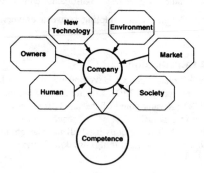

*Figure 1: Companies situation sets the scene for competence requirements*

Except for the previously mentioned requirements, a company has environmental and social responsibilities which adds requirements to the list. New technologies not only increases the variety of possible solutions but also provides new methods and tools for efficient work. The intuitive area is perhaps the information technology area, where new ways of communicating are supported and more sophisticated simulations can be performed using computer aided tools. However, these technology improvements also requires employees to be educated and new organisational forms to be developed.

### 1.2 New and future requirements on competence

Statham and Kleiner (1996) identifies two major premises for efficient development projects;

- use up-front planning and
- cross disciplinary communication

These must be emphasised to reduce the number of late and expensive problems.

When developing competence, the same idea holds true; plan your forthcoming need for competence to avoid late problems with lacking competence. In this work, new tools and methods are being used for project and process planning of competence development.

Competence improvements have to be carried out continuously on several levels;

- development and implementation of new methods
- new and improved methodologies
- development and adoption new technologies
- develop organisations and management techniques

Capbility to synthesise increasingly complex situations is a vital competence. Most work activities have become more theoretical, and *theoretical knowledge* is definitely a core competence. This also increases the need for knowledge about higher education in most companies.

*Social competencies* (communication, flexibility, creativity, adaptable to continuously changing circumstances, express in oral and writing in several languages, management skills, holistic and critical thinking) are increasingly important since more intense communication is required both within the company and between the company and customers/suppliers/partners.

Since the industrial environment is quite turbulent and future changes can be expected the following questions are raised;

- How to prepare students for life-long learning?
- How to educate for continuous re-education?
- How many times must an average co-worker re-educate?

## 2    Methods

### 2.1    Process based competence development

Volk (1992) concluded from a technology development project at Northrop Corporation (USA) that technological improvements (regarding advanced, automated computational tools) themselves will not improve productivity. Increased awareness and control of processes are required to develop and introduce new and improved technological systems.

One way to obtain a good overview of organisational activities, used and developed at Volvo Aero since late 80:th (Loinder, 1996) is to use process mapping to describe activities (Rise & Wiklund, 1993). Customer needs and inputs are identified as well as the products from each process. The *process* is defined as the series of activities required to develop the product based on input from customer needs. The process is directed by management processes and supported by support processes, as illustrated in figure 2.

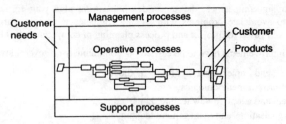

*Figure 2: Illustration of process mapping, describing work at VAC*

Describing work in processes, using process mapping, is helpful when identifying critical competencies in new or excising processes. Thus, the problem of obtaining an overview over the competence situation can be addressed.

The market environment sets the scene and through a careful strategy analysis the product plan is formulated. The product plan sets the requirements on the business plan and the technology plan, respectively. Finally, as the technology requirements are identified, the requirements on forthcoming competence needs can be foreseen and formulated in a competence development plan. The resulting plan is used for personnel and organisational development strategies. In this way competence requirements can be foreseen and planned for in a structured manner. Strategic tools used for this development at Volvo Aero are found in Roussel et al (1992).

The competence development forms at Volvo Aero ranges from short course modules to post doctoral education. The different levels where universities and the company co-operate are shown in figure 3.

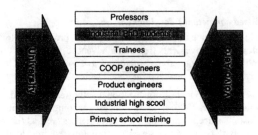

*Figure 3: The different levels of competence development at Volvo Aero and co-operation with universities.*

### 2.2 Learning processes

Organisations need to rapidly adopt to new circumstances and learn how to do things in new and different ways (Dodgson, 1993). As the competitiveness of the company increasingly depends on such capability, the process of organisational learning has been highlighted. Not only has the company to learn from their mistakes, but also consciously and continuously improve current processes and methods. As the need for a specific competence has been identified, the delicate task is to develop and implement this competence into the organisation. Argyris and Schon (1978) describe this as single-loop learning (learning from mistakes), double-loop learning (improve current processes) and deuterio-learning (understand and develop the process of learning itself). Dodgson concludes that an interdisciplinary perspective will have a particular value for studying learning organisations.

Competence follows the individual and therefore the individual co-worker carries the company's competence. To achieve a organisational capability, this has to be done by developing individuals such that these contribute to the organisational competence requirement.

Lunde (1996) studied the effects on co-operation and work culture of a re-organisation. It was found that a re-organisation can be useful when developing competence within a company by identifying the work culture supporting critical processes.

### 2.3 The process of technology development

It is useful to divide the development efforts into product- and process developments to meet the requirement of an effective product and an effective company, respectively. Each is divided into base development phase, demo phase and prototype phase as shown in figure 4.

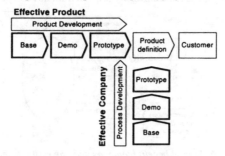

*Figure 4: Process vs. product development*

Project planning can be used to identify expected and forthcoming technology requirements. (Isaksson & Elfström, 1996). New and improved technologies identified can be assessed (upon risk) and an appropriate form of technology development can be initiated. Structured methods (like QFD) are valuable when identifying and assessing these alternatives.

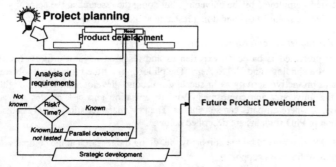

*Figure 5: Assessment of technology requirements*

The same method can be used for strategic competence development. As the technology development is planned future needs of competence are identified which forms input to the competence development plan (see also figure 3).

# 3    A concept for Company and University co-ordinated research

Volvo Aero uses several methods to co-ordinate competence development in an industrial environment. Co-operation within the Volvo Aero group or within the Volvo company, together with partners and suppliers, and co-operation with universities in different forms. Here, the university co-operation projects involving doctoral students will be discussed, and one of them presented in more detail.

## 3.1    General doctoral student models

Co-operation between universities is most often used in base and demo phases of process development, while universities seldom takes part in the core development phases of product development. Research oriented projects and demonstrator projects are often more suitable for university involvement. New methods, techniques and ideas developed at universities often needs an implementation phase before they are productive. The problem discussed often addresses questions important for new engineers, presently under education at the universities. Thus, both the company and the university benefits from this co-operation. Se figure 6.

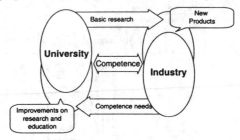

*Figure 6: Mutual benefit (company and university) from co-operation*

These research projects can be realised in several different ways. At VAC we have four different models for involving PhD students;

- Industrial PhD students employed by and doing research at the company
- Industrial PhD students employed by the company and doing research at the university
- PhD students employed by the university, but doing the research at the company
- PhD students employed by- and doing research at the university

## 3.2    The model for co-ordinated research

The model presented is based on experiences and research in joint projects between Luleå university of technology and Volvo Aero. The philosophy of the project is to obtain the same positive and pro-active activity as in successful product development teams. Tight coupling between the university and company in both organisation and task creates a group with a common goal, where all parts can se benefits. The key characteristics, mainly considering the organisation of PhD students are described below;

- PhD students employed by the university, but doing the research at the company
- Government financial support
- Position at operative department, utilising the technology of interest
- Insight in the daily work at the company
- Involved, to some extent, in the university department work
- Involved, to some extent, in the product development project

- Steering group with members from university and company
- Reference group, consisting of company specialists in the area
- Examiner and supervisor at the university
- Supervisor at the company
- Reporting to government, university and company in different forms
- Information and implementation through the government program, the university and direct into the company
- Information to other interested parties through publications, seminars, lectures, and courses

The technology development projects are managed following the same principles as in an IPD project. This means parallel work, cross disciplinary teams and communication, and use of structured support tools (se figure 7). The project steering group consists of seven persons out of which three persons from the university and four from the company. They all represent different interests of the project (customer, supervisor, expert etc.). The entire group meets twice a year, while the company group has four additional meetings a year.

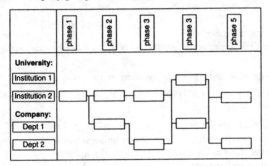

*Figure 7: A process schema used for planning of activities and showing the relations and responsibilities of the work packages*

# 4 Results and conclusions

## 4.1 General observations

The general observations presented are based on several years of research co-operation between Volvo Aero and various Swedish universities.

1. Observed difficulties to establish an efficient form of co-operation

   Universities and companies have by definition different aims of their work and thereby different roles. Universities works on a longer base while companies have to consider short return of their investments and make profit. The academic culture differs from the company culture and this can often lead to mis-understandings and mis-interpretations in meetings and agreements. Especially if the parts only meets occasionally, and does not have a tight communication. Together with a relatively low research competence in industry and low industrial competence at universities, conditions for efficient co-operation are lacking.

2. Continuous change of universities

   Swedish universities are currently undergoing several changes. In industrial terms, they are developing a customer oriented view, with less free founding and competition to get students. Quality questions and educational lead times are frequent issues of discussions.

More research activities are wanted in collaboration with industry. The development of new, regional universities has forced universities to focus on different areas. Small and local universities specialise on regional specialities, young universities on applied research while the old and well established universities are strongest in classical areas of science. This simplified relation is illustrated in figure 8, where the university profiles are related to typical stages in industrial development.

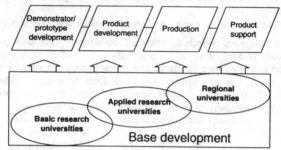

*Figure 8: Types of universities involved in different industrial stages*

### 4.1.1 Conclusions based on general observations

To improve the efficiency for university and company co-ordinated research, the following considerations are vital to deal with

- Obtain an understanding for each roles, culture and language
- Search for equal competence level at both the university and the company in order to get a good dialogue in communication and adaptation of knowledge
- Build cross functional networks
- Increase the amount of research educated co-workers in the companies
- Improve industrial involvement and increase the number of industrially experienced people at the universities
- Develop co-operation forms involving industrial based PhD students

### 4.2 Advantages and disadvantages with the co-ordinated research model

The model for co-ordinated research has influenced the working methods at both the university and the company. Both parts have developed a better understanding for each others expectations and the close coupling has improved communication, something that is vital in technology transfer. Some advantages are summed below;

- High degree of influence on both company and university
- Good forum for co-operation (mixed steering group)
- Fast implementation of new technology
- Fast feedback for university education and research
- High degree of relevancy in research (continuous involvement)
- Industrial PhD student is free to focus on research activities
- Easy access to the company's education for university co-workers
- Easy access to university education for company co-workers
- Real industrial experience during doctoral education
- Direct and simultaneous insight in company and university

However, there are some disadvantages especially for the research student namely;

- Weaker academic environment in companies
- Courses at a distance
- Implementation issues can disturb the research activities
- Less objective position

# 5    Discussion

The perhaps most important recommendation is to not only agree upon the research objectives and goals, but also to understand each others perspective and expectations. As a help in doing so, an illustration of the research perspective has been developed and used in the discussion. Companies expectations on projects are often to find applicable solutions to a problem on an industrial level whereas researchers at the university aims at developing their field from a scientific point of view. Generally, scientists wants a narrow scope to fulfil expectations and industry people a much wider scope. The difference between project expectations    is illustrated in figure 9.

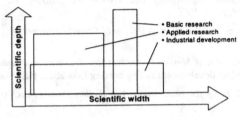

*Figure 9: Different levels of technology projects*

Initially, this might seem like a contradiction in defining objectives that satisfies both aspects. However, the scientific research perspective is beneficial for the broader industrial expectations as well. This is illustrated in figure 10. Typically, a scientific development effort strives for a deeper and more complete understanding of a specific problem or phenomenon. To achieve this, a solid understanding is needed in a wider area. This knowledge rests on a scientifically solid base and does not directly contribute to new scientific results.

For the industrial problem in the same field this basic scientific knowledge might be very useful. It is often not known to a broader community outside the scientific discipline. *A scientific peak effort within a narrow area gives a broader knowledge which contributes to the solution of industrial problems in a much wider sense.*

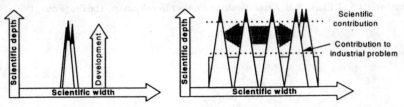

*Figure 10: Scientific development vs. industrial development. The scientific study gives a wider result on an industrial level than what is scientifically interesting.*

On the other hand, applied scientific research directly linked to industrial activities guarantees relevant research topics.

A few scientific (narrow) efforts defined within the industrial problem can cover the broad scope of a project on an industrial level, and still produce relevant and scientifically interesting results.

# 6    Acknowledgement

Financial support from NUTEK (the INPRO programme) is acknowledged.

# 7    References

Argyris, C., Schon, D., *Organizational learning*, London: Addison Wesley, 1978

Conaway, J., Integrated Product development The Technology, White Paper at http://www.pdmic.com/articles/artIPD1.html, December 1995

Couchman, P., Badham, R., *Organizing For Effective Concurrent Engineering: Beyond the Technical Fix*, Manufacturing Agility and Hybrid Automation, R.J. Koubek and W. Karwowski (Eds.), IEA press, 1996

Dodgson, M., *Organizational learning: A Review of Some Literatures*, Organizational Studies 1993, pp 375-394

Isaksson, O., Elfström, B-O., *A Method to Analyze Requirements on Product Technology*, 3:d int symposium on Product development in Engineering Education, Halmstad, 1996

Loinder, A: *Processledning för ökad samverkan mellan företag*, LiU-Tek-Lic-1996:06 (In Swedish)

Lunde, R., *Reorganisation, culture and co-operation*, Manufacturing Agility and Hybrid Automation, R.J. Koubek and W. Karwowski (Eds.), IEA press, 1996

Rise, J, Wiklund, T: *Ericsson Business Process Management*, Ericsson Quality Institute, 1993 (In Swedish)

Roussel, P A, Saad, K N, Erickson, T J: *Third Generation R&D: managing the link to corporate strategy*, Arthur D. Little Inc., 1991

Statham, E., Kleiner, B. H., *Effective project management in aerospace industry*, Aircraft Engineering and Aerospace Technology, vol 68, 1996:4

Volk, J. A., *Multidisciplinary design environment development for air vehicle engineering*, AIAA-92-1113-CP, 1992

Wheelwright S C, Clark, K B, *Revolutionizing Product Development*, The Free Press, 1992

# ORGANIZATIONAL LEARNING AND COMPETITIVENESS: THE CONTRIBUTION OF THE EXPERT SYSTEMS TECHNOLOGY AS A DYNAMIZING TOOL FOR THE ORGANIZATIONAL LEARNING PROCESS

Antonio Domingos Padula, Dr
Universidade Federal do Rio Grande do Sul. UFRGS
Programa de Pós-Graduacao em Administracao- PPGA/UFRGS
Porto Alegre, RS- Brasil

Co-author:  Antonio Carlos Macada, MS
The same address

## ABSTRACT

The demands imposed upon enterprises by the dynamism of their business milieu are forcing them to try to transform, in an increasingly shorter period of time, the individual "know-how" into an organizational learning. The organizational learning is here understood as the process through which both individuals and organizations can acquire new knowledge and skills aiming at improving their future performance.

This transformation does not occur automatically. The difficulty lies in the fact that quite often the individual knowledge is not explicitly presented, thus rendering its systematization and sharing difficult.

A behavioral alternative which may contribute to a greater dynamism in the process of transformation of individual knowledge into organizational learning is the utilization of the informatics technology of the expert systems. One of the objectives of this technology is the capitalization of the individual "know-how" into a software and its availability for utilization in areas of interest of the organization.

In this work, we initially intend to show the strategic role taken up by the generation, capitalization and management of the organizational knowledge for the entrepreneurial competitiveness and the possibilities offered by the informatics technology as support tool in this process (Section 1). Section 2 presents the relevant to the development and the utilization of the technology of the expert systems by the organizations. To illustrate one case of strategic utilization of this technology as a support tool to the organizational learning, one expert system is shown which systematizes, formalizes, and capitalizes the "know-how" (methodology of organizational intervention) developed by French Accountants for management consulting (Section 3). In the conclusion, we make some comments on some strategic contributions which the expert systems might come up with in order to facilitate the organizational learning process, thus providing an improvement of the competitive performance of the management consulting offices.

# 110

## SWITCHING OF WORK OPPORTUNITIES BETWEEN DYING AND GROWING INDUSTRIES - A CASE FROM SWEDISH SHIPBUILDERS

Author:
Horst Mueller, Lic.Sc.E, P.E
Chalmers University of Technology, Department of
Transportation and Logistics, S-412 96 GÖTEBORG, Sweden
Tel:        +46-31-772 41 77
Fax:        +46-31-772 42 40
Email:      horst@mot.chalmers.se

## ABSTRACT

Sweden has experienced massive disturbances in affected industries when a dying industry, with heavy impact on work opportunities, tries to climb into already existing market segments.

Often global needs in tune with technological and financial changes are seen to be involved when impact of industries grow or drop.

The examples below from efforts trying to reach, for them, new market segments are from the Swedish shipbuilding industry with the diminishing market segments such as:

- Crude oil, bulk, obo vessels
- Diesel engines
- Auxiliary equipment
- Installation work and miscellaneous equipment.

Examples of attempts for substitution with new market segments were made as follows:

| | | | |
|---|---|---|---|
| - | Road and railway bridges | - | Process plants |
| - | Barges | X | Drilling, service and hotel platforms |
| X | Diesel engine power plants | - | Solar power plants |
| X | Wind power plants | - | Sea wave power plants |
| X | Nuclear power maintenance | X | Installation of process piping |
| - | Installation electrical wiring | - | Machine tools equipment |
| X | Work shop sub-contracts | X | Off-shore supply vessels |

; and where X stand for market segments which have provided sustainable work opportunities.

Out of broadly based on-hands-experiences there will be discussed, issues as triggers for, possible actions for finding interesting volumes of work opportunities.

Key words:
Switching, work opportunities, shipbuilders, industry, sustainable.

# 111

# How economic institutions influence technological choice

## The case of upgrading steelworks dust

*Keywords*: economic institutions, technological choice, zinc

*Authors:*

Per Storm

Industrial Economics and Management, KTH

Drottning Kristinas väg 35 D

S-100 44 STOCKHOLM

tel. +46/8/790 6743

fax. +46/8/790 6741

e-mail: Per_Storm@lector.kth.se


Professor Gunnar Eliasson

Industrial Economics and Management, KTH

Drottning Kristinas väg 35 D

S-100 44 STOCKHOLM

tel. +46/8/790 6803

fax. +46/8/790 6741

e-mail: gunnar_eliasson@lector.kth.se

Topic C/D: National technology policies for a sustainable society

Category 1: conceptual papers

Form of presentation: c) this paper is suitable for both oral presentation and poster presentation.

# How economic institutions influence technological choice

## The case of upgrading steelworks dust

### Introduction - problem, argument and results summarized

Coated steel is a large and growing part of all steel used in manufacturing industry. With growing environmental awareness, increased attention has been paid to the environmental impact and life-cycle costs. Hence, the entire value chain has become concerned with environmentally sound production and acceptable disposal, not only of waste material but also of products when scrapped as when, e.g., zinc coated steel is used. When re-cycled zinc coated steel is remelted in the steel mill, zinc evaporates to form a zinc-containing dust which constitutes an environmental hazard. Accordingly, attempts have been made to find conversion routes to re-cycle the hazardous waste as a raw material in zinc production.

Sweden has an unusually high concentration of scrap-based steel producers. There is also a long tradition of coôperation between the steel mills and the government. In this specific case, several Swedish steelworks have joined forces with the non-ferrous metal producer Boliden, and the research institute MEFOS to resolve the environmental problem. Our hypothesis is that centralized decision making has pushed for one large-scale solution rather than the experimental application of several competing technologies, some of which may, in the long run, turn out economically and environmentally superior to the actually chosen technology. The logics against one centralized solution is clear. The practical experience in Sweden and in other countries increasingly supports the same result: The case for large economies of scale that favour centralized solutions, is no longer clear, even in the short run, since so many other circumstances influence the economic outcome. The case for a varied, experimental approach becomes even stronger when the technology is rapidly changing. For an economy with such a varied steel industry as Sweden, pluralistic experimentation, decided locally has clear advantages.

## The problem

We claim that the Swedish industry structure (in the metals industry) and technological traditions has influenced technological choices in favour of centralistic technical solutions with limited flexibility rather than promoted a decentralized, technological experimention that may generate better long run (and possibly environmentally preferable) solutions to reclaim the dust.

No technical solutions exist today which allow the dust to be treated as a direct raw material for production of high grade zinc products. Existing technologies only upgrade the dust to an environmentally less hazardous form. Development work directed to using the dust as a high grade raw material is in progress, but far from ready for commercial use. With a strong actor such as the government or a government backed organisation - this is an hypothesis - the centralist focus on what works right now will take priority. Thus a second best solution may be advocated and supported economically. The evidence is as follows.

## Technologies and processes

The two main technologies in the reclamation are *pyrometallurgy* (i.e. high temperature chemistry) and *hydrometallurgy* (i.e. wet chemistry). The latter is carried out at ordinary temperatures. In pyrometallurgy the fundamental step is the heating and melting of incoming raw material. The melted raw material may subsequently be modified through additions which generate chemical reactions of different kinds. Fundamental pyrometallurgical reactions may also take place simultaneously with heating, commonly referred to as smelting. Most pyrometallurgical processes, these included, have inherent economies-of-scale for geometrical reasons.

In hydrometallurgy, the central step is the dissolution of the raw material in a solvent (commonly water). The pregnant solutions will then be modifed (generally purified) and the desired metal will precipitate in an electrolysis. Both of these fundamental technologies have been succesfully used in several processes and may also be combined in different ways. The most common conventional zinc processes today are hydrometallurgical.

The common way to treat zinc containing dust today is the Wealtz-process (Unger 1986, Kola 1990) which upgrades the dust in a rotary furnace process (cp. manufacturing of cement) from where it may be used as a low grade addition to conventional pyrometallurgical zinc production production. As merely an upgrading step, the Wealtz-process can not be considered a commercial process to produce zinc raw material but must be seen as a waste treatment facility (Kola 1990). Alternatives to the Wealtz-process, as well as to conventional pyrometallurgical zinc production, have been developed in Sweden. They are part of a line of pyrometallurgical reduction processes developed by SKF Steel Engineering (presently ScanArc Plasma Technologies) that use plasma generators to generate the energy necessary for the reactions. Two main process lay-outs have been outlined: *Plasmadust* and *Slag Reduction*. The *Plasmadust* process is the most developed and was put forward as an alternative to conventional large scale zinc smelting. This shaft furnace based process was found to function equally well for dust feed. It was thus further developed to treat waste products (dust) from different types of steel production. In 1984, an enterprise to upgrade Swedish steel furnace dust was started in Landskrona (Sweden) as a separate company, *ScanDust AB*. In this facility, both stainless and carbon steel dust was initially treated in separate campaigns. In the ScanDust operation, the plasmadust process has been in continuous operation since the start. The carbon steel dust treatment was closed down in 1987 for both economic and technological reasons; the process is currently operating on 100% stainless dust (Santén 1993).

Based on the experiences on developing plasma based processes, ScanArc Plasma Technologies developed a complementary process called *Slag Reduction* (Santén 1992 & 1993). In Slag Reduction, a slag bath is created by oxidic raw materials and underneath the surface plasma generators are supplying required energy to maintain liquid phase and for required reactions. By feeding a controlled amount of reducing agent, a selective reduction of various metals can be obtained. Due to the intense mixing, it is possible to operate the reducer very close to equilibrium. Compared to the large scale *Plasmadust* process, the *Slag Reduction* process is more suited to treat materials with low metal content, it consumes less energy than the Plasmadust process and may, most reasonably be applied economically also in small scale installations as it does not have a shaft based geometry to begin with.

The alternative way to produce zinc is the hydrometallurgical conversion route (leaching and electrolyses). This is the most common route for conventional zinc production in the world (including Europe) today. Unfortunately, EAF dust often contains high amounts of iron oxide and a zinc-iron compound know as zinc ferrite. Conventional processes are not suited to treat raw materials with a high iron content, nor can the mildly acid solutions used in conventional leaching dissolve ferrites. Since it is - in principle - possible to dissolve zinc oxide in both acid and basic solutions, some basic leaching methods have been proposed such as the Cebedeau process (Frenay et al. 1986) and the Caron zinc process (Nyirenda 1990; van Put et al, 1989). Of these, the most developed is the Cebedeau process. It has been running as a pilot plant but has not yet reached commercialisation. In the Cebedeay process, EAF dust is dissolved in an sodium oxided based solution were iron compounds stay unsolved and is obtained as a leach residue. Zinc powder may then be obtained by electrolyses. However, the zinc powder obtained in the process, does not meet the demand of a special high grade product and must be refluxed to meet such standards (Frenay et. al. 1986).

Hydrometallurgical processes in general (these included) do not have the type

of economies-of-scale that exist in pyrometallurgical processes. Hydrometallurgical processes are, however, more flexible capacitywise (easier to build a
leaching pond than a furnace), less capital intensive but more labour intensive
than pyrometallurgical processes. For a comparison of hydrometallurgical and
pyrometallurgical processes, see Kellog (1980, 1990).

Summarizing, two different routes might be traveled to reach the same goal i.e.
environmentally sound and effective metal production. None of the two
technologies are easily identfied as environmentally "better" than the other. They
both entail environmental problems, although in different form. Pyrometallurgy
generates gasous substances (e.g. carbon monoxide and sulphurs oxide) as well as
needs for bulc transport of the dust to and from the treatment facility.
Hydrometallurgy generates sludges and residues mainly form the leaching steps
that have to be handled in an environmentally sound manner. Which of these
processes is economically superior is dependant on the conditions under which
they are implemented. These conditions differ between product type and
localization and change over time. In general, in a dynamically changing
technological environment, flexibility is a desired property of the technology
itself. For the industry at large, and the economy it is then generally to be prefered
to have several competing technologies represented in the market to avoid
having the whole industry locked into an economically less desired solution. In a
technologically changing environment, multiple approaches, futhermore make a
more varied learning possible, than in a standardized environment. This is the
general case against centralistic standard solutions, when future technologies
cannot be predicted multiple approaches should be stimulated at the local firm
level, And one standardized solution should not be promoted from a central
policy level (Eliasson 1991).

If productivity is central and the future best technology predictable,
pyrometallurgy is generally regarded as superior. If flexibility (in regard to e.g. the
business cycle) is wanted, hydrometallurgy is regarded as superior. In

conventional zinc production (i.e. ore-based production), hydrometallurgy has crowded out pyrometallurgy over the past 50 years. It is, nevertheless not clear if any of the two technologies have been profitable lately (Bué 1987).

As we will now see, the combined influence of resident industry competence, traditions of industry and the influence of centralized coordinating governement bodies favoured the choice of a large scale, and fairly, inflexibe pyrometallurgical process to be applied in production installations.

## The economic institutions

The economic institutions involved in the case we study are of three kinds: (*i*) privately owned metal industry companies; (*ii*) non-profit R&D organisations and coôperative bodies and (*iii*) the governement.

Swedish metallurgical industry is structured into production areas as "one company - one product" lines. In commercial steel, SSAB - the biggest Swedish steel company - has the flat segment (steel sheets) and Fundia the long segment (e.g. rebars). In special steel (stainless steel and high alloyed steel) Avesta-Sheffield produces flat stainless steel, Sandvik long stainless products, Ovako high alloyed ball bearing materials (mainly for its mother company SKF), Böhler-Uddeholm high alloyed tool steel, Erasteel Kloster high alloyed speed steel and Scana non-stainless forgings. All of the steelmills use scrap iron and, hence, have the problem of takning care of the evaporated zinc. Non of them have a zinc treatment of their own. Since the only existing Swedish installation (ScanDust) has closed down its zinc operation, they have to ship the dust abroad for treatment.

The steel industry structure has developed historically but one central feature has been the early focus on the home market. Accordingly, in the latest re-structuring of the industry, following the steel crises in the 1970:s, the specilized industry structure that we now see was enforced by direct interventions from the state (the formation of SSAB) and/or the close interaction between the governement and large companies and conglomerates (SOU 1977:15) as e.g. the Johnsson companies (Avesta) and the sphere around Volvo-Skanska (Sandvik). From being an industry with Swedish owned companies, the international industry (roughly 50 % exports and 50 % imports) of today with several companies wholly or partly owned from abroad has emerged: Scana and Fundia (Norway, Norway & Finland), Avesta-Sheffield (England), Böhler-Uddeholm (Austria), Erasteel Kloster (France).

There is also the R&D structure of joint research. Jernkontoret (today the Swedish Steel Producers Association) was founded in 1747 (as a financial institution) and still functions as a technical coôperation organisation for the steel industry in the Nordic countries. Jernkontoret is also one of the founders of the Swedish Institute for Metals Research (Institutet för Metallforskning, IM) in Stockholm and the applied process metallurgy research institute of MEFOS in Luleå, an institute were large development projects may be carried out (cp. IRSID in France and CRM in Belgium).

However, Jernkontoret and the Swedish steel industry cannot alone afford the luxury of a large, applied research facility, equal to the facilities in larger countries as France and Belgium. Accordlingy, MEFOS has to be supported by the state to an extent of 20 - 25 %.

### How economic institutions influenced technological choice

A few years ago, the Swedish zinc situation was highlighted by Naturvårds-verket (1994). Sweden produced (and produces) roughly 80 ktonnes of zinc dust every year (ibid.). Hence, although the discussion of recirculation of Steel works waste is not a new one (Edström 1980), a R&D venture was initiated to find economical solutions to upgrade the dust and preferably produce zinc using dust as a raw material. In the project, none of the above mentioned pyrometallurgical processes developed in Sweden (Plasmadust or Slag reducer) was chosen, although there existed possibilities of applying the latter in small scale installations with a limitied research effort. Neigher was a more conventional hydrometallurgical approach chosen. Instead, the tasks of the project were formulated as follows:

i) to develop a new, sofar untried, large scale pyrometallurgical process (Falk 1993): remelting the dust in an electric furnace with a hollow electrode into a liquid iron bath. Subsequently, the metal oxides are reduced, re-oxidized in the oxidizing atmosphere of the furnace and a secondary dust is fromed that is rich in zinc oxide. The secondary dust may be used as a raw material for electrolyses.

ii)     to investigate the possibilities to establish a central dust treating facility in Sweden, to take care of contamineted dust from several commercial steelworks, in the same way as Scandust handled stainless dust[1].

The method chosen was akin to the large scale pyrometallurgical technology (Plasmadust) that had not worked well in the zinc case. The new related technology had never been tried before and was supposed to apply to all steel industry.

The project was finance by Swedish Steelworks, Nordic Industrial Investment Fund (Nordisk Industrifond), the Swedish Steelmakers Association (Jernkontoret) and several goverment bodies for environmental resaearch. The project turnover was roughly MSEK 10.

Existing economic instituions influenced the specification of the project in two ways:

1)The long tradition of pyrometallurgical process development established a competence history that favoured the pyrometallurgical solution with its

---

1 This last ambition can not be documented from written records but has been recounted in several interviews

inherent economies-of-scale creating in fact a quasi-monopoly. Process development in Sweden has been going on from the Wiberg and KALDO processes (Wiberg 1958, Kalling & Johansson 1954) via smelting reduction (Edström 1977) to plasma processes (Santén 1992 & 1993) and now to this zinc process.

2) The centralistic structure of the Swedish steel industry together with centralized decision making in the governement (NUTEK, Naturvårdsverket etc.) created a tendency to support this quasi-monopolistic structure. This was also recognized in the Governement Committy on commercial steel production (Handelstålsutredningen, SOU 1977:15) that became the basis for the current steel structure in Sweden. The tendencies to favour large scale, centralistic solutions are, however, older than this. The rationale for the formation of NJA in the 1930:s, the purchase of Grängesbergsbolaget´s shares in LKAB in the 1950:s and the Steelworks 80 venture in the 1970:s belongs to the same central decision pattern.

### The consequences

Whether this choice of technology is economically negative or not, depends on the economic context in which the structure is placed. Monolithic, capital intensive structures are most sensitive to price and output varations. In zinc trade (and non-ferrous trade of the same kind, e.g. copper and lead) this is emphasized by the trade structure. Zinc is generally sold from the smelter to a trading arm of the same company or to an independent broker who puts it on the market, i.e. the metal exchange (London Metal Exchange, LME, or the commodity exchange, COMEX, in New York). Accordingly, price changes are directly reflected in the status of the production and depends on whether the dust is a raw material or not. Since zinc prices over the last twenty years (see figure) have been volatile, there have been even more volatile changes in profitability. Hence, high capital-over-production cost ratio:s are not wanted.

Is there an alternative? Maybe the state-sponsored R&D should focus more on alternative ways to travel, to focus more on possibilities to change the technological future development path (cp. Arthur 1994) than to continue to stroll down "memory lane". If resources are to be created instead of managed, maybe a full scale venture in hydrometallurgy - or in plasma based small scale processes[2] - would lead to both a productivity, a high profitability and a clean environment in the long run. Not only would this solution be more flexible in the current production case, a small scale conversion closer to the source would diminish the need for bulk transport (bulk transport is generally considered to be environmentally negative). It may also have applications outside traditional metallurgical industries such as high tech industries (e.g. precipitation and processing of superconductive oxides; see Medelius 1994) and waste management in other production sectors.

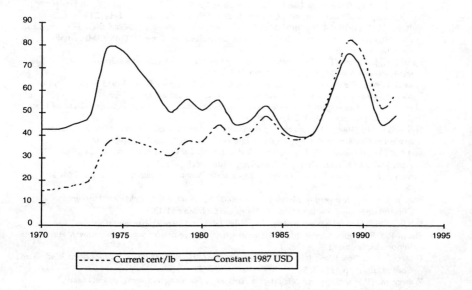

---

[2] the discussed project has been terminated and further development has been moved to Scan Arc Plasma Technologies.

The conclusion is that a standiardized solution for all is not optimal if technologies are not predictable, but liable to change over time and apply very differently in different product categories and markets.

## References

Arthur W. B. (1994): *Increasing Retourns and Path Dependancy in the Economy;* Univ. Michigan Press

Edström J.O. (1977): Råjärnsprocesser - Sveriges FoU-behov; STU-utredning nr. 74-1977; Stockholm

Edström J.O. (1980): *Omhändertagande av stålindustrin restprodukter;* Forskningsrapport, Inst. för produktionsteknik, KTH, Stockholm

Eliasson G. (1991): Modelling the Experimentally Organized Economy; *J. Economic Behavior and Organization,* vol xx, no. pp

Falk T. (1993):*Pilotförsök med insmältning av zinkhaltigt stoft i flytande slagg;* Forskningsrapport MF93024, MEFOS, Luleå

Frenay J., Hissel J., Ferlay S. (1986): *Zinc and lead recovery from EAF dust by caustic soda process;* Proc. 44:the Elec. Furnace Conf., Dallas; pp 417 - 421

Kellogg H.H. (1980): *Energy Use in Zinc Extraction;* Lead-Zinc-Tin '80, Proc. World Symp. Metallurgy and Environmental Control; TMS-AIME, Las Vegas, USA. Febr. 24 - 28

Kellogg H.H. (1990): *A Practical Model of the Imperial Smelting Zinc-Lead Blast Furnace;* Lead-Zinc'90, Proc. World Symp. Metallurgy and Environmental Control; TMS-AIME, Anaheim, USA. Febr. 18 - 21; pp 549 - 569

Kalling B., Johansson F. (1957): Syrgasfärskning i roterande ugn enligt Kaldo-processen; Jernkontorets Annaler, vol. 141, no 4, pp. 189 - 205

Kola R. (1990): *The Processing of Steelworks Waste;* Lead-Zinc'90, Proc. World Symposium of Metallurgy and Environmental Control; TMS-AIME, Anaheim, USA. Febr. 18 - 21; pp 453 - 464

Medelius H. (1994): *Synthesis and Processing of Supercoducting Oxides;* Dr. Diss.; Dept of Material Science and Engineering, KTH, Stockholm

Nyirenda R.L. (1990): *An appraisal of the Caron Zinc Process when Zinc Ferrite is Reduced to a Magnetite Containing Product;* Minerals Engineering, Vol 3, No 3/4; pp 319-329

von Put J.W., de Bruijn W., Duyvesteyn W.P.C. (1988): *The Caron Zinc Process;* Proc. Fine Particles'88 Can. Inst. Mining & Metallurgy, Montreal; pp 641 ff

Santén S. (1992): *Metallurgical Processes Based upon Plasma Technology;* Proc. John Olof Edström Symp. Oct. 29-30; pp 208 - 211

Santén S. (1993): *Recovery of Metals from Steelmaking Dusts;* Proc. McMaster University symp. "Pretreatment and Reclamation... ", Hamilton ON, May 11-13

SOU 1977:15, Handelsstålsindustrin inför 1980-talet, Industridepartementet

Storm P. (1997): *Environmentally induced structural change in zinc production;* Raw Materials Report, forthcoming

Unger T.W. (1986): *Waelz kiln recovery process for electric arc furnace dust;* Proc. 44:th Elec. Furnace Conf., Dallas; pp 413 - 415

Wiberg M. (1958): *Några nya sätt att göra järnsvamp;* Föredrag vid Jernkontorets tekniska diskussionsmöte, 31 maj

**Non written sources**

Sources for this paper (including interviews) have been gathered for several years. A large part of the information which this paper is based on is "common knowledge" for people working in and in connection with the tightly knit network around the Swedish steel industry, e.g. the technical coôperation under the umbrella of Jernkontoret. A small part of the material is restricted and has been given to the authors (mainly Per Storm) more or less in confidence. Hence no person or persons will be named and eventual errors in the paper is to be attributed solely to the authors.

# 112

MOT97

Roger Seaton
Lecturer in Technology Policy
International Ecotechnology Research Centre
Cranfield University, Cranfield
Bedford
MK43 0AL
England.

Telephone: +44 (0) 1234 754097
Fax: +44 (0) 1234 750163
Internet: R.A.Seaton@Cranfield.ac.uk
Compuserve: 100034,2267@Compuserve.com


Dr Dr H. Al-Dhahab Al-Ghailani
Acting Director General for Industry
Industrial Directorate
Ministry of Commerce and Industry
Sultanate of Oman.
Telephone: (00968) 794244/794246
Fax: (00968) 792444/794238
Compuserve: 100734,3405

Title:
## 'Innovative Effort' in small manufacturing companies in development economies.

Keywords:
Technology transfer, innovation process, SME's, Development economies, receptivity, theoretical, empirical, experimental

**TOPIC H CATEGORY 2**

**Oral**

# "Innovative Effort" in small manufacturing companies in development economies

## Introduction

This research is focused on the way in which small and medium sized manufacturing companies who often have little or no internal Research and Development expend their resources on the processes and underlying activities by which they not only implement technical innovation but also develop their capacity to innovate. From the literature, it is not clear how small and medium-sized manufacturing companies behave during the process of innovation, particularly in many development economies.

The research takes a "knowledge" perspective as a way of exploring innovation in such companies and draws upon two broad fields of research literature, those of innovation and technology transfer. The research translates the theoretical and conceptual aspects of relevant research into the operational level (a set of resource consuming and identifiable activities described as Innovative Effort) which then become the subject of field work investigation. The final stage is to translate these activities (as verified and amended in the research activities) back into a conceptual model. Considering innovation in this way and in the context of this type of manufacturing company, a number of issues arise:

- How can research into the determinants of innovation and the process approach be combined to research the innovation process?
- What types of activities are required to perform each element of the overall process of technical change and technological learning?
- How can we identify the activities involved in the innovation process?

Much innovation research has been at the level of the economy or a sector. In addition, much literature focuses on radical change, whereas this research focuses on incremental change, the dominant mode of innovation in companies of interest. Macro and micro technological development theory explains the link between innovation and economic growth and asserts the need to improve innovation inside organisations through improving their competitive. However, this literature mostly uses an analytical approach (often statistical) which cannot reveal the organisations 'internal processes and thus cannot show the way to promote innovation processes intra-company.

The process models on knowledge transfer and knowledge accumulation place an emphasis on these processes of innovation into organisations, on sub-processes and the importance of prior knowledge, key individuals, communication, scanning, and networking. Concepts of human-centred effort to improve individual and organisational learning are also of interest to research in the context of development economies. While Inward Technology Transfer (ITT) and other models study the process in its abstract sense, this research, in contrast, attempts to understand these processes through the **activities** that underlie them and use these activities as building blocks for the proposed notion of 'Innovative Effort'. Thus intangible processes are identified in terms of tangible activities to enable their identification, testing and measurement in the organisations' daily life.

We need to develop a model that addresses the innovation process as it relates to small and medium-sized manufacturing companies with no internal R&D. Such a model would have two important contributions to the field by:

- Linking theoretical levels of process models with operational levels of 'Innovative Effort' by breaking down the innovation process into sub-processes which are further broken down to

their constituent activities. Thus the behaviour of individuals and organisations that can be translated into actions is the focus of the observation and exploration.
- Drawing upon research methods that enable operationalisation and illustration of the process concept.

Since shifting between research levels is a relevant part of the research method it may be helpful to locate this research device and its properties within the literature as shown in Table 1

Table 1   The relevance and the origin of 'Innovative Effort' from the literature

| Research Level | Innovation | Inward Technology Transfer | 'Innovative Effort' |
|---|---|---|---|
| Theoretical | Innovation Models | Process Model of ITT | Model of Innovation in Manufacturing Companies |
| Conceptual | Determinants of innovation | Acquisition, communication, application, and assimilation. Knowledge accumulation Individual and Organisational learning | Nature of 'Innovative Effort' Process thinking approach |
| Operational | Using statistical analysis | Scanning and networking and other activities | A set of operationalised activities |
| Type of Innovation | Organisational Innovation | Technical Innovation | Organisational and Technical Innovations |
| Relevance (Link with IE) | Radical change vs. Incremental change Sectoral vs. organisational | Large vs. small companies With vs. without R&D Units | Incremental technical and organisational change in SMCs with no R&D functions |

Shaded boxes in Table 1 highlight mutual areas on which this research focuses, in order to bridge the limitations of both major strands of the literature. The level of the research activity is operational (the focus of applied research). The types of innovations studied are incremental, organisational, and technical innovations in manufacturing companies. Relevant queries for such a task include:

- What activities need to be included in a study of the innovation process?
- What type of effort in the process of innovation do small and medium-sized companies in manufacturing sector emphasise?
- Do companies invest deliberately in people to improve innovation?
- What will the innovation process model in small companies look like?

## Understanding Innovative Effort

In this research therefore, 'Innovative Effort' refers to the amount of effort (in terms of resources allocated) small and medium-sized manufacturing companies expend to implement technological innovation and develop their capacity to innovate. As a preliminary activity, it will be useful to discuss and explain some important aspects of the notion of 'Innovative Effort' so as to understand the reasons behind proposing its use.
- It is clear that companies acquire different knowledge in management, finance, accountancy and other areas so as to operate effectively.
- The idea of cumulative knowledge is discussed for example by Cohen and Levinthal (1990). The ideas of a firm's prior related knowledge and absorptive capacity are linked to this notion, but the focus is on generating technical knowledge via the firm's own R&D. It is argued that this kind of

2

notion does not accommodate a whole range of firms which are not driven by the desire to gain comparative advantage through acquiring leading edge knowledge.

- The notion of receptivity has been proposed to amend deficiencies in previous technology transfer models. Receptivity, as it is proposed by Seaton and Cordey-Hayes (1993), is: *'a firm's ability to be aware of, acquire and make effective use of technology'*. Receptivity focuses on knowledge acquisition in the context of the technology transfer process, while absorptive capacity focuses on generating knowledge in the context of R&D driven firms. This idea of receptivity denotes the way in which a company relates and uses external knowledge. Receptivity highlights the importance of having certain abilities and qualities to enable a firm to acquire and exploit external knowledge (Trott, 1993, Gilbert, 1995). Receptivity needs to be investigated in more depth so as to understand its importance to the innovation process into manufacturing sector SMCs.

- The qualities of scanning, networking, assimilating, and other activities are seen to be good indicators of the innovation process. The assumption is that the better these qualities are in a firm, the better chance it has to acquire and accumulate technical knowledge. It is important to develop proxies for the innovation process in SMCs so as to identify its intensity

- It is important to acknowledge that 'Innovative Effort' is not only intended to be a device to quantify the capacity to aquifer and exploit knowledge, but also to extend our understanding of the totality of the innovation process and its various sub-processes and activities.

**Research Activity**

The initial phase of the research was to identify from existing research the range of different activities associated with innovation and technology transfer. Research then took place in Oman, a country with a typical development economy as far as manufacturing is concerned. There were three phases to the research activity.

The first involved a scoping questionnaire of some 14 questions obtained from some 50 small and medium sized manufacturing companies. This focused on three themes:

- Corporate change and the role of technological change
- Interactions with between internal staff and external contacts
- The ability to acquire new knowledge and the role of individuals in this process

The aims of the second phase was to:

- Identify the inward technology transfer process
- Expose the activities that constitute this process and the factors affecting it

It consisted of in-depth research in a selection of 10 companies chosen for as much diversity as possible. The research method was to use unstructured thematic interviews which were the analysed individually and collectively using cognitive maps as an interpretative device. It is these which provide much of the material for the synthesis of a new conceptual model at the end of the research. The third phase consisted of work with 8 companies and comprised:

- A questionnaire on the perceptions of the most senior manager about the importance of the component activities of Innovative Effort
- A semi-structured interview of some 88 questions about company resource expenditure on these, the organisational factors which enhance them and the type and role of individuals involved

It is from this third phase that much of the detail of Innovative Effort has been derived. Note that an attempt has been made within the practicalities of the research to involve companies that have considerable differences in order to explore the ability of measures of Innovative Effort to discriminate.

**Table 2   Characteristics of the companies under study**

| Company | 1 | 2 | 3 | 4 | 5 | 6 | 7 | 8 |
|---|---|---|---|---|---|---|---|---|
| Products | Paints | Pumps | Food/ Sweets | Detergents | Food/ Biscuits | Food/ Dairy | Plastic Pipes | Food/ Oil |
| Employees | 104 | 90 | 55 | 210 | 170 | 270 | 270 | 230 |
| Production. | 4.41 | 2.00 | 0.44 | 7.14 | 2.22 | 4.40 | 2.64 | 11.72 |
| Capital | 0.75 | 0.23 | 0.70 | 1.45 | 0.45 | 1.00 | 0.20 | 2.30 |
| Wages | 0.29 | 0.11 | 0.10 | 0.46 | 0.29 | 0.68 | 0.08 | 0.36 |
| Exports | 0.56 | 0.60 | 0.14 | 2.72 | 0.82 | 0.47 | 0.41 | 4.01 |
| Current Assets | 1.63 | 2.18 | 0.49 | 3.79 | 1.22 | 2.24 | 2.14 | 6.69 |
| Current Liabilities | 1.33 | 1.57 | 0.89 | 3.23 | 0.13 | 1.13 | 0.93 | 5.61 |

All the companies involved in the study produce different commodities. The products range from food to engineering products. Four companies are involved in food, one in detergents and cosmetics, one in paints, one in plastic pipes, and one in water pumps. Even the companies in the food industry are different in what they do with one company in each of the following activities; biscuits, dairy, sweets and oil derivatives.

All the companies chosen are a 100% locally owned, as is the case with most companies in the industrial sector in Oman. The major difference is that some companies are independent, whereas others are part of larger corporations that also deal with other related activities.

**'Innovative Effort' Characteristics**

This section describes the practical application of the notion of 'Innovative Effort'. It refers largely to Phase 3 of the study and demonstrates a method for measuring the associated activities. Table 2 shows the range of research relevant activities that have been identified from the literature and the all phases of the research activity.

**Table 3  'Innovative Effort' Activities**

| | | |
|---|---|---|
| Own Research and Development | Short courses, seminars, etc., On-the-job Training | Using IT for accessing an information the firm needs |
| Contracting Research and Development | Off-the-job Training Attending exhibitions and or | Buying and purchasing database, programmes, etc., |
| Product Development | conferences | Committees and or Teams; like |
| Process Development | Buying specific literature; | QC, Suggestion Teams, etc. |
| Patents | journals, books, etc., | Formal Meetings to discuss |
| License | Reading specific literature | issues related to innovation and |
| Royalty | related to the field | technological change |
| Trade Mark | Contacting other people outside | Informal meetings and |
| Copyright | the company | discussions |
| Consultancy | Buying and installing | |
| Formal education of employees | information technology | |

From the activities listed in Table 2, nineteen activities are performed by more than one company, and nine activities are found to be performed by all companies in the Phase 3 research. These are; product development, attending courses and seminars, off-the-job training, attending exhibitions and conferences, buying literature, reading literature, contacting people outside the companies, buying information technology, and using information technology to access outside information. Some activities are not represented in these companies at all. Figure 1 shows the general patterns of Innovative Effort by activity as measured by % of Turnover.

### Figure 1   Innovative Effort by activity as measured by % of Turnover

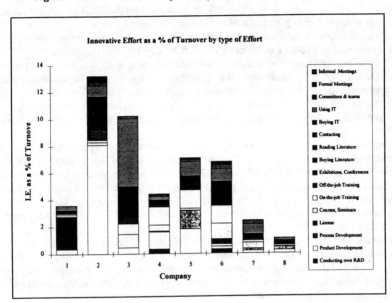

Product development is found to be the most important activity that is performed by all companies. Using information technology is the second most important. Employing information technology in the product line, sales, raw materials, marketing and other areas will improve the efficiency of a companies' performance. Information technology in most companies is not used to access that outside information which might improve and develop technical people's knowledge. All companies, except number 1, have committees and teams. Formal and informal discussions are performed by most companies under study.

Attending courses and seminars is one of the most important activities that is performed by all companies. Most courses and seminars are local and they are attended by technical people. International events are usually attended by the general manager or members of the board of directors.

On-the-job training is another important activity which is performed by all companies. Training is subsidised by the government and mostly focused on non technical aspects; such as secretarial skills, English language, and others.

The data on attending exhibitions and conferences sometimes includes non-technical exhibitions; such as trade exhibitions.

Buying technical literature is also a common activity among all companies involved in the study. Although companies spend relatively little on this activity, owing to the fact that subscription to technical journal is cheap, it expresses the awareness of these companies to the importance of keeping their technical people abreast of new knowledge in the field. The reading of this literature mostly at

**work** expresses management awareness of the importance of reading as a mechanism of knowledge transfer. All of the managers responded positively when managers asked whether they consider reading at work as productive activity.

**Contacting people outside the companies** is one of the important activities performed by all companies. The main contacts for technical people to are suppliers and licensers. Most of the managers give a reasonable amount of freedom to their technical people to talk to their colleagues at the suppliers end without needing prior permission from their superiors.

Process development and formal and informal meetings are performed by five companies, whereas **conducting own R&D and licensing** are performed by only two companies.

Five activities are found to be of no actual importance as none of the companies exert any effort on them. These activities are; **contracting R&D, patents, royalty, trademarks, and copyright**. It is thought that companies acquire most of their knowledge from research through suppliers. Companies have agreements with equipment, raw materials, and ingredients suppliers to furnish them with whatever knowledge, information, experience, and research results are generated by the suppliers or their agents.

Companies do not generally **contract R&D**, but ask their suppliers to perform studies on their behalf to find solutions to their problems. Companies that have a strong linkage through such agreements do not perform their own R&D activities, but rather acquire whatever knowledge they need to update their knowledge from their suppliers. Thus, acquiring the cream of the **suppliers' R&D** is performed through strong linkages with the suppliers and environment scanning. They think this is a cheaper and more effective way to upgrade their companies knowledge without performing their own research, which is costly and time consuming.

As for the other three activities; **royalty, trademark, and copyright**, it is found that the companies under study have passed the licensing period during which they ought to pay royalties, trademark, and copyright fees. All the companies performed these activities in the first five years of their existence but no longer perform them. The relationship between them and their suppliers is now based on mutual benefit for both of them.

## People versus non-people and individual versus organisation Innovative Effort

The research also aimed to explore the differences in the way effort was distributed between these two types of classification. This is because there is an interest in a development economy which is dependent on external knowledge for innovation about the extent to which it itself become engaged in that wider knowledge economy rather than provide capital and labour inputs. This issue in turn places a great deal more emphasis on how organisations use people as a part of their innovation activities and what actions governments can take to equip their populations with the skills required to take part at these two levels. As will be seen in the final part of this paper, models of innovation for companies in these circumstances which focus on the interactions between individuals and organisations and which place a somewhat greater weight on the knowledge and skills aspects are likely to be more helpful in developing policy. It is also relevant for small manufacturing companies in established economies to begin to identify the resource consuming activities that will enhance innovation capability and implementation in such a way that they can compare themselves with peer group companies. It is not possible to discuss the potential of this approach for benchmarking but research is underway to develop this in the UK. The Table below identifies the constituent activities and Figure 2 shows both of these comparisons side by side. The Figure also shows the variation in size of overall Innovative Effort among this disparate group of companies.

## Table 4 People versus non-people and individual versus organisation Innovative Effort

| People centred | Non-people centred | Individual | Organisational |
|---|---|---|---|
| Attending Courses & Seminars | Conducting Own R&D | Attending Courses & Seminars | Committees and Teams |
| 'Attending Exhibitions & Conferences | Conducting Product Development | Attending Exhibitions & Conferences | Informal Discussions |
| Buying Literature | Conducting Process Development | Buying Literature | On-the-job Training |
| Reading Literature | Licensing | Reading Literature | Conducting Own R&D |
| Contacting people outside companies | Buying IT | Contacting Outside Sources | Product Development |
| On-the-job Training | Using IT | Off-the-job Training | Process Development |
| Off-the-job Training | Conducting Formal Meetings | | Licensing |
| Building Committees & Teams | | | Buying IT |
| Formal and Informal Meetings | | | Formal Meeting |
| | | | Using IT |

## Figure 2  Innovative Effort as a % of Sales by Organisational/Individual and Technology/People

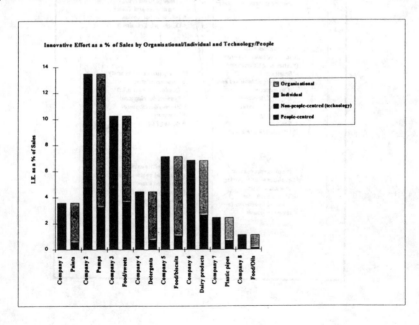

## A Conceptual Model of Innovation using Innovative Effort research

Figure 3 presents a break down of a process model of innovation into activities which are considered as opportunities provided by the companies (Gilbert, 1995). It is depicted in a way that reveals the various concepts and activities that are used and discussed in this research.

First is the concept of prior related knowledge. The literature suggests that prior knowledge increases the ability to acquire new knowledge (Cohen and Levinthal, 1990; Willman, 1991; Nonaka, 1990, 1991). From the literature as well as from the fieldwork, it was concluded that to make use of external knowledge companies need internal capabilities. As knowledge starts with individuals (Cohen and Levinthal, 1990; Nonaka, 1988, 1990, 1991; Leonard-Barton, 1992; Kim *et al.*, 1993), the existence of individuals with certain levels of education, experience, technical skills and personal qualities are the central attributes in the process of innovation. Figure 3 shows those concepts and how they relate to each other.

### Figure 3 A model of innovation based on 'Innovative Effort' activities

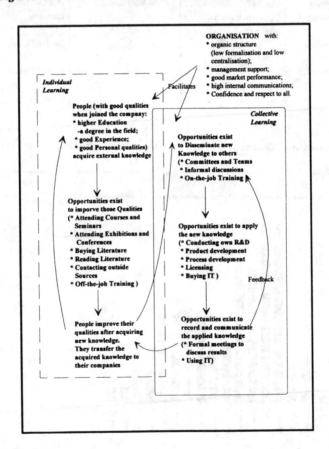

The individuals need to be provided with opportunities to enable them to acquire and make use of external knowledge. The more opportunities these individuals have, the more they will be able to acquire knowledge. It is suggested that organisations with organic structures (Burns and Stalker, 1961; Mintzberg, 1979; Hage and Aiken, 1970; Cohen and Turyn, 1984; Khan and Manopichetwattana, 1989; Damanpour, 1991; Kim *et al.*, 1993), positive market performance (Rothwell, 1986; Storey, 1994), and certain levels of respect and confidence (Trott, 1993) will support opportunities and facilitate these activities. Through these opportunities individuals promote and improve their knowledge, technical skills, experience and personal skills. This description is represented by the arrow in **the 'Individual learning'** area connecting the node **'People improve their qualities'** to the node of **'People with qualities'**. So the first part of the diagram shows an individual learning process where the acquired knowledge improves the level of individual knowledge. When there is no opportunity to communicate this knowledge to the others in the company, the learning can be thought of as a single-loop learning process.

When individuals who acquire external knowledge are provided with opportunities to distribute this knowledge through various internal mechanisms, individual knowledge is transferred into collective knowledge. Organisations with organic structures, management support, positive market performance, and confidence and respect, support these opportunities and facilitate the activities required to perform them. The more opportunities the companies provide to disseminate knowledge, the more knowledge these companies acquire and make use of. The arrow connecting the **node 'People improve their qualities'** to **'Opportunities exist to disseminate'** explains the transformation of individual knowledge to collective knowledge.

The individually acquired knowledge is transferred into collective knowledge where it is evaluated, tested, developed, and applied collectively. The more opportunities the companies have to apply knowledge, the more knowledge they assimilate and accumulate over time. The applied knowledge which is routinised and recorded needs to be communicated back to others inside the companies through the same opportunities to disseminate knowledge. This is represented by the arrow which leads from the node **'Opportunities to record and communicate the applied knowledge'** to the node **'Opportunities to disseminate knowledge'**. This feedback represents a double-loop learning process, where the applied knowledge is routinised and disseminated to others in the company. If the applied knowledge is retained and left with the individuals who applied it, the learning will still be individual, which is represented by the arrow which goes **from 'Opportunities to record and communicate the applied knowledge'** to the node 'People improve their qualities'. Hence the learning will be individual.

## Conclusions

The idea of 'Innovative Effort' is far from complete and the following suggestions for future research are proposed. In depth studies undertaken to establish a comprehensive list of all activities involved in the innovation process. A broad range of companies need to be studied in different sectors with a range of size, age, performance, and organisational and technical capabilities. In addition, cross-sectional studies are needed to understand the perceived and the actual activities involved in the innovation process at all levels within companies. In future research it is suggested that the amount of effort on evaluation and assessing new ideas need to be separated from the amount of effort on product and process development.

The focus of this research has been to develop a practical method by which managers in manufacturing companies can apply (without involving themselves necessarily in understanding) abstract models of innovation. The originality of the idea of 'Innovative Effort' is in the use of tangible day-to-day activities that can be tested, identified and measured in a quantifiable manner. In addition, they can compare themselves with others in the industry using actual measures.

The idea of 'Innovative Effort' also helps government to understand the importance of innovation to their national economic growth and promotes their understanding of the innovation process inside companies in manufacturing sectors and the various activities which constitute it. Government awareness of the innovation process inside manufacturing companies will promote a shift in their focus that considers the manufacturing sector as a homogeneous group of companies that might respond to their policy initiations together.

In the context of Oman, this research suggests that the Omani government might attempt to help the manufacturing sector through promoting its competitive performance and sustaining indigenous involvement in order to improve the national knowledge economy. The Omani government in this context might use 'Innovative Effort' to identify those sectors that have a better capacity to innovate by enhancing and using the skills of the local population.

## References

Burns, T., and Stalker, G. M. (1961). *The management of innovation.* London: Tavistock Publications.
Cohen, W. M. and Levinthal, D. A. (1990*). Absorptive Capacity: A New Perspective on Leaning and Innovation* Administrative Science Quarterly, vol. 35, 128-152.
Cohen, S. F. and Turyn, R. M. (1980*) The structure of the firm and the adoption of process innovations* IEEE Transactions on Engineering Management, vol. 27, 98-102.
Damanpour, F. (1991*) Organisational innovation: a meta-analysis of effects of  determinants and moderators* Academic of Management Journal, vol. 34, no. 3, 555-590.
Gilbert, M. (1995) *Technological Change as a Knowledge Transfer Process.* Ph.D. Thesis, INTA, IERC, Cranfield University, England
Hage, J. and Aiken, M. (1970) *Social Change in Complex Organisation.* Random House, New York.
Khan, A. M. and Manopichetwattana, V. (1989) *Innovative and Noninnovative Small Firms: Types and Characteristics* Management Science, vol. 35, no. 5,  597-606.
Kim, D. H. (1993) *The Link between Individual and Organisational Learning'* Sloan Management Review, 37-50.
Leonard-Barton, D. (1992) *The Factory as a Learning Laboratory* Sloan Management   Review, 23-38.
Mintzberg, H. (1979) *The structuring of Organisations.* Prentice-Hall, Englewood Cliffs, NJ.
Nonaka, I. (1991) *The Knowledge-Creating Company* Harvard Business Review, November-December, 96-104.
Nonaka, I. (1990 *Redundant, Overlapping Organisation: A Japanese Approach to Managing the Innovation Process* California Management Review, 27-38.
Nonaka, I. (1988) *Toward Middle-Up-Down Management: Accelerating Information Creation'.* Sloan Management Review, 9-18.
Rothwell, R. (1986) *The Role of Small Firms in Technological Innovation* in J. Curran,      J. Sanworth and D. Watkins (Ed.), *The Survival of the Small Firms.* vol. 2, Gower, Aldershot.
Seaton, R A. and Cordey-Hayes, M. (1993*) The Development and Application of Interactive Models of Industrial Technology Transfer* Technovation, vol. 13, no. 1, 45-53.
Storey, D. J. (1994) *Understanding the Small Business Sector* Routledge, London, the UK.
Trott, P., Cordey-Hayes, M. and Seaton, R. A. (1995) *'Inward Technology Transfer Process',* Technovation, vol. 15, no. 1, 25-43.
Willman, P. (1991) *Bureaucracy, Innovation and Appropriability* ESRC Industrial Economics Study Group Conference. London Business School, November 1991
Yin, Z. J. (1992) *Technological Capabilities as Determinants of Success in* Technology Transfer Projects Technological Forecasting and Social Change, vol. 42, 17-29.

# 114

INDUSTRIAL PRODUCTION- A WAY OF DESCRIBING, ANALYSING
AND SOLVING PRODUCTION PROBLEMS

Henrik Blomgren and Magnus Aniander
Department of Inudstrial Engineering and Management
Royal Institute of Technology, KTH
100 44 STOCKHOLM

ABSTRACT

The paper claims that one important aspect in the area of industrial
production is to understand the consequences of implementing a
production solution. If we shall become better in solving production
problems it is necessary to understand what happens when we try to solve
them. The paper presents a model (useful for describing and analyzing) and
gives an idea on how an awareness of this consequences can be achieved.
The model visualize effects of change and can thereby help us manage
them.

To begin the model could be synonymous with "placing the problem in
different contexts". Two examples are used to describe the model and how it
can bee used. Just one example "digital printing" are briefly introduced here.
The other example is "the process of making a new production layout".

The first example is from the graphical industry and shows that the effects
of digital printing not just is automated printing. Also other consequences
influences the result of implementing digital printing. For example: how
prepress and postpress are changed is important (the activities before, and
after, printing). Since digitaiprinting gives room for lower production
volumes it becomes important for the company to "get more jobs", which
increases the workload of the department for prepress. Lower volumes also
makes postpress more handicraft-like than before. Printing companys may
even have to invest in machines that they just got rid of. If a company is to
gain something out of digital printing it is important to be aware of these
consequences.

The question raised in the paper is actually: what kind of insights can a
"broader" perspective on production give? Starting from a low context (a
machine, the individual working with it) and taking it higher (other
machines, the layout, other departments and finally the valuechain where
the company is one link) we can se different effects of a production solution.

The example above just showed the points by thinking in terms of different
departrnents. But in the final paper this example (and the other) will be
discussed more deeply and the contexts suggested here will be used more
systematically.

# 116

DESIGN OF INTERFACE BETWEEN INTERNAL AND EXTERNAL
MATERIALS FLOW-SYSTEMS A NEGLECTED ASPECT OF "THE
FACTORY OF THE FUTURE?

Jan-Åke Granath
Department of Architectural Design,
Industrial Architecture and Planning
Chalmers University of Technology
GÖTEBORG, Sweden

Co-author:  Mats Johansson, Tomas Engström
Department of Transportation and Logistics
Chalmers University of Technology
GÖTEBORG, Sweden

ABSTRACT

Proposing future consequences of the application of two production models
for the design of freight depots including loading bays

The production models applied within a specific production system have an
impact on the choice of other sub-systems than the ones traditionally
assumed to be included in a production system. These sub-systems
influenced by aspects such as the choice of e.g. building design or the
influence of infrastructural characteristics on materials feeding system
design, e.g. [1] and [2].

In this paper we will elaborate the impacts of two different production
models on the design of a materials feeding system focusing on freight
depots and loading bays.

The discussion on production models is based on the authors long
experience of design of production systems. We have chosen to study the
application of two different production models. Namely "lean production"
originally coined by [3] and "reflective production" originally coined by [4].

This discussion will be backed up by earlier research on the design of
loading bays and loading areas by [5]. The methods of investigating the
interrelation between different subsystems in production systems have been
developed over a long period of time by own and joint projects concerning
design of production systems, e.g. [6] and [1].

The two models mentioned above will form the base for our discussion of
the design of the interface between internal and external materials flow
systems focusing on freight depots including loading bays. This will enable
us to elaborate the consequences of the application of the two production
models in the form of e.g. reformed materials categories, the consequences

of industrial trends in the form of shorter lead times, extended JIT-deliveries, out-sourcing of subassemblies, reduced product life cycles and increased number of product variants, etc.

The consequences for the design of freight depots and loading bays will be illuminated by the use of space, the layout, the detailed technical solution etc. These aspects will be enlightened by data from our case studies within the Swedish automotive industry. namely the main Volvo Torslanda plant in Goteborg, the Autonova plant in Uddevalla and the Volvo Engine plant in Skovde using our established methods like video recording, work mapping, using the product structure as the base for analyze, etc.

References:

[1] Granath J A (1991). "Architecture Technology and Human Factors. Design in a Socio-Technical Context", Industrial Architecture and Planning, Chalmers University of Technology, Gothenburg (PhD-thesis).

# 117

W. Gary Howard
Department of Government
The University of West Florida
11000 University Parkway
Pensacola, FL 32514
USA
Office: 904-474-2883
FAX: 904-474-2716
Internet: ghoward@uwf.edu


Marcia R. Howard
Office of the Dean of the College of Business
The University of West Florida
11000 University Parkway
Pensacola, FL 32514
Office: 904-474-2348
FAX: 904-474-2716
Internet: mhoward@uwf.edu

**Title:**   **Hypermedia Can Accommodate Needs and Preferences of Individual Learners:  A Boon for Education, Business, and Government**

**Key Words:**  hypermedia, educational technology, interactive technology

**Topic:**   A.   Applications of technology to learning organizations

**Category:**   3.   Case Studies

**Suitable for:**  Oral Presentation

**Hypermedia Can Accommodate
Needs and Preferences of Individual Learners:
A Boon for Education, Business, and Government**

Educators are confronted by a dilemma: Students have become so accustomed to technology that new means must be employed to retain their interest during the educational process. Sitting in front of televisions and computer monitors for hours, they compute, move mice, and pull triggers on joy sticks to solve virtual mysteries, shoot virtual asteroids, or accomplish similar virtual global phenomenon. They are bombarded by noise, color, and fast action. Even toys and games involve interactive technology.

Thus has the influx of media in our society impacted students' everyday lives and, therefore, learning by traditional methods. Because their surroundings and experiences are inundated with noise, color, and action, contemporary students very quickly can become bored by slow-moving, traditional lectures and static textbooks; and effecting learning has become even more difficult. Educators, then, must find ways to exploit these "toys" and capitalize on technology in teaching.

The same phenomenon impacts government and business as they seek effective ways to train workers in various tasks. Industry is searching for means by which it can train employees in-service for changes in technology, processes, and procedures. Add to this additional dilemmas of varying shifts, locations, times, and backgrounds of employees; cut backs and downsizing; technology providing new methods and machines; and the increasingly rapid need to constantly update existing work force. Compound the problem with the need to accommodate individual personalities and learning styles of employees so that requisite training/learning can be achieved, and the dilemma seems insurmountable.

Enter hypermedia, an effective alternative to traditional lecture and a means by which educators and trainers can capitalize on technology. Some have viewed it as an enhanced multimedia. And while instructors and trainers have employed multimedia in teaching to embellish lectures—e.g., opaque and overhead projectors, films, records, audiotapes, photographs and slides, the term has taken a new twist. Today it also implies the use of computers and the capability for learner control.

HyperStudio is one example of hypermedia. Visualize a stack of three-by-five cards that are displayed electronically, one at a time, on a computer monitor. Each card contains buttons, fields, and graphics. By using these cards, many types of instruction can be authored. Pictures or drawings can be created and/or imported from print sources; video sequences can be integrated from a videodisc simply by indicating beginning and ending frame numbers. Voice, music, or other sound can be included using recorded clips or by directly speaking into the microphone. These can be incorporated with relative ease and minimal effort. Programs such as HyperStudio are easy to master and allow for versatility and creativity. However, if pictures (or icons) in a flowchart format are preferred to create lessons, icon-based authoring systems such as AuthorWare Professional also are available (Sharp 1994).

Hypermedia is more than just using several media to present information. It is an efficient multidimensional electronic information system (Merrill, et al., 1996). Worley (1994) defines it as "a computing environment designed for 'intellectual laborers' to help them 'work with ideas'" (86),

> a new and rapidly developing technology that combines text, graphics, animation, video, and sound. With a fully-integrated hypermedia system, a user sitting at a computer screen can, with the click of a mouse button, call up for simultaneous display the text file of a document, a video sequence, a sound track, an animated illustration, or any combination. (85)

And hypermedia has much to offer business. Worley continues, "Frequently used in training programs, hypermedia systems enable employees to choose the pace, level of difficulty, and style of learning that best suits them" (86).

Hypermedia materials have become increasingly popular in both education and industry; they provide for individualized instruction and training. However, research needs to be conducted to ascertain just how effective hypermedia is. Beasley and Waugh (1996) say, "the solid empirical research base necessary for guiding the design of effective hypermedia systems is lagging far behind advances in the capabilities of the technology itself" (272).

The purpose of this paper is to discuss the advantages of hypermedia in learning environments and provide empirical data on how it has been employed successfully with students. It will also demonstrate how hypermedia has been used effectively with various personality types.

**Advantages of Hypermedia in Learning Environments**

Hypermedia provides a number of advantages to the educator and the learner. Among them are the following:

1.  Hypermedia provides the ability for learner control, the degree of personal responsibility a student can exert in an instructional situation. For example, the learner can manage the pace at which he/she proceeds through a lesson or select the sequence of the information. Learner control is a potential solution for boredom and lack of motivation.

2.  Hypermedia presentations are nonlinear. A linear path of learning is similar to reading a book--page by page. With hypermedia, each learner can select a different path,

depending on his or her individual needs or desires. For example, while reading a hypermedia version of a text, a student can click on marked terms (hot words) or phrases to display definitions, cite additional sources of information, or provide additional instruction. Clicking on symbols can activate video clips to demonstrate how a process works or how to perform an activity. The student is free to select many possible paths and the order in which they will be experienced.

3.  Hypermedia is interactive. Students do not have to be just passive viewers of predetermined, sequential presentations (such as videotapes). Instead, they can respond to questions, react to situations, and solve problems presented by the media—and they can review, ask questions, receive feedback, and be referred to additional sources for further study.

4.  As noted previously, hypermedia takes advantage of multimedia. Text, graphics, sound, animation, and video can be used under computer control with a variety of audio and video hardware to present ideas and information (Merrill, et al., 1996).

In his book *Technology, Open Learning and Distance Education* (1995), Bates claims that all four media must be available to teachers and learners because learners

> vary a great deal in terms of educational background, age, experience, and preferred learning styles....Decision-makers should therefore try to ensure that all four medias (print, audio, television, computers) are available for teaching purposes in one technological form or another. This will give variety to a course, not only providing an individual learner with different ways of approaching the same material, but accommodating different learning styles. (13)

5.  Developing and producing hypermedia learning modules does not require a computer specialist or a programmer—only an understanding of how learning occurs and how instruction should be designed. Therefore, development of hypermedia learning modules with the user-friendly software can be low cost.

6.  Hypermedia lessons can easily be adapted and edited. New information can be added and changes made as situations require. Furthermore, updates in text and information are easily accommodated. Bates writes,

> What is much more significant about multimedia are the user-friendly software tools that allow teachers and learners to add, adapt, remove and edit material. This adds a different dimension to computer-based learning. Instead then of the computer program being all-inclusive, controlling both the content and the instructional methodology, reducing or eliminating the role of the human teacher, and forcing the learner into a narrow range of response modes, it is possible to develop instructional strategies that enable joint input from teachers and learners,

683

allowing learners not only to transform learning materials into forms that have personal relevance and meaning, but also to construct new knowledge, new ways of understanding. (193-194)

## Success of Hypermedia as a Teaching Tool

With such possibilities in mind, we set out to see if hypermedia was a teaching tool that could be effectively employed in the fields of government and business. To determine how successfully students learned, a pre-test/post-test study (n=239) was conducted.

Prior to assignment of the hypermedia module, students were administered an in-class pre-test. Then they had two weeks in which to complete a hypermedia lesson. They were able to undertake the project according to their own schedules and as often as they desired. At the end of the two-week period, an in-class post-test was administered. The test, employing Bloom's taxonomy of educational objectives, was designed to assess which levels of learning could be achieved by hypermedia. Additionally, the Myers Briggs Type Indicator was administered to see if certain personality types performed better by use of hypermedia. These results were compared to other case studies we have done on technology and computer learning over a ten-year period.

Highlights of the findings follow:

1.  Results from using the hypermedia module support the conclusion that students can and did learn by this method. Overall, significant learning occurred in all groups using hypermedia. In fact, in every case positive gains were recorded. Using pair t-tests, statistical analysis revealed a significant difference between pre-test and post-test scores (t=16.87, p<.0001).

    *   A control group which did not receive hypermedia instruction had no significant gains, but the mean score doubled for students who completed the module yet had no prior knowledge.

    *   Two groups were tested: one with prior information of the topic and one without. At the end of the hypermedia application, both groups averaged the same mean scores. The advantage of prior knowledge had been overcome on one application.

    *   Students using hypermedia were able to score as well as students receiving instruction through other traditional methods.

    *   Student evaluation of hypermedia was universally positive. Words like "fun," "awesome," and "helpful" are expressions students used to describe their experiences. They particularly like the multi-media effect combining visual and audio components. The ability to control the pace and steps of learning is also appealing.

2.	Learners can achieve all levels of learning through hypermedia lessons, from the most fundamental to the most comprehensive.

•	In his classic work on educational objectives, Benjamin Bloom (1959) delineates six levels of learning: knowledge, comprehension, application, analysis, synthesis, and evaluation. These levels are presented as a hierarchy because they span a continuum from the simple to the complex, from the concrete to the abstract. The assumption is made that the learner must be able to perform at each subordinate level as he/she ascends the hierarchy. Therefore, in order to comprehend, one must also have knowledge; in order to apply, one must know and comprehend, etc. Evaluation is defined as making "judgments about the value....It is placed at this point in the taxonomy because it is regarded as being at a relatively late stage in a complex process which involves some combination of all the other behaviors" (Bloom, 1966, 185).

Results of the study indicate that students were able to achieve even the highest levels of learning via the hypermedia module. They were able to break material down into constituent parts, put elements and parts together to form a whole, and appraise "the extent to which particulars are accurate, effective, economical or satisfying" (Bloom, 185).

Therefore, hypermedia can be viewed as a successful teaching tool which can do more than just teach facts. It has the capability for encouraging and guiding students into the more advanced stages of education.

3.	Personality type is not a significant factor in learning via computerized instruction.

•	The Myers Briggs Type Indicator has been widely used for nearly 50 years. It is based on C.G. Jung's concept that human behavior is not random but follows patterns. Lawrence (1979) summarizes Jung's intricate analysis of the basic modes of variation in human experience:

In Jung's theory, all conscious mental activity can be classified into four mental processes—two perception processes (sensing and intuition) and two judgment process (thinking and feeling). What comes into consciousness, moment by moment, comes either through the senses or through intuition. To remain conscious, perceptions must be used. They are used—sorted, weighed, analyzed, evaluated—by the judgment process, thinking and feeling. (6)

Lawrence continues,

If the best learning is to happen, thinking types must pursue logical order;

feeling types must follow their hearts; sensing types must strive to engage their senses in the mastery of practical skills; and intuitive types must follow whatever inspires. To capture the interest of diverse students requires real artistry in teaching. (17)

- Four analyses of covariance, one for each of the classifications of personality characteristics, were run to examine the effect of personality characteristics on achievement; the achievement pre-test scores served as the covariant in each case; the post-test was the dependent variable in each. All statistical tests were conducted at the .05 level of significance.

The statistics indicated that there was a highly significant difference in the post-test scores for each of the classifications. For each of the four ANCOVAs that were run, the associated p-value was .0001, indicating that the data were significant beyond the .05 level.

No significant differences in achievement were observed within each of the four personality classifications: extraversion/intraversion (f=3.12, p-value= .080), sensing/intuition (f=1.88, p-value=.173), thinking/feeling (f=1.88, p-value=.173), judging/perceiving (f=.02, p-value=.895).

Based upon these data, one can conclude that while learning does take place via hypermedia, one's personality traits do not necessarily affect how well learning occurs by hypermedia. Thus, hypermedia can be an effective tool for all.

## Implications for Education, Business and Government

Today, education, business, and government share the same challenge of doing more with less. Yet, education and training require more attention to keep the work force current with the ever-changing technology. Thus, there is a constant search for educational tools which will accomplish educational/training goals and be more cost effective.

Hypermedia has shown great potential for accomplishing both objectives. Without question, there are times when a live trainer/teacher is necessary; but in the times that the human element is not essential, hypermedia is a cost effective alternative. With the advent of personal computers and the minimal cost of the software, hypermedia is a delivery system available to all.

Actually, minimum equipment is required, and the authoring systems do not require specialists or programmers to design the learning modules. Hypermedia modules are simple and inexpensive to upgrade; thus, sessions can be updated quickly.

For the user, learning can be personalized; it can address individualized needs. All levels of learning can be taught, from the concrete to the abstract; and learners can proceed at their own pace. Repeating and reviewing previous information are accommodated as is the option for exploring supplementary materials. Visual and auditory examples can be employed based on the individual's preference. New skills can be taught in various formats. Individuals can complete a training module or groups can be taught at once; or, if one prefers, both can be done simultaneously. Add the advantage for the public and private sectors that hypermedia learning fits any schedule, a boon for shift workers or a company that must release employees one at a time to receive in-service training.

In the search for those universal tools of education, there is still much to learn; and educators continue to search for ways to maximize learning experiences. Our experience (and the experience of many of our students) is that hypermedia is a tool to add to our arsenal.

# References

Bates, A. W. (1995). *Technology, Open Learning and Distance Education.* New York: Routledge.

Beasley, R.E. and Waugh, M.L. (Spring 1996). The effects of content-structure focusing on learner structural knowledge acquisition, retention, and disorientation in a hypermedia environment. *Journal of research on computing in education,* 271-281.

Bloom, B. (Ed.) (1966). *Taxonomy of educational objectives, handbook I: Cognitive domain.* New York: David McKay Company, Inc.

Lawrence, G. (1982). *People types & tiger stripes: A practical guide to learning styles.* 2nd ed. Gainesville, FL: Center for Applications of Psychological Type, Inc.

Merrill, P.E., Hammon, K., Vincent, B.R., Reynolds, P.L., Christiansen, L., and Tolman, M.N. (1996). *Computers in education.* Boston: Allyn and Bacon.

Sharp, V. (1994). *Hyperstudio in one hour.* 2nd ed. Eugene, OR: International Society for Technology in Education.

Worley, R.B. (1994). Hypermedia. In Williams, A. (ed.) *Communication and technology today and tomorrow.* Denton, TX: The Association for Business Communication, 85-97.

# 118

DISTRIBUTED EFFORT IN R&D AND ITS ROLE IN ECONOMIC
DEVELOPMENT
- THE CASE OF SINGAPORE

Author:
K J Yeo
Centre of Engineering and Technology Management
Nanyang Technological University
Nanyang Avenue, Singapore 639798

## ABSTRACT

Singapore is entering a new phase of its economic development. The threats
of 'hollowing out' and the need to upgrade industry's technological
capabilities are critical issues. The government is proactively directing
investments and R&D in strategic areas to ensure long term economic
growth. Large scale strategic investments in modern wafer fabrication parks
in anticipation of an increased demand in semiconductor industry is one
such example. International mobility of technology and manufacturing
bases of the MNCs has long term implication for Singapore The response is
to intensify the nation's R&D efforts and to raise technological capabilities
in strategic areas. This paper addresses the role of public and private ate
sectors in the promotion of R&D effort in Singapore.

A R&D distribution matrix is developed which illustrates the actual
perceived and desired level of R&D effort by the various technology
providers or originators, in Singapore's namely: the multi-national
corporations (MNCs), Government-linked companies (GLCs), local private
enterprises and universities and public research institutes and centers. The
nature of R&D efforts are broadly delineated into three types (Type I, II & III)
which are defined by the state of technology application and problem-
solving capability required.

The distribution profile is constructed on a the basis of a recent survey of 60
R&D managers in both and private and public sectors, on the nature and
types of ongoing research and development work in their respective
organizations. The profile reflects the current perception of the level of
R&D in Singapore and what constitute a reasonable division of Labor in
R&D among the major technology originators. A partial objective of the
study is to find ways to promote closer R&D cooperation and collaboration
among the public and private sectors, mainly between the
universities/research institutes and the industry.

# 119

# A COMPETENCY MODEL OF R&D LEADERSHIP

### K T Yeo

Centre of Engineering and Technology Management
School of Mechanical and Production Engineering
Nanyang Technological University
Nanyang Avenue, Singapore 639798

## ABSTRACT

This paper proposes an enhanced leadership model in R&D and investigates some aspects of competency of successful R&D project leaders in Singapore. The model defines leadership (L) process as a function of the leader (l), team members (m), task (t) and situational variables (x), i.e.. L=f (l, m, t, x). Special interest is given to the delineation of tasks as an influencing factor on R&D leadership performance. The technological tasks are categorized into three broad types  defined by the level of technology applications and the problem-solving capability required. The leadership model then provides a framework for an industry survey on successful R&D leadership in Singapore in their perceived competencies and motivation. The findings are useful to provide ideas for the development of research scientists and  engineers.

[ Keyword:  R&D, Leadership, Competency Model ]

## INTRODUCTION

Management and leadership are more commonly thought of as two distinct concepts. In the proposed leadership competency model, a successful leader is one who possesses both management competence and leadership qualities that are required in his work environment. The management competence is reflected in the leader's ability to meet organisational and task goals; while leadership qualities are more personal,  independent of time and place,  and usually reflected in the leader's ability to influence the behaviour of others.

This paper proposes an enhanced leadership competency model relevant to a research and development environment. The leadership model is defined as a process and function of four components namely :

- the project leader himself (l)
- the project team members (m)
- the task (t) and
- relevant  situational variables (x).

Thus, Leadership Process = f(l, m, t, x). The leader's personal qualities are reflected in his behaviour style and personality traits. The team member's characteristics are those represented their task preferences and motivational needs. The R&D tasks are defined by the degree of structureness in problem-solving requirements and level of technology applications.  The situational variables are those existing in the internal and external environments of the organisation.

One of the main contributions of this paper is to incorporate task(t) as a necessary component in the situational leadership competency model.  The paper hence gives the assertion that leadership effectiveness and performance is contingent to specific task requirements which, in an R&D environment,  are inevitably affected by the level of technology involved and the structureness in problem definition.

In technology application, the task requirements are defined by the newness and provency of technology applied. The technology types can be identified as proven or basic, familiar, new or emerging technology. In problem definition and solving requirements, the task performance will be affected by the presence or absence of clear and defined task objectives, requirements, and scope; and the availability or the lack of it, of an appropriate and effective problem-solving methodology.

## Need to delineate task requirements

In many of the traditional leadership models, the task environment, in terms of nature and characteristics of tasks undertaken, has not been systematically studied and often omitted from the situational model. The traditional models mainly give emphasis to the behaviour of the leader (l), his follower or group members (m), and situational variables (x) [1]. The task (t) as a relevant and significant contingent factor had been omitted.

McGregor [1] identified four major variables that influence leadership as a dynamic behaviour form as: characteristics of the leader, followers and organisation; and the prevailing social, economic and political environment. Though tasks and structure are included in defining the organisation, no working definition on the nature of tasks undertaken by leaders was given.

The management or leadership grid, by Blake and Mouton [1] defines a useful conceptual framework combining a concern for task accomplishment and a concern for people. The grid assumes that the most effective leadership style is one that achieves the highest (9,9) position on the grid, which gives simultaneously maximum concerns for both task and people. Again, there was no attempt made to delineate the nature or characteristics of task and how leadership performance may be affected.

Other similar work like those from the University of Michigan[1] identified leadership behaviour as production-centred and employee-centred. A two-factor theory developed at the Ohio State University[1], focused attention on the leader's role as initiating structure and giving consideration. The two factors are separate and independent dimensions of leadership behaviour. Initiating structure is concerned with task accomplishment and consideration is about showing friendship, mutual trust, warmth and concern for subordinates.

## AN ENHANCED SITUATIONAL LEADERSHIP MODEL

The proposed and enhanced leadership model is one that determined by the behaviour and personality traits of the leader, the work preferences and motivational needs of the followers or team members, the nature and requirements of task, and other situational variables- both internal and external to the organisation. Special emphasis will be given to the delineation of the tasks into types defined by its structureness or the lack of it.

A highly effective leadership style is contingent to the nature of the technological task and its problem-solving requirements. A highly structured task with clear objectives, defined scope, and firm delivery requirements may need a more task-centred and control oriented leadership style. The leadership may take on a stringent management-by-objective(MBO) mentality. Similarly, the followers or team members are likely be more disciplined, goal-accomplishment oriented, willing to accept authority of the leader, and have strong tendency to quickly converging to a single 'best' or definitive solution. The task-oriented leadership is one who is more likely to have a well developed left hemisphere of his brain [2]. This could also be true for his followers.

Conversely, in a highly innovative environment dealing with relatively ill-structured task requirements, the effective leader is likely to have a high tolerance for initial task ambiguity and uncertainty. The ambiguity is mainly due the initial lack of definition in objectives and requirements, or lack of prior experience and availability internal capability. Achieving a balanced concern for both people and task will be a hallmark of a successful R&D leader in such innovative environment. His success will depend on his ability in creating a learning organisation, and in helping team members to rapidly build up personal mastery over the challenging technological tasks.

The team members in a highly creative environment may need minimal guidance and direction from their leader. The management system will be less procedural with minimum requirements for compliance of set rules and standards. The dominance of right hemisphere of the brain may be required in generating innovative and previously unknown ideas, which are essential in a R&D environment.

## A Framework to delineate technological tasks

Traditionally, R&D work are classified as basic research, applied research, or product and process development. However, this classification is rather static and does not represent the dynamic and shifting nature of technological learning and development. Here, the a problem-framing approach [3] is proposed which categorises the R&D task into three broad types according to the level of technology application and the problem-solving capability required. The problem framing approach encorages the company in critical self assessment of its current level of technological development and accumulated capabilities.

Table 1 defines the three types of technological tasks as Type I, II and III, which are characterised by relative certainty, controlled uncertainty, and uncontrolled uncertainty. The uncontrolled uncertainty is also characterised as the problem of high ambiguity.

**Table 1 Delineation of Tasks**

| Types of Task | State of technology application in organisation | Nature of Problem-solving |
|---|---|---|
| Type I<br><br>Relative Certainty | - Apply basic or proven technology already commonly available and in use.<br>- Use basic and well established process and facilities commonly available.<br>- Well informed on related technology trend and potential.<br>- Mainly basic development work in products and processes, including enhancement and modification work. little or no research content. | - Solving mainly routine and well defined and structured problems.<br>- Well constructed and relevant mental models available.<br>- Adopt well-developed methodologies and procedures.<br>- Clear project objectives, scope and requirements.<br>- High predictability of problem variables and outcomes. |
| Type II<br><br>Controlled Uncertainty | - Adopt known technology that has not been embodied into existing products and processes in the company or local industry.<br>- Well informed of the potential and possess internal knowledge and skills of relevant technology from R&D.<br>- Required facilities not yet established.<br>- Mainly new product or process development using proven and advanced technology. | - Solving broadly defined and structured problems.<br>- Adequate relevant mental models available.<br>- Broadly defined objectives, scope and requirements.<br>- Moderate predictability of problem variables and outcomes. |
| Type III<br><br>Uncontrolled Uncertainty or Ambiguity | - Use new and emerging product and process technology dissimilar to the current base technology.<br>- Lack of internal knowledge and skills and facilities to support the new technology.<br>- Informed about the potential and risk involved.<br>- Mainly advanced technology development involving sustained research. | - Solving mainly and ill-structured and ambiguous problems.<br>- Absence of an adequate mental model. Fragmented images of the problem situation.<br>- Fuzzy and ill-structured problem formulation.<br>- Outcome not yet determinable. |

Type I task represents a condition of 'relative certainty' with high predictability of developmental outcome. It uses base and proven technology in product and process development work. The company is likely to have accumulated prior experience in the application of the relevant technology. The Type I condition is one that has reached a mature stage of development and is ready for project implementation and realisation. A Type I project would have clear objectives, well defined requirements and scope of work. The scenario is that a project team of engineers has been assembled to develop an enhanced version of an existing product using existing process with only minor modifications, and drawing support from existing internal expertise and resources. In this scenario, the project leader and his team are likely to have possess the necessary mental model to deal with the problem situation at hand. The Type I problem situation is perceived to be well defined and structured.

Type II task is a condition of 'controlled uncertainty' with moderate predictability of outcomes. It involves the use of new but familiar technology in the development of a new or radically improved product or process. The company has broad knowledge of the advanced technology and is well informed of its potentials, except that the technology has not yet been embedded in its existing products or processes. A Type II project has broadly defined objectives, scope and requirements. The project leader and his team are likely to possess relevant and adequate mental model and broad images of problem situation. The Type II task situation is perceived to be moderately and broadly defined and structured.

Type III task is a condition of great ambiguity or 'uncontrolled uncertainty'. The scenario is a company forming a R&D team to develop a radically improved and new product or process using new and emerging advanced technology involving undefined or competing technological standards or paradigms. The project leader and his team are not likely to already possess the necessary and relevant mental models at this early stage of research and development. The mental images of the problem situation are likely to be fragmented, fuzzy and messy with developmental outcomes not yet determinable. Type III task situation is perceived to be ill-defined and ill-structured.

**The Leader, the team and situational variables**

The other three main components of the leadership competency model are illustrated in Table 2. The description of these three components in addition to the task definition described in the earlier section will provide a basis for a field survey and data collection to determine aspects of R&D project leadership process and current level of perceived R&D leadership competence in the context of Singapore.

**Table 2 The Leader, Team and Situational Variables**

| The Leader | Leadership traits:<br><br>- Physical: physique, energy and appearance.<br>- Education and scholarship: about his specialist knowledge.<br>- Mental intelligence: on his mental capacity and problem-solving capability.<br>- Emotional intelligence: emotional or psychological maturity, self-confidence, cooperativeness and adaptability, honesty, integrity.<br><br>Behavioral style: on his relationship with the subordinates, followers or team members; Eg. concern for people vs concern for task or production. |
| --- | --- |

| The Team | Characteristics of team members: |
|---|---|
| | Behavioural types based on modified Theory X and Theory Y assumptions, and a mix of motivational needs. Type X: highly motivated by monetary & material needs, take direction and follow instructions, not naturally creative, and have low tolerance of ambiguity, disciplined and left-brain inclined Type Y: highly motivated by self-esteem and self-actualisation needs, strong desire to exercise self-direction and control, appreciate intrinsic value of work, desire to achieve the fullest of potentials, creative with balanced development of right brain capacity and preferences, tolerance for ambiguity. |
| Situational Variables | Internal variables: top management support, culture & value, internal business processes and systems, core company competency, human resource, organisational learning etc. External variables: Societal networking, relationships with major customers and suppliers; macro social, economic and political environment, competition, access to sources of new and advanced technologies, etc. |

*The Leader:*

The studies of leader mainly focus on personality traits and behavioural style. The former is on personal qualities of successful R&D leaders. These qualities are defined in terms of physical traits, mental and emotional intelligence, and other personality traits. The behavioural style can be described, as in some studies, as directive, supportive, participative, or achievement oriented; or democratic vs authoritative.

Research shows that there are indeed some correlation between leadership effectiveness and personal traits; but they are more complex that they first appear. The effectiveness of leadership does not depend solely on a combination of personality traits. Other situational variables such as the characteristics of tasks, motivation of followers, and the organisational and macro environments are also important and must be examined on their on leadership performance.

*The Team Members:*

The behavioural characteristics of team members can be conveniently appreciated with reference to McGregor' Theory X and Theory Y assumptions. However, these assumption of behaviour is modified in conjunction with Maslow's[1] hierarchy of motivational needs. The modified behavioural types of subordinates are referred as Type X and Type Y behaviour.

Type X people are those who are relatively more highly motivated by material needs in terms of monetary rewards, salary and bonuses, job security, promotional prospects; tend to take direction and follow instructions from the leaders; not naturally creative, and have low tolerance of ambiguity. They are disciplined and left-brain inclined workers who are generally systematic in approach, reliable but not innovative. Type X members' mix of motivational needs are more concentrated at the lower levels of Maslow's hierarchy of needs.

A leader who takes a Theory X view of his subordinates are likely to be directive, authoritative and highly disciplined in his behavior in dealing with his people. He is likely to exercise more control and expect compliance of rules and procedures. The control is perceived to be necessary for task accomplishment and to better serve the project and organisational goals. The Theory X leaders tend to believe that people are more driven by material or monetary rewards, and not necessarily find their work enjoyable and meaningful.

Type Y people are those who are more highly motivated by self-esteem and self-actualisation needs. They have the strong desire to exercise self-direction and control. They appreciate the more intrinsic value of work. The achievement and recognition derived from work are important intrinsic rewards and motivating forces. Monetary and material rewards after a certain level are only 'good-to-have', but not critical. They have great desire to achieve the fullest of their intellectual potentials. They are generally more creative and innovative and with balanced development of right brian capacity and preferences. Their tolerance for initial ambiguity is high and can hold on to tension of opposing views for a sustained period of time until a creative solution is found.

Theory Y leaders tend to take a more positive and dynamic view of his people, and are interested in finding and promoting ways of empowering and enabling their subordinates to attain their higher level needs. Building up a learning organisation and promoting team learning are some of the ways to motivate people to develop to the maximum of their capabilities in teams and organisation.

### The Situational Variables:

The leadership process can be influenced by contingent or situational variables, both internal and external to the organisation. Examples of internal variables are: organisational structure, top management support and commitment, internal corporate business processes, empowering culture, internal core competency and capability, inhouse quality assurance systems. The leader's ability to handle interdepartmental tasks and relationship are important influencing factors on effective leadership performance.

Some examples of external variables are relationships with key customers and suppliers; macro social, economic and political environment; industry structure and competition; access to sources of new and advanced technologies.


## SURVEY ON COMPETENCY OF R&D LEADERS

The competency model of R&D leadership was developed to provide a framework for the design of an survey instrument to gauge and determine some aspects of R&D leadership qualities in Singapore. In this survey companies and research institutes were asked to identify one or two of their successful R&D leaders to respond to the questionnaire on aspects of competency and leadership process. A total of 50 useful returns were received and analysed.

The breakdown of the respondents' companies in terms of ownership is as follows:

| | |
|---|---|
| Multi-national Corporations (MNCs) | 54.2% |
| Government Linked Companies (GLCs) | 12.5% |
| Local Private Enterprises | 12.5% |
| Universities and Public Research Institutes | 20.8% |
| | 100% |

The MNCs represent a major player in the current R&D scence in Singapore as they have the technological capabilities and capital to conduct R&D activities. The GLCs and local enterprises are increasingly playing an important in promoting R&D in terms of R&D expenditure and manpower development.

The survey questions were designed to be as objective as possible so as not to favour any particular outcomes. The questionnaire has eight sections to survey on: the responding company's background and business, education and experience of the respondents identified as company's successful R&D leaders, their response on balancing the concern for people and task, on framing and managing the types of technical tasks, on identifying and managing the types of team members, on desired R&D leadership qualities, on managing situational variables, and finally on on-going training and development of R&D leaders. Selected results of the survey are presented in this paper.

## 1. Age and education of successful R&D Leaders

The age profile of these respondents is as follows:

| | |
|---|---|
| Below 30s | 12% |
| 30-35 | 40% |
| 36-40 | 19% |
| Over 40 | 29% |
| | 100% |

The concentration is between age 30-35 with 40%, which is indicative of the relatively young R&D workforce in Singapore. The first five-year National Technology Plan (NTP I) was only launched in 1990, as the first major national science and technology policy initiative to prepare country for a new innovative phase of her economic development and meet new global competition and challenges.

The educational level of these R&D leaders is high with the great majority holding a university degree. A good proportion of them, about 58%, also possess graduate degrees, masters or doctorate. The competent R&D leaders in the Singapore context, are highly qualified academically, as shown below:

| | |
|---|---|
| Polytechnic diploma | 4% |
| First degree | 38% |
| MSc and MEng | 29% |
| PhD | 29% |
| | 100% |

## 2. On balancing concern for people and task

When asked whether leadership performance was contingent to the nature of task and people, the response was overwhelmingly positive with 93%. Many respondents commented that leadership effectiveness is unavoidably dependent on the nature and challenge of the task as well as the maturity and technical depth of the team.

On the balance between concern for people and concern for task on the (9, 9) Leadership Grid, the respondents gave an effective zone around (7.6, 7.6). Many commented that it is not necessary nor possible to achieve a perfect 9,9 position which represents an idealistic goal. The survey shows that a successful R&D leader is 'balanced' with sufficiently high concern for both people and task. The image of competent R&D leadership is a process of bringing a multi-disciplinary team together, to develop and commit to a shared vision and goal, and nurture a strong team spirit. The leader will ensure that while the team is result-oriented, appropriate extrinsic and intrinsic rewards and recognition must also be given to the successful team.

There are varied views on concern for people and task. Some view that overly concern for people may breed ill-discipline. The existence of the task is the primary reason for the existence of the leader and his team. Moreover, due to competition and shortening of product life cycle, people are pressurized to focus on accomplishing the task in a shorter time. On the other hand, in a crunch meeting the needs of the talented people is more important than short term task objectives. R&D staff are perceived to be a unique breed of people who are creative but not good in conforming to rules and regulations. They must be handled with special concern, both individually and as a team. With their needs met, they are more likely to deliver results. The competent leaders must be able to hold these varied demands in a creative tension. Without a balanced focus on people and task, disarray and ad-hoc management may arise.

## 3. Types of task managed

The nature of task is defined by its structureness and categorised into three broad types on a scale 1-9, as illustrated below:

| TYPE I | | | TYPE II | | | TYPE III | | |
|---|---|---|---|---|---|---|---|---|
| Highly structured | | | Moderately structured | | | Ill-structured | | |
| 1 | 2 | 3 | 4 *<br>(4.5) | 5 | 6 | 7 | 8 | 9 |

The mean value from the respondents' assessment on the nature of task they currently perform is around 4.5, on the average, which is moderately structured and classified as Type II task. It is believed that given time the type of R&D work conducted in Singapore will and should move to higher level of Type II and progressively into Type III tasks. Most of the companies are adopting proven technologies to enhance their existing products and processes, but gradually working on new and emerging ones. The survey shows the distribution of task types as follows:

| | |
|---|---|
| Type I | 24 % |
| Type II | 66 % |
| Type III | 10 % |
| | ------- |
| | 100% |
| | ------- |

## 4. Type of People Managed

One a scale of 1-9, from highly Type X to Type Y people, the respondents were asked to assess the types of people they managed in their successful R&D teams. The result of assessment is centred around 6.9, as shown below:

| Highly Type X | | | | | | Highly Type Y | | |
|---|---|---|---|---|---|---|---|---|
| 1 | 2 | 3 | 4 | 5 | 6 *<br>(6.9) | 7 | 8 | 9 |

The implication of the survey is that successful teams are those with people who are more Type Y than Type X, though only by a certain margin. When asked what would be the most effective in motivating the team members. The following is the ranking of the findings based on a maximum scale of 5.

| Rank | Most Effective<br>in Motivating | Mean<br>Value |
|---|---|---|
| 1 | Challenging nature of work | 4.40 |
| 2 | Opportunity for personal fulfillment | 4.27 |
| 3 | Opportunity for career advancement | 4.23 |
| 4 | Learning opportunity | 4.10 |
| 5 | Prestige of project | 3.94 |
| 6 | Monetary reward | 3.79 |
| 7 | Job security | 3.50 |
| 8 | Association with exciting people | 3.33 |

By assigning this list on Maslow's hierarchy of needs as shown below, in Figure 1, it is interesting to note that the respondents believe that the R&D people are motivated by a mix of needs of various levels. Motivating factors like challenging nature of work, opportunity for personal fulfillment and career advancement, prestige of project, and learning opportunity are high on the list. These represents have the higher levels of needs for self-actualization and self-esteem. The needs for job security and monetary reward are perceived to be of lesser importance. It is of course quite likely that these lower levels of needs are already quite adequately satisfied as these R&D engineers are highly qualified and enjoy reasonably good remuneration.

**Figure 1: Hierarch of Motivational Needs of Successful R&D People**

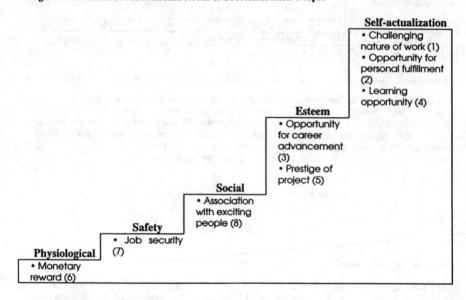

## 5. Competencies of R&D leadership

The respondents are asked to respond to a long list of professional competencies of R&D leadership. The following shows only the top ten competencies that scored over 4.0 on a scale of 5.

1. Ability and willingness for continuous learning
2. Capability to lead
3. Willingness to lead
4. Appreciating and developing talents in his people
5. Technically competent
6. A sense of mission and purpose
7. Good people skills
8. Good communication skills
9. Highly creative in generating ideas
10. Emotionally stable, self control.

The survey shows that the highly competent R&D leaders are those who possess the ability and willingness to lead and for continuous learning, technically competent, and possess good people skills. The emotional or 'soft' intelligence are high on the list.

## 6. Managing situational variables

The ability to deal with internal and external situational variables is an integral part of the leadership competency model. The following partial list respondents what the respondents see as representative of the required competencies:

1. Accurate understanding and interpretation of customers' needs and R&D requirements
2. Secure top management support and commitment

3. Keep abreast with technological trends
4. Develop and nurture internal core competency
5. Appreciate the needs and concern of his people
6. Strive for continuous improvement
7. Anticipate customers latent requirements
8. Appreciating the external business environment, market trends and competition.

The result shows that competent R&D leaders are very much market and business oriented and who appreciate the need to compete by satisfying customers' known and anticipate needs and latent requirements. Internally, they are good at securing management support and commitment on the R&D work initiated.

## Conclusion

The level of R&D efforts in Singapore depends on both the quantity and quality of her R&D manpower and the availability of competent R&D leadership. By the end of 1995, Singapore had achieved 45 research scientists and engineers (RSEs) per 10,000 work force. The target for 2000 is 65 RSEs. It has been a remarkable achievement for a small and newly industrializing country without a strong R&D tradition and culture. However, qualitatively, the competence level of the R&D manpower had not been systematically assessed. The objectives of the study to investigate some aspects of the competency of successful R&D leadership in the context of Singapore have been achieved. An enhanced situational leadership model has also been formulated in the course of this study.

## References

[1] Hersey P and Blanchard K H *Management of Organisational Behaviour*, 5th Ed., Prentice Hall, 1988.

[2] Mintzberg H "Planning on the left side and managing on the right", *Harvard Business Review*, 1976, 54(4) 49-58.

[3] Yeo K T "Strategy for risk management through problem framing in technology acquisition", *International Journal of Project Management*, 13(4), 219-224, 1995.

*Acknowledgment*: My 1995/96 final year student Khee Yu has assisted in the conduct of the survey and compilation of the data. His help is much appreciated.

# 121

# INDUSTRIAL AND TECHNOLOGY POLICIES FOR SMES IN THE NAFTA REGION. TOWARDS A NORTH AMERICAN SYSTEM OF INNOVATION.

Author:
Jose Luis Solleiro
Centro para la Innovacion Tecnologica-UNAM
Apartado Postal 20-103
01000, Mexico D.F.
Fax and Tel.:      +52-5- 6225200 to 03
e-mail :      solleiro@servidor.unam.mx

Co-authors:
Vijaya Ramachandran
Center for International Development Research
Sanford Institute
Duke University
BOX 90237
Durham, North Carolina 27708-0237
U.S.A.
Tel:      +1-919-613-7333
Fax:      +1-919-684-2861
e-mail:      VIJAYA@pps.duke.edu

Charles Davis
International Development Research Center
Regional Office for Latin America and the Caribbean
Plaza Cagancha 1335, 9th Floor
Casilla de Correo 6379,
11100 Montevideo, Uruguay
Tel:      +598-613-2366163
Fax:      +598-613-5630815
e-mail:      cdavis@idrc.ca

Rosario Castanon
Centro para la Innovacion Tecnologica-UNAM

## ABSTRACT

Small and Medium Enterprises (SME's) play an important role in developed  and developing economies because they contribute a high share of GDP and generate employment. Furthermore, their organizational structure is more flexible than that of larger companies which means that SME's can survive more easily during crisis periods.

In the case of Mexico, more than 98% of the manufacturing enterprises are micro, small and medium, and they play an important role in the economic and social sectors. The Mexican Government, at this moment, has neither an explicit nor implicit policy to support SME's although authorities have recognized that one is needed.

This paper presents the first results of a study aimed at identifying the possibilities of trinational instruments of industrial and technology policies for SME's as well as opportunities for industrial collaboration among North American small firms.

Our research is based upon an analysis of the Mexican, American and Canadian systems to improve the innovative behavior and competitiveness of small firms as well as on discussions with some of the key actors of the implementation of such policies in the three countries.

This analysis allows us to draw conclusions on following subjects:

- A system of bench marks for industrial and technology policy design in North America.
- Concrete proposals for the instrumentation and implementation of the Mexican Industrial Policy putting emphasis on mechanisms to foster innovation in SME's
-Opportunities for the establishment of partnerships among SME's of the three countries.
- An agenda for future research.


Key words: Small and Medium Enterprises, industrial policy, technological policy.

# 122

- First author:

  José Luis Solleiro
  Centro para la Innovación Tecnológica
  Costado Norte del Edificio "D" de la Facultad de Química
  Circuito de la Investigación Científica
  Ciudad Universitaria
  04510 México, D.F.
  Tel.: (52 5) 622 5200
  Fax: (52 5) 622 5221
  E-mail: solleiro@servidor.unam.mx


- Co-author

  Rosario Castañón
  Centro para la Innovación Tecnológica
  Costado Norte del Edificio "D" de la Facultad de Química
  Circuito de la Investigación Científica
  Ciudad Universitaria
  04510 México, D.F.
  Tel.: (52 5) 622 5200
  Fax: (52 5) 622 5221
  E-mail: rosarioc@servidor.unam.mx

- Title
  Global Technology Partnerships and North-South Collaboration. The Case of CamBioTec


- Key words: Technology Transfer; international networks; biotechnology.


- Topic letter: H (Technology transfer)
  Category: Empirical


- The paper is suitable for oral presentation

# Global Technology Partnerships and North-South Collaboration. The Case of CamBioTec

## 1. Introduction

The recent biotechnological revolution represents the hope for a more sustainable agriculture in developing countries with potential benefits for small farmers, rural producers and agroindustries. The reason for this is that biotechnology has two attributes that distinguish it from prior agricultural technologies: (1) biotechnology can be used to increase product quality by improving the characteristics of plants and animals; and (2) biotechnology has the potential of conserving natural resources and improving environmental quality. Furthermore, from a global perspective, there are two elements that characterize biotechnology: first, its development is almost exclusively concentrated in highly industrialized countries; and second, innovations have been gradually controlled by large multinational companies. Paradoxically, however, many of the applications of these products will have a potential market in third world countries.

In some countries of Latin America, an incipient biotechnology industry has appeared and some governments are beginning to recognize the promises of biotechnology through the establishment of specific policies in this area. However, there are still numerous bottlenecks that must be overcome if they wish to gain the benefits offered by biotechnology. Some of the most important characteristics of biotechnology in Latin America are the following (Quintero, 1994):

- Most of the research is carried out in academic institutions
- There is very little private participation and in some countries it is almost non-existent
- The main area of application is the health sector, followed by agriculture, the environment and the industrial sector. Livestock has been neglected, even though it is a very important economic activity in some countries.
- The main objective of research has been in basic disciplines and there has been little interest in engineering and its applications
- Biotechnology projects have been largely monodisciplinary and conducted at a laboratory level.

Thus, in the light of the events in biotechnology over the last twenty-five years, it can be observed that one way for the developing countries to gain access to technology is mainly through the purchase of technology, principally from the developed contries, which have invested considerable resources in research and development to help them obtain several profitable products and processes.

Solleiro and his collaborators (1996) suggest that the best technological strategy Latin American countries could use to gain access to biotechnology is that of becoming a good follower. In this way, they can become competitive even though leadership level cannot be reached given the entry barriers to biotechnology and the enormous control over fundamental research in the most advanced countries and enterprises in the area. In a good follower strategy, one basic aspect is to have highly trained human resources that can develop research projects and also select and rapidly assimilate existing technologies. Institutions and firms must be highly competent if they are to gain access to generic technologies and use them to develop applications and products for specific markets and demands.

Strategic alliances have been an important factor in the biotechnological sector in achieving the competitiveness of firms. This industry in particular needs heavy investment in R&D, knowledge of different scientific areas for integration in the form of products and/or processes, highly trained human resources, flexibility of organization in order to develop specific products, knowledge of the market and highly efficient commercialization mechanisms. Only by bringing together these factors is it possible to guarantee the success and survival of firms. However, it is extremely difficult for one organization to have all these elements, hence the importance of combining efforts and resources. The type of alliances that have been established can be seen to present different modalities, the most notable of which are: cooperation between small firms that have a large scientific capacity and large firms that know the market and have the means to sell the product; intra and inter-regional cooperation; alliances with Universities and public research centers; etc. Similarly, various objectives are pursued with this type of partnership, but the following can be mentioned: collaboration in advertising; joint R&D activities; joint distribution; technology transfer; shared use of installations; spin-offs; industry-government collaboration, etc.

Given this evidence, the Canadian Government, through the International Development Research Center (IDRC), in cooperation with the Technology Innovation Center (an institution belonging to the National Autonomous University of Mexico), decided to explore the feasibility of establishing a multinational entrepreneurial cooperation network. With this idea in mind, a project was begun in 1995 to construct a technology transfer network in the biotechnological sector, particularly in the agricultural, livestock and environmental areas. The project is financed by the IDRC and six Latin American countries are participating in it (Argentina, Brazil, Cuba, Colombia, Chile and Mexico) and, of course, Canada. The network has been called the Canada-Latin America Initiative in Biotechnology for Sustainable Development (CamBioTec) and its main objective is to establish effective mechanisms for the introduction of the necessary biotechnology applications for its member countries. Almost two years after the commencement of activities, favourable results have been obtained that show that multinational technological cooperation is feasible. However, difficulties have also arisen that have proved to be obstacles to its functioning. The purpose of this document is therefore to discuss the operation of the network and the elements that must be improved if success is to be attained in this undertaking.

## 2. CamBioTec's Program

### 2.1 Objectives

The general objective of CamBioTec is to promote the introduction of biotechnological products and applications to satisfy the needs of the agri-food and environmental management sectors in some selected countries of Latin America. In order to achieve this objective, technological cooperation management activities are being carried out within CamBioTec to enable the fulfillment of the following specific objectives:

(a) To implement foresighting methodologies and priority setting in research and development in order to identify the opportunities for biotechnological applications in the participating countries.

(b) To strengthen public policy in biotechnology through the fostering of research, consultation with experts and the stimulus of consensus building exercises. To strengthen the capacity to monitor the environmental and socio-economic impacts of applying biotechnology.
(c) To promote a better administration of innovation in biotechnological enterprises through executive seminars and the exchange of information among network members.
(d) To promote technological alliances between Canada and Latin America through an agile intermediation mechanism that makes it possible to help entrepreneurs identify potential partners, available technologies and financing mechanisms.

## 2.2 Network operation

In the first stage, the countries comprising the network were: Canada, Mexico, Cuba, Colombia and Argentina. Later, Chile and Brazil were invited to form part of the network and were incorporated into it in 1996. The Latin American countries were chosen in accordance with the importance of their biotechnological sector within the region and because they offer a wide field of action for the application of biotechnology and for the development of possible partnerships with Canadian firms. The possibility of subsequently including other Latin American countries in the network has not been discarded, however. The growth of the network will depend on the possibility of obtaining additional resources to finance activities and the existence of an organization that has the technical and managerial means necessary to carry out the tasks it is charged with.

CamBioTec is a decentralized network, flexibly organized around "Focal Points" in each of the participating countries. The focal points are responsible for implementing a program of activities at a national level in order to act as a link with the national biotechnological communities, research organizations and government authorities (Herbert-Copley, 1995). Table 1 shows the focal points currently in the network. The principal activities are shown in Table 2.

Table 1. Focal Point Members of CamBioTec

| Country | Institution | Brief Description |
|---|---|---|
| Argentina | Foro Argentino de Biotecnologia (FAB) | FAB is a private organization with the mission of diffusing biotechnology in Argentina, promoting policies in the area and fostering debate and cooperation among industry, government and the academic sector. |
| Brazil | Empresa Brasileira de Pesquisa Agropecuaria (EMBRAPA) - Centro Nacional de Pesquisa de Recursos Geneticos e Biotecnologia (CENARGEN) | EMBRAPA is a public institution which is responsible for carrying out research in the field of agriculture and livestock. CENARGEN belongs to EMBRAPA and is the main center in the country doing research in biotechnology especially in fields such as animal reproduction, biological control of pests, somoclonal variation, and genetic manipulation of crops. |

| Country | Institution | Brief Description |
|---------|-------------|-------------------|
| Canada | Canadian Institute of Biotechnology (CIB) | A non-profit making organization that supports the Canadian biotechnology community in technology transfer. |
| Colombia | 1) Fundación Tecnos | TECNOS's mission is to promote technological development in Colombia and the Andean countries. Its principal activities include the elaboration of foresighting exercises, the development of technological strategies for enterprises and technology administration. |
|  | 2) Instituto de Biotecnología | The Institute is the principal research institution in biotechnology in the country. |
| Cuba | Centro de Ingeniería Genética y Biotecnología (CIGB) | CIGB is the leading institution in Cuba and probably in Latin America in biotechnological research using recombinant DNA techniques. |
| Chile | Facultad de Medicina - Universidad de Chile | The Medicine Faculty is in charge of linking the University with Industry. It also participates in the Euro-Chile project, a program aimed at establishing strategic alliances between Chilean firms and enterprises from the European Union. It has excellent contacts in the national biotechnology industry |
| Mexico* | Centro para la Innnovación Tecnológica** | Forms part of the National University of Mexico (UNAM) and its principal goals include linking the technolgical potential of UNAM with the demands of the industrial sector, consultancy and technical training |

\*  Given the geographical extension of the country, it was considered convenient to open "regional offices" of focal point Mexico. The first is located in the University of Chihuahua (in the North of the country) and the second in the University of Sinaloa (in the North West of Mexico).

\*\*  The Technology Innovation Center is headquarters of focal point Mexico and the General Coordination of CamBioTec.

It should also be mentioned that the network structure is complemented by a governing committee with headquarters in Ottawa, Canada, which is made up of one official from the IDRC, the General Coordinator of CamBioTec and some focal point coordinators.

Table 2.  Main Activities of the Focal Points

---

- Identify priority application areas in biotechnology for the sectors of interest
- Define requirements for integrating and introducing technological packages that will make it possible to attend to priority demands
- Design action plans to link different institutions and available mechanisms in the member countries of the network
- Identify potential partners in the different member countries of the network
- Collect and diffuse relevant technical and commercial information that could lead to the identification of opportunities for collaboration, technology transfer and joint investment with institutions and firms
- Provide support for negotiations derived from potential alliances and the resulting projects
- Negotiate economic support to finance the organizations or alliances arising from CamBioTec

---

## 3. CamBioTec's Roles

CamBioTec has performed various functions including:  promoter of biotechnological research and development priority setting; gatekeeper with regards to market opportunities, generic technologies of interest to the region and specific technologies required by organizations; promoter of alliances between firms; and promoter of discussions on national biotechnology policies.  The activities performed for each of the functions mentioned are described below.

### 3.1 CamBioTec as a promoter for identifying biotechnology R&D priorities

The identification of priority areas has been considered to be fundamental in focussing all efforts towards the most promising sectors and thus obtain a greater impact with the planned activities and a higher probability of success in promoting partnerships.  To this end planning exercises have been promoted that will lead to the identification of priority areas in the biotechnology sector and of the necessary changes in countries in order for them to satisfy priority needs and capitalize on opportunities.  To this end, a methodology developed by Solleiro and his collaborators (1993) was used.  This is an exercise in consensus building in which experts from academic, entrepreneurial and governmental sectors participate. The process is divided into three main stages (figure 1 is a schematic presentation of the process):

I.  Identification and hierarchization of biotechnology applications based on three criteria:  (1) socio-economic adaptation (this factor makes it possible to adapt decisions to the needs, socio-economic conditions and particular resources of each country or region); (2) technological feasibility (the technico-economic possibilities of developing the biotechnology application in question at a commercial level are considered, taking into account not only the potential of the research system but also the regulatory framework, entrepreneurial network and commercialization channels that will allow for market insertion); and (3) market attractiveness (this item considers potential economic benefits, the existing entrepreneurial base, skills needed to achieve benefits, market opportunities and availability of financial resources).

II. Identification of the generic areas of knowledge necessary for developing priority applications at a commercial level and thus clearly determining market opportunities; and

III. Determination of the advance that would need to be made in the generic areas of knowledge in order to reach the level of development desired in accordance with the proposed technological strategy (to reach "good follower" level). The results of this phase make it possible to clearly identify needs in building up capacities so that the country can reach adequate dominion of the technology.

This methodology has been successfully applied in Argentina and Mexico. In Mexico the exercise was carried out in two modalities: at a country (in 1993) and at a state level (in 1996). Table 3 summarizes the most important results.

As can be observed, in spite of the particular conditions of each region at all levels (political, economic, social, geographical, etc.) there are common areas in which biotechnologies are needed to obtain an increase in yields and product quality. The priority list is an excellent starting point to determine concrete technological needs and identify different alternatives for the acquisition of the required techniques, whether by means of licences, alliances, joint developments between firms or with public and/or private research centers, etc.

## 3.2 CamBioTec as gatekeeper

CamBioTec formally offers a technological and commercial opportunities information service for firms in network countries. It does so by replying to specific requests for consultancy. However, it has also been considered that CamBioTec should have a more proactive attitude. Thus, an initiative was launched concerning the characterization of the national biotechnology industry, including the identification of the type of firm that forms CamBioTec's work universe, the technologies currently used and the occasional demands and concrete supply of products, services and technologies. Without any doubt, this approach has significantly contributed to the orientation of the network's efforts, since the focal points can identify more fully with the problems and main players in the industry.

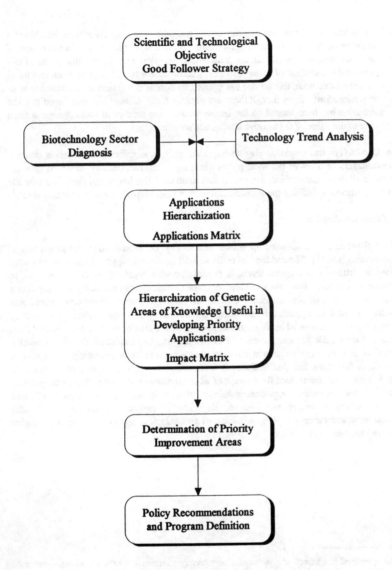

Figure 1. Methodology for identifying biotechnology R&D priorities.

CamBioTec has also introduced a technology monitoring program in priority areas with the objective of determining the state of the art and technological trends. As well as offering a complete overview of the main innovation currents for developing concrete biotechnological applications, the results of this initiative have generated the interest of entrepreneurs in gaining access to attractive technologies up to then unknown. At the same time, this service has opened up spaces and generated creditability as to CamBioTec's professionalism. Even though these are positive traits, it should be mentioned that the demand for information has been limited so far, largely because the number of Latin American firms that are fully aware of the value of competitive intelligence services is low.

Nevertheless, CamBioTec has begun to play an important role as an informal information channel, thanks to the managers of most of the focal points adopting a "mouse" strategy, in which they are foraging around in all the corners of industry and its surroundings. This has turned them into valuable informers who are efficiently fulfilling the technical and market "gatekeeper" role on a continental scale.

## 3.3 CamBioTec as matchmaker

This role of CamBioTec can be summed up in two points: (1) the identification and promotion of business opportunities; and (2) "Transducer" of technological needs and supply. Both functions have been developed at national and regional levels, in accordance with firms' expectations. In order to carry out activities at a regional level, the good level of communication between focal points has been a decisive factor. The quality of communication depends on keeping constant, direct contact, and also on the capacity and skill in opportunely detecting, understanding and transmitting clear, precise information on potential business. This is a difficult task given the lack of reliable data on firms and markets that is a characteristic of Latin America. It is also important to emphasize that the promotion of partnerships has been principally aimed at ones centered around technology transfer. However, it has been possible to detect the fact that flexibility is fundamental for the success of a network of this kind. Indeed, it is not advisable to limit the concept of interentrepreneurial cooperation or the possible areas of work[1]. Various recent experiences indicate that it is necessary to explore different cooperation mechanisms including the joint development of products, distribution and sales agreements, technical assistance activities, provision of technological services, linkage with higher education institutions, etc.

---

[1] CamBioTec has specialized in agrifood and environmental biotechnologies. However, the first project to give rise to the signing of an alliance was for the joint development of a product for human health.

Table 3. Results of priority definition in Agricultural Biotechnology

| Country | Priority biotechnology applications (five most important) | | |
| --- | --- | --- | --- |
| | Agricultural Sector | Livestock Sector | Agroindustrial Sector |
| Mexico (Country Level) | Post-harvest biotechnology in vegetables<br>Control of pathogens in vegetables<br>Control of insects in vegetables<br>Control of pathogens in fruit<br>Insect control in fruit | Waste treatment (cattle)<br>Waste treatment (pigs)<br>Waste treatment (poultry)<br>Genetic disease resistance (bees)<br>Poultry vaccines | Industrialization of maize<br>Industrialization of sugar cane<br>Processes to obtain balanced feed<br>Industrialization of tomato<br>Traditional products of the chemical industry (additives and enzymes) |
| Mexico (Chihuahua State) | Industrial crop harvest improvement<br>Vegetable harvest improvement<br>Fruit harvest improvement<br>Vegetable breeding<br>Post-harvest vegetable conservation | Beef cattle feed<br>Dairy cattle feed<br>Growth promoters for broilers<br>Probiotics and additives for broilers<br>Bio-indicators | Fruit industrialization processes<br>Effluent treatment<br>New products - meat industry<br>New processes - meat industry<br>New processes - vegetable industry |
| Argentina | Pathogen control in ornamental plants<br>Insect control in ornamental plants<br>Vegetable, oilseed and cereal breeding<br>Pathogen control in cereal, oilseeds and vegetables<br>Insect control in cereals, oilseeds, vegetables and fodder | Vaccine against foot and mouth disease for beef cattle<br>Vaccine against mastitis for dairy cattle<br>Vaccine against babesia for beef cattle<br>Tuberculosis diagnosis system for dairy and beef cattle<br>Vaccine against brucellosis for dairy cattle | Effluent treatment<br>New processes for yeast<br>Industrialization of milk<br>Raw material (wheat)<br>New sorghum products |

Partnership promotion has come across serious obstacles. On the one hand, in the Latin American environment alliances between firms have not yet been completely accepted, basically because there is no experience in managing them and this has generated an unwillingness, due to lack of trust, to disclose information and a fear of risking scarce resources without receiving anything in return. The attitudes of many entrepreneurs is thus highly conservative, their number is so small that they do not have sufficient resources to explore opportunities and their sight is too firmly fixed on the local market (Jaffé, 1992; Solleiro et al., 1996).

On the other hand, some entrepreneurs find it difficult to determine exactly what type of partnership they are looking for and the results they can expect from it, because they do not have explicit technological strategies, and this complicates the expression of their technological demands. This situation must be worked on by the focal points: it is necessary to support entrepreneurs in diagnosing their technological needs and clearly explaining opportunities for collaboration with other firms.

It is worth mentioning that CamBioTec has used the organization of executive seminars on biotechnology management as a dual purpose instrument: i) to create awareness in firms about the critical elements for the success of biotechnology derived businesses; and ii) to provide a space where entrepreneurs with interests in common can meet. To reinforce this last point, business round-tables to promote interentrepreneurial partnerships were organized in Mexico with encouraging results, as they helped to "break the ice" between entrepreneurs from different countries[2] and allowed for the exchange of non confidential information aimed at identifying opportunities for collaboration and completely unexpected potential business. We learnt an important lesson from this: in spite of having worked for several months before the business rounds to draw up a list of entrepreneurial appointments based on concrete opportunities, nothing can take the place of direct contact between entrepreneurs.

## 3.4 CamBioTec and policy development

In the Latin American context, the elaboration of development policies for industry in general and for biotechnology in particular is barely beginning. Within CamBioTec, it is considered that the strengthening of the sector can only take place if significant progress is made in this subject, since the policy and regulations environment has a critical influence on the competitiveness of the industry (OTA, 1991).

Nevertheless, the construction of a development policy and a regulatory framework is not a simple task since studies for their design, stakeholder agreement and the political will of the authorities for their introduction are required. CamBioTec is therefore promoting studies, seminars, diffusion of information and consensus searching meetings that could lead to the development of biotechnological policies in the region.

---

[2] Approximately 60 firms from Argentina, Brazil, Canada, Chile, Colombia and Mexico took part in the executive seminar and business round-tables

## 4. CamBioTec focal points

### 4.1 Institutional profile and focal point staff

CamBioTec has been formed by offices specialized in innovation management that act as focal points. From the moment the idea of establishing a network was conceived, attempts have been made to build it up on the basis of existing organizations with experience in the subject. An effort has been made to avoid resources being channelled towards the creation of new structures or the purchase of equipment. Thus, it has proved possible to advance very quickly towards the operation of the network (see Table 4) and efficiently administer an extremely limited budget.

The contracting of people with wide experience in technology management activities is crucial for success, but this is a complex task as there is no plentiful supply of this type of staff in the region. Four of the seven focal points have put a binomial into practice that combines the experience and vision of a senior technology manager with the push, enthusiasm and creativity of a young professional with a solid background in engineering. This formula is yielding dividends.

However, experience in technology management has not been the only condition for the good functioning of the focal points. It is also essential to know the local business environment, have an excellent network of contacts and fluency in the network's working languages (Spanish and English).

Furthermore, it has been observed that the most successful focal points have been those whose members can devote a large part of their time to the network and have a proactive attitude, always seeking to satisfy the needs of the firms with which they are working.

### 4.2 Networking: in-country and international

CamBioTec has been very active in establishing links with other institutions and networks. Networking with domestic institutions has been critical in gaining the support of the local biotech community for CamBioTec's concept and goals. Most of the focal point representatives have been active in "internal" networking, but a systematic approach is still missing. External networks, on the other hand, refer to cooperation with international agencies and other programs and networks. It has proved important to draw up collaboration agendas, basically with the aim of achieving some degree of synergy. Resources from international organizations for this kind of undertaking in Latin America are limited and it is therefore mandatory to include cooperative efforts to raise resources and increase program reach. Another motivation behind cooperation is that it would be very negative to compete against other initiatives when common goals are quite easy to find. The existence of these motivations, however, does not mean that the establishment and management of "networks of networks" are simple tasks. There is still a long way to go for the formalization and consolidation of CamBioTec's external relations, even though excellent informal contacts have already been established.

713

## 4.3 Differences among countries

Undoubtedly, multinational collaboration has many advantages (complementing skills, resources, knowledge and markets). Cooperation management, however, is extremely complex, mainly due to the cultural differences between nations. In the case of CamBioTec, it was surprising to find that, in spite of the generalized belief that there is just one Latin American culture, there are many differences in customs, laws, procedures and bureaucratic expression which makes it impossible to assume that a business formula that works in Mexico will also work in Colombia (not to mention Cuba). Another difference to be found in the national context of each country must be mentioned which refers to the level of institutional and personal commitment detected in focal point performance. Here, the challenge is to reach a more homogeneous level as regards the dedication of effort and talent by focal points. Another considerable difference can be found in the possibility of access to a telecommunications infrastructure since the problems in using Internet that a couple of focal points have has limited possibilities of exchange. These deficiencies must be overcome.

## 5. Challenges for the consolidation of CamBioTec

The balance of the first 18 months of CamBioTec's operations is highly positive. The network has been built up and has begun to give concrete results. However, it is not yet the moment to state that it has been successful. Consolidation requires greater professionalism and commitment. As a result of our first experience, we conclude that priority must be given to strengthening the following actions:

Even though the focal points have experience, the level is heterogeneous and we still do not have common procedures for managing innovation projects arising from CamBioTec's promotional activities. Given that there is now a large number of potential alliances, a technology management manual must be urgently developed. This manual should deal with subjects like how to calculate royalties in biotechnology, contract structure, intellectual property protection at an international level, financing and managing strategic alliances. The idea of having a manual is simply to have a practical, useful guide and it in no way implies inflexible handling of work procedures in the focal points.

It will also be necessary to develop effective tools to identify needs related to entrepreneurial technologies, follow up, and assessment of the interentrepreneurial contacts that have been identified so that project accompaniment can optimize the probability of success. It is worth stressing here that CamBioTec's most important success indicator must be its effectiveness in promoting alliances, that is, that they exist.

The achievement of this final purpose can simultaneously offer a powerful stimulus to raising the commitment of the focal points, strengthen the network and convince entrepreneurs that cooperation with firms in the region is viable. Furthermore, if it can be shown that CamBioTec works, firm bases will be laid to permit us to advance in another priority task: the define and implementation of a strategy to generate income that will assure the provision of resources to give continuity to the operation of the network once initial financing has run out.

Table 4. Principal Results of CamBioTec's Priority Action Lines (1995-1996)

| Biotechnology R&D Priorities | Gatekeeper | Matchmaker | Policy Development |
|---|---|---|---|
| Workshop on R&D priority definition methodologies | Information services for firms | Promotion of business opportunities<br>Organization of seminars on biotechnological innovation management | Courses on intellectual property management<br>Courses on risk assessment and biosafety<br>Courses on biotechnological trends in the agricultural, livestock and environmental sectors |
| Workshop on the application of methodologies for biotechnological research priority setting | Technological monitoring in priority area, for example biopesticides, vegetables, waste water, potato | "Transducer" of technological needs and supply:<br>Identification of a firm's technological needs (technological package)<br>Organization of business rounds<br>Detection of potential partners<br>Diffusion of technological needs | Workshops on impact assessment in agricultural biotechnologies |
| Biotechnology diagnosis:<br><br>Argentina<br>Canada<br>Chile<br>Colombia<br>Mexico | Networking with international institutions:<br>OECD Development Centre<br>IBS/ISNAR<br>IICA<br>Tufts University<br>ISAAA<br>Bolivar Programme | Organization of seminars on business opportunities in specific countries<br>Studies of business plans on specific subjects, for example Bacillus thuringiensis<br>More than 25 potential interentrepreneurial alliances<br>Concrete results:<br>Technology transfer - University of Chihuahua-firm (production of onion seeds)<br>Contract between a Canadian and a Mexican firm (clinical tests and commmercialization of a pharmaceutical product) | Seminars on planning, priorities and agricultural biotechnological policy in Latin America and the Caribbean |

Finally, one recommendation is to follow the example of the Argentinian focal point which created an advisory committee composed of biotechnology researchers and entrepreneurs who have contributed valuable advice for more effective management and to foster a greater approach to the entrepreneurial sector.

References

Herbert-Copley, B. 1995 (editor) "Assessing the impacts of agricultural biotechnologies: Canadian-Latin American Perspectives" Proceedings of the workshop held in Ottawa, Canada, 16 to 17 May. IDRC.

Jaffé, W. 1992 "Agricultural biotechnology research and development investment in some Latin American Countries" Science and Public Policy, Vol. 19, Number 4, August, 229-240.

OTA (Office of Technology Assessment), 1991. "Biotechnology in a Global Economic", OTA-BA-494, Washington D.C.

Quintero, R. 1994, "Biotechnology and bioengineering in Latin America: main areas and approaches for development"; in Aguilera et al (eds) "Bioengineering and bioprocesses. Needs and opportunities in Latin America"; Editorial Universidad de Santiago; Santiago de Chile.

Solleiro, J.L. et al 1993; "Research and development priorities in agri-food biotechnology"; Research report submitted to the International Development Research Center; Ottawa, Canada.

Solleiro, J.L. et al 1996 "Innovation strategies for follower biotechnology firms: Business development under adversity" in Proceedings of the Fifth International Conference on Management of Technology "Technology Management in a Changing World" Robert Mason, Louis Lefebvre and Tarek Khalil (editors). February 27-March 1, Miami, Florida, 243-252.

# 123

# Strategic Information Systems - Developing a Simulation Game for Virtual Supplies

**Heli Laurikkala**
M. Sc., Researcher
Tampere University of Technology
P.O. Box 541
33101 Tampere
tel. +358 3 365 3665
fax. +358 3 365 2027
e-mail: helil@cc.tut.fi

Petri Härkönen
M. Sc., Researcher
Tampere University of Technology
P.O. Box 541
33101 Tampere
tel. +358 3 365 3662
fax. +358 3 365 2027
e-mail: petrih@cc.tut.fi

## Abstract

The aim of the paper is to discuss the Strategic Information Systems and to study the main characteristics of them. Various forms of SIS are also described. The basic goal is to show the importance of networking and cooperation between different organizations. Supplier networking, its present stage, disadvantages and advantages are also studied. The approach is strategic, because the model is built for future purposes i.e. for the year 2005. The strategic study concentrates on the issues important for modelling and for functioning in the virtual economy. The important strategic factors to be found out before building the simulation model are e.g. prerequisites for networking, competitive situation, constituent groups, cost drivers, technology development and competitive advantages.

Networking has to be a strategic decision, the company should not just float into it. Networking should be economically profitable and every partner should get some advantages out of it. So it's quite a demanding task to define with whom to build a network and when. There are several problems related to openness of the information and the network security. Also the willingness of taking risks and sharing profits are important strategic questions to be studied when planning a network.

As an example of a SIS, the simulation model called Virtual Supplies is introduced. The model is used for studying different alternatives for organizing process plant deliveries. The structure of the product needs to be known in advance and the information is loaded into the system in a tree-like product structure. The process model should be able to serve both the strategic management and persons responsible for operational functions of the organization.

Key words: strategy, information systems, supply chain management, networking, virtual supplies.

# 124

TAMPERE UNIVERSITY
OF TECHNOLOGY
Institute of Industrial Management
Strategic Studies

# Generation of the Technology Outline for the Finnish Metal, Engineering and Electrotechnical Industries for the Planning Period 1996 - 2005

**The Sixth International Conference on Management of Technology, MOT 97
25-28 June 1997, Göteborg, Sweden**

**Ulla Niemi-Ylänen**
Tampere University of Technology
Industrial Management: Strategic Studies
P O Box 541, FIN-33101 Tampere, Finland

Telephone  + 358   3   365 3965
Telefax      + 358   3   365 2027
Email        ullany@tut.fi

**Abstract**

The Federation of Finnish Metal, Engineering and Electrotechnical Industries, FIMET, is the central co-ordinating organisation of the Finnish basic metal, mechanical engineering, electronics and electrotechnical industries. Foresight is needed concerning the future competitive position of these industries and the critical technologies, procedures and developmental activities influencing it. To provide the necessary information, FIMET has produced Technology Outlines for the Finnish Metal, Engineering and Electrotechnical Industries in 1992, 1994, and 1996. The purpose of this presentation is to discuss the generation and the contents of the Technology Outline 1996.

The generation process of the third Technology Outline is described. The main objective set in the Technology Outline for the Finnish metal, engineering and electrotechnical industries is to promote world-class performance. New applications of technology in products and processes are superior methods for improving competitiveness. To achieve global competitiveness several initiatives for action are presented that are included in the following four main points: targeting investment, promoting commercialisation, being aware of the risks of narrow internationalisation, and developing entrepreneurship and competence.

# 1    Introduction

## 1.1    Background

The Federation of Finnish Metal, Engineering and Electrotechnical Industries, FIMET, is the central co-ordinating organisation of the Finnish metal, engineering and electrotechnical industries (hereafter referred to as "the industries") and is the largest industrial association in Finland. The 1000 member companies with a total of 1300 plants operate in the following sectors: the basic metal, mechanical engineering, electronics and electrotechnical industries. FIMET member companies represent 90% of the output, labour and exports of these industries.

**FIMET Technology** is one of the five subdivisions within FIMET. The business idea of **FIMET Technology** is to actively improve the operating preconditions and competitiveness of the industries through development of technology and standardisation. **FIMET Technology** also promotes and co-ordinates co-operation between its member companies and research bodies to develop the competitiveness of the industries. Development targets include product, production, materials, environmental and information technologies as well as quality and management. Development is promoted through programmes consisting of a number of projects. Therefore foresight is needed concerning the future competitive position of the industries and the critical technologies, procedures and developmental activities influencing it. This information is needed by FIMET, research bodies and the entire national innovation support system.

To provide the necessary information, FIMET has previously produced Technology Outlines for the Finnish Metal, Engineering, and Electrotechnical Industries in 1992 and 1994. The 1992 report was the first technology strategy for a single industrial sector in Finland. The FIMET Technical Committee, which directs the development activities of **FIMET Technology**, decided in September 1995 that a new technology outline should be prepared in 1996.

Companies may use the Technology Outline when formulating their technology strategies, an essential part of their overall business strategy. The Technology Outline also serves as the basis for the long-term strategic plan of **FIMET Technology**, to be reviewed annually, from which an action plan will be derived.

## 1.2    Objectives of the Technology Outline 1996

The main objective set for the industries is to promote world-class performance. The objective of the Technology Outline is to indicate, by way of concrete action plans, the direction in which the industries should develop. Its purpose is to define the most important investment targets, areas for development of technology and the actions needed to advance the developmental activities. It will be discussed how investments in research and development and the principles for actions should be made to coincide with the needs of the industries. The Technology Outline can be used by research bodies in directing their resources and activities in line with the needs of the industries.

One aim of this report is to influence the technology policy implemented by the science and technology institutions and authorities of the Finnish government and those of the European Union. It also serves as a guideline for the activities of FIMET itself. The FIMET subdivisions will be required to systematically follow the principles presented there when taking a position on the technological development both nationally and internationally.

## 1.3 Scope of the study

The planning period of the Technology Outline for the Finnish Metal, Engineering and Electrotechnical Industries is 1996 - 2005. The purpose of this presentation is to discuss the generation and the contents of the Technology Outline 1996.

## 2 Description of the generation process

## 2.1 Procedure, methods and timetable

The objectives and timetable of the Technology Outline were introduced by a group of specialists at the meeting of the FIMET Technical Committee on January 17, 1996. The group formulated preliminary initiatives for improving the industrial competitiveness of the industries. These were reviewed and augmented at the meeting of the FIMET Technical Committee Executive Group on March 26, 1996.

The practical benefit to the industries of the Technology Outlines 1992 and 1994 became apparent in interviews with present and former members of the FIMET Technical Committee. Company representatives were interviewed on the developmental needs of the industries and their visions covering the next three to five years.

The first iterative round on initiatives ended on June 6, 1996 when the initiatives were reviewed by the FIMET Technical Committee and were then reformulated by the specialists. During another round, meetings were held with company representatives from various FIMET business sectors and with **FIMET Technology** expert groups. They were interviewed to record the matters about which they were unanimous, to note differences in opinion and to specify concrete targets for development.

Senior specialists selected and analysed the critical targets for development regarding the global competitiveness of the industries in the light of their visions for the next five to twelve years.

The second round ended on August 21, 1996 when the initiatives were thoroughly reviewed at the annual seminar of **FIMET Technology** and were then rewritten in their final form by the specialists. The Technology Outline was presented for approval to the FIMET Board on October 16, 1996. The generation process employed is summarised in the following chart, Figure 1.

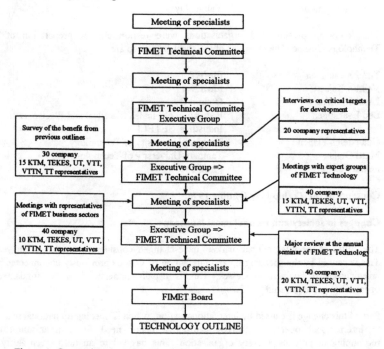

Figure 1. Generating the Technology Outline

FIMET = Federation of Finnish Metal, Engineering and Electrotechnical Industries
KTM = Ministry of Trade and Industry
TEKES = Technology Development Centre
VTT = Technical Research Centre of Finland
UT = Universities of Technology
VTTN = Science and Technology Policy Council of Finland
TT = Confederation of Finnish Industry and Employers

## 2.2 Organisation

The Executive Group of the FIMET Technical Committee has acted as the steering group
in generating the present Technology Outline. The members of the group are:

Kaarlo Kankaala          Oy E. Sarlin Ab
Ilkka Eerola             High Speed Tech Ltd. Oy
Matti Kilpi              Nokia Oy Research Centre

Rauno Mattila                    Trafotek Oy
Jorma Veräjänkorva               Valmet Oy

The following persons and organisations were responsible for preparation of the
Technology Outline. The members of the specialist group are:

Timo Airaksinen                  FIMET
Veikko Kajaste                   FIMET
Lasse Kivikko                    Otakon Oy
Leo Laaksonen                    Federation of Finnish Electrical and Electronic
                                 Industries, SETELI
Ulla Niemi-Ylänen                Tampere University of Technology
Matti Otala                      Tampere University of Technology
Pekka Pokela                     FIMET

## 3    Contents of the Technology Outline 1996

### 3.1    Changes in society and technological landscape

The "rules of the international market" have changed considerably in the recent years.
This is caused by the speeding up and interaction of various previously unconnected and
unsynchronised business processes. This is usually understood as a "fundamental
operational paradigm shift".

Part of this change is caused by internationalisation, which is opening up national markets
to international operators, thereby causing a major need for reorganisation and
regrouping in practically every organisation. This has led to an unforeseen flurry of
business process reengineering projects, alliances and business or technology networking
initiatives, mostly based on state-of-the-art approaches to technology management and
assessment. Moreover, the era of sustainable development has increased customer
interest in ecological issues and resulted in broader legal involvement in operations
affecting the environment. Taking account of total quality management and
environmental issues in products and operations sets new challenges and opportunities for
technology and competitiveness.

The character of technological development has changed fundamentally. The
improvements in technologies are based on reciprocal co-operation between
manufacturing, product and process developers, and researchers. The ideology of
"breakthrough innovation" is being replaced by "continuous improvement", the concept
of "product" has been replaced by "modifiable product platform", and that of "market" is
being replaced by "glocal", a culturally consistent globally local operation.

## 3.2 Future success factors

The importance of rapid, flexible just-in-time deliveries will grow. Distribution and marketing channels will be the key success factors. The management of logistics and process streamlining will become increasingly important and will require improved methods and systems for product data management (PDM) which combine standard solutions with the individual needs of the customer. It is essential to thoroughly understand the business of the customer and the applications he or she needs. In addition to rapid product development, rapid market entry is part of process streamlining and a decisive factor in competition.

Intelligent and communicative products are coming and improved know-how is needed in control systems and applied electronics. The characteristics of intelligent products include self-configuration, self-diagnostics, redundancy, operating reliability, remote diagnostics, remote programming and remote maintenance; however, these must not increase the manufacturing or implementation cost.

Better quality in products, processes and especially services is required, as is a greater recognition of environmental considerations and lower prices. This will entail increased automation, more effective processes, life-cycle analysis of products, and environmentally sound processes. It will also be extremely important for companies to build themselves an image as being ecologically minded.

The use of expert systems (knowledge-based systems) will increase; these systems cover project know-how, product development, production management and marketing. Involvement of human resources is the driving force in company success. The appropriate utilisation of information and communication technologies coupled with the ability to innovate may form a competitive edge for the company. This would need to be continuously improved through training. Electronic communication will be utilised in user and maintenance manuals, and telephone or computer-based help desks will become more common.

World-wide liberalisation and deregulation of trade has led to the globalisation of markets. The emerging of new markets on the Pacific Rim should be considered in the marketing strategies of Finnish engineering and electronics companies with sufficient potential and capacity to operate there.

## 3.3 World-class tomorrow - development towards 2005

### 3.3.1 Targeting investment

**Continuous process**

In each FIMET business sector a continuous, real-time identification process is needed to identify targets for investment in technology. The basic principles of the process are well known and implemented in many countries *(see References 1-5)*. Targets should be continuously assessed and corrections made immediately when an error is noticed. This process should be supported by a modern, world-wide information-gathering system providing relevant market and technology information and promoting technology transfer. Within this process, target areas would be prioritised according to the following criteria:

1) Strong, existing business areas
2) Emerging demand areas with obvious growth potential
3) New, generic features and priorities in product and process technology
4) Strengthening research and development

**Global market leaders**

The world-wide trends described in Chapter 3.1 provide convincing evidence that in the future more numerous and smaller globally operating corporations will exist in each field of business. Only companies exhibiting excellence will succeed in competition. It will be a world of black or white. It is therefore important to identify the strategic business areas and support potential market leaders at their early stages of development - even beginning with the establishment of the company.

**Technology fusion**

New opportunities will emerge from the innovative fusion of key technologies. Research and technology development work should not only be done on the basis of the narrow interests of companies but also encouraged with an eye towards combining technologies of various fields in different industrial sectors.

Technology fusion can be promoted by lowering boundaries between various fields of technology. Therefore improvement of the structure of research and development bodies will be needed. The aim is to identify opportunities for blending incremental technical improvements from previously separate fields of technology. This way new innovative products that will revolutionise the markets are created.

**3.3.2 Promoting commercialisation**

**Promoting lead users**

The high risk involved with the accelerated development of technology should be reduced. The commercialisation of new technologies is a problem for which solutions should be found. One solution is to encourage successful development by aiding the commercialisation of new products.

**Launching products just-in-time**

Product engineering is much more than just engineering, since it is also extremely important to be on the market at the right time with the right product. By accelerating the research and development process, a more appropriate reaction is generated within the rapidly changing markets. Accelerated development of technology demands the speeding up of product launching with simultaneous or concurrent engineering and activation of innovation processes. It implies the parallel execution of product, production and investment plans using cross-functional teams, resulting in a considerable reduction of the time-to-market of the product, while simultaneously reducing the possibilities of problems related to product and production. The implementation of simultaneous or concurrent engineering principles includes activities with well co-ordinated targets, careful planning and good discipline, resulting in better management of the project, improved efficiency and considerably shortened development times. It is important, however, that the new product also be reliable. One must assess the risks involved when applying new technologies.

### 3.3.3 Being aware of the risks of narrow internationalisation

**Partnerships in new emerging markets**

World-wide liberalisation and deregulation of trade have led to the globalisation of markets. The opening of Russia and the Baltic States will mean new emerging markets for the industries. The market and technological potential of these regions are expected to rise rapidly, and partnerships and networks should therefore be established in the Baltic States and in the Commonwealth of Independent States. It is also important to shift the focus away from excessive concentration on the European market, e.g., towards the Pacific Rim and South America. In these areas a closer working partnership among industry, governments and universities should be established. Contract research and development centres giving small businesses easy access to technical innovations and know-how should be advanced.

### 3.3.4 Developing entrepreneurship and competence

**Technology entrepreneurs in Finland**

Accelerated development of technology leads to new research and technology development efforts, which involve higher risks for companies and a need for more rapid development and investment cycles. But successful development of technology also leads to new business opportunities and gives new entrepreneurs a chance to enter new markets.

The general conditions conducive to becoming an entrepreneur should be developed further. A new type of company - the microcompany - is emerging, which should be easier to set up and unbureaucratic to run. Therefore legislative and operational barriers, e.g. risk taking, should be eased.

**Creation of "learning companies"**

The skills of those within the company should be improved by increasing the productivity of and accessibility to education and training. Education and training programmes should be updated to ensure continuous learning opportunities for all employees. Everybody should improve his or her vocational skills to make this increased competence immediately applicable to the benefit of the entire organisation and thus of society.

**Activation of employee initiative process**

Implementation of a continuous improvement process (CIP) should be encouraged. At the same time, a fundamental reform of employee initiative activities is recommended. Employee initiatives should be supported by short and long-term recognition, aiming at a considerable rise in the amount of employee initiatives.

**Securing the availability of skilled technical personnel**

As jobs become more demanding and responsibilities more extensive, the quality of education should be raised to the level needed by the industry. Based on a study *(see Reference 6)* it is likely that a shortage of workers with a vocational training in mechanical engineering technology will occur in the industries as well as of engineers in electricity and electronics. Particular attention should be given to educating more engineers with academic and non-academic degrees in the fields of electronics and information technology.

**3.3.5 New project initiatives**

New projects should be started in the following fields

- rapid and flexible deliveries, process streamlining
- rapid product development and market implementation
- development of intelligent and communicative products
- quality improvement in products, processes and services
- new engineering services and expert systems
- emerging forms of electronic communication.

**3.4 Proposal for an action plan**

The following table lists the principal organisations responsible for formulating strategies to implement the initiatives mentioned above, Table 1. FIMET will formulate those strategies for which it is responsible; however, in many cases the implementing organisation will be other than FIMET. Through successful co-operation, results can be achieved that meet the objectives set in the present Outline.

Table 1. The principal organisations responsible for formulating strategies to implement the initiatives.

| INITIATIVE | IMPLEMENTING ORGANISATION |
|---|---|
| **Targeting investment** | |
| Continuous process | Ministry of Trade and Industry and Technology Development Centre |
| Global market leaders | Ministry of Trade and Industry |
| Technology fusion | Technology Development Centre, companies and research bodies |
| **Promoting commercialisation** | |
| Promoting lead users | Ministry of Trade and Industry and Technology Development Centre |
| Launching products just-in-time | Companies |
| **Being aware of the risks of narrow internationalisation** | |
| Partnerships in new emerging markets | Companies |
| **Developing entrepreneurship and competence** | |
| Technology entrepreneurs in Finland | Ministry of Trade and Industry |
| Creation of "learning companies" | Companies, Ministry of Education and FIMET |
| Activation of employee initiative process | Companies |
| Securing the availability of skilled technical personnel | Companies, Ministry of Education and FIMET |
| **New project initiatives** | Companies, Technology Development Centre and FIMET |

## References

1) Europe and the global information society. 1994. Recommendations to the European Council. Bangemann report. Brussels, 26 May.
Internet: http://guagua.echo.1u/eudocs/en/report.html

2) United Kingdom Office of Science and Technology. 1995. Progress through Partnership: Technology Foresight Programme. HMSO, London.

3) National Institute of Science and Technology Policy (NISTEP) and the Institute for Future Technology (IFTECH). 1993. The Fifth Technology Forecast Survey, Future Technology in Japan toward the Year 2020. Tokyo.

4) Organisation for Economic Co-operation and Development, OECD. 1996. Science Technology industry Review No. 17. Special Issue on Government Technology Foresight Exercises. Paris.

5) Office of Science and Technology Policy. 1995. National Critical Technologies Report. Executive Office of the President. Washington.

6) Federation of Finnish Metal, Engineering and Electrotechnical Industries, FIMET. 1996. Need of Technical Personnel in the Finnish Engineering Industry by the Year 2005. FIMET Report (in Finnish). Helsinki.

# 125

CONSTRUCTIVE LEARNING: A NEW APPROACH TO DEPLOYING
TECHNOLOGY-INTENSIVE PRODUCTION SYSTEMS IN THE
WORKPLACE

Author:
J.C. Spender, Dean,
Sch of Mgt, NYIT, POBox 8000 Old Westbury NY 11568
USA or
411 East 57th Street New York, NY, USA
Tel + Fax:    +1-212-759-6451 (privat)
Tel:          +1-516-686-7423
Fax:          +1-516-484-8328
Email:     spender@worldnet.att.net - spender@admin.nyit.edu

ABSTRACT


The much remarked rise of knowledge-work is the result of employees
needing new knowledge and skills as high-technology production and
information systems become increasingly common in the workplace. This
is as true in the office environment as on the shop-floor and in the service
industries. Employees now need formal and knowledge-intensive skills
that match the way these increasingly complex systems work. They become
post-modern 'system minders', checking the system's operation and fixing
it when it fails to operate correctly, rather than cogs in the system. This
requires deep knowledge of the system, and one consequence is the
traditional methods of workplace education, learning-by-doing from others
already skilled, or from the equipment and systems suppliers, prove risky,
expensive and inefficient. While it is common to note that the employees
knowledge and skills are the firm's principal assets, it is not so clear how
these are to be managed and built up. Throughout the Westerndemocracies
there is an impending crisis in employee training which cannot be solved by
merely providing incentives and tax penalties to those firms who fail to
spend a preset amount of turnover on training. How is post-modern
employee training to be done? We know that classroom training does not
work well and that new thinking is required. In this paper, which is based
on Vygotskian developmental theory, we describe 2-day constructive
learning workshops designed to help introduce MRPII, the widely used
computer-based inventory and production management system, into a
major transportation maintenance facility in New York City. MRPII is
notoriously difficult to install successfully, and it is also difficult to evaluate
its value when installed. We report both the training and the outcomes
evaluation methods, and show that the workshops worked well and
reduced the operatives' learning period by upwards of a year.

# 126

FUNCTIONAL MODELLING AS A TOOL FOR THE INTEGRATION OF
NEW TECHNOLOGIES

MAGNER-CANET Sophie
Ecole Centrale Paris Laboratoire Productique - Logistique
Grande Voie des Vignes
92295 Chatenay Malabry Cedex
France
Tel:      +33-1-41-13-15-68
Fax:      +33-1-41-13-12-72

ABSTRACT

The integration of a new process technology within a manufacturing
company turns out to be a complex process which involves many actors of
various knowledge domains and responsibility areas. This integration
process becomes more difficult when in the mass production of mechanical
parts, product development deadlines and constrains are present.
Particularly, decisions regarding heavy investments have to be taken
quickly.
In order to face up to this challenge, we propose a model that allows, at the
early stage, to evaluate the potential of the technology in spite of its novelty,
with regard to uncertain and evolving internal requirements. This model is
based upon a teleological (in order to link the means to the goals)
representation of the technology, taking into account its functional and
structural aspects, as well as mapping relationships between function and
structure (machines, tools, process plannings...). This representation allows
to integrate and to couple objectives of designers, strategic managers,
manufacturers, suppliers and R&D. Such a model has been adopted in order
to support integration process, from its technical advance identification
until the regular use of the technology, providing a judicious representation
for both a proactive approach (from technology to product) and a reactive
approach (from product to technology). Both integration approaches must
be undertaken either independently or simultaneously with the processes of
the new product development and the manufacturing processes
optimization. Firstly, this model will help to evaluate the functional
potential of a new technology and to position it within the technology
portfolio. Secondly, the technology could be molded to evolve to better fit
the implementation environment (products, complementary technologies,
standards, organization...). Finally, some technical and organizational
improvements could be suggested to make the company more adapted to
the technology.
By the implementation of this conceptual viewpoint of new technologies,
we hope to contribute to the identification and to the reduction of the costly
and late modifications risks, the useless studies and investments risks, or
the risk of giving up without justification of what could have become a
competitive advantage.
This research work is done in collaboration with Peugeot-Citroen company.

## MANAGING TOOL SUPPLY IN ASSEMBLY OF COMPLEX PRODUCTS

Roland Kadefors and Mats Eklöf
Lindholmen Development and Department of Injury Prevention, Chalmers
University of Technology, Göteborg, Sweden
Contact address: Lindholmen Utveckling, Box 8714, 402 75 Göteborg

## ABSTRACT

In a study of the organization of powered tool supply in Swedish
manufacturing industry, it was found that organizational obstacles existed,
hampering acquisition of adequate tools for a given purpose. In a common
organizational model, responsibility for tool selection rests with a
purchasing department with little knowledge of the precise intended use of
the tools. Incentives are often limited to prize, technical specifications and
personal relations to suppliers. In another organizational model, acquisition
is placed with the foremen; here, acquisition is often on an ad hoc basis. In
both cases, quality problems, maintenance problems and ergonomic
problems are likely to occur.

A case study was undertaken to analyze the properties of a unique
organizational model introduced at Volvo Cars in Göteborg, Sweden. Here,
a Tool Center was created in the workshop hall, containing an exhibit of
approved powered tools, as well as test equipment. This center was
managed by a senior production engineer with expert knowledge of
powered tools. Whenever a problem occurred linked to hand tools, the
Tool Center could be consulted. The problems, which could be technical or
ergonomic in nature, were analyzed by the manager of the Center. Technical
malfunctions motivating repairs could be identified. All repairs were
carried out by the tool supplier. Tools could be chosen only from the
exhibit, and were selected by a panel of experts, including quality engineers
and ergonomists. All purchases were done by the Center manager, who had
a budget for the purpose.

Analysis of the Volvo model showed that (a) the number of tool variants
was reduced significantly; (b) the project had helped improve quality and
productivity; (c) ergonomically better tools were used. The end user
influence on the acquisition of tools was changed dramatically.

## A Step by Step Implementation Model for Computer-based Technologies

Mohini Singh, Department of Information Systems, Victoria University of Technology, P O Box 14428, MCMC, Melbourne 8001, Victoria, Australia Email: MohiniSingh@vut.edu.au

### Introduction

Computer-based technologies generally referred to as new technologies have been classified by Youssef (1994) as hardware and related software based technologies used in designing, manufacturing and managing all necessary activities to produce a product or provide a service such that all non value added activities are eliminated. Dean et. al. (1990) referred to new technologies as those that have evolved over the last decade and hold the promise of revolutionising manufacturing. These include robotics, computer-aided design, engineering and manufacturing (CAD, CAE, CAM) and manufacturing resource planning (MRP II).

An increased investment in new computer-based technologies by the Australian establishments instigated the need to carry out an intensive study of the implementation and management of these technologies. Five detailed case studies were conducted through semi-structured interviews with senior and middle managers and shop floor workers. The reality of a company emerges through the activities of everyday life, and is shaped by the managers and employees involved. Such aspects and other technology related events were perceived through case studies which identified the benefits of technology achieved, factors that contributed to success and problems experienced during implementation. A comparative study of the case studies revealed that time scales for implementation in all the cases were lengthened, costs spiralled and that only some of the anticipated benefits were realised. However, findings of the five case studies were not sufficient to say that this was true for all Australian companies, therefore a postal questionnaire survey of 335 companies was conducted to confirm the findings of the case studies.

The findings of this research project indicated that Australian companies implementing new technologies took a long time to realise the benefits of technology. It was also evident that although companies were aware of factors that can contribute to success, application of these factors were not as effective as they should have been. The existence of problems identified from research clearly calls for support and guidance in the implementation and management of technology. Ineffective implementation and management of new technologies leads to lost opportunities in competitive advantage which intensified the need for strategies that would close the gap between current performance and desired performance.

To assist the organisations avoid pitfalls throughout the acquisition and implementation process a model for successful implementation and exploitation of technology is presented in this paper. The adoption of this model should be especially useful for Australian companies because current literature on implementation and management of technology in Australia is not immense, and according to research findings of the case studies and the postal questionnaire, guidance and support in the implementation process is needed to avoid pitfalls. Existing models largely deal with disparate aspects of technology management. A comprehensive model addressing all issues related to technology implementation is not available. The model presented in this paper is based on the research findings discussed earlier and is particularly pertinent to the Australian manufacturing industries.

**The Model**
The model incorporates a step by step implementation process. It is made up of seven steps that are presented in Figure One on the next page. Most of the technology issues addressed in each step of the model has been supported by the findings of research which justifies the need for it to be incorporated in the model. Issues that are not research outcomes but important for successful implementation of technologies are also included. Each step of the model is made up of a number of variables that need to be modified and adjusted so that a proper combination of these is applied for successful implementation.

The seven steps of the model are:
*Step One. Technology concept and its strategic definition.* This step identifies the strategic opportunities the firm will attain from technology and the need for technology for the company.

*Step Two. Technology configuration and development of a database.* This step specifies the relevance of new technology to the manufacturing function, compatibility of technology with existing technology, sources of technology and the need for a database to store the technology details, supplier information and negotiation documents for future reference.

*Step Three. Technology Planning.* Technology planning involves thorough planning of technology finance, sociotechnical issues, technology integration, composition of the project team, supplier of technology, production during technology installation and the organisation structure.

*Step Four. Installation and Commissioning of Technology.* Technology installation suggests a number of implementation strategies that can be used for technology installation. It also lists a number of success factors and possible problems that should be avoided.

*Step Five. Performance Evaluation.* Step Five highlights the need for post implementation audit of the implemented technology. It presents ideas for evaluating the performance of technology so that all existing problems and negative repercussions can be minimised.

*Step Six. Suggestions for Improvement.* Step Six provides a number of suggestions for improving the performance of technology. The suggestion most relevant to the problem identified in Step Five should be chosen. It also allows for a combination of suggestions to rectify the situation.

*Step Seven. Plan for a New Technology.* Step Seven provides the option of a new incremental technology for the organisation, for continuous improvement to sustain core competencies and to formulate and further improve business strategies.

The model is presented as Figure One on the next page.

The following section describes the model by discussing the issues incorporated in each step of the model. One, all or a combination of the issues can be applied in each step. To conceptualise the model it is imperative to understand each of the steps in detail.

**Step One:    Technology Concept and its Strategic Definition.**
New technologies in manufacturing are linked with the growth in the use and application of computers. The concept of computer-based technologies is essential for companies competing in sophisticated markets to achieve consistent quality, dependable deliveries and rapid design changes. The concept first of all has to be evaluated to see if it is worthwhile. The strategic opportunities that the firm will attain from technology and the impact of technology on the whole organisation structure should then be assessed. Justification of the concept is then directed to the senior management to make them understand the strategic implications of technology and its beneficial impact on the organisation. The idea of a computer based technology could enhance the achievement of a specific strategic objective, such as improved flexibility and responsiveness, increased productivity, a highly skilled workforce and superior goods and services. It is then necessary to learn if the proposed technology is strategically, technically and financially feasible. Alternative designs and evaluation may be conducted to test its economic feasibility. A complete understanding of the technology concept is needed before financial justification can be undertaken.

Issues addressed in step one are:

*1. Source of Information.* Sources of technology information can also be internal as well as external to the organisation. Internal sources are in-house research and development, joint venture, research consortium, technology alliances and key personnel. External sources include employees, industrial exhibitions and seminars, consultants, etc.

*2. Strategic Implications*
The first step would be to identify the strategic advantages of technology and make them known to senior management and other employees. The strategic importance of technology is such that it contributes positively to the competitive edge of a company through the benefits it offers.

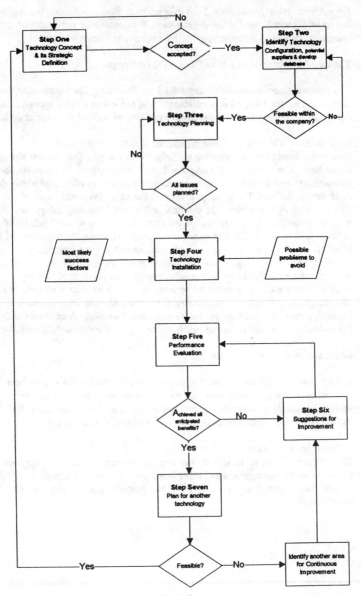

Figure One

### 3. Reasons for New Technology.

Companies compete on cost and customer-focused performance factors such as quality, delivery reliability, design lead times, flexibility and response to customer requirements which are attainable from the use of new technologies. New computer based technologies allow for increased accuracy, flexibility and uniformity, making a firm's operations more competitive by increasing productivity, decreasing cost of production and improved quality. It also increases a company's ability to respond quickly to the changing market demand.

### 4. Justification Techniques for New Technology

Acquiring new technologies usually require large expenditure, thus a well conceived methodology for their selection is required to ensure that the decision to invest is based on sound business strategies which are developed to serve the long and short term interests of the company.

### 5. Communication of the Technology Idea

Once the technology concept is accepted, it should be communicated to the employees because as suggested by Saraph and Sabastian (1992) a well-planned communications program is vital in the introduction of new technologies.

### Step Two:    Technology Configuration

Once the technology concept is accepted, it is important to obtain technology specifications to analyse its relevance to the manufacturing function. A list of suitable technology with equipment description, age, flexibility, capacity and constraints are required to decide on the most appropriate technology as well as potential suppliers.

Issues discussed in this step are:

### 1. Identification of technology's suitability to the company's needs

The most obvious thing to look at in selecting technology is whether the technology is suitable for the business requirements.

### 2. Feasibility of technology

Feasibility of technology is an important issue to consider to avoid cost overruns.

### 3. Compatibility

Compatibility of hardware, software, and integration with existing and incremental technologies will require careful analysis.

### 4. Input requirements

The input required for new technology either in the form of raw materials or in the form of data will have to be scrutinised for quality, format, and the associated costs. It is important to note that quality requirements of inputs to new technologies may need to be re-examined.

### 5. Potential Suppliers
A complete description of the technology configuration from all potential suppliers will indicate who should supply the technology. One or two suppliers who have the capability to develop the required technology will be chosen at this stage.

### 6. Development of a Database
A database is a collection of data that is shared and used for multiple purposes. Data are organised around files and arranged so that duplication and redundancy are avoided. Information concerning ongoing activities is captured once, validated and entered into the proper location in the data base (Kanter, 1992). Manufacturing firms according to Bordoloi et.al. (1993) develop databases and implement data base management systems for computer integrated manufacturing which calls for high levels of data sharing among subsystems. However, a database for technology implementation and management should be developed to hold a record of implementation issues which can be retrieved to formulate solutions to similar situations during the implementation of other technologies.

### Step Three: Technology Planning
An effective technology concept and identification of a suitable technology configuration is not sufficient for the successful implementation and exploitation of technology. Creative planning of the project incorporating decisions to determine the sequence of pre- and post-implementation events is required. Failure to create the proper environment for computer based technologies may produce negative results. The role of senior and middle management in managing technological change, creating the right environment and organisational culture and keeping abreast of the progress of the project team will ascertain their commitment to the project. The plans for implementation, organisational changes and sociotechnical issues in relation to technology and their association with the strategic objectives established in step one are aligned at this stage. A long term view to technology strategy, organisational and sociotechnical issues is essential for successful implementation. According to Zairi (1992) the sequence in which new technology is implemented will have marked effects on all aspects of a company's business. Therefore thorough planning and vigorous management control of the following issues is needed:

### 1. Organisation Structure
Existing organisational arrangements may need to be examined so that an accurate picture of the synergistic potential of new technologies can be realised.

### 2. Financing the Technology Project
Once the technology concept is accepted and some indication of the cost of technology has been attained from the supplier, the company faces the task of appropriating sufficient funds for the project. Planning for costs of training, reorganising and making changes to the current operations and engineering of new processes is essential to avoid cost overruns during and after implementation.

### 3. Sociotechnical Issues
It is essential to consider people factors right from the onset of new technologies and not after implementation as it happened in most Australian companies. Zairi (1992) suggests that human resource justification needs should be considered alongside technological justification. Proper planning of staffing, new job design, training, reward system, gain sharing, safety issues and union-management relationship is required before implementing a new technology. The social implications of new technology are just as significant as its economic effects (Noori 1990).

### 4. Technology Integration
Detailed aspects of technology implementation and its integration with the existing and future technologies should be considered to avoid the high costs of islands of technology.

### 5. Project Leader and Project Team
New technology projects require a leader who is willing to take risks and provide tenacious commitment to ensure that the technology is implemented successfully. Whether the project leader is going to be someone from the company or a consultant is to be hired from outside should be decided at this stage. Research findings indicated that non cross-functional teams encountered a lack of support from those sections of the organisation that were not represented on the team.

### 6. Supplier of Technology
Assessing technology capability in Step Two will also identify potential suppliers. Proper coordination is required in case of multi-vendor equipment and operations control software.

### 7. Work / Production during Implementation
It is important to consider how work will be handled during implementation and who will be involved. Proper planning will avoid disruption to the usual business which may affect the profits of the organisation.

### Step Four:    Installation and Commissioning of Technology
Proper planning of the factors discussed above will result in the technology being installed within the time and resources designated for it. Successful implementation will depend on the quality of decisions made regarding resources, impact of technology on people, training, and integration of technologies with existing technologies. Clearcut responsibilities and action plan of the project team, management and employees must be established for the implementation. This step discusses direct cutover, pilot conversion, parallel conversion and phased conversion strategies for new technology. It also highlights the success and failure factors.

### Factors that are likely to bring success.
The following were identified from research as success factors:
Top management support for the project.

A competent project leader to implement the technology and sell the idea, benefits and requirements to superiors, subordinates and peers.

Cross-functional project teams for cross pollination of ideas and techniques and for analysis of problems through the eyes of the workers in their sections is essential.

An appropriate organisation structure. Complex equipment, highly skilled employees and a dynamic external environment propel the organisation design toward an adaptable structure that facilitates innovation and rapid change and bolsters creative input from employees.

Communication of the Technology Idea. Early communication of the technology idea and its impact on the company is essential to create a climate for technology within the organisation.

Adequate Education and Training. Education and training act as a catalyst for changes that accompany new technology. It constitutes an essential basis for employee empowerment.

Good Relationship with the Vendor. The relationship between the vendor of technology and user should be permanent and a long term partnership.

## Problem to Avoid during Implementation
The problems discussed below were identified from the research discussed above.
Inadequate training will lead to 'trial and error' and 'wait and see' or 'learn as you go' principles that can result in a costly outcome for the company.

Inadequate Resources. A lack of both financial and non financial resources such as human, technical and managerial are also required.

Overestimation of gains in efficiency. Unrealistic expectations from new technologies eventuate in disappointments.

Supplier. The user-supplier relationship should be one that is based on trust and ability to cooperate to avoid problems.

Improper record keeping. In the absence of formal record keeping methods the gap between performance forecasts and results will not be identified.

Opposition from workers. A well planned communications program is vital in combating resistance to the introduction of new technologies.

Lack of expert advice. A lack of experience with computer based technologies for many Australian companies and consultants constraint referral to past experience for solutions to problems associated with these technologies.

Lack of a cross functional team. Non representation from any one of the functions or departments lead to opposition from that department because they feel deprived of opportunities.

Disruptions during implementation. Behavioural and organisational reasons such as opposition from workers and project leaders can delay or abandon the project.

Incompatible or obsolete technology. With the rapid changes in computer based technologies it is possible that by the time a technology is implemented it is obsolete.

### Step Five     Performance Evaluation
Once the technology is implemented it is unwise to assume that it is operating successfully as was the case in the companies investigated. Continuous monitoring of technology will highlight its progress and improve its utilisation. Step Five suggests measures for the evaluation of new technologies.

### Step Six     Suggestions for Improvement
If the performance evaluation of technology indicate that the hoped-for productivity gains have not been achieved then the project team should refer to the suggestions for improvement discussed in the following section. These suggestions were formulated to help the companies improve their current positions.

*1. Redefine the Firm's Mission Statement.* Business goals should be examined with an emphasis on the role of technology in achieving it.

*2. Evaluate the Compatibility of Hardware, Software and Human Resource.* It is important to assess the compatibility of hardware, software and the users for successful operation of the technology.

*3. Integrate Islands of Technology.* Companies should take an undertaking to integrate all islands of technology so that a continuous flow of information and processes is achieved.

*4. Organisation Structure.* Major technological changes induce significant organisational changes, which if not appropriately incorporated can become suboptimal for new technology potential. Organisation structures should be such that they form effective communication, mutual trust and information sharing.

*5. Human Resource Strategy.* The impact of technology on the employees should be assessed to establish whether they have realised the beneficial effects of new technology. Incentives and rewards, health and safety policy and education and training policies should be re-examined.

*6. Impact of recent Economic Trends / Government Policies.* It will be useful to check if the technology is in compliance with government regulations, corporate policy and ethical standards.

*7. Risk Management.* A company's reputation and possibly its existence will be at risk if incorrect information such as cost estimates or sales are used. Failure of computer controlled machinery can sometimes lead to the use of faulty information.

**Step Seven    Plan for a New Technology**
If the performance evaluation after incorporating improvement measures reveal success then the committee responsible should store the procedure and achievements in the database in step two for future reference and plan for another new technology for the organisation if it is financially feasible or identify another area for continuous improvement. For continuous improvement or technology upgrade the success attained from technology should be sustained, and core competencies and technologies implemented should be used to formulate and further improve business strategies.

**Conclusion**
Research findings discussed earlier lead to the development of the model (Figure One) which is intended to guide companies successfully implement new technologies.

With various tools available to guide companies in technology investment, the general outcome of research is that companies are managing the first four steps although in a time period much longer than essential. Steps five to seven are not addressed at all. The model is intended to guide the companies so that the time spent on the first four steps are reduced, allowing them to enjoy a longer time in the effective utilisation of technology bearing in mind that all computer based technologies have a limited life.

This model was presented to four companies that had recently implemented new computer-based technologies in Australia. Their response to the model was that it is a practical tool, especially for companies implementing technologies for the first time.

**References.**
1. Bordoloi, B., Agarwal, A. and Sircar, S., 1993, 'Relational or Object-oriented or Hybrid? A Framework for Selecting Appropriate Database Management System Type in a Computer Integrated Manufacturing Setting', *International Journal of Operations & Production Management*, Vol 14, No 9, pp 32 - 44.
2. Dean, J. W., Susman, G. and Porter, P., 1990, 'Technical, Economic and Political Factors in Advanced Manufacturing Technology Implementation', *Journal of Engineering and Technology Management*, 7 pp 129 - 144.
3. Kanter, J., 1992, Managing With Information Fourth Edition, Prentice Hall, New Jersey.
4. Noori, H., 1990, *Managing the Dynamics of New Technology - Issues in Manufacturing Management*, Prentice Hall New Jersey.
5. Saraph, J. and Sabatian, R., 1992, 'Human Resource Strategies for Effective Introduction of Advanced Manufacturing Technologies', *Production and Inventory Management Journal*, First Quarter, pp 64 - 70.

6. Youssef, M., 1994, 'The Impact of the Intensity Level of Computer-based Technologies on Quality', *International Journal of Operations & Production Management*, Vol 14 No 4 pp 4 - 25.
7. Zairi, M., 1992, Management of Advanced Manufacturing Technology, Sigma Press Wimslow, U. K.

COMPETITIVENESS OF TWO COMPANIES WITH DIFFERENT
TECHNOLOGICAL CAPABILITIES

Francisco V Barbosa
Aston Business School
Aston University
1th Floor - South Wing
Birmingham - UK

Tel:          +44-121-359 3611
Fax:          +44-121-333 5620
Email:     barbosfv@aston.ac.uk

## ABSTRACT

This paper examines to what extent two companies' competitiveness with
different technological capabilities is affected by privatisation. The study
focuses on the Brazilian steel industry which has an important role in the
Brazilian econmy. The research examines the privatisation process and
competitiveness outcome in two major steel companies located in the state
of Minas Gerais. These enterprises carried out privatisation between 1991
and 1993. The Brazilian steel industry has been totally privatised since the
end of 1993, when the last company went into private hands.

The case study method was adopted in this research due to its strengths as a
useful technique allowing an in-depth analysis of an event and the context
within it happens. The paper also develops a company analysis model
consisting of three distinct components: input, process and outcome.

The research data suggest that there is not a straightforward link between
privatisation and competitiveness. Privatisation may bring profound
changes in many areas of the company. Nevertheless it is no guarantee that
a shift in company ownership alone will bring success and improve
competitiveness. The research results are based mainly on the analysis of
the added value, value added, net profit, trends, and factors influencing a
firm's competitiveness.

Most studies of competitiveness have neither considered privatisation as an
aspect that may have a major influence on the improvement of a
company's performance nor examined privatisation as a turning-point to
evaluate changes in competitiveness of large enterprises in industrialising
countries. It seems that the use of the case study methodology associated
with privatisation as a watershed in measuring competitiveness, at the
company level, in industrialising countries, has not been tried before.

# IMPLICATIONS OF RESTRUCTURING AND PRIVATISATION FOR COMPETITIVENESS AND PERFORMANCE: TWO BRAZILIAN COMPANIES WITH DIFFERENT TECHNOLOGICAL CAPABILITIES

## Introduction

This paper is about how privatisation and restructuring affect the competitiveness and performance of two manufacturing enterprises with different technological capabilities in Brazil. The study focuses on the Brazilian steel industry which has an important role both economic and social. As an example, iron and steel products account for 14.0% of the total Brazilian exports [1]. Brazil is the world's eighth largest steel producer and accounts for 3% of the world's production. It is the main Latin America steel maker [2]. Just as a matter of comparison, in 1994, the Brazilian steel industry output was approximately 50% higher than the British [3]. In 1994, the twenty largest steel producers employed over 85,000 employees and turnover was approximately $13.2bn in US dollars for that year [4].

This investigation has two main objectives. They are:

- Within the Brazilian steel industry, to examine two steel producers with different technological capabilities that underwent privatisation and the consequences this may have for performance and competitiveness
- To identify the characteristics that lead some companies to improve their competitiveness and performance under privatisation and others not to do so

This paper reports the findings of a research project which began at the end of 1992 and finished in 1996. The aim was to analyse the changes in performance and competitiveness of companies that underwent a privatisation process.

## Research framework and privatisation

In order to investigate the relationships between restructuring and privatisation and its implications on performance and competitiveness, this study has devised a framework based on Buckley, Pass and Prescott[5].

The privatisation of Brazilian state-owned steel companies started in the mid 1980s under the supervision of the Brazilian Development Bank (BNDES). However, privatisation only gained momentum after the introduction of structural reforms initiated by the Brazilian Government in 1990. The privatisations of Alpha and Beta, the two firms studied, are a consequence of that reform and change of people's attitude.

Preparations for privatisation of Alpha and Beta demanded a restructuring programme that began a few years before privatisation itself and is still continuing. The restructuring process was important to give to the then-state-owned companies financial viability and a shape that could attract as many buyers as possible. From the steel industry, Alpha was chosen as a show-case since it was considered by experts to be the best "performer" in the steel industry. Doing so, the government of the day expected to raise the privatisation process profile in the general public and encourage a wider share ownership. Beta was the last steel company to be privatisated after it underwent a rigorous restructuring programme.

Privatisation is a widely discussed and controversial issue. The debate and subsequent implementation of the privatisation programme first started in the United Kingdom under the Conservative Government in the early 1980s. After that, privatisation has been a focus of attention and argument all over the world. Nowadays, privatisation is an integral part of business restructuring of a great number of state-owned companies worldwide. For many governments, it is a means of reducing the burden on public finances and easing the problem of controlling public expenditure.

The key question, of course, is to what extent the privatisation process enhances competitiveness and performance capacity of an organization. This appears a deceptively easy question to address at first sight. However, the multiple definitions and criteria for defining organizational *performance* and the multiple levels of analysis through which one might examine *competitiveness* (industry, firm and international levels, for example) create a complex and intricate web of possible relationships. Before outlining the framework for this research, it is first necessary to examine in some detail what is meant by the terms competitiveness and performance -

and at which level of analysis any potential links between privatisation and performance might be empirically revealed.

## Competitiveness and performance

Over the last decade sweeping changes have affected the whole world economy, characterised by a structural shift in most international markets [6]. New players have appeared in the international arena, countries such as South Korea, Taiwan, Singapore, Thailand, Malaysia, Indonesia, Brazil, Mexico, China, India, and so on that are willing to improve their profile and their role as distinguished players in the world economy. A way such countries devised to achieve that has been through a range of economic and political measures to help their enterprises to succeed. Economic reforms, reduction of import tariffs on hardware and technology, incentives to export, introduction of economic stabilization programmes, privatisation of state-owned enterprises, and so on.

Economic activity is becoming increasingly globalized, the world is facing an unusual and more sophisticated integration of scattered activities. Globalization of economic activities has led to an 'era of turbulence and volatility in which economic life in general is being restructured and reorganized both rapidly and fundamentally' [6]. The economic and social certainties of the 1950s seem to have vanished.

The last two decades have been inundated with transnational corporation cases that have failed to keep up with the competition. Companies such as IBM, General Motors, ICI, GEC, Olivetti, Phillips once considered the *"prima donnas"* by industry, are now struggling to survive and compete against newcomers [7]. They did not realize or maybe did not want to recognize how fast things had changed over the past decades making products, companies, and economies outdated in a very short period of time. The increasing globalization of economic activities has demanded an almost total different approach from most economic players. The economic environment has never ever been like that before.

Readiness, planned and quick adjustments or sometimes radical shifts are far too important to be left to chance. Due to the relentless and swift changes that are taking place worldwide one needs to build and improve constantly to keep abreast with the new realities that come up so quickly and in such generous doses. Anyone that wants to survive in this 'global village' should be concerned with those factors that allow growth and prosperity to take place, in spite of the fierce and sometimes fatal competition. Such factors are flexibility, strategic vision, integration, partnerships, environmental pressure, competitiveness and performance.

Competitiveness has been considered the key issue to economic success and future prosperity in this new globalized economic reality. The astonishing economic growth of Far Eastern countries has led the USA, the European Community, Australia, Brazil, and others, to consider competitiveness as the number one priority. There is no light at the end of the tunnel if one is not able to produce goods and services that will meet the needs of potential clients.

To understand competitiveness one is required to look at different levels of analysis, productivity, the role of government, the standard of living, the institutional reality, education and training, quality of management, innovation and technology, creativity, risk-taking attitudes, entrepreneurship, and so on. It is clear that competitiveness is not a one-shot goal since it involves and requires multidisciplinary and multifarious viewpoints.

This research argues that, even when studying firms which trade internationally, competitiveness is more fruitfully studied at the level of the firm. The assumption here is that without the basic competences and resources in place at the level of the individual firm, competitiveness at the international level will be at worst, impossible and, at best, extremely short lived.

A key question, therefore, is what factors might constitute competitiveness at the level of the firm to enable some degree of advantage when trading in an international context. Buckley, Pass and Prescott [5] argue generally that the firm level of analysis is crucial since competitiveness comprises a combination of firm performance, potential and management. More specifically, such factors can be narrowed down interalia to the ability of a firm to transform and renew; to innovate; to learn and to develop a culture or climate to foster competitiveness. The research question, at this level of analysis, thus becomes to what extent government macro strategies, such as privatisation, facilitate or hinder such firm level factors of competitiveness. In the extreme, it may be that privatisation has virtually no influence over these factors.

744

### R&D and Technological capabilities

Technology is another factor considered by both companies to be fundamental to any serious improvement in performance and competitiveness. In terms of discourse, one can feel quite impressed by the commitment expressed by both firms. But reality is not quite like that. There are palpable differences between the two companies relative to their technological apparatus as, for example, in terms of having a technology center and technical information department. Alpha has a much better technological structure and has been able to upgrade some of its products and sell technological assistance services more consistently.

Despite this relative success, there is a group of people in those organizations that is firmly against expending resources to develop new products and processes. The most common reason put forward is that it is much cheaper to buy technology from an outsider than develop it. As a short-term approach this can be true. Yet as a long-term strategy it is questionable as the company will probably never be able to have any product at the top of the market range and at the same time will depend constantly on the supplier. Continuous dependency is a risky strategy as the supplier might change its mind and refuse to sell a more up-to-date technology.

Over the last years, R&D expenses by the two Brazilian steel producers have been less than 0.6 percent of total sales. When compared with the major Japanese steelmakers, this figure seems quite small. In 1987, these companies expended on average about 3.0 percent of total sales on R&D [8]. So it is no surprise why Japanese steel companies are in the forefront of technological development, displaying some of the most advanced products and processes worldwide.

Besides R&D, there are other characteristics that describe the technology factor. Number of patents, royalty income and licensing, percentage of sales and number of qualified scientists and engineers are among those features that allow one to measure and evaluate if a company is as committed to technology as it says. At present, there is an evident difference between the two case studies concerning their outcome relative to technological achievements. Alpha has been able to develop indigenous technology in its research institute and render technological services to some Brazilian and foreign companies. On the other hand, Beta is far behind compared to Alpha. It has not been able to develop in full its technological capability potential primarily due to lack of resources and uncertainties that have hampered any serious attempt to set up a technology center.

Technological upgrading is another element to be considered. Alpha has established major partnerships with Brazilian and foreign companies seeking to improve its technological capability. It has a long established relationship with a Japanese Steel Corporation which has been one the main suppliers of hardware and software in technology. These partnerships and its Steel Technology Center have been the source that provide the company with the necessary conditions to upgrade its range of products. As a result, the mix of products available for customers is becoming increasingly more sophisticated. Given that, the company aims to further its higher value-added products' availability as these products can bring a greater profit margin.

There has been a stronger emphasis on applied research at the cost of basic research projects. Alpha's technological capabilities have been enhanced through new partnerships established in 1992 with British Steel, Ahlstrom Equipment, Hitachi, Nippon Steel, and Chugai-Ro. The company is investing in new hardware to upgrade the mix of products, eg galvanized steel plates.

Beta is not very strong in R&D. It lacks a Research Centre, a Technical Information Department, and a firm commitment from the top management to invest time and money in R&D. Beta's technological capability to a certain extent is dependent on other Brazilian steelmaker as well as some foreign companies. The company does not have as many technological partnerships as Alpha. In this moment of transition, Beta does not see enhancing technological capability as being a major priority.

### The company analysis framework

The aim of the research framework is to provide an overview and description of the main aspects and components involved in the restructuring and privatisation of the two case studies.

Figure 1 displays the main constituents of a "Company Analysis Framework" used in this research. The framework is based on Buckley, Pass and Prescott [5] study on measures of international competitiveness. It is a modified version of the framework in the study mentioned above and focuses on competitiveness at the firm level. The company analysis framework is an attempt to explain the process of change in ownership, mentioned previously, and its consequences on a company. It comprises three groups: management, competitiveness/productivity, and performance.

Each group embodies a number of measures, indicators and qualitative assessments intended to explain the dynamics behind the process undergone by the two case study companies. The items in the three groups help to assess the implications of privatisation for competitiveness and performance.

As the focus is on the firm level, it is necessary to distinguish between changes internal to the firm and one in which the management have control and the external changes such as shifts in government policies. The external environment of the firm comprises all those influences that intervene in the enterprise's performance and the way the top management take decisions. Among the external influences is the neo-liberal policy adopted by the Brazilian government, in the beginning of 1990's, intended to expand foreign trade, curb inflation, reduce import tariffs, reduce the public burden, increase competition, and deregulate the business activities. Other external influences are the creation of the Mercosul common market (Brazil, Argentina, Uruguay, and Paraguay) that opened new business opportunities for a great number of companies, recovery of the domestic economy in the outset of 1990's, the implementation of a economic stabilization programme, lifting of the domestic market steel price controls, car makers increasing demand, and recovery of the steel industry worldwide.

Among the internal influences are the drastic reduction of the workforce, different goals and values of the two companies, different technological capabilities, excessive hierarchical levels, management affected by political interference, great uncertainty on the boardroom and among employees, relationships with competitors, suppliers and customers.

Management components in the framework are those related to the way a company is constituted and organized, formulates and implements strategies and policies. These strategies and policies are the main internal influences on the competitiveness and performance of the companies. Broadly, management decision-making acts on the "Competitiveness/Productivity" components to improve them as well as the performance. Management is a critical aspect that plays an important role in any organization. Six components of management identified as having the most significant influence on competitiveness and performance are ownership, governance, autonomy, incentives, organizational structure, and strategy.

Competitiveness/productivity group embodies those measures that help the management to achieve a better performance and makes performance sustainable. It is the link between management and performance. The success of a company is dependent on the way management deals with the competitiveness components. These measures influence productivity in quantity and value/unit terms. They are mainly internal: workforce, R&D, technological capabilities, production capability and finance/investment; and external/internal: products, price/deregulation, market strategy and relationship with customers.

Performance group is constituted of those measures that provides management the information needed to improve and assess the outcome of a company's operations. It helps the management to carry out changes according to the results achieved. Performance measures the success or failure of a management and bears a close link with the competitiveness/productivity group. Performance is dependent on management and competitiveness/productivity measures groups as well as influence them.

Productivity is one of the most common used and accepted measure of performance. Also, Profits and Earnings per share are the two most used measures of financial performance [8]. PBIT (profit before interest and taxation)/total assets and PBIT/sales are amongst the most popular profitability ratios [9]. Sales margin (net profit over sales) and return on equity (net profit over stockholders equity) are also very often used as a profitability ratios that take into account net profit. Sales/total assets or asset turnover is an important ratio that indicates how a company is capable to produce profits. Further measures used are costs, sales, market share, exports and value added. Most of the ratios and other measures listed are widely used by the main Brazilian business magazine to evaluate the largest 500 industrial, commercial and service companies in the private sector and the top market leaders in 23 main sectors of the Brazilian economy [10] and accepted by experts to be relevant to the Brazilian business environment.

### Analysis of the case studies

Comparative analysis of the two cases (Alpha and Beta) focuses initially on the differences in levels of competitiveness between them. Subsequently, the analysis then examines to what extent a change of ownership through privatisation enhanced or hampered such levels of competitiveness. Of course, the comparison of the two case studies inevitably introduces constraints in generalisations that may be gleaned from this analysis.

Nevertheless, taking two firms in the same sector, subject to the same privatisation processes, provides both depth and allows a detailed examination of context, the role of company history as well as provide rich data on performance and competitiveness. It would also be noted that Beta was privatised more recently than Alpha, so some post-privatisation results cannot be known. Yet, there are sufficient data to allow comparisons between the two firms especially at the firm level of analysis.

### Applying the Company Analysis Framework

For reasons of difficulty in comparability over time, no analysis is made of stock market data or other macro indicators since they could produce erroneous post hoc rationalisations in both cases, and they go beyond the parameters of the company analysis framework of this study. The comparative results are tabulated on Tables 1 and 2. In each case the three factors of Management, Competitiveness and Performance are utilised to facilitate comparison of Alpha and Beta. Analysis of the macro-economic climate, both nationally and internationally, is beyond the scope of the current research but would, of course, be a key item in any future research agenda, especially when a greater number of organizations could be compared empirically. That is for the future.

### Conclusions

Comparisons of the two cases reveals that the influence of privatisation at the company level is rarely, if ever, direct. Changes of ownership and direction can set the agenda for the direction of the changes, but appear not to constrict or restrain managers in their choice of implementation of strategies [11]. As Galal et al [12] states of other "Latin" privatisations "... (it is) merely one act in a larger play - a lesson most developing countries have been slow to grasp."

The cases act as examples of relatively more successful change (Alpha) and rather less successful change (Beta). The comparisons reveal some stark differences between the firms. Most revealing of all, perhaps, is the centrally important role played by corporate strategy in both cases (a finding supported by Pettigrew and Whipp [13]). Both Alpha and Beta had identifiable corporate strategies (see Tables 2 and 3). But privatisation for Alpha meant that its managers could shake off some of the shackles of regulation and exploit new business opportunities, especially in partnership. For Beta, privatisation merely added to a corporate strategy which was arguably already going wrong. Downsizing and the reduction of functional specialisation resulted in a marked diminution of core competences. Recourse to shareholding strategies brought further problems.

Beta was troubled by shareholding disputes after privatisation. Its main shareholder - GMJ - after the change in ownership, turned out to be in a big financial crisis. After some months of dispute, eventually GMJ was obliged to sell its stake in the company and to withdraw its representatives from the Administrative Council and Board of Directors.

So, at the company level, managerial agency has the greater influence over strategic direction and performance of the firm. The process of privatisation merely gives the direction and context for those changes. The relative lack of success of Beta, when compared to Alpha, is almost wholly due to management strategy rather than privatisation.

Indeed, there is strong supporting evidence for this conclusion since Beta's management was already pursuing strategies of downsizing and reduction in the functions prior to privatisation (whether they were doing this in anticipation of privatisation is impossible to tell). So, strategy in Beta post-privatisation became dominantly (but not wholly) more of the same. Privatisation provided a new context in which the existing portfolio of strategies could be pursued in greater breadth and depth.

To a large extent, the management strategies pursued in Beta post-privatisation exacerbated a cost-cutting frame of mind that was always in place. For example, labour productivity in both firms rose post-privatisation, but Alpha's came from modernization and expansionist strategies, whilst Beta's are rooted in cost reduction through workforce cuts. Labour cost savings were 30 per cent (of operating costs). Alpha's were 5 per cent. Such cost reduction strategies have a finite life - there is a point at which it is impossible to progress - and in Beta's case this seems to have been accelerated by the privatisation process. At present, Beta is holding ground especially by developing its export markets, but the financial performance data indicate a firm which soon may be in trouble. For example, PBIT/Sales and PBIT/Sales margin as well as ROE have decreased markedly (more than four times) over the last four years. Earnings per share have also been inherently unstable in Beta, whilst Alpha's have increased steadily.

Returning to the research questions raised at the beginning of this paper, the data from the two Brazilian firms support the view that managerial agency rather than privatisation per se is the key influence over both what decisions are subsequently taken and over long-term performance. This raises a cautionary signal, particularly amongst those scholars who are anti-privatisation on social policy or political grounds. From this sample, one could conclude that the impact of privatisation and performance is slight and indirect. There is no indication of 'sudden' exposure to competitive markets and the onset of Darwinistic economies of survival. These appeared to be happening *before* privatisation. What privatisation did do was to accelerate the change process by forcing management's hand to make quicker decisions - especially over markets and customers [14].

## References

[1] *Exame* (1996) Brasil em Exame: Quem esta pronto para o ano 2000. Sao Paulo, June, pp. 12-23.

[2] Baring Securities (1993) *Brazilian Company Report*. Sao Paulo, 22 June

[3]*The Economist* (1995) Half-empty or half full? Survey of Brazil. Insert, 29 April, pp. 4-34.

[4] *Exame Melhores e Maiores* (1995) Siderurgia. Longe do Governo ha um ceu mais azul. Sao Paulo, p. 238-241.

[5] Buckley, P. J., Pass, C. L., and Prescott, K (1988) Measures of International Competitiveness: a Critical Survey. *Journal of Marketing Management*, Vol. 4, no. 2, pp. 175-200.

[6] Dicken, P. (1992) *Global Shift: the Internationalization of Economic Activity*. Paul Chapman, London.

[7] Doyle, P. (1994) *Marketing Management & Strategy*. Prentice Hall. New York.

[8] Bowonder, B. and Miyake, T. (1990) Technology Development and Japanese Industrial Competitiveness. *Futures*, Vol. 22, no. 1, pp. 21-45.

[9] Kay, J. (1993) *Foundations of Corporate Success*. Oxford University Press, London.

[10] Samuels, J. M., Wilkes, F. M. and Brayshaw, R. E. (1995) *Management of Company Finance*. Chapman & Hall, London.

[11] *Exame Melhores e Maiores* (1995) Siderurgia. Longe do Governo ha um ceu mais azul. Sao Paulo, p. 238-241.

[12] Wilson, D. C. (1992) *A Strategy of Change. Concepts and controversies in the management of change*. Routledge, London.

[13] Galal, A., Leroy, L., Pankaj, T. and Vogelsang, I. (1993) *Welfare Consequences of Selling Public Enterprises: Case Studies from Chile, Malaysia, Mexico and the United Kingdom*. New York, Oxford University Press.

[14] Pettigrew, A. and Whipp, R. (1991) *Managing Change for Competitive Success*. Blackwell, London.

[15] Bishop, M. and Thompson, D. (1992) Privatisation in the UK, in Ramanadham, V. V. (ed) *Privatisation: Global Perspective*. London, Routledge.

## Address for Correspondence

Francisco Vidal Barbosa
University of Minas Gerais
Faculdade de Ciencias Economicas
Rua Curitiba, 832 - 10. andar
Belo Horizonte - MG
CEP: 30170-120
BRASIL
Fax: 00 55 31 2126561

Table 1 A summary of changes in ALPHA due to restructuring and privatisation and its implications for performance and competitiveness within "the company analysis framework"

| GROUP | MEASURES | CHANGES | IMPLICATIONS |
|---|---|---|---|
| | • Ownership | - public to private | • Greater entrepreneurship, flexibility, autonomy, teamworking, faster decision making, leaner administrative structure, and less red tape. Greater freedom to establish new partnerships and alliances |
| | • Governance | - centralized to more participatory decisions | |
| | • Autonomy | - dependence to greater autonomy and initiative | |
| • Management | • Incentive | - shareholding and performance-related pay | |
| | • Organizational structure | - fewer hierarchical levels<br>- functional units were reduced by about 50 per cent over a five-year period | |
| | • Strategy | - establishment of partnerships and alliances. Acquisition of stakes in companies | |
| | • Workforce | - reduction of workforce by about 25 per cent over a five-year period | • greater reduction of workforce, closeness to customers, market deregulation, and improved product-mix |
| | • R&D and Technological capabilities | - no evident changes | |
| | • Production capacity | - no evident changes | |
| • Competitiveness/ Productivity | • Finance/ Investment | - acquisition of shares in companies | |
| | • Products | - production of galvanized plates started in 1993. | |
| | • Price/ Deregulation | - lifting of price control in 1991 and greater market deregulation | |
| | • Market strategy | - improve product-mix through higher value-added products | |
| | • Relationship with customers | - greater closeness to customers | |

| GROUP | MEASURES | CHANGES | IMPLICATIONS |
|---|---|---|---|
| • Performance | • Labour productivity | - increased by about 20 per cent over a five-year period | • greater labour productivity, labour cost savings, sales per employee, and profitability |
| | • Costs | - cost of products and services has been stable as a percentage of net revenue<br>- labour cost savings: more than 5 per cent as a percentage of operating costs | |
| | • Sales/market share | - sales (value) per employee increased by more than 50 per cent over a five-year period<br>- market share has been stable | |
| | • Exports | - exports have been reduced | |
| | • Profitability and asset turnover ratios<br>• Profits/EPS | - profitability ratios have improved since 1991<br>- asset turnover has decreased<br>- profits as a percentage of net revenues have increased by more than three times since 1991<br>- EPS has increased since 1991 | |
| | • Value added | - it has been stable | |

Table 2 A summary of changes in BETA due to restructuring and privatisation and its implications for performance and competitiveness within "the company analysis framework"

| GROUP | MEASURES | CHANGES | IMPLICATIONS |
|---|---|---|---|
| • Management | • Ownership | - public to private | • Greater flexibility, autonomy, teamworking, faster decision making, leaner administrative structure, and lesser red tape. Profound reduction of functional units. |
| | • Governance | - centralized to more participatory decisions<br>- Board of Directors replaced | |
| | • Autonomy | - dependence to greater autonomy and initiative | |
| | • Incentive | - shareholding and performance-related pay | |
| | • Organizational structure | - fewer hierarchical levels<br>- functional units were reduced by about 60 per cent over a four-year period | |
| | • Strategy | - establishment of partnerships and alliances. | |

|  |  |  |  |
|---|---|---|---|
| Competitiveness/ Productivity | • Workforce | - reduction of workforce by more than 40 per cent over a five-year period | • profound reduction of workforce, greater closeness to customers, market deregulation. |
| | • R&D and Technological capabilities | - no evident changes | |
| | • Production capacity | - no evident changes | |
| | • Finance/ Investment | - overhauling of the financial situation | |
| | • Products | - no evident changes | |
| | • Price/ Deregulation | - lifting of price control in 1991 and greater market deregulation | |
| | • Market strategy | - improve product-mix through higher value-added products | |
| | • Relationship with customers | - greater closeness to customers | |
| | • Labour productivity | - increased by about 60 per cent over a four-year period | • greater labour productivity, labour cost savings, and sales per employee. Profitability have not improved |
| | • Costs | - cost of products and services has increased as a percentage of net revenues<br>- labour cost savings: about 30 per cent as a percentage of operating costs over a four-year period | |
| Performance | • Sales/ market share | - sales (value) per employee increased by more than 75 per cent over a five-year period<br>- market share has been stable | |
| | • Exports | - exports as a percentage of total sales have been stable | |
| | • Profitability and asset turnover ratios | - profitability ratios have worsened since 1991<br>- asset turnover has been stable | |
| | • Profits/EPS | - profits as a percentage of net revenues have decreased since 1991<br>- EPS has not been stable | |
| | • Value added | - it has decreased since 1991 | |

751

# Figure 1 Company Analysis Framework

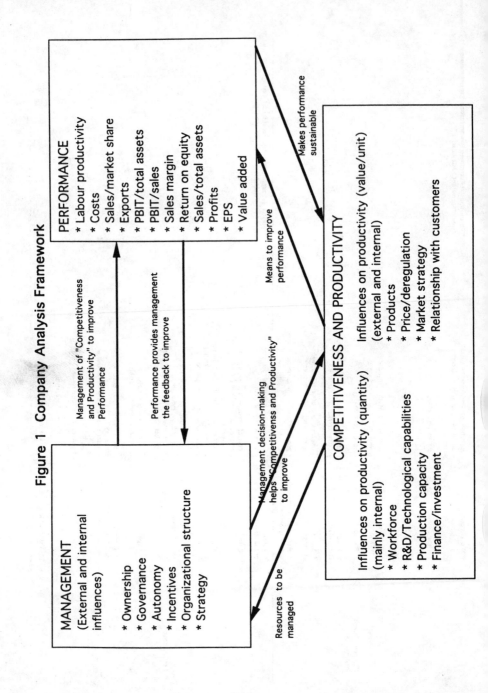

MANAGEMENT
(External and internal influences)

* Ownership
* Governance
* Autonomy
* Incentives
* Organizational structure
* Strategy

PERFORMANCE

* Labour productivity
* Costs
* Sales/market share
* Exports
* PBIT/total assets
* PBIT/sales
* Sales margin
* Return on equity
* Sales/total assets
* Profits
* EPS
* Value added

Management of "Competitiveness and Productivity" to improve Performance

Performance provides management the feedback to improve

Management decision-making helps "Competitivenss and Productivity" to improve

Resources to be managed

Means to improve performance

Makes performance sustainable

COMPETITIVENESS AND PRODUCTIVITY

Influences on productivity (quantity) (mainly internal)

* Workforce
* R&D/Technological capabilities
* Production capacity
* Finance/investment

Influences on productivity (value/unit) (external and internal)

* Products
* Price/deregulation
* Market strategy
* Relationship with customers